An Introduction to
Music Therapy
Research

THIRD EDITION

EDITED BY

Barbara L. Wheeler
& Kathleen Murphy

Barcelona
PUBLISHERS

An Introduction to Music Therapy Research

(Third Edition)

Copyright © 2016

Print ISBN: 9781945411120

Distributed throughout the world by:
Barcelona Publishers
10231 Plano Road
Dallas TX 75238

www.barcelonapublishers.com
SAN 298-6299

Cover design: © 2016 Frank McShane

Permissions

The editors thank the following for permission to reprint materials in this book:

American Music Therapy Association
Figure: Percentage of Positive Peer Interactions for Each Child for Each Condition. From Kern, P., & Aldridge, D. (2006), Using embedded music therapy interventions to support outdoor play of young children with autism in an inclusive community-based child care program. *Journal of Music Therapy, 43,* 270–294.
Figure: Frequency of Rummaging in Kitchen During Each Design Phase. From Pasiali, V. (2004), The use of prescriptive therapeutic songs in a home-based environment to promote social skills acquisition by children with autism: Three case studies. *Music Therapy Perspectives, 22,* 11–20.
Portions of article and an adapted table: From O'Callaghan, C. (2012), Grounded theory in music therapy. *Journal of Music Therapy, 49,* 236–277.
Table: Excerpt from a Delphi Questionnaire for Round Two, Model 1. From Cassity, M. D. (2007), Psychiatric music therapy in 2016: A Delphi poll of the future. *Music Therapy Perspectives, 25*(2), 86–93.

American Psychological Association
Figure: Sample Search in the EBSCOhost-PsychINFO Engine (PsycINFO® Database screen shot).

ATLAS.ti
Figure: Standard Display Window for ATLAS.ti 7 (iPad Version). From ATLAS.ti for ATLAS.ti Version 7 [Computer software] (2012). Berlin, Germany: Scientific Software Development.

Barcelona Publishers
Figure: The Affective-Expressive Contour (dynamic profile) of the GIM Music Program *Positive Affect.* From Bonny, H. (1978). *GIM monograph #2: The role of taped music programs in the GIM process.* Salina, KS: Bonny Foundation. (Portions reprinted in H. Bonny (2002a) & L. Summer (Ed.), *Music consciousness: The evolution of Guided Imagery and Music,* pp. 301–321. Gilsum, NH: Barcelona.)
Table: Refereed Journals in Music Therapy Published in English. Updated from Edwards, J. (2005), Developments and issues in music therapy research. In B. L. Wheeler (Ed.), *Music therapy research* (2nd ed.; pp. 20–32).
Table: Stages of Analyzing Phenomenological Interview Protocols: A Comparison of Approaches. From M. Forinash, & D. Grocke. (2005), Phenomenological inquiry. In B. L. Wheeler (Ed.), *Music therapy research* (2nd ed.; pp. 321–334).
Tables: Interpretivist Research Questions: Foci, and Interpretivist Research Questions: Purpose. Adapted from Bruscia, K. E. (2005), Topics and questions. In B. L. Wheeler (Ed.), *Music therapy research* (2nd ed.; pp. 8–93).

British Journal of Music Therapy
Excerpts from *British Journal of Music Therapy:* From Stige, B. (2006), The problem of pleasure in music therapy. *British Journal of Music Therapy, 20*(1), 39–51.

Anita Gadberry
Figure: Number of Intentional Communicative Acts per Participant. From Gadberry, A. (2010), *Communicative acts in music therapy interventions with and without aided augmentative and alternative communication systems* (Doctoral dissertation). Retrieved from ProQuest Digital Dissertations & Theses (UMI No. 3458215).

Guilford Press
Table: Hierarchies of Evidence. Adapted from Oxford University Centre for Evidence-Based Medicine's Levels of Evidence by F. Baker and printed in Baker, F. A. (2015), Evidence-based practice in music therapy. In B. L. Wheeler (Ed.), *Music therapy handbook* (pp. 103–115).

Centre for Evidence-Based Medicine
Table: Hierarchies of Evidence. Adapted from Oxford University Centre for Evidence-Based Medicine's Levels of Evidence (2009).

Hans Reitzels Forlag
Figure: A Multi-Structure Combination of CSR Components. From Ramian, K. (2012), *Introduktion til Casestudiet i praksis.*

ACKNOWLEDGMENTS

From the Editor

Putting together a book of this scope and magnitude is bound to involve many people. This may be especially true for me, since I tend to seek information and feedback broadly. I am fortunate to have many good and knowledgeable friends and colleagues and have received assistance from more of them than I could thank in this brief section. I would like to acknowledge Kenneth Bruscia for his vision of a music therapy research book way back in the early '90s, which led to *Music Therapy Research: Quantitative and Qualitative Perspectives* and then, of course, to the next two editions of the book *Music Therapy Research*. His role has changed over the years, but he has continued to provide guidance and astute input into many aspects of the book. It has been a pleasure working with Kathleen Murphy, Associate Editor, whose contribution to this third edition is immense. And, of course, the authors have contributed their expertise to the chapters.

In the process of editing the book and writing my contributions, I have reached out to many people. I cannot thank all of them but would like to mention some who have made major contributions. These include Eric Waldon, who provided input on one major section of the book; Douglas Keith, who has helped with a variety of concerns; and Margaret Mukherjee, who gave extensive feedback on the glossary. I also want to acknowledge some others who have been available for repeated questions over the years that this book has been in progress (again stating that many people whom I am not thanking here have been very gracious in giving input): Gene Ann Behrens, Lars Ole Bonde, Joke Bradt, Virginia Driscoll, Barbara Else, Susan Hadley, James Hiller, Cathy McKinney, Anthony Meadows, Even Ruud, Brynjulf Stige, and Arthur Sullivan.

Barbara L. Wheeler
Editor

From the Associate Editor

The process of putting this book together has been humbling and eye-opening. I, too, would like to acknowledge Kenneth Bruscia for his vision and guidance. Barbara Wheeler also needs to be acknowledged for her perseverance and dedication to the music therapy research community. Undertaking this project was no small task, and I am grateful for the opportunity that Kenneth Bruscia and Barbara Wheeler offered. I also want to acknowledge and thank all of the authors for their contributions of time and research knowledge, as well as their willingness to answer questions and offer guidance. Lastly, I want to acknowledge my husband, Michael Mulligan, for his ongoing support and encouragement.

Kathleen M. Murphy
Associate Editor

AUTHOR LISTING

Elaine A. Abbott, PhD, MT-BC
Director of Music Therapy
Duquesne University
Pittsburgh, PA, USA

Brian Abrams, PhD, MT-BC
Associate Professor of Music and Coordinator of Music
Therapy
Montclair State University
Montclair, NJ, USA

Kenneth E. Bruscia, PhD, MT-BC
Professor Emeritus of Music Therapy
Temple University
Philadelphia, PA, USA

Nicki S. Cohen, PhD, MT-BC
Professor of Music Therapy and Voice
Texas Woman's University
Denton, TX, USA

Alice-Ann Darrow, PhD, MT-BC
Irvin Cooper Professor of Music Therapy and Music
Education
Florida State University
Tallahassee, FL, USA

Cochavit Elefant, PhD, MT
Head of Graduate School of Creative Arts Therapies
University of Haifa
Haifa, Israel

Susan C. Gardstrom, PhD, MT-BC
Professor and Coordinator of Music Therapy
University of Dayton
Dayton, OH, USA

James Hiller, PhD, MT-BC
Assistant Professor
University of Dayton
Dayton, OH, USA

Douglas R. Keith, PhD, MT-BC
Professor of Music Therapy
Georgia College
Milledgeville, GA, USA

Seung-A Kim, PhD, MT-BC
Director of Undergraduate Music Therapy
Molloy College
Rockville Centre, NY, USA

Cathy H. McKinney, PhD, MT-BC
Professor and Coordinator of Music Therapy
Appalachian State University
Boone, NC, USA

Anthony Meadows, PhD, MT-BC
Director of Graduate Music Therapy Studies
Shenandoah University
Winchester, VA, USA

Theresa R. Merrill, PhD, MT-BC
Director of Music Therapy
Eastern Michigan University
Ypsilanti, MI, USA

Kathleen M. Murphy, PhD, MT-BC
Assistant Professor and Coordinator of Music Therapy
Loyola University
New Orleans, LA

Arthur P. Sullivan, PhD
Professor of Psychology & Education
Touro School of Health Sciences
New York, NY, USA

John A. Sullivan, MD, PhD
Resident Physician
Stony Brook University Hospital
Stony Brook, NY, USA

Eric G. Waldon, PhD, MT-BC
Assistant Professor, Music Therapy
University of the Pacific
Stockton, CA, USA

Barbara L. Wheeler, PhD, MT-BC
Professor Emerita
Montclair State University
Montclair, NJ, USA

TABLE OF CONTENTS

FOREWORD

Donald A. Hodges

I was an undergraduate student during the time that E. Thayer Gaston was working on his landmark publication *Music in Therapy* (1968), as it came out the year after I graduated. Although it is a simplistic comparison, it is instructive to note some gross indicators of just how much the professional literature in music therapy has grown and developed. Gaston's book contained 39 chapters, with three of them focused specifically on research. Contrast this with the third edition of *Music Therapy Research* (MTR3), standing at 68 chapters, all focused upon research.

Setting content and quality aside for a moment, MTR3 is a monumental achievement in size and scope. It compares very favorably to similar compilations in the sister fields of music education and music psychology, as can be seen in Table 1. Note that although the other books include research as one of the content areas, all of them have a much broader focus. Thus, this edition of MTR is the largest and most detailed exploration of research in this or related fields. Another point to note concerning size is the obvious expansion from the first to the third edition.

Consider the microscope as an analogy for the scope of MTR3. This compendium focuses on only one particular aspect of music therapy in the same way a microscope concentrates on a small portion of a larger object. However, just as a microscope reveals a myriad of minutiae lurking below the surface, so does MTR3 present for the reader's consideration a wealth of detail that underscores a conception of research as a multifaceted discipline. Topics range from relationships between research and theory to the use of the Delphi technique to ways of combining interpretivist (qualitative) and objectivist (quantitative) methods. Sixty-eight chapters are arranged in nine units that demonstrate a clear organizational scheme:

- Unit One: Introduction
- Unit Two: Preparations
- Unit Three: Foundations and Principles
- Unit Four: Methodological Concerns in Objectivist Research
- Unit Five: Methodological Concerns in Interpretivist Research
- Unit Six: Objectivist Designs
- Unit Seven: Interpretivist Designs
- Unit Eight: Other Types of Research
- Unit Nine: Evaluating, Reading, Writing, and Submitting Music Therapy Research

This, then, is the extensive scope of MTR3.

A person reading from cover to cover—quite an undertaking in and of itself—would receive a comprehensive overview of the field of research in music therapy. Likely to be more common, however, is the perusal of specific chapters or sections. Novice researchers can begin their study in these pages, but even experienced researchers can return time and again not only to glean explicit details on selected topics, but also to gain insights into broader issues and concerns. Research methods, statistical techniques, notions about relationships among theory, practice, and research, and many other aspects are all subject to change over time. Three editions, each subsequent volume more expansive than the previous, are evidence of the currency of MTR3.

Another great strength of MTR3 is the roster of 71 authors from 12 countries who have contributed. Some of the writers are scholars who have made substantial contributions to the field of music therapy for many years. Many of them have held important leadership positions, contributed significant

Table 1. Comparison of Selected Reference Books in Music Therapy, Music Education, and Music Psychology

Editor(s)	Title	Year	Number of Chapters
Colwell	*Handbook of Research on Music Teaching and Learning*	1992	55
Wheeler	***Music Therapy Research: Quantitative and Qualitative Perspectives***	**1995**	**24**
Colwell & Richardson	*New Handbook of Research on Music Teaching and Learning*	2002	61
Wheeler	***Music Therapy Research* (2nd ed.)**	**2005**	**41**
Juslin & Sloboda	*Oxford Handbook on Music and Emotion* (2nd ed.)	2010	33
McPherson & Welch	*Oxford Handbook of Music Education*, 2 volumes	2012	116
Hallam, Cross, & Thaut	*Oxford Handbook of Music Psychology* (2nd ed.)	2016	55
Edwards	*Oxford Handbook of Music Therapy*	2016	48
Wheeler & Murphy	***Music Therapy Research* (3rd ed.)**	**2016**	**68**

research findings, and trained generations of music therapists. Others are newcomers, with more recent training. They provide fresh insights, new ideas, and an eagerness to influence the profession. Each author possesses individual strengths and experiences. Collectively, they represent a wealth of expertise, based on a variety of training and educational experiences, as well as enormous diversity in working with a wide range of clients.

MTR3 documents the important role that research plays in moving the field of music therapy forward. It provides not only theoretical ideas about why research is important, but also ways to think about research and specific instructions on how to conduct research. In short, MTR3 represents an impressive achievement. It will serve as a guiding star for the profession, for beginning researchers as well as old hands. To all of those who participated in the creation of this marvelous anthology—and especially Barbara Wheeler, who has been the constant driving force on this project since the first edition (joined now by Kathleen Murphy as Associate Editor)—congratulations and thank you. The late night hours, struggles with a blank computer screen, frantic hunts for the just the right word, and all of the other frustrations and joys of committing words to paper were worth it. You have given your profession a most invaluable resource, one that will continue to be a well-used reference tool … until such time as MTR4 makes its timely appearance.

Donald A. Hodges
Professor of Music Education
University of North Carolina at Greensboro
Greensboro, NC, USA

References

Colwell, R. (Ed.). (1992). *Handbook of research on music teaching and learning.* New York, NY: Schirmer Books.

Colwell, R., & Richardson, C. (Eds.). (2002). *The new handbook of research on music teaching and learning.* New York, NY: Oxford University Press.

Edwards, J. (Ed.). (2016). *Oxford handbook of music therapy.* London, UK: Oxford University Press.

Gaston, E. T. (Ed.). (1968). *Music in therapy.* New York, NY: Macmillan.

Hallam, S., Cross, I., & Thaut, M. (Eds.). (2016). *The Oxford handbook of music psychology* (2nd ed.). Oxford, UK: Oxford University Press.

Juslin, P., & Sloboda, J. (Eds.). (2010). *The Oxford handbook on music and emotion: Theory, research, and applications.* Oxford, UK: Oxford University Press.

McPherson, G., & Welch, G. (Eds.). (2012). *The Oxford handbook of music education* (Vols. 1 & 2). Oxford, UK: Oxford University Press.

Wheeler, B. L. (Ed.). (1995). *Music therapy research: Quantitative and Qualitative Perspectives.* Gilsum, NH: Barcelona.

Wheeler, B. L. (Ed.). (2005). *Music therapy research* (2nd ed.). Gilsum, NH: Barcelona.

Wheeler, B. L., & Murphy, K. M. (Eds.). *Music therapy research* (3rd ed.). Dallas, TX: Barcelona.

PREFACE

The aim of this book is to provide an introductory overview of how research has been conceived and implemented in music therapy over the last several decades. It was designed for those who are beginning their studies in music therapy research, and it is especially well-suited for use as an accompaniment to classroom instruction.

Seventeen of the chapters were excerpted from *Music Therapy Research (3rd Edition)*, a much larger volume of 68 chapters that gives considerable detail on the topic and its numerous sub-topics. In addition, three chapters (15, 16, 17) were specially written to provide a birds-eye view of some of the chapters that were not included, and in particular, those chapters in the larger book that examined the numerous methodological designs and approaches used in objectivist, interpretivist and other types of music therapy research.

Kenneth E. Bruscia

An Introduction to
Music Therapy
Research

THIRD EDITION

Chapter 1

OVERVIEW OF MUSIC THERAPY RESEARCH[1]

Barbara L. Wheeler • Kenneth E. Bruscia

Music therapy is a diverse and evolving field, and its research both reflects and guides that diversity and change. This chapter examines some salient features and concerns in music therapy research. Rather than look at all aspects—which is the purpose of the book—this chapter focuses on major concepts and issues that run throughout the book. We will look first at some definitions of music therapy research, also considering topics of research, its relationship to practice and theory, and what distinguishes research from other professional tasks performed by music therapists. Then we will consider reasons why people do research and the various ways of conceptualizing and classifying research. Finally, we will examine two issues confronting music therapy researchers: evidence-based practice and the relevance of research.

Defining and Distinguishing Music Therapy Research

What is *research?* It may be defined as "careful or diligent search" or "careful study that is done to find and report new knowledge about something" ("Research," 2015). Many years ago, Charles Eagle used the word to remind us that we must *re-search*—embark again and again on a journey of discovery and exploration (Charles T. Eagle, personal communication, June, 1982). Bruscia (2014) says that research is "a systematic, self-monitored inquiry which leads to a discovery or new insight, which, when documented and disseminated, contributes to or modifies existing knowledge or practice" (p. 196). Although many definitions of research have been formulated, all suggest that it leads to the discovery of new things, the reaffirmation of what we already know, or changes in the way that we view things. It is these possibilities of discovery and change that make research so exciting!

Topics of music therapy research may be divided into discipline, profession, and foundational (Bruscia, 2005). *Discipline research* looks at what music therapists do in the areas of assessment, treatment, and evaluation. *Profession research* covers a range of topics that concern music therapists as a group and the contexts in which they work. *Foundational research* often originates in other disciplines but provides the foundations for what music therapist do. All of these can contribute to our understanding of music therapy.

Research, Practice, and Theory

Research, theory, and practice are closely related but different, and each has its own role in the formation of a discipline. Thus it is important to see not only how they overlap and relate, but also how they differ. Bruscia (2014) has defined all three, and only the main points are included here. The basic difference between clinical practice and research is that research intends to increase or modify the knowledge base in music therapy, while clinical practice intends to help particular clients address health matters. The purpose of theory, on the other hand, is "to enlarge our perspectives on what we know, while the purpose of research is to establish what we know by describing and explaining what occurred or what was observed. … A theory tells us how to make sense out of the facts; research tells us what the facts are" (Bruscia, p. 201).

Music therapists undertake many professional tasks that are not research. Clinical work in and of itself is not research, although at times it shares some elements of the research process. For example, when music therapists assess client needs and evaluate client progress, the gathering and analysis of data differ from research in both purpose and outcome. And when we write about or share our clinical work so that others may learn from it, it is not necessarily research, although under certain conditions it may meet the criteria for research. To gain a better sense of what distinguishes clinical work, assessment and evaluation, and sharing our clinical experiences from research, we can look back to the definitions of research. The most important difference may be the goals: The goal of research is to inform the scholarly community about the nature of music therapy, whereas the goals of the clinical pursuits mentioned are to gain the knowledge needed to help specific clients.

Research is also different from yet related to theory. The scope of theory is much broader than the scope of research. Theory can deal with a broad realm with many topics and subtopics or can combine and include many research studies and models of practice, while research must have a limited focus and purpose. Theory plays a different role in quantitative (or objectivist) research than it does in qualitative (or interpretivist) research. Objectivist researchers believe that facts are objective truths that are discovered through systematic inquiry by disinterested researchers, whereas interpretivist researchers believe that all research findings are constructions of the researcher. Since a theory intends to explicate what is known, the two types of researchers see the role of theory differently: Objectivist researchers see research and theory as continually adding to existing knowledge, whereas interpretivist researchers believe that research and theory increase our understanding of existing constructions, leading to more relevant reconstructions. Because of these different views of the role of research, there is a clearer boundary between theory and research among objectivist researchers than among interpretivist ones.

The distinctions and overlap among the three areas are discussed more completely in other chapters of the book.

Ways of Conceptualizing Research

Numerous ways of conceptualizing research have been developed. Three will be described here. These have been selected for different reasons. Objectivist and interpretivist research are the divisions of research as presented in this book. Basic research and applied research are traditional divisions and distinguish different applications of music therapy research. Research frameworks, or stages in the research process, reflect types of research that are useful at different points in the research process and are important to consider in the planning process for research.

Objectivism and Interpretivism

Music therapy research can be classified as objectivist or interpretivist based on the purpose and design of the research. In *objectivist research,* the purpose is to determine what is true or not true—to confirm or deny a focused and well-defined hypothesis established at the very beginning of a study. In *interpretivist research,* the purpose is to explore a particular phenomenon as it unfolds and reveals itself during the study, the aim being to explicate and understand the phenomenon. Thus, the outcome of objectivist research is fact, and the outcome of interpretivist research is a better construction.

As for design, objectivist research is built upon the belief that methodological design is crucial to the establishment of what is true or not true. Thus, objectivist designs and methods are carefully created or selected at the onset of the study and then scrutinized by the scholarly community to determine whether the hypotheses have been confirmed. In contrast, in interpretivist research, the very terms *design* and *method* may be misleading; probably a better term for them would be *approach* or *perspective.* For example, we can say that a study exemplifies phenomenology in design or method, but, in actuality, this means only that the focus of the study is on understanding the nature of a particular human experience (e.g., being understood) and that whatever strategies are needed to gain that understanding will emerge as data are gathered and analyzed on that experience. Thus, in interpretivist research, there are no formulaic designs or methods that must be carried out without modification throughout the study.

Taking our discussion one step further, the purpose and design of a study, and its classification as objectivist or interpretivist, depend upon the philosophical notions of ontology and epistemology. Since this is the classification around which this book is organized, it is important to understand what these terms mean and how they influence our understanding of different types of research.

Ontology is the study of what exists or what is real. *Epistemology* is the study of what is possible to know, and how it is possible know it. Ontological and epistemological beliefs are inextricably linked; we have to know the natures of reality and truth before we can determine how they can be known. Ontology precedes and limits epistemology, and together they lead to different beliefs about the intent and design of research, as manifested in objectivist and interpretivist approaches. More information on these topics appears in Chapter 11, Epistemological Foundations of Objectivist and Interpretivist Research.

Objectivist research assumes that there is a single reality that exists independent of humans' experience of it (ontology) and that it is possible to increasingly know this reality through the senses (epistemology). Reality and truth are not determined by our subjective constructions and interpretations; instead, they are obtained through repeated observations of reality in highly controlled situations, that is, through designs and methods of research that eliminate the researcher's subjectivity. Two variations of objectivist research are the theoretical perspectives of positivism and postpositivism. *Positivism* is a philosophical system of knowledge that accepts only observable or measurable (i.e., empirical) experiences of the world as data for analysis, the findings from which are considered positive or absolute truths about reality. *Postpositivism* understands that, "regardless of a researcher's faithful adherence to objectivist *scientific* methods, findings are not considered absolute truths but rather are *conjectural* and *circumstantial* … and that, given new evidence, it is always possible for alternate explanations of data and findings to be articulated" (Hiller, 2016, p. 101). This was the dominant way of viewing music therapy research during the first decades of its existence.

Interpretivist research assumes that reality and truth are multiple human constructions rather than objective absolutes. There is not one reality or truth—there are many. Thus, humans construct reality and truth as they interpret their experiences of and in the world; all knowledge is grounded in our unique experiences. Interpretivist research then focuses on gaining understanding and making meaning from what the researcher has discovered. Interpretive research findings, then, reflect the researcher's own values and insights and therefore are not considered absolute, universal, or generalizable. The goal is to expand and diversify our constructions of reality and truth, rather than to discover how they exist out there apart from us. There are various interpretive theories and paradigms (see Denzin & Lincoln, 2008, for an overview). One of the most dominant in music therapy research is *constructivism,* which acknowledges that the reality we perceive is constructed by our social, historical, and individual contexts.

Whereas objectivism is primarily concerned with the world of objects, that is, reality and truth as they manifest objectively, interpretivism is primarily concerned with the world of subjects, that is, reality and truth as they manifest subjectively. This distinction implies that objectivism is relevant for the natural sciences, and interpretivism is relevant for the arts and social sciences. This has important implications for music therapy research: When music therapy is viewed as a natural science, researchers will seek to discover absolute and universal realities and truths about the world of objects, whereas when music therapy is viewed as an art or social science, researchers are seeking to discover better insights and constructions of the world of subjects. This in turn has major implications for the kinds of data that are greater interest to objectivists and interpretivists.

Objectivist research relies primarily on objective forms of data, and most often this requires quantification and statistical analysis. Thus, objectivist research is frequently referred to as *quantitative research.* In contrast, interpretivist research relies primarily on subjective data, and this most often involves gathering and analyzing other types of data such as verbal, musical, and artistic materials or qualities. Thus, interpretivist research is frequently referred to as *qualitative research.* A growing trend in today's research is to combine quantitative and qualitative methods of gathering and analyzing data. This type of research is frequently referred to as *mixed methods research* (Creswell & Plano Clark, 2011; see also Chapters 56 and 57 in this book).

The distinction between objectivist or quantitative and interpretivist or qualitative research is useful to focus on differences in ways of approaching research. Music therapy researchers and others, though, find problems with making such a clear-cut split between these two approaches. It is too simplistic to equate quantitative research with the use of numbers and statistical analysis and qualitative research with greater emphasis on nonnumerical data and theoretical or interpretive analysis. In relation to this, Edwards (1999) said:

> Quantitative research can involve nonnumerical data; it is not the presence or absence of numbers which provides information as to the methodological orientation. This limiting of qualitative and quantitative distinctions to enumeration can mean that researchers comparing their studies in purely methodological terms might not be aware that their ontologies conflict, however similar their methodologies may appear to one another. Analyses of videos of music therapy sessions, for example, are undertaken differently according to the ontology which frames the method of inquiry and the epistemology which directs the method applied. (p. 78)

Put another way, quantitative data can be interpreted from an objectivist or interpretivist stance, and so can qualitative data. This in turn can pose particularly difficult epistemological questions when both types of data are used, as in mixed methods research.

If we realize that they have different purposes and are suitable for answering different questions, the reason for conflicts between objectivist and interpretivist research fade.

Music therapists seem to be less concerned about these differences than in the past, at least in terms of viewing them from adversarial positions. Some of this is because mixed methods research has become more popular, both inside and outside of music therapy. Mixed methods are used increasingly in music therapy research and have made possible the exploration of certain questions appropriately investigated using both objectivist and interpretivist methods. It is important that those using these methods be aware of the differences in questions that are appropriate using each paradigm and the epistemologies that go with each. This brings to mind Bruscia's (1995) caution that "notwithstanding the possibility of collecting both quantitative and qualitative data in the same study, and combining the different interests and methodologies, the two philosophical paradigms cannot be integrated or combined" (p. 73). Essentially, this means that the ontologies and epistemologies of objectivist and interpretivist research are different, if not incompatible, and these differences must be considered in forming conclusions about the data, regardless of whether the data are quantitative or qualitative. Objective conclusions cannot be drawn from interpretivist research, and subjective conclusions cannot be drawn from objectivist research.

Basic Versus Applied Research

Research can also be classified as basic or applied. *Basic research* is defined as "systematic study directed toward fuller knowledge or understanding of the fundamental aspects of phenomena and of observable facts without specific applications toward processes or products in mind," while *applied research* is "systematic study to gain knowledge or understanding necessary to determine the means by which a recognized and specific need may be met" (National Science Foundation, 2015).

Basic research is done more often in some other disciplines than in music therapy. Much quantitative research in the physical sciences and psychology is done with no immediate practical goal in mind. Experiments on how cells divide, laboratory research on reinforcement of rats, or studies on which part of the brain is activated by certain stimuli are examples of basic quantitative research. Basic qualitative or interpretivist research might involve looking at how people experience a particular phenomenon but without focusing on a practical application of that information.

Basic research, labeled by Bruscia (2005) as *foundational,* provides the foundation for much of what music therapists do and includes much of the research that is done in the psychology of music. Studies of reinforcement (originally in rats and other animals), how the brain processes music, and how music affects muscles are basic research.

At the point that results from basic research are applied to real problems, the research becomes applied. Because the purpose of music therapy is to help people, research in this discipline is generally applied. Music therapy assessment, treatment, and evaluation studies are all applied research. When researchers began investigating how reinforcement could be applied to education and therapy using behavior modification, this was applied research. When the research on the brain and music was applied to understanding people's responses to music and how they might apply in music therapy or those of neurologic development were applied to the development of Neurologic Music Therapy, this was also applied research.

There are many examples of applied music therapy research that grew from basic research. Examples from research that was conducted in reinforcement include Hanser's (1974) application of behavior modification to her research on group-contingent music listening for boys with emotional disturbances and Jorgenson's (1974) use of behavior modification in her multiple baseline study of the use of a contingent music activity to modify behaviors that interfered with learning.

Basic research on the functioning of the brain has been followed by research on how the brain processes music, both of which led to applied research on how the brain is affected by different kinds of music therapy interventions. Koelsch (2009) provides a number of examples of basic research on functions of the brain and cites applied research on their connections to music therapy in the areas of attention, emotion, cognition, behavior, communication, and perception.

The presentation of research on the Neurologic Music Therapy (NMT) website (nmtacademy.co) makes the distinction and progression from basic to applied research clear, with separate listings for basic and clinical (applied) research in three areas: cognitive, speech and language, and sensorimotor. The *sensorimotor basic* listing includes, for instance, a study by Thaut, McIntosh, Prassas, and Rice (1992), "The Effect of Rhythmic Auditory Cuing on Temporal Stride and EMG Patterns in Normal Gait." It is easy to see how that and other studies led to the development of the NMT technique of rhythmic auditory stimulation (RAS), an example of which is shown in the applied research study, "Rhythmic Auditory Stimulation Improves Gait More Than NDT/Bobath Training in Near-Ambulatory Patients Early Poststroke: A Single-Blind, Randomized Trial" (Thaut et al., 2007). These studies show the progression of research from basic to applied.

Interpretivist research can also be basic research. Racette's (2004) study "A Phenomenological Analysis of the Experience of Listening to Music When Upset" could be considered basic research. Racette was interested in people's experience of using music when they were upset. In its most basic form, this study did not purport to use the results to help people use music as a tool to overcome being upset. A therapist who

uses Racette's results to formulate clinical interventions that use music to help clients who are upset and who then gathers information (possibly using the same phenomenological methods that Racette used) would be doing applied research. The lines between basic and applied research are not always clear. For example, since Racette made suggestions for practical uses of her results, her research would be classified as applied.

Research Frameworks

As used here, *framework* refers to the stages of doing a research study as well as the sequences for following up on previous research studies. Frameworks, then, provide guidance on how the different types of research should be sequenced in the knowledge-building process. Robb and Meadows (2015) explain:

> Research frameworks illustrate and describe the progression of research, including basic and exploratory concepts, theoretical and developmental studies, and evaluative studies examining intervention effects and translation of findings to clinical practice. Older models were criticized for their depiction of research as a linear process; newer models emphasize a more cyclical, interdependent process. (p. 21)

The Medical Research Council has identified four key stages in researching treatment strategies such as those used in music therapy. First is the development stage, which involves defining the treatment strategies clearly in terms of both process and outcome, while also ensuring that there is sufficient evidential and theoretical justification for studying the strategy. Second is the feasibility and piloting stage, which involves addressing all issues regarding the recruitment, selection, and randomization of the participants, estimating sample size, and using pilot studies to determine the suitability of the design for the participants selected. Third is the evaluation stage, involving assessing the effectiveness of the strategy in producing the desired outcome, understanding the process of change undergone during treatment, and assessing the cost effectiveness of the treatment. Fourth is the implementation stage, which involves finding the best ways to disseminate findings of the study to the target audiences (e.g., practitioners, researchers, decision-makers), disseminating the findings, and then monitoring how well the findings are being utilized.

As music therapy researchers recognize the different needs and purposes of research at each stage, music therapy research will develop more efficiently, leading to more useful results. This awareness will also assist music therapy researchers in acquiring funding for research, as the research proposals will fit the most appropriate point of the process.

Classifications of Research

Research is often classified according to the methodological design or approach employed in a study. In objectivist research, the term *design* is used to distinguish one method of research from another. A design describes various ways of doing objectivist research. Key variables are (a) whether the study involves one or more groups, (b) whether the group(s) are already existing or purposely created for the research study, (c) whether the study involves one or more treatments, (d) how observation and treatment are sequenced, and (e) the strength of the evidence, that is, the extent to which if–then and cause–effect relationships can be proven. The section below describes the larger divisions of objectivist research, and later chapters in this book give specific details about the variations within each of these divisions (Bruscia, in press a).

Interpretivist research is more difficult to classify than objectivist research. The main reason is that it does not involve standard designs uniformly used by researchers across different fields. Instead, interpretivist research involves as many designs as there are researchers, studies, and disciplines. As a result, classifications of interpretivist research in education, for example, may be irrelevant for research in psychology, which may be inadequate for music therapy research. With this mind, the following classification scheme was formulated (Bruscia, in press b) to embrace a wide range of interpretivist research in music therapy. The classification is based on the focus or purpose of the research and/or the method of data processing.

Other types of research are also used in music therapy, and these do not easily fit within either objectivist or interpretivist approaches or fit easily within both.

Types of Objectivist Research

The typology of objectivist research presented is traditionally accepted by the natural and social sciences, and the definitions have been constructed to include all the variations contained within each type (Bruscia, in press a). Notice the sequence: No experimental manipulation moves up the evidence ladder to manipulation of individual participants or very small groups, to manipulation of one experimental group, to the comparison of an existing group with a matched group, then to a comparison of experimental and control group(s), to the comparison of the effects of manipulation on several groups, and finally to a synthesis of research on a particular question.

- *Single subject and small* n *research* involves the analysis and comparison of the effects of one or more treatments on an individual or group of individuals, accomplished through the repeated measurement of the baseline (dependent) variable) before and after treatment(s) (independent variable). These designs differ from the others in that in-depth and rich data are collected for single or small samples, rather than limited data on larger samples.
- *Descriptive research* is the study of the characteristics of a population or phenomenon when the researcher does not manipulate any of the variables. The aims are to describe: the incidence of selected variable(s), the degree to which they vary in relation to one another, and the extent to which they change as a function of time or age.
- *Pre-experimental designs* are those that involve one group of participants that receive treatment and are then measured to determine the effects of treatment.
- *Quasi-experimental designs* are those that compare the effects of treatment on an existing group with another existing group that has not received the treatment. The groups have to be closely matched.
- *Experimental designs* are those wherein two or more groups are created specifically for purposes of experimentation. Ideally, participants of each group are randomly selected from a defined population. Pretests may or may not be administered. The groups then receive the same or different treatments, and posttests are administered. Experiments are designed to determine if–then or cause–effect relationships.

Types of Interpretivist Research

The types of interpretivist research presented here were developed by Bruscia (in press b). The main basis for this typology is the focus and purpose of the research, then the methods or techniques used in collecting and analyzing the data; it is not the truth value of the findings. The typology parallels the process of clinical work in music therapy: The client and therapist act and interact in a real-life setting (*natural setting approaches*), using various media (*music-focused, language-focused,* and *meaning-focused approaches*) to engage the client (*case approaches*) in therapeutic experiences (*phenomenological approaches*) that can be understood in various ways (*theoretical approaches*). (Note: Music-focused research will be discussed in the next section.)

- *Natural setting approaches* are concerned with what happens, what people do, or how people interact in a specifically defined situation or context. The aim is to discover how people fulfill their needs, influence others, and derive meaning out of their actions and interactions. Observations may focus on in-vivo behaviors, actions, interactions, and events, as well as the environments, conditions, or circumstances of their occurrence. In clinical practice, the focus may be on what happens in an actual music therapy session or environment, how clients and therapists spontaneously act and interact, and what significances or meanings their actions and experiences have. Related chapters in this book include naturalistic inquiry, ethnography, and action research.
- *Phenomenological approaches* are concerned with how a person perceives, feels, thinks, and derives meaning from

a *lived* phenomenon, that is, something that a person has actually experienced. For example, in clinical practice, how do clients describe their experiences of improvising with the therapist, or how does a therapist experience working with a particular client? Related chapters in this book include phenomenological inquiry and first-person research, as well as the numerous variations within these two approaches.

- *Meaning-focused approaches* are concerned with the various meanings that are given to actions, experiences, and materials and how these meanings affect people. Of particular interest in music therapy is what the various clinical data mean. How can various types of clinical data be interpreted in order to gain insights into the client, the therapist, and the therapeutic process? In music therapy, the focus is on different interpretations of the various verbal and nonverbal materials that result from the actions and experiences of client and therapist during a session. This may include an audio or video recording of a session or the music made by the client and therapist, a musical score or graph of the music, a drawing or sculpture, a journal entry, a poem or story, or a transcript of imagery or verbal dialogue. Related chapters in this book include hermeneutics, critical inquiry, arts-based research, and morphological research.

- *Language-focused approaches* are concerned with how people use words to express themselves, communicate with and influence others, and find meaning in their events, experiences, and materials. In clinical practice, an example would be to study the language that clients use to describe their own encounters with making and listening to music. Related chapters in this book include discourse analysis, content analysis, and narrative inquiry.

- *Theoretical approaches* are those that derive theories from analyzing the regularities, themes, and relationships in data of all types. These are methods of data processing, rather than research paradigms. Related chapters in this book include grounded theory, repertory-grid technique, consensual qualitative research, and thematic analysis.

- *Case approaches* are concerned with a particular individual or group or a particular phenomenon (e.g., songwriting, client anger). Here the focus shifts from particular aspects of a phenomenon, such as events, experiences, etc., to the very nature of the person or group involved in them or the very nature of the phenomenon itself. In clinical practice, an example would be to study many aspects of an individual or group or many different occurrences of the same phenomenon. Related chapters in this book include case study research, first-person research, and those chapters on other methods that focus on cases.

Other Types of Research

Other types of research is a group of approaches used in music therapy that, for one reason or another, cannot be easily classified as either objectivist or interpretivist (Bruscia, in press c):

- *Microanalysis* is a method of collecting data rather than a complete research method in itself, and the data gathered may be processed in either an objectivist or interpretivist fashion. It involves studying very small segments of an unfolding stream of data (such as an improvisation, or session, or series of sessions) in order to discover recurring themes or other regularities that might characterize the entire data stream.

- *Music research* is a focus rather than a method of research. It deals with the music created by client or therapist in a session or the music that the client and therapist listen to as part of the therapy. It can be implemented with either an objectivist or interpretivist perspective.

- *Mixed methods research* involves collecting a combination of quantitative and/or qualitative data in the same study in order to enrich and extend the findings.

- *Systematic review, meta-analysis,* and *interpretivist synthesis* are methods of integrating previous findings of either objectivist studies only, interpretive studies only, or a combination of both, all dealing with the same topic or research question. The studies are carefully selected and analyzed to yield more definitive conclusions about the findings.

- *Historical research* is different from all other research in that new data are not generated or collected; instead, already existing sources of data are carefully analyzed. The aim is either to assemble facts about the past or to interpret the past to gain further insight.

- *Philosophical inquiries* are different from all other research in that they scrutinize ideas and ways of thinking rather than gathering and analyzing traditional forms of data. They also do not favor one epistemology over another, but rather continually challenge their assumptions, meanings, and implications.

Issues in Music Therapy Research

There are, of course, numerous issues in music therapy research, many of which are discussed in chapters of this book. Two—evidence-based practice and the relevance of research to practice—will be discussed here. Both of these have significant implications for research in the field.

Evidence-Based Practice

Evidence-based practice (EBP) is defined as the "conscientious, explicit, and judicious use of current best evidence in making decisions about care of individual patients. The practice of evidence-based medicine means integrating individual clinical expertise with the best available external clinical evidence from systematic research" (Sackett, Rosenberg, Gray, Haynes, & Richardson, 1996, p. 71). EBP represents the combined use of (a) systematic reviews of the scientific literature, (b) practitioner experience and opinion, and (c) patient or client preferences and values for making clinical decisions and treatment and intervention planning. All three elements of EBP are important for a full understanding: Systematic reviews summarize the results of a number of studies in an area, either verbally or numerically, according to criteria that determine which studies will be included. The inclusion of practitioner experience and opinion takes into account the expertise of the clinician (which would include the music therapist), and the inclusion of patient or client preferences and values means that the needs and wishes of the client are considered.

Many music therapists acknowledge the need for EBP. The American Music Therapy Association (AMTA) includes the following statement as part of the AMTA Strategic Priority on Research: "Evidence-based practice: MTs will adopt nationally endorsed evidence-based protocols founded in sound theory and demonstrated via outcomes studies of efficacy and/or effectiveness" (American Music Therapy Association, 2015).

Some music therapists, though, share a concern that the types of evidence that are generally considered acceptable in EBP do not reflect the goals that they have in therapy and thus their work with clients. One important reason is that EBP stems from an objectivist approach to research and does not always address the issues important to interpretivist research. Abrams (2010) addressed this concern when he explored four contrasting ways of understanding evidence-based practice in music therapy. He used Wilber's (2001) Integral Model to explore four worldviews, which he labels "epistemological domains of evidence" (p. 354), and suggests that EBP can be understood using any of these. These worldviews, based on Wilber's quadrants, accept different types of evidence for music therapy. *Objective music therapy evidence* looks for causal relationships between music therapy interventions and specific clinical outcomes. *Interobjective music therapy evidence* examines systemic relationships among music therapy variables. *Subjective music therapy evidence* is concerned with personal experiences about and the meaning of music therapy processes and outcomes. Finally, *intersubjective music therapy evidence* demonstrates the role of the client's cultural, historical, and political contexts. More recently, Aigen (2015) has critiqued EBP, suggesting that effectiveness is only one thing upon which we might seek information on the benefits of music therapy. Other possibilities are: (a) whether clients are satisfied with music therapy services, (b) whether other individuals are satisfied with music therapy services, (c) whether music therapy benefits clients' lives in some way, and (d) whether music therapy benefits the institutions and communities in which it is offered.

Relevance of Research

Concerns about the relevance of research to music therapists' clinical practice have existed for many years. Several surveys of the attitudes of music therapy clinicians toward research, all done several decades ago, found that clinicians rated knowledge of research literature as low in importance (Braswell, DeCuir, & Maranto, 1980) or felt that the research that was published was not very relevant to their work (Nicholas & Gilbert, 1980). Gfeller (1995), after reviewing these and other studies, suggested that a problem in applying the results of research to the needs of clinicians might be that the research did not address the populations with which people work.

Aigen (2005) wrote about this concern and his analysis of the reasons for it, saying, "We begin with the 'real-world' problem that is at the source of the study, namely: There has been, and continues to be, a schism between researchers and clinicians in music therapy. Clinicians have continually observed that the research base of the field has been of limited applicability and relevance to actual clinical work" (pp. 470–471). Aigen provided a strong argument for the need for qualitative research as a way of making research match the clinical work that music therapists do in his doctoral dissertation, titled *The Roots of Music Therapy: Towards an Indigenous Research Paradigm* (Aigen, 1991). Recently, Aigen wrote, "The study demonstrated that music therapy research methodologists operated from a view of science congruent with the received view and that the philosophical assumptions of this view conflicted with the premises of creative and improvisational approaches to music therapy" (2015, p. 13).

Although there is without a doubt a large increase in the amount of qualitative, or interpretivist, research, it is not clear whether this has led to an increase in how relevant music therapists find research to be.

One effort to bridge the gap between research and clinical practice is the Music Therapy Research Blog (http://www.musictherapyresearchblog.com), co-hosted by Blythe LaGasse and Andrew Knight, which includes the subtitle: "Bringing current research to music therapy clinicians." The information about the blog says:

> This site is for the working music therapy clinician in order to help with the goal of maintaining evidence-based practice. The purpose of this blog is to provide a resource for the music therapy clinician—where you can find unsolicited information on current research, ways to generalize findings into practice, and tips about maintaining an evidence-based practice.

Two recent studies address music therapists' perception of the relevance of research. In a survey of AMTA members, Waldon (2015) examined perceived barriers to integrating research into practice and the frequency of research-related activities. Respondents reported setting constraints (e.g., inadequate time or institutional support) and the inaccessibility of research findings (e.g., unclear research findings or perceived irrelevance of findings) as interfering most with the ability to integrate research evidence into clinical practice. Waldon also discovered that those with graduate degrees, working in medical or rehabilitation settings, and serving in research or academic capacities tended to engage in research activities (e.g., reading journals, attending research conference session, conducting research, and discussing research with colleagues) more frequently than other respondents.

In an attempt to assess current attitudes about the relevance of research among music therapists from around the world, Waldon and Wheeler (2015) surveyed music therapists to assess current attitudes toward research and its relevance to clinical practice. Based on 1,261 survey responses, including 787 from the United States and 474 from other countries, perceptions of relevance appear to be based on both cognitive features (e.g., how well features of research are understood) and affective features (e.g., questioning beliefs about research and practice). Additionally, perceived relevance appears to vary by: (a) sample, with international respondents perceiving research as more relevant than those from the United States; (b) educational attainment, with those who have higher degrees perceiving research as more relevant than as considered by others; and (c) occupational role, with those in research or academic roles perceiving research as more relevant than as viewed by clinicians or administrators.

Conclusion

This chapter has defined terms and concepts that are important in music therapy research. It has also provided an overview of some of the issues that are relevant to music therapy research. Many of the topics introduced here are covered in much more detail in other chapters.

At least one topic, though—stages in the research process—is discussed here but not elsewhere. It is introduced here because of its importance to many as they conceptualize at which point in the research process their study will fall. While this is currently most important for those applying for funding (at least in the United States), due to the focus of some of the U.S. funding agencies on where in the research process a particular study falls, it is likely to become more important as music therapists become more adept at identifying the point in the process at which their research study falls.

Many of the subjects introduced in this chapter, as well as in other parts of the book, can be viewed from many perspectives. Other chapters will, indeed, look at them from the viewpoints of their chapter authors and the focus of the chapter content.

Music therapy research is a huge and evolving area. This chapter—and this book—will help the reader to enter and participate in it.

References

Abrams, B. (2010). Evidence-based music therapy practice: An integral understanding. *Journal of Music Therapy, 47*(4), 351–379. doi:10.1093/jmt/47.4.351

Aigen, K. (1991). The roots of music therapy: Towards an indigenous research paradigm (Doctoral dissertation, New York University, 1990). *Dissertation Abstracts International, 52*(6), 1933A. (UMI No. DEY91–34717)

Aigen, K. (2005). Philosophical inquiry. In B. L. Wheeler (Ed.), *Music therapy research* (2nd ed., pp. 526–539). Gilsum, NH: Barcelona.

Aigen, K. (2015). A critique of evidence-based practice in music therapy. *Music Therapy Perspectives, 33*(1), 12–24. doi:10.1093/mtp/miv013

American Music Therapy Association. (2015). Strategic priority on research. Retrieved from http://www.musictherapy.org/research/strategic_priority_on_research/overview

Braswell, C., DeCuir, A., & Maranto, C. D. (1980). Ratings of entry level skills by music therapy clinicians, educators, and interns. *Journal of Music Therapy, 17*, 133–147. doi:10.1093/jmt/17.3.133

Bruscia, K. E. (1995). Differences between quantitative and qualitative research paradigms: Implications for music therapy. In B. L. Wheeler (Ed.), *Music therapy research: Quantitative and qualitative perspectives* (pp. 65–76). Gilsum, NH: Barcelona.

Bruscia, K. E. (2005). Research topics and questions in music therapy. In B. L. Wheeler (Ed.), *Music therapy research* (2nd ed.; pp. 81–93). Gilsum, NH: Barcelona.

Bruscia, K. E. (2014). *Defining music therapy* (3rd ed.). University Park, IL: Barcelona.

Bruscia, K. E. (in press a). Types of objectivist research. In B. L. Wheeler & K. M. Murphy (Eds.), *Introduction to music therapy research* (3rd ed.). Dallas, TX: Barcelona

Bruscia, K. E. (in press b). Types of interpretivist research. In B. L. Wheeler & K. M. Murphy (Eds.), *Introduction to music therapy research* (3rd ed.). Dallas, TX: Barcelona.

Bruscia, K. E. (in press c). Other types of research. In B. L. Wheeler & K. M. Murphy (Eds.), *Introduction to music therapy research* (3rd ed.). Dallas, TX: Barcelona.

Creswell, J. W., & Plano Clark, V. L. (2011). *Designing and conducting mixed methods research.* Thousands Oak, CA: Sage.

Denzin, N. K., & Lincoln, Y. S. (2008). Introduction: The discipline and practice of qualitative research. In N. K. Denzin & Y. S. Lincoln (Eds.), *The landscape of qualitative research* (3rd ed.; pp. 1–43). Los Angeles, CA: Sage.

Edwards, J. (1999). Considering the paradigmatic frame: Social science research approaches relevant to research in music therapy. *Arts in Psychotherapy, 26*, 73–80. doi:10.1016/S0197-4556(98)00049-5

Gfeller, K. (1995). The status of music therapy research. In B. L. Wheeler (Ed.), *Music therapy research: Quantitative and* qualitative perspectives (pp. 29–63). Gilsum, NH: Barcelona.

Hanser, S. B. (1974). Group-contingent music listening with emotionally disturbed boys. *Journal of Music Therapy, 11*(4), 220–225. doi:10.1093/jmt/11.4.220

Hiller, J. (2016). Epistemological foundations of objectivist and interpretivist research. In B. L. Wheeler & K. M. Murphy (Eds.), *Music therapy research* (3rd ed.; pp. 99–117). Dallas, TX: Barcelona.

Jorgenson, H. (1974). The use of a contingent music activity to modify behaviors which interfere with learning. *Journal of Music Therapy, 11*(1), 41–46. doi:10.1093/jmt/11.1.41

Koelsch, S. (2009). A neuroscientific perspective on music therapy. *The neurosciences and music III—Disorders and plasticity: Annals of the New York Academy of Sciences, 1169,* 374–384. doi:10.1111/j.1749-6632.2009.04592.x

National Science Foundation. (2015). Retrieved from http://www.nsf.gov/statistics/randdef/fedgov.cfm

Nicholas, M. J., & Gilbert, J. P. (1980). Research in music therapy: A survey of music therapists' attitudes and knowledge. *Journal of Music Therapy, 17,* 207–213. doi:10.1093/jmt/17.4.207

Racette, K. (2004). A phenomenological analysis of the experience of listening to music when upset. *Qualitative Inquiries in Music Therapy, 1,* 1–18.

Research. (2015). In *Merriam-Webster online dictionary.* Retrieved from http://www.merriam-webster.com/dictionary/research

Robb, S. L., & Meadows, A. (2015). Research frameworks: Ways to communicate about the state of the science and develop comprehensive programs of research. In B. A. Else & A. F. Farbman (Eds.), *Proceedings from*

MTR2025: Improving quality and access: Music therapy research 2025 (pp. 114–115). Silver Spring, MD: American Music Therapy Association.

Sackett, D. L., Rosenberg, W. M. C., Gray, J. A. M., Haynes, R. B., & Richardson, W. D. (1996, Jan. 13). Evidence-based medicine: What it is and what it isn't. *British Medical Journal, 312,* 71–72.

Thaut, M. H., Leins, A. K., Rice, R. R., Argstatter, H., Kenyon, G. P., McIntosh, G. C., Bolay, H. V., & Fetter, M. (2007). Rhythmic auditory stimulation improves gait more than NDT/Bobath training in near-ambulatory patients early poststroke: A single-blind, randomized trial. *Neurorehabilitation and Neural Repair, 21*(5), 455–459. doi:10.1177/1545968307300523

Thaut, M. H., McIntosh, G. C., Prassas, S. G., & Rice, R. R. (1992). The effect of rhythmic auditory cuing on temporal stride and EMG patterns in normal gait. *Journal of Neurologic Rehabilitation, 6,* 185–190. doi:10.1525/MP.2010.27.4.263

Waldon, E. G. (2015). Music therapists' research activity and utilization barriers: A survey of the membership. *Journal of Music Therapy, 52*(1), 168–194. doi:10.1093/jmt/thv001

Waldon, E. G., & Wheeler, B. L. (2015). [Perceived research relevance: A survey of music therapists]. Unpublished data.

Wilber, K. E. (2001). *A theory of everything.* Boston, MA: Shambhala.

1. Portions of this chapter are based on "Overview of Music Therapy Research" by B. L. Wheeler, in B. L. Wheeler (Ed.), *Music Therapy Research* (2nd ed.; pp. 3–19). Gilsum, NH: Barcelona.

Chapter 2

MUSIC THERAPY RESEARCH: A HISTORICAL PORTRAIT

Theresa R. Merrill

I thought how lovely and how strange a river is. A river is a river, always there, and yet the water flowing through it is never the same water and is never still. It's always changing and is always on the move. And over time the river itself changes too. It widens and deepens as it rubs and scours, gnaws and kneads, eats and bores its way through the land.
—Aidan Chambers, *This Is All: The Pillow Book of Cordelia Kenn* (2006, p. 371)

The image of a river of music winding through time has been an enduring metaphor as I explored our collective research history. Historically speaking, music therapy research is linked with theory, practice, and culture, and nowhere is that more clear that when one attempts the historical view. Looking within, one can be overcome with the details … but from above one is able to view a winding progression. Through this portrait, I hope to convey a sense of movement and overview. In framing *our story* of research, I am informed by the reflexive method of *Portraiture*, an arts-based phenomenological methodology (Lawrence-Lightfoot & Hoffman-Davis, 1997).

Introduction and Critique

The portraiture methodology (as with other interpretivist methods) examines the perspective of the portraitist (narrator) explicitly in order to provide an understanding of bias. While the context of this particular text does not allow for an in-depth self-hermeneutic, I am aware that narratives are reflective of the context of the writer and the time, place, and culture within which they are written. As a pluralist and English-speaking North American, I feel careful, perhaps even reticent, to presume a definitive narrative of music therapy research. So, for me, this exploration must begin with cautious criticism of the notion of *history.*

Histories are reductive and selective in nature (Carr, 1962). Any person who would write a history will naturally allow some things to rise to the surface of significance and others to recede. Music therapy is a relatively young profession, with published research in peer-reviewed journals dating only from 1964 (Gfeller, 1987). Histories can be problematic, as they frequently reflect the socially constructed perspective of the author and of a dominant group or groups for whom this *history* is true. Hadley (2013) reminds music therapists to be "vigilant and ever-mindful" of dominant narratives within our profession (p. 380) and to recognize the larger (possibly

political) implications of what we construct as *truth*. This pertains to implied truths of what music is, what healing is and who does the healing, what therapy is, how that is defined, and even what research is. Kenny (2006) cautions toward an awareness of research hegemony: where Western values exert influence (even dominance) over non-Western cultures of inquiry. I agree with her statement "we embody many histories" and the description of history as a "complex web of narratives, characteristics, qualities, and customs that bring an array of worldviews, values, aesthetic preferences, and skills into our field as a whole" (Kenny, 1998, p. 202).

"The belief in a hard core of historical facts existing objectively and independently of the interpretation of the historian is a preposterous fallacy, but one which is very hard to eradicate" (Carr, 1962 p. 10). Historical studies in music therapy have utilized the quantitative epistemological stance for the most part, yet there is evidence that some music therapist researchers employ qualitative epistemologies (Sewell, 2005) that include multiple ways of knowing and interpreting oral histories and lived experiences. Aigen (1996) and Hadley (1998) offer examples of qualitative approaches to understanding and interpreting past events and processes as they developed in both clinical models (Nordoff-Robbins Music Therapy and Analytical Music Therapy) and the founders of these models (Clive Robbins and Mary Priestley), respectively.

Caution acknowledged, histories have the potential to construct important narratives about formative events, processes, people, trends, and ideas. In the case of music therapy research, these narratives can be seen as an organic process of unfolding and generative meaning-making that has arisen (and continues to arise) within a broader context of ideas as they have unfolded in and between different cultural contexts. This portrait will frame music therapy research as being central to the development of our discipline globally. I believe that research will continue to exert tremendous influence as the discipline moves into the future nonmonolithically. Histories will serve our development most when written from the perspectives of the particular cultures within which the narratives emerged.

Historical narratives are particularly relevant now, as the discipline seems to be at a pivotal point in its development. In North America particularly, the discipline is dividing into specializations, with institutes, specialist certifications, specialist conferences, and symposia offering multiple opportunities for growth and development outside of academia. The extent to which this is a global phenomenon is unclear. Surely a reflection of organic growth within the discipline and profession, it is also a potent opportunity to reflect on our own development as a discipline—including the role of research (which can be seen as holding a central role in the development of specializations). This chapter offers a portrait of research history in music therapy through the portraitist's cultural lens, humbly acknowledging cultural stories that have yet to be told. Indeed, as Carr (1962) points out, "the content of history can be realized only as we experience it" (p. 153). Although I have made an attempt to reflect a cross-cultural narrative, access issues (including language) have necessarily limited the extent to which this is possible. Thus, while I am the *author of record*, this portrait is painted by many hands and by many voices. I hope that at some future date more detailed descriptions and oral histories will emerge from within non-English-speaking contexts.

Frameworks

Music therapy as a clinical and theoretical discipline is not monolithic. We are diverse in our inquiries. In the past 60 years, research has informed theoretical development, clinical practice, ethics, an understanding of music, and education and training. More recently, researchers seem to be exploring the profession through a postmodern framework: its position in society, its relation to other disciplines, including critical discourse of dominant narratives within the profession. It is an incredibly rich time. Never before have music therapy authors and researchers published so prolifically. Still, the discipline is marginalized in terms of funding for a broad range of research questions, methodologies, and cultures. In many parts of the world, music therapy research is dominated by universities and institutes and thus reflects bias within those cultures that further influence practice, research, reflection, and, most importantly, our ideas of what constitutes music therapy. In many parts of the world, music therapy is described as being *evidence-based,* yet some forms of evidence are emphasized over others. The deeper question of what constitutes evidence and how that evidence is obtained is an important one to ask. Abrams (2010) suggests that nondichotomous, integral understanding of this issue is meaningful to contemporary discourse on evidence-based practice. The current text, along with previous editions, offers the implicit suggestion that evidence lies across a continuum of philosophical, epistemological, and methodological contexts (Wheeler, 2005).

Definition

In creating a framework around which to view this historical portrait, it is helpful to define what is meant by *music therapy* and by *research.*

Bruscia maintains that defining the discipline is an important activity. In the recently published edition of *Defining Music Therapy* (Bruscia, 2014), he discusses the ongoing need for definition as a possible antidote for "continual soul-searching" (p. xxii). He also points out that the discipline is a dynamic one and that the process of defining needs to be flexible and responsive to changes within the practice (Bruscia, 2014). The fact that the discipline is performed differently in different contexts makes a strong case for pluralism in research as well as in practice. In the current professional climate, research drives the development of the discipline in every respect. This idea of a dynamic and unfolding discipline is germane to a historical viewpoint of research in that we have built upon knowledge, experience, and ideas since the seeds of our discipline were planted around the turn of the last century and especially since the *Journal of Music Therapy (JMT)* was first published in 1964. For purposes of this historical review, music therapy is defined by music experiences within the context of the therapeutic relationship and where a professional music therapist guides or contributes significantly to the study. I have chosen to relax the boundary of this definition somewhat in order to include research conducted prior to the emergence of the profession of music therapy in the 1950s.

Bruscia (2014) defines music therapy research as "a systematic, self-monitored inquiry which leads to a discovery or new insight, which, when documented and disseminated, contributes to or modifies existing knowledge or practice" (p. 196). This definition is an expansive one and covers those influential, early studies that served to inform the earliest music therapists in North America. At the present time and within a culture of specialization, a wealth of information arrives upon us from our own interdisciplinarity: from our interface with medicine, neuroscience, and other allied health fields; from musicology and ethnomusicology; and from the impact of the social sciences in the form of women's and gender studies, disabilities studies, theories of race, and so forth. These interfaces influence the shape of research as well. Locating music therapy research within larger theoretical, philosophical, and cultural frameworks that inform practice serves to shape theory and practice and gives voice to a broadening description of music therapy that is inclusive of multiple perspectives. Simultaneously and perhaps because of this trend toward specialization and interdisciplinarity, more depth is possible, and we see greater complexity and sophistication within methods than in previous years. For purposes of this chapter, I have chosen to focus on research that is conducted under the auspices of music therapy as a distinct discipline, interdisciplinarity notwithstanding. I am guided by my own understanding and interpretation of Bruscia's definition: Music therapy research is systematic investigation across a continuum of paradigms conducted by music therapists to understand a range of phenomena—effects of music, effects of music as therapy, music as experienced in therapy, the shared musical experience, the therapeutic relationship as experienced through or with music, and social issues arising within music therapy, in both clinical and community contexts.

Preparing the Canvas

Inquiry into the therapeutic uses and effects of music in human life has been going on for centuries, perhaps from the first time a patterned response was noted. Music therapy research as a distinct focus must clearly be viewed as emerging from within aesthetic philosophy, music psychology, and medicine. The recorded relationship between music and health can be traced back to the Greek philosophers Plato and Aristotle, whose philosophical research provides a foundation for any depth treatment of music therapy. Anthropological research offers that as an aesthetic, creative endeavor, humans use music for a number of social and perhaps survival purposes (Dissanayake, 2001; Levitin, 2006). Multiple artifact-style data suggest that music has been a human occupation for 40 million years. Research (as we currently define it) on music and health has taken place for hundreds of years, with more formalized research into music as therapy in the mid-1900s.

The question remains: Where should we begin? Music therapists are fond of reflecting upon the work of the early philosophers, and I mention it here to illustrate a development of human thought and inquiry and because I believe that we are still creating this path of inquiry. Philosophers and scientists explored phenomena with methods available to them that are reflective of the intellectual culture of the moment. Projecting ahead, it is poignant to think that our own methods and discourse will one day be analyzed from a larger context and seen as reflective of our own *moment*. Nevertheless, standing on one another's shoulders, the early philosophers built a scaffold of knowledge that continues.

Headwaters:
Origins of Music Therapy Research

A history of music therapy research can be framed as existing in two periods: the preprofessional and professional eras. By preprofessional, I refer to research that occurred prior to the establishment of the first professional association of music therapy, the National Association for Music Therapy (NAMT), in 1950.

Research in the Preprofessional Era

Gold and Rolvsjord (2006) suggest that music therapy research "can be understood as a loose web of ideas which are linked to each other and influence each other over time" (p. 140). The image of the loose web is evident when examining the literature that exists prior to the existence of an organized or professional discipline.

Before the establishment of the NAMT in 1950, an impressive and diverse body of literature contributed to the birth of the profession in the United States. Prior to that time, effects were noted, studied, and presented in a variety of research styles (Davis, 1987, 1993; Rorke, 2001). The International Society for Musical Therapists, founded by Eva August Vescelius in 1903, is evidence of the beginnings of interest in the effects of music on human behavior (Davis, 1993). It is unclear whether members of this group conducted systematic research. Perhaps the earliest evidence of a disseminated single case study design was in Sydney, Australia, in 1926, at a conference (Edwards, 2005).

Evaluating *research* prior to the 20th century is problematic. Ideas about research and what constitutes research have evolved over time, but it is interesting to track these origins and the ways in which people thought about music, how effects were deduced or induced, and the ways in which music was then applied therapeutically. Another problem in tracking early research lies in the nature of music therapy as an art/science hybrid. Considerable philosophical treatment of music as an art form (what we would now describe as philosophical inquiry) is traceable in written history to Plato and the early Greek philosophers (Ross, 1994). Through the centuries, the effects of music on humans and the ways in which humans use music in society have fascinated philosophers from multiple traditions. In later centuries, these philosophical writings reflected upon observable patterns of both effects and lived experiences that amounted to an empirical process of noticing patterns of observable effects over time within the music condition. These ideas would coalesce into a philosophical dialectic between empiricists (those who believed that knowledge is derived purely from the senses and through experience) and rationalists (those who believed that knowledge is gained through a process of deduction and logical experimentation (http:// plato.stanford.edu/ entries/rationalism-empiricism/ #pagetopright). This philosophical interest in music and its effects continued until around the 18th century, when observation (empiricism) and experimentation (rationalism) merged and became the foundation for medical practice from that time forward (Rorke, 2001). Indeed, this important philosophical movement is influential on the ways in which music therapy research has evolved and is still relevant to contemporary discourse and our current understanding of music therapy research.

18th Century. In 1749, in England, Richard Brocklesby published a medical treatise on the use of music in the cure of disease. The *experiments* cited were systematic in their time, but are presented in a way that contemporary researchers might describe as being isolated narratives depicting idiosyncratic responses to music. Still, they reflect the state of scientific inquiry of the time and seek to influence a theory and practice of music used for medical or therapeutic purposes. Indeed, Brocklesby begins his treatise with a hypothesis: that "the further and more frequent application of music will cure or mitigate various disorders" (Rorke, 2001, pp. 68–69), and the author aspires to an investigation that is the result of "prolonged observation and experiment" (Carapetyan, 1948, in Rorke, 2001, p. 67).

19th Century. Davis (1987) notes the work of two early scholars with dissertations published in 1804 and 1806 by the University of Pennsylvania Medical School: Atlee's *An Inaugural Essay on the Influence of Music in the Cure of Diseases* and Mathews' *On the Effects of Music in Curing and Palliating Diseases.* Again, these dissertations did not reflect experimentation in the current understanding of the practice but reflected 19th-century empiricism and speculation. Davis notes that both dissertations note effects and make recommendations that have stood the test of time and been verified by contemporary studies: the *Iso principle* and the importance of personally significant musics in therapy. These two works may document the first systematic investigation of music as a therapeutic modality in North America and, along with Brocklesby, may well be the first set of *shoulders* on which we built the scaffold of practical knowledge about the effects of music and its use in medicine.

Throughout the 19th century, a handful of papers published mostly by psychiatrists attested to positive effects of music used in and as therapy. An early example of experimental research can be observed in a report in an 1878 issue of the *Virginia Medical Monthly.* In this experiment, music sessions were conducted from a piano while physicians recorded physiological data and behavioral observations. Unfortunately, none of these data survived, and the report is nonspecific; however, the effects were apparently compelling enough that funding was obtained for additional research (Davis, 1987).

James L. Corning published the first systematic experimental research in music therapy in North America, "The Use of Musical Vibrations Before and During Sleep: Supplementary Employment of Chromatoscopic Figures: A Contribution to the Therapeutics of the Emotions," in 1899 in *Medical Record.* The therapeutic method combined listening to recorded classical music with visual imagery prior to sleep. Corning deduced that this method reduced the presence of morbid thoughts during the waking hours (Davis, 1987).

20th Century Renaissance: The Water Is Wide. Compared with the previous century, the 20th century (prior to 1950) represents a renaissance of research into therapeutic music phenomena. In the early 20th century in North America, three American women began the practice of music therapy and studied the effects of that work empirically (Davis, 1993).

The National Association for Music Therapy (NAMT) published its first journal, the *Journal of Music Therapy,* in 1964. The second issue, also published in 1964, featured an extensive article by William and Margaret Sears, who reviewed music therapy research abstracts from 1921–1958. They reprinted 170 abstracts that highlight the presence of a burgeoning culture of music therapy research in the early and mid–20th century (preprofessionally). Indeed, this review of abstracts encompassed the entire issue of *JMT.* The stated purpose was to review research from the early years of the 20th century. The authors identified certain criteria for inclusion in this list of abstracts: "Each abstract was to be of sufficient length, detail and thoroughness for it to stand for the original article for most reference purposes" (p. 33). Perhaps the authors did not imagine that some materials would be of interest to future generations of music therapists, as they omitted research abstracts from NAMT yearbooks 1951–1958, stating that "the committee members would have access to them" (p. 33).

The authors developed a coding device that classified each abstract descriptively, including a code to indicate the presence of a bibliography, followed by the number of references that were included. They then described the source of data, the *method of treatment* (which seems to refer to research method), and the *manner of treatment* (e.g., general, intensive). The methodological reference (method of treatment) is of particular relevance to this historical inquiry. Multiple references to methodology were used to classify each abstract, so frequency ratings would not be an accurate portrayal of discrete methods; however, it is interesting to note the prevalence of experimental, comparative, analytical, statistical, and descriptive codes used to classify the majority of the abstracts (though no definition of these terms is contained within the article). From my cursory review, it seems that in the early 20th century there were attempts to control variables; to compare treatment groups with control groups; to measure effects, outcomes, and behaviors; and to describe the application of music as a therapeutic modality.

The Widening River. The 20th century saw the growth and development of the profession in Australia. Indeed, the first music therapy case study research was presented in 1926 in Sydney (Edwards, 2005). In the first self-report study in that country (1950), patients were asked for their responses to attending a concert as part of therapy (Edwards, 2005).

An important text, *Therapeutic Music Pedagogy,* was published by music educators in Argentina around 1948 (Wagner & Benenzon, 1993). This text is reported to have stimulated the development of research in Argentina, but there is little evidence to suggest published studies existing prior to the 1970s.

Preprofessional Themes: Priming the Canvas. Within the portraiture methodology, the process of unfolding themes is iterative, and while the presentation of this process for this publication is by necessity brief and truncated, the process for this author represents an unfolding narrative of early music therapy researchers. This involved keen observation, a commitment to recognizing patterns of responses, and studying these effects within contemporary frameworks that defined research at the time and with a seeming sense of *foundation.* These clinician–researchers (many of whom were physicians) established a strong background on which to build.

Of course, by the time the 20th century is examined, a reader can begin to recognize research methodology that is familiar to us. It appears that the growing profession of music therapy in the United States, Argentina, and Australia used early studies as seminal sources of evidence on which to build an established professional practice of music therapy. These were in addition to research being conducted on medical aspects of music in many countries, English and non–English-speaking. For example, a listing of PhD dissertations done in German universities traces them in 1822, 1824, 1836, 1934, 1939, and later (Pfeifer, 2015); an overview of the use of music in hospitals (Taylor, 1981) includes a number of examples of early research on the use of music in medical treatment; and a report by Lecourt (1993) describes early research using music in psychiatry in France by Pinel and his followers. Coupled with a deep conviction that music held potential to powerfully affect a range of human conditions and suffering, these seminal sources provided impetus for clinical work and for the education of music therapists in a distinct discipline. These early, committed researchers *primed the canvas* for practice, theory, and contemporary approaches to music therapy research.

Research in the Professional Era

I have chosen to date this period from 1950, which marks the founding of the first professional organization designated as music therapy–related, NAMT. That being said, it is important to note that music therapy as a profession was established at different times in different countries, so the notion that the professional era has a singular start date is necessarily arbitrary and reflective of a North American worldview. For example, an important early text in the German language, *Musik in der medizin. Beiträge zur musiktherapie* (Teirich, 1958), was written in 1958. This text contained theoretical and historical chapters as well as medical research on the use of music as therapy. By my definition, this would be considered a preprofessional work in German, as music therapy was not established as a profession in Germany until 1978, but I include this work in *professional era* publications because it is subsequent to the formation of NAMT in the United States.

As previously noted, the first professional organization for music therapists, NAMT, was formed in 1950. Those early leaders understood the role of research in the emerging profession. In 1951, the research committee identified an important role as "publicizing information on experiments, findings, conclusions, and research projects" ("Research," 1952, p. 179). In the same year, Gilliland notes: "While many of the effects of music on the human organism have been measured scientifically, it has been pointed out that more research is necessary. It is expected that those trained in therapeutic procedures will be able to spend a portion of their time in research" (1952, p. xii).

In 1958, Juliette Alvin and some others formed the British Society for Music Therapy and Remedial Music, but there is every indication that there was a significant practice of music therapy in the UK for at least 20 years prior to that. Edwards

(2005) notes that the practice in the UK developed experientially and that these foundational therapists (Alvin, Nordoff and Robbins, Priestley) contributed mightily to the research literature through the use of single case study designs and were less behaviorally focused in their work than their American counterparts. The *British Journal of Music Therapy* began in 1968. The journal has undergone several changes of name and focus over the years, including a re-envisioning and the beginning of the *Journal of British Music Therapy* in 1987, with a notable commitment to the publication of empirical research (Wigram, Rogers, & Odell-Miller, 1993). The journal is moving to online publishing with Sage of the *British Journal of Music Therapy* in 2016.

The first issue of the *Journal of Music Therapy* was published in the United States in 1964. That first issue contained no research, but the theoretical papers allude to current research that seemed to be taking place at the time. Supporting and publishing research was clearly a mission for the journal. Indeed, in his regional report, Dr. John D. Graham of the New England Chapter of NAMT writes, "research will lead to music therapy being established on a sound scientific basis so that treatment can be appropriately prescribed and effectively carried out" ("Association Activities," 1964a, p. 31). Clearly there was a sense that research should inform practice. Further, in that same report of association activities, it is reported that "Members of the NAMT Research Committee are initiating a study of music therapist classifications and salary ranges in various types of hospitals in the United States. The committee also is identifying specific areas of needed research in music therapy" (p. 30). While not clinical research, this proposed study may have been one of the first demographic studies within the newly established profession ("Association Activities," 1964b, p. 30).

In the United States, the important volume edited by E. Thayer Gaston, *Music in Therapy,* was published in 1968. This book contains a chapter by George L. Duerksen (1968), "The Research Process," which gives clear direction for research that is situated within the American cultural context and is reflective of the dominant narrative of that time as it was unfolding in the United States. This is distinguished from European thought, which will be discussed at a later time.

Canadian music therapists contributed important history during the 1970s. The *Canadian Journal of Music Therapy* was published in 1973 in both English and French languages. Canada is perhaps unique in the world in that there are distinct and unique cultures, languages, and models of practice defined by region and culture within a single country. To my knowledge, *CJMT* is the only explicitly bilingual music therapy journal. Canadian music therapy research practice has explored multiple identities over time, and the research culture blends both American and European perspectives with a distinctive Canadian social context to contribute unique research grounded in clinical work. More recent developments in Canadian research will be discussed later.

Gfeller (1995) compiled data from Jellison (1973) and

Gilbert (1979) that analyzed trends in music therapy research in the *Journal of Music Therapy* from 1964–1979 and noted the following trends: a significant increase (from 13% to 45%) in experimental studies, a significant decrease (from 41% to 7%) in philosophical studies, and relative stability in both descriptive and historical studies (from 44% to 48% and 2% to 0%, respectively). It is important to note that these trends are reflective of the *Journal of Music Therapy* only and do not include other forms of dissemination. Moreover, use of the word *trends* seems to refer exclusively to methodological trends. Bunt (1994) had earlier compared British publication trends with those of both Jellison and Gilbert and found similar trends in the UK publication as in the U.S. publication.

Two surveys of journals examined trends from 1964, when the first *Journal of Music* Therapy was published, until early parts of the 21st century. Brooks (2003) examined articles from nine music therapy journals over a 37-year period, from the time that they were first published until 2001, looking for trends and types of articles and comparing them across journals. Silverman (2006) examined the rich history of case study research in the *Journal of Music Therapy, Music Therapy,* and *Music Therapy Perspectives* from 1964–2003. While single case studies are at times viewed as subordinate to experimental research and randomized controlled trials, others maintain the importance of this research genre (Aigen, 1995; Aldridge, 2005; Barlow & Hersen, 1984; Hanser, 1999; Silverman, 2006; Smeijsters, 1996).

Edwards (2005) compiled a list of refereed journals in music therapy that were published in English; it is reproduced with additions in Table 1. Although only *the Journal of Music Therapy* began publication in the early professional era to which this section refers, it is useful to

view the table at this time—noting the intervening years and speculating on the influences that precipitated the birth of these English-language journals. All that were published at these times continue to be published. Some more recent developments will be discussed in a later section. *Musiktherapeutische Umschau,* the publication of the German Music Therapy Society (DMTG), an important non-English music therapy journal, has been published since 1979. Other non-English journals, some of which will be introduced later in this chapter, are also published.

The growth of research appears to be influenced by several other developments in a country: (a) the initiation of music therapy training programs, which have an impact on the development of music therapy and thus research; (b) the establishment of doctoral programs, which is probably related to the availability of music therapists who have PhDs and can thus supervise PhD students; (c) the existence of a professional association in the country; and (d) the publication of a journal. All of these influence the development of research and will be considered in the upcoming discussion.

The 1970s: Slack Tide. A slack tide is a time in the circadian rhythm of a body of tidal water when the tide is neither ebbing nor flowing. It is a calmer and less active period. Of course, it is the action and movement of a tidal body that carves the land, but it is the slack of the tide that settles the landscape and reinforces it in its stillness. My study of history as a discipline of inquiry indicates that human endeavor does not always move in a forward fashion. Carr, in his classic University of Cambridge lecture series (1962), notes that "no person ever believed in a kind of progress

Journal	Country of Publication	First Year of Issue
Journal of Music Therapy (JMT)	United States	1964
Canadian Journal of Music Therapy (CAM)	Canada	1973
Music Therapy: Journal of the American Association for Music Therapy (MT)	United States	1981(–96)
Music Therapy Perspectives (MTP)	United States	1982
British Journal of Music Therapy (BJMT)	UK	1987
Australian Journal of Music Therapy (AJMT)	Australia	1990
Nordic Journal of Music Therapy (NJMT)	Norway	1992
New Zealand Journal of Music Therapy (NZJMT)	New Zealand	1994
Voices: A World Forum for Music Therapy	Norway	2001
Approaches: An Interdisciplinary Journal of Music Therapy	Greece	2009

Table 1. Refereed Journals in Music Therapy Published in English*

*This list does not include the many creative arts therapy journals and bulletins published internationally or online publications in music therapy. The *South African Journal of Music Therapy,* no longer in publication, was not consulted.

Updated from J. Edwards (2005). Developments and Issues in Music Therapy Research. In B. L. Wheeler (Ed.), *Music Therapy Research* (2nd ed.), p. 21. Gilsum, NH: Barcelona. Used with permission

which advanced without reverses and deviations" (p. 153). He states also that the "effort which is needed to drive civilization forward dies away in one place and is later resumed in another" (p. 154). Music therapy research in the 1970s can be likened to a slack tide.

There were notable landscape-shaping developments in research during these years. The *Canadian Journal of Music Therapy* began publication in 1973. The *Journal of Music Therapy* published a number of empirical studies during the 1970s, many of which focused on the effects of reinforcement and aspects of behavior modification (Edwards, 2005). Even Ruud, a Norwegian who received his master's degree at Florida State University, did a theoretical research study for his master's thesis. *Music Therapy and its Relationship to Current Treatment Theories,* completed in 1973, was published in 1980 (Ruud, 1980) and later translated into several other languages, an indication of its value for the generation of knowledge internationally.

Christoph Schwabe was the first European music therapist to establish a clinical practice based upon an empirical grounding in East Germany (E. Ruud, personal communication, Dec. 14, 2015). His edited book from 1979 includes chapters on research (Schwabe, 1979). The first all–German-speaking music therapy conference (East and West Germany and Austria) took place in 1969 in Leipzig, Germany. Empirical research in music psychology and in musical experience in music therapy was presented (T. Wosch, personal communication, Dec. 15, 2015).

Perhaps most significantly, the first World Congress of Music Therapy took place in Paris, France, in 1974 (Wheeler, 2008). Conference chair Edith Lecourt noted that the general timbre of the conference was clinical and *pragmatic*. Rolando Benenzon (2009) reflects that this congress seemed to be one of giving papers on clinical work. Diverse in interest and foci, it was not research-oriented; however, this congress serves as a baseline for this historical exploration, a barometer for the progress of research globally. In contrast, the most recent world congress in Krems, Austria, hosted 125 research posters and 212 concurrent sessions (not all of which were research presentations; Fachner, Kern, & Tucek, 2014).

An important international gathering of music therapists occurred in Witten-Herdecke, Germany, in 1978 (Wheeler, 2003). A number of academically trained people from 12 countries met there for a symposium that helped to launch the *Mentorenkurs,* a course that was held from 1978 to 1980 and was the vision of the late Johannes Th. Eschen, who built an eclectic training course that included Nordoff-Robbins Music Therapy and Priestley's Analytical Music Therapy. Students from this course later became prominent clinicians, educators, and researchers around the world (L. O. Bonde, personal communication, Dec. 15, 2015). This gathering has been considered by some to be the beginning of what became much larger international collaboration among music therapists. One outgrowth of the Herdecke symposium was another symposium on the development of music therapy

theory, in Dallas, TX, in 1979, as well as later symposia and communications.

The 1980s and 1990s: Crosscurrents. A number of things occurred to influence music therapy research in the 1980s and 1990s. Just like crosscurrents in a river, they impacted other ongoing events.

Music therapists were conducting research in many European countries. Compendiums of music therapy research were compiled in two issues of the *European Music Therapy Research Register* (Smeijsters & Rogers, 1993; Smeijsters, Rogers, Kortegaard, Lehtonen, & Scanlon, 1995).

In the UK, City University in London provided a fulcrum for the development of research in the early 1980s. The Music Therapy Charity sponsored the first Research Fellowship in Music Therapy at a British University in 1980, leading in the early part of the 1980s to a series of outcome-based research studies with a strong ethological underpinning. The Music Therapy Charity was established in the UK in 1969 and, since that time, has enabled countless music therapists to undertake research at the postgraduate and doctoral level, helping the profession to flourish. For many years, the Music Therapy Charity funded a PhD position at The City University, London, and it has supported a number of key UK music therapists in completing their doctoral studies (Penny Rogers, personal communication, Jan. 3, 2016).

German music therapy has a long history, beginning well before the formal development of music therapy with studies on music and medicine. Austria, another German-speaking country, is also part of this history. Schwabe's work in East Germany has already been mentioned, as have the journal *Musiktherapeutische Umschau* and the Herdecke Symposium and *Mentorenkurs* in Witten-Herdecke. Other publications that included research were also being produced. Two compilations of research are important and give a sense of the breadth of the research that was and is being done. Pfeiffer (2015) compiled a listing of doctoral dissertations in music therapy or in other disciplines with a connection to music therapy. Monika Nöcker-Ribaupierre (2013) surveyed the heads of university music therapy programs in Germany, Austria, and Switzerland to learn of research that was being conducted. She reports information beginning with the PhD programs, then the different university programs and research projects related to them, and finally scientific research from other related disciplines, providing relevant knowledge for music therapy research and practice.

The following was reported on music therapy research in The Netherlands:

> Since 2003 at the Universities of Applied Sciences, research centres have been established for research into the arts therapies. One of these centres is KenVaK, in which Zuyd UAS, Utrecht UAS, ArtEZ UAS, and Stenden UAS cooperate. Another centre has been established at Arnhem-

Nijmegen UAS. In these research centres, research into all arts therapies (drama, music, art, dance–movement) takes place. There is cooperation between the research centres at UASs and scientific universities, where students after their master's degree from UASs can do their PhD. At this time, several PhD studies on music therapy are in progress. (Smeijsters & Vink, 2010)

After 30 years of professional published research, a critique arose from within the ranks of clinicians (especially in North America) that research had *lost touch* with the real-life practice of clinicians in clinical settings and had ceased to be relevant (Braswell, DeCuir, & Maranto, 1980). Nicholas and Gilbert (1980) explored attitudes of music therapists toward research, and their findings indicate that a gap had arisen between clinicians and researchers. Some concern arose among the respondents about the use of *distancing* jargon in research that served to further alienate clinicians. Survey respondents soundly critiqued the overall usefulness of research. Finally, the authors indicated that clinicians reported feeling unprepared to read and understand research reports and posed the question of whether to "distill research results for readers or to train readers to become more proficient in comprehending research studies" (p. 212). This study seemed to reflect an emerging narrative that clinicians needed research to be directly applicable to their lived experiences. It is unclear whether a similar *revolution* occurred in other countries and cultures.

Around this same time, Canadian authors spoke to a sense of isolation with regard to research (Moffitt, 1993), as they described education, training, and research as being siloed by region and institutional context. Also critical of a perceived gap between research and the lived experience of clinical work, several Canadian researchers began exploring qualitative methodologies linked with the first master's degree in Canada, developed by Carolyn Kenny at Open University in British Columbia. Perhaps some of the earliest iterations of arts-based research emerged in western Canada at this time (Bird, 1998; Merrill, 1998).

Confluence. A confluence is a geographical term used to refer to the point where two or more streams flow together, merging to create a single stream. What began as a critique of the dominant research paradigm in the early '80s became a robust critique and theoretical exploration that was firmly rooted in the qualitative discourse. Research was seen to inform theory development directly, and thus the *how* question arose in earnest. *How* is knowledge generated in this art/science/social hybrid discipline? What *is* music therapy, and where is the music experience reflected in our research tradition? These questions and more were central to discourse that shaped important changes in the research climate within the discipline.

Aigen (personal communication, Apr. 13, 2015) believes

that the qualitative movement actually began in 1982 at the International Symposium on Music in the Life of Man: Toward a Theory of Music Therapy. The symposium brought together a wide range of individuals, many of whom were music therapists, from around the globe to explore the topic of *music in the life of man.* In the study group titled "What are the appropriate/acceptable approaches to study musical experiences?," led by Clifford Madsen, the following were noted as possible approaches to study musical experience: historical descriptive (case study, interview, survey, observation), correlational analysis, experimental (probability theory, acoustics), phenomenological (eidetic, descriptive), semiotic, structural, introspective (insight and descriptions including meditation [zen]), and meta-analysis (Forinash & Kenny, 2015). Another subgroup discussed research and assessment in music therapy. This group identified feelings of frustration with the state of music therapy research and the problem of objectifying language (Kenny, 1989). A statement from the research/client assessment group (in reference to the musical content of therapy sessions) reads, "There was a sense of frustration that this material was not being shared effectively" and "This seemed to stem from the difficulty of objectively describing what happened within the sessions" (Kenny, 1989, p. 81). In this setting, participants identified qualitative research as a new area of inquiry for the field and a possible antidote to the *problem* of supposed objectivity. Later, Kenny presented phenomenology (both as philosophy and inquiry) as a bridge between the scientific and the artistic (1983, 1987, 1989). (One of the participants in the symposium, Danish philosopher Siggaard Jensen, 1981, had written an article, "Die 'Phänomenologie' der Musiktherapie," which may have been the first writing that made the connection between music therapy and phenomenology; E. Ruud, personal communication, Dec. 14, 2015.)

The first large-scale qualitative studies in the English language were published in the late 1980s, beginning with Kenny's (1987) doctoral dissertation *The Field of Play: A Theoretical Study of Music Therapy Process.* Also in 1987, Ruud explored an adaptation of phenomenology in his dissertation titled *Music as Communication and Interaction* (English translation; dissertation is in Norwegian; Forinash & Grocke, 2005). Forinash and Gonzalez (1989) presented a music-centered phenomenological methodology that they hoped would provide a way of representing "the heart of the work" (p. 36). They implemented a seven-step method to explore the experience of a terminally ill client who received music therapy.

By 1990, *Music Therapy: Journal of the American Association for Music Therapy* published two additional qualitative studies (Aigen, 1990; Amir, 1990). Both authors provide examples of sophisticated methodology offering nuanced meaning to the reader. Meanwhile, the qualitative movement was well under way in Europe. Kenny acknowledged European colleagues' contributions to the International Symposium on Music in the Life of Man in a personal communication: "The Europeans brought phenomenology and semiotics into our discussions. Even though they did not advocate phenomenological 'methods' in qualitative research, it was a powerful addition to the conversation for all of us. ¼ This is where I took my inspiration for 'The Field of Play' initially" (C. Kenny, personal communication, Apr. 21, 2015).

In the 1990s, Langenberg, Frommer, and Tress (1993) published a pivotal study utilizing *qualitative methodology* informed by social inquiry and utilizing triangulation to analyze improvisations in the Analytical Music Therapy tradition. Later, Langenberg (1996) reflected on early plans for an international symposium for qualitative research in music therapy during 1990 (1996, p. 4). With the support of David Aldridge of the University of Witten-Herdeke and Henk Smeijsters from The Netherlands, the first symposium was held in Dusseldorf, Germany, in 1994. Participants began a formal collaboration whose stated purpose was to "enter into dialogue about research methodology, cultural identity, subjective influences on each researcher's approach," and, further, "We are interested in developing qualitative research approaches to obtain a better understanding of our clinical work, our patients, and ourselves, while placing a high priority on communicating what we learn to other professionals" (Langenberg, Aigen, & Frommer, 1996, p. 1). Several International Symposia for Qualitative Music Therapy Research were held over the next years, with the last one in 2007. Sponsored by Mechtild Jahn-Langenberg and the Universität der Künste, Berlin, the symposium attracted qualitative research scholars from all over the world who gathered to discuss and develop their thinking about qualitative research. The first of these discourses (1994) was published in the 1996 text *Qualitative Music Therapy Research: Beginning Dialogues* (Langenberg, Aigen, & Frommer). Merrill (2002) and Edwards (2004) chronicled the content of the 2002 and 2004 symposia.

Another important voice emerged in the 1990s in the United States during this time of confluence: Cheryl Dileo initiated an important ethical discourse that deepened and expanded the traditional view of research to encompass the unique condition of music within the therapeutic relationship and the vulnerable populations with which music therapists work (Dileo Maranto, 1990). This was an important contribution and marked a scholarly agenda for Dileo that has benefited the profession as a whole and culminated in a broad treatise on *Ethical Thinking in Music Therapy* practice (including research; Dileo Maranto, 2000).

Music Therapy Research: Quantitative and Qualitative Perspectives, edited by Barbara Wheeler, was published in 1995. This book was important as the most comprehensive overview of music therapy research methods to date and paved the way for increasing international awareness of music therapy research. The 2005 edition of the book was much larger, more comprehensive, and more international than the first edition and reflected much of the growth of music therapy research.

In Scandinavia, the Nordic Network of Music Therapy Research (NorFa Network), led by Aalborg University from 1993 to 1996 (Pedersen & Mahns, 1996), was the beginning of Aalborg University's music therapy research program under the guidance of Inge Nygaard Pedersen and Lars Ole Bonde. The development of the Aalborg University program is presented later in the chapter, along with other developments of the 21st century.

The Delta. As a river nears its joining with the sea, the tempo of the current slows, and the land widens out into broad deltas. A delta is a rich ecosystem, often described as being a *cradle of civilization*.

Music Therapy: International Perspectives, edited by Cheryl Dileo Maranto (1993b), includes information by more than 67 authors who wrote about music therapy in 36 countries. Each author addressed research in his or her particular country. This book was important in advancing awareness of international music therapy before the Internet was available. Later, *Voices: A World Forum for Music Therapy* provided a way to learn about music therapy in other countries through its Country of the Month section.

Although the World Wide Web was launched in 1991, it did not have a discernable impact on the dissemination of music therapy research until later in the decade. Databases made many studies available to individual scholars and researchers who would not ordinarily have had direct access to them. This trend in information technology and the prevalence of the personal computer have impacted dissemination in ways early music therapy researchers could not have imagined.

The 21st Century: 2001 and Beyond

I want to reiterate that I write this historiographical portrait from the perspective of an English-speaking music therapist with Canadian roots living in the United States, and that a *history* of music therapy and music therapy research is an ongoing, living, dynamic, and generative process of cultural narrative. The discipline is developing in different and non–English-speaking parts of the world in ways that are unique to those cultures. The developments that are reported here are by necessity dictated by the information that has been available, much of which has been gathered from colleagues, and therefore does not include all countries in either Asia or Latin America.

Research in parts of Asia began with medical research. A variety of research on the effects of music in medical settings, beginning in 1990, is described in a Chinese publication (Du, 2007); information on this early research is not available in English.

In China, music therapy is reported to have a 30-year history, which places the beginning of modern music therapy at about 1985. The first graduate program in China was initiated in 1997 (Zhang, Gao, & Liu, 2016). It has been reported that the Japanese Music Therapy Association "recently started funding research in the area of EBM (Evidence-Based Medicine). There are quite a number of doctors and therapists working in this area, and this kind of quantitative research is also required by the government in order for music therapy to obtain public recognition" (Okazaki-Sakaue, 2003). In South Korea, recent music therapy research has been documented in a number of sources (summarized by Lee & Lee, 2016), covers a range of topics, and uses various methodologies. In South Korea, the first master's degree program began in 1997 (Lee & Lee, 2016). These are indications of a much shorter history of music therapy education and research in Asia and illustrate (as this history has endeavored to communicate) that the development of music therapy research is at different points in different countries at different times. No doubt, developing research cultures are influenced by more contemporary trends rather than those in the more distant past and cannot be understood as existing within a cultural vacuum, yet these developments *may* illustrate both indigenous ways of generating knowledge that is culturally unique and specific and ways that contemporary Western research is interpreted and experienced within varied cultural and intellectual contexts (due largely to Internet accessibility).

Music therapy and thus music therapy research also has been developing in Eastern Europe but, again, more recently than in some other parts of the world. Case studies are most commonly used in music therapy research at this time, although some researchers are conducting and publishing research using RCTs and other experimental designs. Published examples of experimental research by Eastern European researchers, included because they are available to the author and not claiming to be a comprehensive list, are by researchers from Estonia (Rüütel, Ratnik, Tamm, & Zilensk, 2004), Croatia (Katusic, Alimovic, & Mejaski-Bosnjak, 2013), and Poland (Bukowska, Kręẓałek, Mirek, Bujas, & Marchewska, 2016; Konieczna-Nowak, 2015; Stachyra, 2015).

Music therapy research in Latin America is expanding. It is guided by the Research Commission for the Latin American Committee of Music Therapy (CLAM). Gustavo Gattino, head of this commission, summarizes the development of music therapy research in Latin America as:

> Research activities have represented an important development in these last 10 years in Latin America with important research studies in many fields using different designs (qualitative and quantitative). These include case studies, theoretical studies, randomized controlled studies, translation and validation of assessments, phenomenological [studies], and naturalistic studies. Moreover, [in] the number of publications from Latin America in the Scopus database (realized 27 January 2016), [there] are found 11 publications from Latin America: Brazil

(6), Cuba (2), México (2) and Argentina (1). (G. Gattino, personal communication, Jan. 30, 2016 [slightly edited for English])

Also related to music therapy research in Latin America, Karina Ferrari (Argentina) and Gustavo Gattino (Brazil) created the Ibero-American Group of Research in Music Therapy (GIIMT; **www.giimt.com**) to generate opportunities for training and spreading research in the region. This group is working on assessment research and their validation and sponsors a conference every three years (K. Ferrari, personal communication, Jan. 28, 2016). And in Brazil, since 2009, Claudia Zanini and Clara Piazzetta have been documenting the research that Brazilian music therapists are doing in graduate programs (C. Zanini, personal communication, Sept. 18, 2015).

As another indication, the publication of non–English-language journals is on the rise. Latin American journals—of which there are now three—were initiated in the following years: *Brazilian Journal of Music Therapy* in 1996, *InCantare* (Brazil) in 2010, and *Ecos* (Argentina), planned for 2016. All three journals are open-access and accept publications in Spanish, Portuguese, and English. Similarly, in South Korea, in 1999, the *Korean Journal of Music Therapy (KJMT)* emerged as the first journal dedicated to the field of music therapy, and the *Journal of Music and Human Behavior (JMHB)*, formerly known as *Korean Journal of Music Therapy Education,* followed this development in 2004. The first issue of *Frontiers of Creative Arts Therapy and Education in China,* which includes music therapy articles, published its first issue in 2015. Poland has two journals, both Web-based: *Therapy through Art* (published since 2009) and *Polish Journal of Music Therapy* (published since 2014). These are provided as indications of both the emergence and development of music therapy research and as a reminder of the dynamic life of a discipline (including research) that is still growing.

Finally, important developments in Scandinavian countries have made significant contributions to the music therapy research culture. The international doctoral program at Aalborg University, begun as part of the NorFa Network and mentioned earlier in the chapter, grew under the leadership of Tony Wigram, who headed it from 1997 to 2010. Now led by Hanne Mette Ridder, the program includes PhD courses, supervisor training, and postdoctoral support. Young as well as mature clinicians from five continents have studied and received their PhDs through the program. The Aalborg University PhD program has had an enormous impact on music therapy research, stimulating collaboration and research far beyond those enrolled in it. As of February 2016, 41 PhD theses (dissertations) have been completed.

Brynjulf Stige and colleagues in Norway have done extensive research through GAMUT—The Grieg Academy Music Therapy Research Centre, which aims to provide research relevant to the professional practice of music therapy as well as to the understanding of music and health in society.

It is closely linked to the research institute Uni Research Health as well as to the music therapy education at the University of Bergen and aims to ensure a connection between research, academic training, and practice. Research initiated through GAMUT spans a range of topics. GAMUT is also a leader in other initiatives regarding music and health and the publisher of *Voices: A World Forum for Music Therapy* and the *Nordic Journal of Music Therapy.*

Jaakko Erkkilä at the University of Jyväskylä in Finland has pioneered work integrating theories of psychotherapy, music psychology, and music therapy and investigating, among other things, clinical improvisation and the effects of music therapy on depression through the Finnish Centre of Excellence in Interdisciplinary Music Research.

In North America, as graduate programs emerged in Canada, the research profile expanded to draw upon multiple theoretical influences. Graduate theses from Open University (directed by Carolyn Kenny) offered innovative explorations of qualitative inquiry across themes of culture and social justice. Theses from Wilfrid Laurier University draw on a range of research methodologies and reflect broad influences of their faculty. Graduate theses and other published work from individuals affiliated with Concordia University in Montreal indicate a diversity of research methodologies and areas, including Community Music Therapy, feminism, social issues (Curtis, 2012a, 2012b; Vaillancourt, 2011, 2012), and social gerontology (Young, 2013).

History and Contemporary *Moments*

"Situating ourselves in time is a basic human need" (Wineburg, 2001, p. 6). Historians differ in their beliefs about what constitutes *history* in terms of time frames. Some English texts assert that events or moments within the previous 50 years are considered contemporary events and thus do not characterize history. Other authors bracket *history* as that which occurs beyond a 20-year time frame (Hoffer, 2008; Wineburg, 2001). For a discipline as young as music therapy, I feel that it is useful to consider an alternate and constructivist view: that history is created *as* contemporary events occur in relation to past events (Carr, 1962). As a musician, I understand this philosophy of temporality, relation, and interpretation, as music is a phenomenon that arises and passes away in relatively short time frames, with sounds occurring in relation to one another. The interpretation of meaning is complex but subjective and context-bound, allowing for particular significance to arise from within specific contexts. Perhaps music therapists are well positioned to adopt a similar view of history. One purpose of historiography is to go beyond *reporting* events toward interpretation of the significance of events and processes (Hoffer, 2008).

In attempting to reflect on more recent events and trends (some of which may come to be interpreted as historically significant to music therapy research), I am influenced by

Lincoln and Denzin (1998), who note, "Writing the present is always dangerous" (p. 407). Those authors' characterization of *current history* of qualitative research as occurring in *moments* (Denzin & Lincoln, 2000) stands out as being a useful vehicle for presenting contemporary trends which (through the author's lens and in no particular or hierarchical order) may be deemed as holding significant impact for the present and future of music therapy research.

Moment 1: The Communication Age—Information Technology. Information technology as a social force for equalization and open access to research is an important trend that began at the opening of this century. In 2001, *Voices: A World Forum for Music Therapy* was launched with the express purpose of enabling international dialogue about multiple aspects of music therapy, including research (Kenny & Stige, 2001). *Voices* has since become a refereed journal. The impact of *Voices* on the dissemination of information and communication about music therapy has been tremendous. The website for the World Federation of Music Therapy (WFMT; http://www.wfmt.info/) includes many resources. Of particular interest in terms of publications is http://www.wfmt.info/music-therapy-today/, which includes links to the current issue, recent issues, and the archive *(Music Therapy World: 2000–2008).*

Approaches: An Interdisciplinary Journal of Music Therapy, is an open-access peer-reviewed journal that was first published in 2009. *Approaches* invites "diverse perspectives on music therapy practice, profession, and discipline. As a Hellenic-English publication, *Approaches* fosters interdisciplinary dialogue bridging local and global aspects of music, health, and well-being" (http://approaches.gr/).

The *Nordic Journal of Music Therapy* also began offering selected articles within issues as open-access from their website. These include various types of research articles. Databases such as Psych Abstracts, PsycINFO, and CINAHL have offered access to research across disciplines for many years, but subscriptions were expensive and access limited to music therapists who worked within institutions who owned subscriptions. As early as 1993, Dileo Maranto noted that, "American researchers and clinical authors need more access to international researchers and literature through online data-banks and electronic mail" (1993a, p. 650). In or around the year 2000, music therapy studies published in the *Journal of Music Therapy* and *Music Therapy Perspectives* became available to readers via several databases: Medline, PubMed, and Index Medicus (American Music Therapy Association, personal communication, Aug. 11, 2015). Dissemination of theses and dissertations has been available to researchers through the Educational Resources Information Center (ERIC) database and *Dissertations Abstracts International* (DAI) for several decades. The impact of this access to journals and papers on contemporary music therapy research cannot be overstated. Information technology makes advances in research possible through exhaustive reviews of literature, examinations, and improvements in research methodologies and makes the all-important practice of replication possible. Regrettably, the *Journal of Music Therapy* and *Music Therapy Perspectives* are no longer accessible to nonmember individuals and organizations.

Moment 2: Collating and Interpreting Primary Research—Cochrane Reviews. Cochrane reviews are systematic reviews of primary research in human health care and health policy. Cochrane reviews are essentially meta-analyses of primary research across a range of interventions that assess efficacy of treatment (http:// community. cochrane.org/cochrane-reviews). They are widely regarded as a source of reliable information on evidence-based approaches to care. The first Cochrane review of music therapy research for individuals with autism spectrum disorder was published in 2006 (Gold, Wigram, Elefant; it was revised in 2014 as Geretsegger, Elefant, Mössler, & Gold). Cochrane reviews on the efficacy of music therapy as intervention for a range of conditions are now published regularly. Most Cochrane author groups note inconclusive evidence on the efficacy of music therapy, citing overall low methodological quality, problems with short-term treatment, and small numbers of participants. Perhaps as a consequence of this, many researchers call for a greater number of randomized controlled trial studies within the positivist/postpositivist paradigm. Cochrane reviews of music therapy research may be historically significant as historical place-markers in the positivist tradition. As meta-analyses of primary research, the reviews imply that there is a body of research to collate and analyze. Seventy years into the professional era, Cochrane reviews may offer both longitudinal perspective and evaluative statements on the efficacy of treatment and the quality of research (from the perspective of the authors).

Moment 3: Expanded Ways of Living Music Therapy Research. Since 2000, music therapy researchers have made methodological advancements of understanding, implementation, and evaluation across ontological and epistemological paradigms. Moreover, modes of dissemination have expanded to offer greater possibilities for presentation of findings. The expansive nature of interpretivist studies has made it difficult to find music therapy journals willing to publish these larger and often arts-based works. Because online and open-access journals do not have the same imitations as paper journals, a greater number of large-scale studies have been able to be published intact in various sources. In 2004, Barcelona Publishers began publishing the *Qualitative Inquiries in Music Therapy: A Monograph Series.* This electronic format series offers qualitative researchers a venue for intact dissemination of qualitative research and makes a significant contribution to the literature. Viewing this present text along with its previous (Wheeler, 1995, 2005) editions, the reader readily

notices an increase from 24 chapters in 1995 to 41 in 2005. This present edition includes 68 chapters offering detail and depth across a range of epistemologies. Great attention is paid to in-depth treatments of methodologies and issues related to research design and interpretation (Wheeler & Murphy, 2016), with a wider range of authors than previously. This may be an indication that there is increased capacity for reading, understanding, and conducting research among a wider range of clinicians and scholars than at any previous time in the profession's history.

The increased availability of published music therapy research to researchers across disciplines is a welcome change that supports new research. Although undocumented, there is an impression that the number of clinician-researchers is increasing. That is, qualified researchers whose primary affiliation is with a clinical institution rather than an academic institution seem to be represented within the literature with greater prevalence than previously. This in stark contrast to the previously cited survey of clinicians (Nicholas & Gilbert, 1980), which concluded that research was out of touch with the experience of music therapy clinicians. It is truly the age of the clinician-researcher. This speaks to the need for quality education in research methods at all levels of education.

Moment 4: Specialization and Interdisciplinarity. With greater interdisciplinarity and collaboration, with increased opportunities and modes of dissemination available to music therapists, and with more music therapists reading, understanding, and conducting research, it stands to reason that music therapists are poised to contribute more substantially to the discourse on research itself. This has the potential of furthering an understanding of what the arts and humanities may contribute to living research, from the (possibly) unique effects of music on human neurophysiology to an ever-expanding exploration of arts-based ways of knowing, performing, and transforming. The development of clinical specializations within the profession may become one of the most influential trends in music therapy research in our history. The inaugural meeting of the International Association for Music & Medicine (www.iammonline.com), at which the by-laws of the association were agreed upon and the *Music and Medicine* journal launched, was held at the University of Limerick in 2009. The Association for Music and Imagery is another example of an organization that holds conferences and publishes music therapy research in their refereed journals.

Conclusion

At the time of this publication, the prevalence and importance of research to the practice of music therapy is almost incalculable.

The intention of this historical portrait of words is to offer an image of research within the discipline of music therapy as a river might move and develop through time. Our culture of research began as headwaters inspired by a belief in the effects of music for individuals experiencing various disabling conditions. Over time, music therapy practice has bridged multiple paradigms, worldviews, ontologies, and epistemologies. The phenomenon of music as experienced through a necessarily social context and joined to values of human caring has inspired scholars to explore questions about music in and as therapy. I agree with Stige (2015), who argues that research questions emerge directly from the practical contexts (p. 1) and are likewise not independent of theoretical constructs. Music therapy research paradigms and methodologies that have emerged over time offer multiple ways of creating knowledge, informing practice and building theory. Our rich history contributes mightily to an increased understanding of the ways in which music is brought to serve individuals, groups, communities, and societies in need.

Acknowledgments

While I am the acknowledged author, this portrait is a narrative constructed by many hands and voices. Over 30 individuals contributed to this chapter. Special acknowledgment must go to Barbara Wheeler, whose vast network of colleagues provided valuable input that would have otherwise been unavailable to me. Her skillful editing assisted in ensuring that as many voices as possible were included. Thanks and acknowledgement go to those individuals who allowed me to interview them, including Liz Moffitt, Kerry Burke, Carolyn Kenny, and Kenneth Aigen, and to my colleague Susan Hadley, whose shared interest in constructivist narrative provided opportunities for lively discourse during the writing and revision process. I further acknowledge and extend gratitude to the faculty of History and Philosophy at Eastern Michigan University for their generosity in discussing their discipline with me and in offering a contemporary discourse on qualitative and critical history and philosophy.

References

Abrams, B. (2010). Evidence-based music therapy practice: An integral understanding. *Journal of Music Therapy, 47*, 351–379. doi:10.1093/jmt/47.4.351

Aigen, K. (1990). Echoes of silence. *Music Therapy, 9*, 44–61. doi:10.1093/mt/9.1.44

Aigen, K. (1995). Cognitive and affective processes in music therapy with individuals with developmental delays: A preliminary model for contemporary Nordoff-Robbins practice. *Music Therapy, 13*, 13–46. doi:10.1093/mt/13.1.13

Aigen, K. (1996). *Being in music: Foundations of Nordoff Robbins Music Therapy*. Gilsum, NH: Barcelona.

Aldridge, D. (2005). *Case study designs in music therapy*. London, UK: Jessica Kingsley.

Amir, D. (1990). A song is born: Discovering meaning in

improvised songs through a phenomenological analysis of two music therapy sessions with a traumatic spinal cord injured young adult. *Music Therapy, 9*, 62–81. doi:10.1093/mt/9.1.62

Association activities. (1964a). New England Regional Chapter. *Journal of Music Therapy, 1*(1), 30–31. doi:10.1093/jmt/1.1.30

Association activities. (1964b). Research Committee. *Journal of Music Therapy, 1*(1), 30. doi:10.1093/jmt/1.1.30

Barlow, D. H., & Hersen, M. (1984). *Single-case experimental designs: Strategies for studying behavior change* (2nd ed.). Elmsford, NY: Pergamon Press.

Benenzon, R. (2009). The first nine World Congresses of Music Therapy. *Voices: A World Forum for Music Therapy, 9*(1). doi:10.15845/voices.v9i1.370. Retrieved from https://voices.no/index.php/voices/article/view/370/293

Bird, N. (1998). *I'm dangerous with sound: Music therapy with street-involved youth* (Unpublished master's thesis). British Columbia Open University, Burnaby, British Columbia, Canada.

Braswell, C., DeCuir, A., & Maranto, C. D. (1980). Ratings of entry-level skills by music therapy clinicians, educators, and interns. *Journal of Music Therapy, 17*, 133–147. doi:10.1093/jmt/17.3.133

Brooks, D. (2003). A history of music therapy journal articles published in the English language. *Journal of Music Therapy, 40*(2), 151–168. doi:10.1093/jmt/40.2.151

Bruscia, K. E. (2014). *Defining music therapy* (3rd ed.). University Park, IL: Barcelona.

Bukowska, A. A., Krężałek, P., Mirek, E., Bujas, P., & Marchewska, A. (2016). Neurologic Music Therapy training for mobility and stability rehabilitation with Parkinson's disease—A pilot study. *Frontiers in Human Neuroscience.* doi:10.3389/fnhum.2015.00710

Bunt, L. (1994). *Music therapy: An art beyond words*. London, UK: Routledge.

Carr, E. H. (1962). *What is history?* New York, NY: Alfred A. Knopf.

Chambers, A. (2006). *This is all: The pillow book of Cordelia Kenn*. London, UK: Random House.

Curtis, S. L. (2012a). Feminist music therapy: Transforming theory, transforming lives. In K. E. Bruscia (Ed.), *Readings in music therapy theory* (pp. 227–244). Gilsum, NH: Barcelona.

Curtis, S. L. (2012b). Music therapy and social justice: A personal journey. *Arts in Psychotherapy. 39*(3), 209–213. doi:10.1016/j.aip.2011.12.004

Davis, W. B. (1987). Music therapy in 19th-century America. *Journal of Music Therapy, 24*, 76–87. doi:10.1093/jmt/24.2.76

Davis, W. B. (1993). Keeping the dream alive: Profiles of three early twentieth-century music therapists. *Journal of Music Therapy, 30*, 34–45. doi:10.1093/jmt/24.2.76

Denzin, N. K., & Lincoln, Y. S. (2000). The discipline and

practice of qualitative research. In N. K. Denzin & Y. S. Lincoln (Eds.), *Sage handbook of qualitative research* (2nd ed., pp. 1–28). Thousand Oaks, CA: Sage.

Dileo, C. (2000). *Ethical thinking in music therapy*. Cherry Hill, NJ: Jeffrey Books.

Dileo Maranto, C. (1990). Ethical precautions in music therapy research. *Music Therapy Perspectives, 8,* 76–79. doi:10.1093/mtp/8.1.76

Dileo Maranto, C. (1993a). Music therapy in the United States of America. In C. Dileo Maranto (Ed.), *Music therapy: International perspectives* (pp. 606–662). Pipersville, PA: Jeffrey Books.

Dileo Maranto, C. (Ed.). (1993b). *Music therapy: International perspectives.* Pipersville, PA: Jeffrey Books.

Dissanayake, E. (2001). An ethological view of music and its relevance to music therapy. *Nordic Journal of Music Therapy 10*(2), 159–175. doi:10.1080/08098130109478029

Du, L. (2007). [Application of music therapy in medical fields in mainland of China]. *Si-Zhu, 13*(1).

Duerkson, G. L. (1968). The research process. In E. T. Gaston (Ed.), *Music in therapy* (pp. 409–424). New York, NY: Macmillan.

Edwards, J. (2004). Report of the 5th International Symposium for Qualitative Music Therapy Research. *Music Therapy Perspectives, 22*(2), 116–117. doi:10.1093/mtp/22.2.116

Edwards, J. (2005). Developments and issues in music therapy research. In B. L. Wheeler (Ed.), *Music therapy research* (2nd ed.; pp. 20–32). Gilsum, NH: Barcelona.

Fachner, J., Kern, P., & Tucek, G. (2014). 14th World Congress of Music Therapy: Cultural diversity in music therapy, practice, research and education. *Proceedings of the 14th World Congress of Music Therapy: Special issue of Music Therapy Today, 10,* 8–9. Retrieved from http://www.musictherapy2014.org/fileadmin/download/Congress_Proceedings.pdf

Forinash, M., & Gonzalez, D. (1989). A phenomenological perspective of music therapy. *Music Therapy, 8,* 35–46. doi:10.1093/mt/8.1.35

Forinash, M., & Grocke, D. (2005). Phenomenological inquiry. In B. L. Wheeler (Ed.), *Music therapy research* (2nd ed.; pp. 321–334). Gilsum, NH: Barcelona.

Forinash, M., & Kenny, C. (2015). *The 1982 Symposium on "Music in the Life of Man": The beginnings of music therapy theory.* University Park, IL: Barcelona.

Gaston, E. T. (Ed.). (1968). *Music in therapy.* New York, NY: Macmillan.

Geretsegger, M., Elefant, C., Mössler, K. A., & Gold, C. (2014). Music therapy for people with autism spectrum disorder. *Cochrane Database of Systematic Reviews*, 2014(3). doi:10.1002/14651858.CD004381.pub3

Gfeller, K. (1987). Music therapy theory and practice as reflected in the research literature. *Journal of Music Therapy, 14,* 178–194. doi:10.1093/jmt/24.4.178

Gfeller, K. (1995). The status of music therapy research. In B.

L. Wheeler (Ed.), *Music therapy research: Quantitative and qualitative perspectives* (pp. 29–64). Phoenixville, PA: Barcelona.

Gilbert, J. P. (1979). Published research in music therapy, 1973–1978: Content, focus, and implications for future research. *Journal of Music Therapy, 16*(3), 102–110. doi:10.1093/jmt/16.3.102

Gilliland, E. G. (1952). The development of music therapy as a profession. In E. Gilliland (Ed.), *Music therapy 1951* (p. xii). Lawrence, KS: The Allen Press.

Gold, C., & Rolvsjord, R. (2006). Citations patterns and scientific impact of the *Nordic Journal of Music Therapy,* 1992–2005. *Nordic Journal of Music Therapy, 15*(2), 139–153. doi:10.1080/08098130609478160

Gold, C., Wigram, T., & Elefant, C. (2006). Music therapy for autistic spectrum disorder. *Cochrane Database of Systematic Reviews*, 2006(2). doi:10.1002/14651858.CD004381.pub2

Hadley, S. J. (1998). *Exploring relationships between life and work in music therapy: The stories of Mary Priestley and Clive Robbins* (Doctoral dissertation, Temple University, 1998). Retrieved from ProQuest Dissertations and Theses Global. (UMI No. 9911013)

Hadley, S. (2013). Dominant narratives: Complicity and the need for vigilance in the creative arts therapies. *Arts in Psychotherapy, 40,* 373–381. doi:10.1016/j.aip.2013.05.007

Jellison, J. A. (1973). The frequency and general mode of inquiry of research in music therapy. *Council for Research in Music Education, 35,* 1–8.

Jensen, H. S. (1981). Die "Phänomenologie" der Musiktherapie [The phenomenology of music therapy]. *Musiktherapeutische Umschau, 2*(Helt 1), 29–37.

Hanser, S. B. (1999). *The new music therapist's handbook* (2nd ed.). Boston, MA: Berklee Press.

Hoffer, P. C. (2008). *The historian's paradox.* New York, NY: New York University Press.

Jellison, J. A. (1973). The frequency and general mode of inquiry of research in music therapy. *Council for Research in Music Education, 35,* 1–8.

Katusic, A., Alimovic, S., & Mejaski-Bosnjak, V. (2013). The effect of vibration therapy on spasticity and motor function in children with cerebral palsy: A randomized controlled trial. *NeuroRehabilitation, 32*(1), 1–8. doi:10.3233/NRE-130817

Kenny, C. (1983). Phenomenological research: A promise for the healing arts. In C. Kenny (2006), *Music & Life in the Field of Play: An anthology* (pp. 194–195). Gilsum, NH: Barcelona.

Kenny, C. (1987). The field of play: A theoretical study of music therapy process (Doctoral dissertation, The Fielding Institute, 1987). *Dissertation Abstracts International, 48*(12), 3067A. (UMI No. DEV88–02367)

Kenny, C. (1989). *The Field of Play: A guide for the theory and practice of music therapy.* Atascadero, CA: Ridgeview.

Kenny, C. B. (1998). Embracing complexity: The creation of

a comprehensive research culture in music therapy. *Journal of Music Therapy, 35*(3), 201–217. doi:10.1093/jmt/35.3.201

Kenny, C. (2006). A world full of voices. *Voices: A World Forum for Music Therapy, 6*(2). doi:10.15845/voices.v6i2.248. Retrieved from https://voices.no/index.php/voices/article/view/248

Kenny, C., & Stige, B. (2001). *Voices: A World Forum for Music Therapy:* A new avenue for communication among music therapy communities. *Voices: A World Forum for Music Therapy, 1*(1). doi:10.15845/voices.v1i1.35. Retrieved from https://voices.no/index.php/voices/article/view/35

Konieczna-Nowak, L. (2015). Music, text, music-and-text, and psychophysiological responses: A randomized controlled trial. *Arts in Psychotherapy, 42,* 57–62. doi:10.1016/j.aip.2014.12.004

Langenberg, M. (1996). Prologue. In M. Langenberg, K. Aigen, & J. Frommer (Eds.), *Qualitative music therapy research: Beginning dialogues* (pp. 1–5). Gilsum, NH: Barcelona.

Langenberg, M., Aigen, K., & Frommer, J. (1996). *Qualitative music therapy research: Beginning dialogues.* Gilsum, NH: Barcelona.

Lawrence-Lightfoot, S., & Hoffman Davis, J. (1997). *The art and science of Portraiture.* San Francisco, CA: Jossey-Bass.

Lecourt, E. (1993). Music therapy in France. In C. Dileo Maranto (Ed.), *Music therapy: International perspectives* (pp. 221–237). Pipersville, PA: Jeffrey Books.

Lee, L., & Lee, J. H. (2016). *An overview of South Korean music therapy research.* Unpublished manuscript, National Association of Korean Music Therapists.

Levitin, D. J. (2006). *This is your brain on music: The science of a human obsession.* Toronto, Ontario, Canada: Penguin.

Lincoln, Y. S., & Denzin, N. K. (1998). The fifth moment. In N. K. Denzin & Y. S. Lincoln (Eds.), *The landscape of qualitative research: Theories and issues* (pp. 407–429). Thousand Oaks, CA: Sage.

Merrill, T. R. (1998). *Rise up singing: A model for consciousness through the therapist's reflections on an improvisational music therapy group for persons with end-stage dementia* (Unpublished master's thesis). British Columbia Open University, Burnaby, British Columbia, Canada.

Merrill, T. R. (2002). Beginner's mind: Personal reflections on the Fourth International Symposium on Qualitative Music Therapy Research. *Nordic Journal of Music Therapy, 11,* 61–64. doi:10.1080/08098130209478-47.

Moffitt, E. (1993). Music therapy in Canada. In C. Dileo Maranto (Ed.), *Music therapy: International perspectives* (pp. 131–155). Pipersville, PA: Jeffrey Books.

Nicholas, M. J., & Gilbert, J. P. (1980). Research in music therapy: A survey of music therapists' attitudes and knowledge. *Journal of Music Therapy, 17,* 207–213. doi:10.1093/jmt/17.4.207

Nöcker-Ribaupierre, M. (2013). Research overview of German-speaking countries. *Voices: A World Forum for Music Therapy, 13*(2). doi:10.15845/voices.v13i2.720. Retrieved from https://voices.no/index.php/voices/article/view/720/619

Okazaki-Sakaue, K. (2003). Music therapy in Japan. *Voices Resources.* Retrieved from https://voices.no/community/?q=country/monthjapan_may2003

Pedersen, I. N., & Mahns, W. (1996). *Nordic Network in music therapy research 1993–1996.* Aalborg, Denmark: NorFa Nordisk Forskerakademi.

Pfeiffer, E. (2015). *Gesammelte Dissertationen über musiktherapeutische Themen bzw, mit musiktherapeutischem Bezug* [Collected dissertations in music therapy or on closely related topics]. Augsburg, Germany: Leopold-Mozart-Zentrum der Universität Augsburg. Retrieved from http://www.philso.uni-augsburg.de/lmz/institute/mmm/Musiktherapie/downloads/Dissertationen.pdf

Research. (1952). Report of the Research Committee. In E. Gilliland (Ed.), *Music Therapy 1951* (p. 179). Lawrence, KS: The Allen Press.

Rorke, M. A. (2001). Music therapy in the Age of Enlightenment. *Journal of Music Therapy, 38,* 66–73. doi:10.1093/jmt/38.1.66

Ross, S. D. (1994). *Art and its significance: An anthology of aesthetic theory* (3rd ed.). Albany, NY: State University of New York Press.

Ruud, E. (1980). *Music therapy and its relationship to current treatment theories.* St. Louis, MO: MMB Music.

Ruud, E. (1987). *Musikk som kommunikasjon og samhandling* [Music as communication and interaction] (Unpublished doctoral dissertation). Institutt for musikk og teate, Oslo University, Oslo, Norway.

Rüütel, E., Ratnik, M., Tamm, E., & Zilensk, H. (2004). The experience of vibroacoustic therapy in the self-development of adolescent girls. *Nordic Journal of Music Therapy, 13*(1), 33–46. doi:10.1080/08098130409478096

Schwabe, C. (Ed.). (1979). *Regulative Musiktherapie* [Regulative music therapy]. Stuttgart, Germany: Gustav Fischer Verlag.

Sears, M. L., & Sears, W. W. (1964). Abstracts of research in music therapy. *Journal of Music Therapy, 1,* 33–60. doi:10.1093/jmt/1.2.33

Sewell, W. H. (2005). *Logics of history: Social theory and social transformation.* Chicago, IL: University of Chicago Press.

Silverman, M. (2006). Forty years of case studies: A history of clinical case studies in the journal of music therapy, music therapy, and music therapy perspectives. *Music Therapy Perspectives, 24,* 4–12. doi:10.1093/mtp/24.1.4

Smeijsters, H. (1996). Qualitative single-case research in practice: A necessary, reliable design and valid alternative for music therapy research. In M. Langenberg, K. Aigen, & J. Frommer (Eds.), *Qualitative music therapy research: Beginning dialogues* (pp. 35–53). Gilsum, NH: Barcelona.

Smeijsters, H., & Rogers, P. (Eds.). (1993). *European music therapy research register*. Utrecht, The Netherlands: Werkgroep Onderzoek Muziektherapie/NVKT.

Smeijsters, H., Rogers, P., Kortegaard, H-M., Lehtonen, K., & Scanlon, P. (1995). *European music therapy research register* (Vol. 2). Castricum, The Netherlands: Stichting Muziektherapie.

Smeijsters, H., & Vink, A. (2010). Developments in music therapy in the Netherlands. *Voices Resources*. Retrieved from http://testvoices.uib.no/community/?q=country/mont hnetherlands_october2010

Stachyra, K. (2015). The effectiveness of receptive music therapy programming in the development of university students' emotional competence. In P. Kraj i & K. Priesterová (Eds.), *Dimenzia muzikoterapie v praxi, výskume a edukácii* (pp. 73–87). Bratislava, Slovakia: IRIS.

Stige, B. (2015). The practice turn in music therapy theory. *Music Therapy Perspectives, 33*(1), 3-11. doi:10.1093/mtp/miu050

Taylor, D. B. (1981). Music in general hospital treatment from 1900 to 1950. *Journal of Music Therapy, 18*(2), 62–73. doi:10.1093/jmt/18.2.62

Teirich, H. R. (1958). *Musik in der medizin. Beiträge zur musiktherapie* [Music in medical contributions to music therapy]. Stuttgart, Germany: Fischer Verlag.

Vaillancourt, G. (2011). Creating an apprenticeship music therapy model through arts-based research. *Voices: A World Forum for Music Therapy, 11*(1). doi:10.15845/voices.v11i1.341. Retrieved from https://normt.uib.no/index.php/voices/article/view/341

Vaillancourt, G. (2012). Music therapy: A community approach to social justice. *Arts in Psychotherapy, 39*, 173–178. doi:10.1016/j.aip.2011.12.011

Wagner, G., & Benenzon, R. (1993). Music therapy in Argentina. In C. Dileo Maranto (Ed.), *Music therapy: International perspectives* (pp. 5–34). Pipersville, PA: Jeffrey Books.

Wheeler, B. L. (Ed.). (1995). *Music therapy research: Quantitative and qualitative perspectives*. Phoenixville, PA: Barcelona.

Wheeler, B. L. (2003). First International Symposium on Music Therapy Training: A retrospective examination. *Nordic Journal of Music Therapy, 12*, 54–66. doi:10.1080/08098130309478072

Wheeler, B. L. (2005). *Music therapy research* (2nd ed.). Gilsum, NH: Barcelona.

Wheeler, B. (2008). 1st International Music Therapy Congress, Paris 1974: Edith Lecourt interviewed by Barbara Wheeler. *Voices: A World Forum for Music Therapy, 8*(3). doi:10.15845/voices.v8i3.425. Retrieved from https://voices.no/index.php/voices/article/view/425

Wheeler, B. L., & Murphy, K. M. (Eds.). (2016). *Music therapy research* (3rd ed.). Dallas, TX: Barcelona.

Wigram, T., Rogers, P., & Odell-Miller, H. (1993) Music therapy in the United Kingdom. In C. Dileo Maranto (Ed.), *Music therapy: International perspectives* (pp. 574–604). Pipersville, PA: Jeffrey Books.

Wineburg, S. (2001). *Historical thinking and other unnatural acts: Charting the future of teaching the past*. Philadelphia, PA: Temple University Press.

Young, L. (2013). Persons with Alzheimer's and other dementias. In L. Eyre (Ed.), *Guidelines for music therapy practice in mental health* (pp. 952–1013). Gilsum, NH: Barcelona.

Zhang, J.-W., Gao, T., & Liu, M.-M. (2016). Music therapy in China. *Music and Medicine, 8*(1), 67–70.

Chapter 3
DEVELOPING A TOPIC
Alice-Ann Darrow

Developing a research topic requires disciplined thought and logical ideas, for these ideas must eventually evolve into clearly formulated questions, questions that will ultimately guide the design of the research, method of data collection, and subsequent data analysis. Developing a research topic also requires a curious and open mind, one that is free of biases and preconceived notions of where the research will lead. Having an open mind also necessitates avoiding *habits of thought,* which are common in academic communities and are often discipline specific (White, 2009). Finally, though perhaps most important, developing a research topic requires time—time for thinking, reading, imagining, reflecting, discussing, and questioning. In the *publish or perish* world of academia, or graduate students' desire to complete a degree, thinking about research is often denied its due process. A *doing* mind-set ought not shortchange the *thinking* mind-set. Setting aside time to think and ponder is an important part of the research process. A researcher might begin with "What if ...?" or "I wonder ...." "What if music could be used to assist people with debilitating diseases?" or "I wonder what music therapists doing clinical improvisation think and feel during the process." Eventually, "What if" and "I wonder" develop and evolve into research problems.

Most good researchers are innately curious people who take delight in the unexpected. Curiosity is a state of active interest that leads one to genuinely want to know more. An inquisitive mind is open to discovery and exploration. Fortunately, curiosity can be developed; consequently, many research advisors spend considerable time and energy nurturing curiosity in their students. They do so by asking students to think, observe, question, make connections, and converse about topics of interest. While curiosity is a vital and useful trait, White (2009) warns against idle curiosity and suggests systematic and disciplined curiosity—the former prompting haphazard practices and the latter promoting clarity and precision.

In addition to curiosity, good researchers also have a passion for finding answers. Good researchers are more concerned with answering questions honestly than with how they will find the answers. Sincere researchers care little about what method of discovery they will use. Their primary concern is finding the most logical and trustworthy answer to a burning question. Novice researchers, and even experienced researchers, often become comfortable with a particular research paradigm, and then only ask questions that fit within that paradigm. Janesik (2000) uses the term *methodolatry* to describe this habitual attachment to a particular method, which in turn belittles the question. In addition, various methods are sometimes set against each other, with advocates touting one or the other as being more rigorous or thorough. Comfort or familiarity with a particular methodology should not play a role in determining the question to be asked or how it is to be answered. A number of contemporary authors (Creswell, 2009; Johnson & Christensen, 2012; Johnson & Onwuegbuzie, 2004) suggest that having a pluralistic mind-set—both philosophically and methodologically—leads to the most intellectually honest research. It is with that mind-set this chapter is written.

The typical research process involves: (a) identifying a topic of interest, (b) formulating a research problem, (c) developing procedures to address the problem, (d) successfully implementing these procedures, and (e) carefully interpreting the results (Phelps, Sadoff, Warburton, & Ferrara, 2005). This chapter is concerned with the first two steps of the research process. Before we look at these procedural steps, we will consider the role of one's beliefs and research paradigm in developing a topic.

The Role of Paradigms in Developing a Topic

According to Willis (2007), a **paradigm** is a comprehensive belief system, worldview, or framework that guides research and practice in a field. Johnson and Christensen (2013) describe a paradigm in more general terms as a set of shared assumptions, values, concepts, and practices. From these descriptions, it is easy to understand how a research paradigm might influence one's work. It is important to realize the strong relationship between philosophy and research paradigms. Researchers come from many schools of thought, and consequently their views vary as to what research is and how it relates to the development of knowledge. Rubin and Rubin (2012) summarize these schools of thought in the following way:

> Researchers who use quantitative tools, techniques that emphasize measuring and counting, are called *positivists;* and those who prefer the qualitative tools of observation, questioning, and description are called *naturalists.* Positivists and naturalists differ in their assumptions about what is important to study, what can be known, what research tools and designs are appropriate, and what standards should be used to judge the quality of the research. Taken together, these assumptions are termed research paradigms or research philosophies. (p. 14)

Research paradigms are distinguished by two basic characteristics: (a) *ontology*, or *what* constitutes reality?, and (b) *epistemology*, or *how* do we know reality? The answers to these questions may assist the researcher in responding to the fundamental research question: *How and in what ways do I feel most comfortable investigating my questions?* The answer to this question is likely to predispose a researcher to a particular paradigm. As a music therapy researcher, I find that it is helpful to have first developed a personal philosophy of practice. A personal philosophy influences one's approach to music therapy practice. It is important to remember that there are numerous legitimate approaches to music therapy and, hence, various approaches to music therapy research (Darrow, 2008). No research paradigm is superior to another; all are of equal importance and have a place within the field of music therapy. Each paradigm has a specific purpose and a way of producing knowledge that is important to music therapists. Denscombe (2002) suggests that the "guiding principle for research is not its paradigm, but how well it addresses the topic it is investigating" (p. 23).

More and more music therapists are acknowledging the notion that any research question can be approached in different ways, and that an eclectic approach perhaps provides a more comprehensive answer. In addition, research questions within the same study can be addressed by different methods (Johnson, Darrow, & Eason, 2008). A number of authors advocate embracing a mixed methods approach to research, and going further to state that mixed methods constitute their own new research paradigm (Johnson & Christensen, 2012; Johnson & Onwuegbuzie, 2004). Researchers have been informally mixing methods in their studies for many years, though the *Journal of Mixed Methods Research* published its first issue in January of 2007.

Most graduate students, and particularly those who plan to do research, will want to spend considerable time contemplating and formulating their personal philosophy of music therapy, familiarizing themselves with the various research paradigms, and determining how well their philosophy of practice fits into these research paradigms. To do so properly involves reading, thinking, reflecting, discussing, and questioning, the same activities suggested at the beginning of this chapter to determine a research topic. Reading studies in both domestic and international music therapy journals will assist students in developing a good working knowledge of the different approaches used in music therapy research. Thinking about and discussing the studies they read will help students to truly align their personal philosophy to the research approaches and topics with which they feel most comfortable. Graduate theses and dissertations often take a year or more to complete; consequently, both comfort and compatibility with the selected approach and a genuine interest in the topic are vital to the research process.

Identifying a Topic of Interest

Deciding on a research problem and determining the subsequent questions to be asked require considerable time spent both reading and thinking about a specific topic of interest. Conducting quality research requires sustained attention and attentiveness to detail, both of which are much easier and enjoyable when the research topic is of great interest to the researcher. White (2009) makes an important distinction between interest in the research topic and interest in the research results. Researchers must always guard against their own beliefs and predilections. If researchers have a vested interest in the outcome of a study, they may not be the best candidates to carry out the study. It is unlikely that researchers will be totally free from expectations and notions about what their investigations will find, but they should be prepared and willing to report results that may not align with their original hypotheses or their professional beliefs. Responsible researchers should also initially consider all possible approaches to answering the research question and all possible outcomes to their research.

The process of conducting quality research is often fraught with roadblocks and is nearly always time-consuming. Having a keen interest in the topic under investigation can make the research process more enjoyable and less arduous. Passion for a research topic can be kindled in different ways. Many researchers become interested in a particular topic because of their discussions with colleagues. If they work in research teams, time is often deliberately set aside for collegial brainstorming and bantering. Such activities often result in collaborative works that possess an inherent system of accountability and that are perhaps more creative than they would have been if designed by a single investigator. Investigators who have colleagues, friends, or students who enjoy discussing research are fortunate, for these kinds of discussions often serve as the impetus for collaborative and groundbreaking research. Research teams are often formed because of members' mutual interest in a particular topic.

Music therapists may also develop a passion for a particular research topic based on their personal or professional experiences (Darrow, 2006). Having work experience or a child or a family member with a particular illness or disability has prompted many researchers to investigate best practices with various populations (Lerner, 2013). In addition, calls for increasing accountability for practice outcomes have intensified the research in music therapy as well as many other professions (Glidden, 2005). As resources for professional support become more limited, research is often motivated by a desire to secure funding and to set the direction of future clinical practices. Commitment to a topic of interest is one of the most influential contributors to quality research and to the development of clinical practices.

If a topic of interest has not been identified via one's professional or personal experiences, reading is a promising and productive way to stimulate an idea for research, and not necessarily research readings. For example, and from the author's personal experience, reading an article in the *The New York Times* or a chapter from a textbook can stimulate a research idea. Good researchers are also active readers, not just of research, but of all sources of knowledge. Reading the news and other publications dedicated to reporting on social, medical, educational, political, and policy concerns can help to generate research ideas that are currently topical (White, 2009). Examining the popular media has considerable potential to inform, if not influence, research in music therapy and all the social sciences.

Reviewing the Literature

Although reviewing the literature is a separate stage in the research process, it is included in this section, Identifying a Topic of Interest, because it can be viewed as an aspect of this step in the process. This chapter gives an overview of this process; additional information and a somewhat different perspective on preparing a literature review can be found in Chapter 6 of this book.

Once a topic of interest has been identified, the researcher will want to become familiar with as much information as possible on the topic, usually accomplished by reading related literature. Research does not take place in a vacuum. It is meant to fill a void. It should fit into the present state of knowledge on a particular topic. Without knowing the place of a particular piece of research within the literature, one risks needlessly replicating previous works or failing to avoid the problems and limitations of previous studies. In addition, placing the research in the broader context helps to establish its significance and contribution to the field of study. Original research cannot take place without knowing what has been done in the past. Reviewing the literature can be enormously useful in helping to clarify the research problem and the questions that need to be asked.

Although most researchers find reviewing the literature to be important, for the reasons just presented, some approaches to interpretivist research "discourage researchers from reviewing the literature early in the study, believing that it is important that the focus of the [study] emerge from the research [itself] rather than being imposed by the literature or an outside theoretical framework" (Wheeler, 2005, p. 95).

Student researchers are often in a quandary as to where to start and what to be looking for in the literature. Bloomberg and Volpe (2012, p. 82) provide five questions that can be used to guide a review of the related literature:

- What are the origins and definitions of the topic?
- What are the key theories, concepts, and ideas?
- What are the major debates, arguments, and issues surrounding the topic?
- What are the key questions and problems that have been addressed to date?
- Are there any important issues that have been insufficiently addressed or not addressed at all?

Too often, student researchers are eager to get on with the business of collecting data and consider the literature review to be a peripheral task that interrupts the research process. This mind-set is most often due to their lack of understanding about the value and purpose of reviewing the literature. Reviewing the related literature is one of the most important steps in the research process, and should generally be done before any data are collected. The main purposes of reviewing the research are to:

- Gain an understanding of the current state of knowledge about the selected topic,
- Identify what has already been investigated related to the topic,
- Identify what approaches have been used to investigate the topic,
- Identify any methodological problems specific to the topic,
- Identify specific research approaches or measures that might be useful.

In addition, familiarity with the related literature ultimately allows an investigator to report the study's findings in the context of extant knowledge and the most relevant and recent research. In summary, the related literature allows a researcher to narrow a topic, identify a pertinent research problem, and then pose relevant questions; however, the literature review may serve an additional purpose in qualitative research. The literature review is often integrated throughout a qualitative study to stimulate new insights and concepts (Johnson & Christensen, 2012).

Finally, the literature review can constitute a form of objectivist or interpretivist research in itself. Objectivist researchers review all of the available research studies on a particular topic and utilize meta-analysis to determine the effects of one variable on another directly or indirectly. Interpretivist researchers conduct a critical analysis of extant literature in order to formulate theories applicable to a particular field of study or to determine what future research is needed (Creswell, 2009).

Determining the Feasibility of the Study

Once the topic of interest has been identified and related literature has been read, the researcher generally has an idea of what he or she is interested in studying and a possible research problem to be investigated. Research questions can be evoked at any time, even before the related literature is read; however, reading relevant research is helpful in understanding other researchers' perspectives on the topic. After reviewing related literature, the feasibility of a study must be considered. Possible questions a researcher might ask are:

- Am I genuinely interested in this topic?
- Am I free from strong biases related to the topic?
- Do I have the background knowledge and necessary skills to carry out the research?
- Do I have the resources, personal and financial, required to carry out the research?
- Do I have the time to do the study justice?
- Do I have access to the materials, equipment, or participants I will need to carry out the study?
- Will the study contribute to the professional field in any significant way?

If the answer to any of these questions is no, prudent researchers will consider going in a slightly different direction or scaling down the study such that it is feasible within the resources available to them. Nearly every researcher has had the experience of setting a lofty research goal that ultimately needs to be revisited and revised.

Formulating a Research Problem

Identifying and focusing on a specific problem to investigate is one of the first steps in conducting research. Brewer and Hunter (2006) offer a healthy perspective on research problems. They muse that in everyday life, we attempt to avoid problems, yet researchers seek out problems and regard them as opportunities to learn. They further state that knowledge is provisional and that all research findings and theories are problematic in principle and are, therefore, subject to further investigation. Problems, then, not only prompt research but also drive its continuation.

After completing the first step in the research process and choosing the topic, then reviewing the related literature as appropriate and identifying a specific study of interest and determining its feasibility, the researcher then formulates the research problem. The research problem, or phenomenon as it might be called, in many forms of interpretivist research is the topic you would like to address, investigate, or study (Boudah, 2011). A research problem indicates a gap in the extent or the certainty of our knowledge on a particular topic. Research problems point to problematic phenomena, pinpoint observed events, and identify theories or current ideas that should be challenged (Brewer & Hunter, 2006). As Northrop (1966) writes, "Inquiry starts only when something is unsatisfactory, when traditional beliefs are inadequate or in question, when the facts necessary to resolve one's uncertainties are not known, when the likely relevant hypotheses are not even imagined. What one has at the beginning of inquiry is merely the problem" (p. 17).

Some authors (e.g., Andrews, 2003; White, 2009) consider identifying and formulating the research problem to be the most important phase of the research process. The problem and the subsequent questions the researcher seeks to answer generally determine the approach that is to be taken in the study. Research approaches are a means to an end; they must

be employed purposefully and intelligently. To do so requires the researcher have a clear understanding of the problem he or she is attempting to address. Brewer and Hunter (2006) emphasize the importance of the problem to the researcher: "A compelling research problem must marshal support in advance of research and, if it is sufficiently compelling, can sustain that support through the sometimes fruitless periods that researchers experience" (p. 40). Carefully considering and formulating the research problem, then, is the most logical first step toward carrying out a research study. Kumar (1996) says, "The formulation of a research problem … is like the identification of a destination before undertaking a journey. As in the absence of a destination, it is impossible to identify the shortest—or indeed any—route, in the absence of a clear research problem, a clear and economical plan is impossible" (p. 35).

A debate as to how and when the research problems are to be formulated (Brewer & Hunter, 2006; Johnson & Christensen, 2012) occurs among both objectivist and interpretivist researchers, although the reasoning that informs researchers' decisions varies, depending upon each researcher's beliefs and approach to research. Researchers on both sides of the debate—that research problems should be defined *a priori* and be based on previous findings or that they should emerge and develop throughout the research process—continue the process of developing the topic by stating the research problem. Although the remaining steps are similar in some ways for objectivist and interpretivist research, they vary in other ways and, for this reason, will be presented separately in this chapter.

Objectivist Research

Stating the Research Problem

Because identifying and formulating the nature and dimensions of the research problem define the course of the study, doing so is a task that requires careful consideration. Analyzing a research problem involves gathering information or facts that are related to the problem, identifying possible relevant relationships, and questioning related assumptions. As an example:

Problem: Persons with hearing loss are not generally considered musical, or persons with hearing loss are not generally considered good candidates for music therapy services.

Gathering relevant information: What musical tests or studies have been carried out with persons who have hearing loss? What types of tests were administered? Are music therapy outcomes for persons with hearing loss documented in the literature? What types of hearing loss did the individuals have? What type of amplification was used during testing?

Identifying possible relationships: Is there a relationship between an individual's musical test score (rhythmic or tonal) and an individual's degree of loss (mild, moderate, severe, or profound) or type of hearing loss (conductive or sensorineural)? Is there a relationship between an individual's musical test scores and the individual's age at the time of onset? Is there a relationship between an individual's musical test scores and the type of amplification he or she used during testing (aided, unaided, hearing aid, or cochlear implant)?

Questioning related assumptions: Based on the information gathered, do assumptions about the musicality of persons with hearing loss seem to be accurate? If so, under what conditions? If not, what specific assumptions should be challenged?

Research problems that are stated in specific terms ensure the researcher has a good understanding of the variables under investigation. Specificity also assists the researcher in designing and conducting the study. The problem statement can be expressed in the declarative or interrogatory form, and how it is stated is the first clue as to the type of methodology that might be most appropriate

In objectivist research, the problem statement can also be presented in the declarative form but is most often posed in the interrogatory form—as a question (Johnson & Christensen, 2012). Here is an example: "What is the relationship between preschool children's type and degree of hearing loss and their ability to execute age-appropriate musical games designed to develop rhythm skills?"

Stating the research problem as a question indicates the type of data that will be collected and the method of analysis. In this example, the children's demographic data (type and degree of hearing loss) will be collected, as well as their performance data for the musical games. With these data, correlation analyses will determine if any relationships exist between the children's type and/or degree of hearing loss and how well the they performed on the various musical games.

Asking the Research Question(s)

The problem statement leads to the research question in objectivist research. The research question is a formal statement of the purpose for the investigation. The question states what the researcher will investigate or attempt to find out. The research problem and question both progress from what is known—as determined by the literature review—to that which is unknown and requires validation. It is important to establish a clear question or questions from the research problem. When the researcher can establish the specific question is to be asked, it is generally a relief, as the question sets up the rest of the study: what literature needs to be reviewed, what approach might be best to address the question, and some idea of how the data will be gathered.

Research questions are often formulated at the beginning of a project. The research answer can only be as good as the question asked. Research questions should be clear and specific to the problem under study. There may be more than one research question, depending on the complexity and breadth of the study. The question should be intriguing enough that the researcher is willing to continue until an answer is found and the reader is sufficiently compelled to continue reading in order to learn the answer. Maxwell (2005) offers three purposes for research questions: (a) they help to focus the study, (b) they offer guidance on how to carry out the study, and (c) they communicate the goals of the research to others.

Research questions need not be original. They may have been asked in previous studies but were not answered sufficiently, or there were problems with how they were addressed. Some graduate programs require that theses research questions be original, and most require dissertations have some aspect that is original. Generally speaking, however, the question may be the same as or similar to those asked in previous research, but approached differently. If research is in an area that has not previously been investigated, it is considered original by that fact alone, but it is also considered original if it is carried out using a different method, produces different data, or uses different analyses (Denscombe, 2002) or a different population (White, 2009). Some researchers might suggest that no research idea is entirely original, particularly if it is based on or is an extension of past research.

Beginning researchers often have difficulty in posing a question that is well defined. Research questions are rarely too minor or insignificant, but they are often too broad or complex. The latter are usually revised and refined to be more manageable. For example, the question "What are the musical characteristics of children with hearing loss?" needs to be more specific as to which musical characteristics are being investigated and what types and degrees of hearing loss are represented among the sample population. A more refined question would be, "What are the rhythm replication abilities of children with mild to severe degrees of hearing loss?" The population description might further define whether the children observed were aided or unaided or had cochlear implants or used acoustic amplification. Nearly all researchers go through a process of refining and delimiting their original research question. Delimitation is simply setting the boundaries of the research question, and it is generally wise to do so before deciding how the question will be approached or before any data collection begins.

Research usually begins with a primary question the study intends to address, but there are often secondary questions, related to the primary question, that are also posed. The answers to these secondary questions add clarification to the primary question. In addition, there may be secondary questions that become apparent as the data are collected. These questions are frequently instrumental in defining future research projects. Secondary questions are not required, but they often add to the information gathered and provide a valuable contribution to the overall research.

Formulating a Hypothesis

A *hypothesis* is a predicted answer to a research question. Although a hypothesis predicts what a researcher will find, it matters little, if at all, that the hypothesis is confirmed or, in other words, that the predicted answer is found to be correct. Many fine researchers have found that the results of their studies did not support their original hypotheses. The goal of research is to determine the most trustworthy answer to the question. Hypotheses are often associated with objectivist research, though White (2009) and others believe they should not be restricted to a particular methodology as they often provide focus and direction. It is important to note that hypotheses are not required to carry out studies, and some authors believe they can contribute to perceived notions of where a study will lead and are not appropriate for research that is intended to be emergent (Creswell, 2005). Most authors agree, however, that a hypothesis is useful when testing an established theory (Johnson & Christensen, 2012).

Hypotheses are often related to a particular theory and the related body of research literature. The hypothesis should progress from the research idea to the literature review, to the theoretical framework (e.g., self-efficacy or self-validation), and finally to the research question or hypothesis. An example of a study related to theory is "The effects of musical activity on the self-esteem and self-efficacy of patients with schizophrenia" (Hovey, 2013). In such a study, the investigator should fully understand self-efficacy theory, the related research literature, and, of course, any studies having to do with music therapy and self-efficacy.

A hypothesis can be stated in the *directional* or *null* form. The null form is open-ended and states no expectation as to what will be found. The directional form predicts a specific finding. Examples of both forms are:

Null hypothesis: There will be no relationship found between clients' musical aptitude and their receptivity to music therapy services.
Directional hypothesis: A positive relationship will be found between clients' musical aptitude and their receptivity to music therapy services. (As clients' musical aptitude increases, so will their receptivity to music therapy services.)

Null hypothesis: No differences will be found in the anxiety of children receiving and children not receiving bedside music therapy during blood draw procedures.
Directional hypothesis: Children receiving bedside music therapy will experience less anxiety during blood draw procedures than children who do not receive music therapy services during the same procedures.

A hypothesis can also be stated as a premise in an argument or as an assumption, such as *music is a universal language.* Such hypotheses are open to testing and are often the impetus for investigations, though they are usually quite broad and not generally advised for student researchers.

Interpretivist Research

In interpretivist research, formulation of the research problem, purpose, and question is often not a linear process. In fact, a question may lead to the identification of a problem or help to clarify the purpose. The reader should remember that interpretivist research is an iterative process that begins with a general curiosity about a phenomenon or personal experience.

Stating the Research Problem

The problem statement, which is also referred to as the need for the study, is a broad description of the phenomenon of interest that provides the rationale for the research being undertaken (Creswell, 2007). Careful crafting of the research problem moves this general curiosity into a specific topic, which can be studied through an interpretivist method (Creswell, 2007). In interpretivist research, the research problem often comes from the personal or professional experience of the researcher or an awareness that there is a "deficiency in the literature" on a given topic (Creswell, 2007, p. 42). Often a combination of these two origins will lead to a *problem* worthy of investigation. For example, Young (2012) noted that, in her experience, the most interesting differences in BMGIM therapists were found in the facilitation of the postlude discussion phase of the process. She also noted that there was a dearth of literature exploring the postlude discussion.

Specifying a Focus and Purpose

Problem statements are usually quite broad and need to be narrowed and focused so that the ensuing research study will be manageable. Therefore, the next step in the process is to identify a focus and purpose. Bruscia (2005) has identified and defined several foci/purposes of interpretivist research (see Tables 1 and 2). The focus typically suggests the type of data to be collected, while the purpose identifies what the researcher is hoping to discover (Bruscia, 2005).

The purpose statement identifies the boundaries of the research study, though in interpretivist research these are not cast in stone, and they may be altered as the study progresses (Lincoln & Guba, 1985). The literature may also be consulted in the formulation of the purpose statement and setting the boundaries for the study. After a thorough review of the literature, Young (2010) refined her problem statement and identified the purpose of her study as "understanding the essence and quality of clients' described experiences of the postlude discussion phase in GIM" (p. 41). This statement identifies the focus on an event (the postlude discussion in a GIM session), while the purpose was to describe the essence (Young, 2012).

Events, Actions, and Interactions	Focus is on anything observable that happens in-vivo within a defined, real-world context
Experiences	Focus is on how a person apprehends, perceives, feels, and thinks about something; covert and unobservable processes that occur in relation to an event, object, or person
Written and Spoken Language	Focus is on how people communicate and act upon one another through verbal means
Art Works	Focus is on the materials that result from participation in music, dance, or visual art activities
Persons	Focus is on understanding an individual, group, community, or culture within a defined setting or context by studying how they constitute and find meaning through their actions, interactions, experiences, language, and artworks

Table 1. Interpretivist Research Questions: Foci

Adapted from "Topics and Questions" by K. E. Bruscia (2005). In B. L. Wheeler (Ed.), *Music Therapy Research* (2nd ed.; pp. 87–89). Gilsum, NH: Barcelona. Used with permission

Holistic Description	Researcher attempts to provide a composite picture of all findings of the study with minimum interpretation
Definition of Essence	Researcher seeks to identify those essential or defining properties that give the phenomenon its basic meaning, character, structure, or identity and, in that process, to discover which of its elements must be minimally present for the phenomenon to exist and be defined as such
Analysis	Researcher seeks to identify regularities, recurrent themes, relationships, and patterns embedded in the data, and, based on these, to offer meaningful explanations of the phenomenon
Theory Building	Researcher hypothesizes or speculates about the phenomenon in order to develop a schematic conceptualization of some kind
Interpretation	Researcher uses his or her own tacit understanding of the phenomenon, often in conjunction with relevant theories or previous interpretations by others, to derive or create meaning out of the data
Artistic Re-creation	Researcher gives his or her own rendering of the data or re-creates the phenomenon under investigation, based on artistic interpretation of the data
Criticism	Researcher evaluates the data, phenomenon, or research study itself according to a particular value system, such as personal opinion or expertise, aesthetic standards, research criteria, logic, clinical efficacy, ethics, cultural or linguistic bias, politics, and so forth
Self-reflection	Researcher examines his or her own actions, interactions, experiences, language, or artworks, and then compares them to those of others

Table 2. Interpretivist Research Questions: Purpose

Adapted from "Topics and Questions" by K. E. Bruscia (2005). In B. L. Wheeler (Ed.), *Music Therapy Research* (2nd ed.; pp. 89–93). Gilsum, NH: Barcelona. Used with permission

Developing the Research Questions

Finally, researchers will develop specific research questions based on the problem and purpose. Interpretivist research questions are typically open-ended and nondirectional, beginning with *what* or *how* (Creswell, 2007; Yin, 2014). The following research questions identified by Young (2010) meet these criteria as they are open-ended and nondirectional: (a) What experiences do clients perceive as helpful in GIM postludes?, (b) What experiences do clients perceive as not helpful in GIM postludes?, and (c) What common themes exist among these experiences? Additionally, interpretivist research questions should also reflect the "emerging design" of the study (Creswell, 2014, p. 141). The questions above would suggest a phenomenological design, whereas Sorel's (2010) research question, "What occurs in a mother–son dyad in Nordoff-Robbins music therapy?" (p. 173), suggests a naturalistic inquiry.

Conclusion

The first steps in planning a research study involve much of the material presented in this chapter: engaging in disciplined thought, adopting a researcher's mind-set, identifying a topic of interest, reviewing the literature, and formulating a research problem. The next steps for objectivist research are asking the research question(s) and formulating a hypothesis or hypotheses, while for interpretivist research, they are specifying a focus and purpose and developing the research question(s).

Not all research projects will require all of these steps, but all require developing a topic of interest. Some steps will need to be repeated or refined. Several of the other topics introduced in this chapter will be revisited and discussed more fully in later chapters.

Research is a rewarding endeavor, and one in which many of the authors in this text have engaged for many years. We hope to model for our students and colleagues the joy of seeking answers to questions and then applying those answers to practice. If it were it not for that joy, none of us would continue to do research. The purpose of research is to inform practice, and we would all likely agree that we are better therapists because of our research. Fortunately, we enjoy what we do, and you will as well.

References

Andrews, R. (2003). *Research questions.* New York, NY: Continuum.

Bloomberg, L. D., & Volpe, M. (2012). *Completing your qualitative dissertation: A roadmap from beginning to end.* Thousand Oaks, CA: Sage.

Brewer, J., & Hunter, A. (2006). *Foundations of multimethod research: Synthesizing styles.* Thousand Oaks, CA: Sage.

Boudah, D. J. (2011). *Conducting educational research.* Thousand Oaks, CA: Sage.

Bruscia, K. E. (2005). Topics and questions. In B. L. Wheeler (Ed.), *Music therapy research* (2nd ed.; pp. 8–93). Gilsum, NH: Barcelona.

Creswell, J. W. (2005). *Educational research: Planning, conducting, and evaluating quantitative and qualitative research.* Upper Saddle River, NJ: Pearson Education.

Creswell, J. W. (2007). *Qualitative inquiry and research design: Choosing among five approaches* (2nd ed.). Thousand Oaks, CA: Sage

Creswell, J. W. (2009). *Research design: Qualitative, quantitative and mixed methods approaches* (3rd ed.). Thousand Oaks, CA: Sage.

Creswell, J. W. (2014). *Research design: Qualitative, quantitative and mixed methods approaches* (4th ed.). Thousand Oaks, CA: Sage.

Darrow, A. A. (2006). Sounds in the silence: Research on music and deafness. *Update: Applications of Research in Music Education, 25*(1), 5–14. doi:10.1177/87551233060250010102

Darrow, A. A. (Ed.). (2008). *Introduction to approaches in music therapy* (2nd ed.). Silver Spring, MD: American Music Therapy Association.

Denscombe, M. (2002) *Ground rules for good research.* Berkshire, UK: Open University Press and McGraw-Hill.

Glidden, M. D. (2005). *Improving the effectiveness of the helping professions: An evidence-based approach to practice.* Thousand Oaks, CA: Sage.

Hovey, S. A. (2013). The effects of musical activity on the self-esteem and self-efficacy of patients with schizophrenia: A cultural study in West Bengal, India. *Music and Medicine, 5*(1), NP1–NP4.

Janesik, V. (2000). The choreography of qualitative research design. In N. K. Denzin & Y. S. Lincoln (Eds.), *Handbook of qualitative research* (2nd ed.; pp. 379–399). Thousand Oaks, CA: Sage.

Johnson, B., & Christensen, L. B. (2012) *Educational research: Quantitative, qualitative and mixed approaches.* Thousand Oaks, CA: Sage.

Johnson, C., Darrow, A. A., & Eason, B. J. (2008). Novice and skilled music teachers' nonverbal behaviors and their relationship to perceived effectiveness and rapport. *Bulletin of the Council for Research in Music Education, 178,* 73–83.

Johnson, B., & Onwuegbuzie, A. J. (2004). Mixed methods research: A research paradigm whose time has come. *Educational Researcher, 33*(7), 14–26. doi:10.3102/0013189X033007014

Kumar, R. (1996). *Research methodology: A step-by-step guide for beginners.* Thousand Oaks, CA: Sage.

Lerner, B. (2013, October 30). A father who fought for Lorenzo's Oil. *The New York Times.* Retrieved from http://nyti.ms/1aorWF0

Lincoln, Y. S., & Guba, E. G. (1985). *Naturalistic inquiry.*

Thousand Oaks, CA: Sage.

Maxwell, J. A. (2005). *Qualitative research design: An interactive approach.* Thousand Oaks, CA: Sage.

Northrop, F. S. C. (1966). *The logic of the sciences and the humanities.* Cleveland, OH: World Publishing.

Phelps, R. P., Sadoff, R. H., Warburton, E. C., & Ferrara, L. (2005). *A guide to research in music education* (5th ed.). Lanham, MD: Scarecrow Press.

Rubin, H. J., & Rubin, S. R. (2012). *Qualitative interviewing: The art of hearing data.* Thousand Oaks, CA: Sage.

Sorel, S. (2010). Presenting Carly and Elliott: Exploring roles and relationships in a mother–son dyad in Nordoff-Robbins Music Therapy. *Qualitative Inquiries in Music Therapy, 5,* 173–238.

Wheeler, B. L. (2005). Developing a topic. In B. L. Wheeler (Ed.), *Music therapy research* (2nd ed.; pp. 94–104). Gilsum, NH: Barcelona.

White, P. (2009). *Developing research questions: A guide for social scientists.* New York, NY: Palgrave Macmillan.

Willis, J. W. (2007). *Foundations of qualitative research: Interpretive and critical approaches.* Thousand Oaks, CA: Sage.

Yin, R. K. (2014). *Case study research: Design and methods* (5th ed.). Thousand Oaks, CA: Sage.

Young, L. (2012). Client experiences in postlude discussion in Guided Imagery and Music. *Qualitative Inquires in Music Therapy, 7,* 33–70.

Chapter 4
REVIEWING THE LITERATURE[1]

Elaine A. Abbott

The purpose of this chapter is to describe tasks typically associated with creating a *narrative literature review*. As defined by Margery, Veale, and Rogers (2001), "this type of review involves performing thorough literature searches, describing how these were done, grouping findings according to themes, critically discussing findings, and placing the proposed research in context" (p. 1013).

There are many reasons to review scholarly literature, and the scope of a review will depend on its purpose. Writing a research paper for an undergraduate college course will require a different breadth and depth of search than writing a literature review for a master's thesis, dissertation, or scholarly publication. Guidance from a professor or advisor may help to determine the scope of a review.

There are many different ways to construct a literature review. The intent of this chapter is not to delineate a specific set of steps that every researcher must do, but rather to describe tasks that may be associated with producing a review. Whether an author uses all of the described tasks, and how an author completes any given task, is dependent on the individual.

What Is a Literature Review?

A *literature review* is a discussion "based on a line of reasoning that identifies important previous investigations and theoretical perspectives" related to a research topic and "reveals a next logical task in advancing" research on that topic (Kucan, 2011, p. 234). A literature review orients readers to key issues on a topic (Gray & Acierno, 2003) and describes a rationale for a study (Dileo, 2005).

Reviewing related literature helps a researcher to define, delimit, and conceptualize a research topic (Dileo, 2005). The researcher learns what is and is not known about the topic, gains awareness of its scope, and gains insight into it (Dileo, 2005). Review of previous studies may foster reconceptualization of a topic and allow a researcher to avoid unsuccessful approaches to it (Dileo, 2005). A researcher may also find useful recommendations from previous researchers (Dileo, 2005). Additionally, once data have been analyzed, the literature review "allows investigators to compare their findings with those of others" (Dileo, 2005, p. 105).

A quality literature review is delimited, comprehensive, coherent, synthesized, and well referenced. Literature reviews are *delimited* when they contain only information that is clearly relevant to a research topic. They are *comprehensive* when they provide diverse, unbiased information that includes all known, relevant, and accessible publications on

the topic (Landrum, 2012). *Coherent* literature reviews present a well-structured thought process that is logically connected. Literature reviews are *synthesized* when information from different authors is gathered together, organized, and analytically discussed under topic headings (Landrum, 2012). Analytical discussion includes, for example, a comparison of competing ideas related to a topic and a determination of what needs to be known about it. A *well-referenced* review cites the work of prior scholars and researchers and, in so doing, acknowledges them. Further information can be found in the chapter "Manuscript Structure and Content" of the *Publication Manual of the American Psychological Association* (6th ed.; 2010).

Conducting the Literature Review

Writing a literature review is typically an iterative process; several tasks are performed and some are repeated. Throughout the process, information is gathered and built upon while understanding about a research topic increases. Figure 1 depicts a sample process of enumerated tasks that might be followed while constructing a literature review. Task 6, Assess, could be a particular catalyst for making decisions about which tasks to repeat and when to repeat them (see dotted arrows). Tasks 2 through 7 are discussed below.

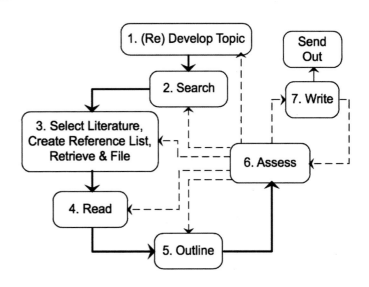

Figure 1. Sample Literature Review Tasks and Process

Task 1. Develop the Topic

This important step is described in Chapter 5, Developing a Topic.

Task 2. Search the Literature

Before beginning a search, it is important to delimit the scope of a topic; a researcher should be able to make a clear, preliminary statement regarding what a study is about and what a study is not about. Finding literature related to a research topic requires knowing for what to search, in what to search, and where and how to search for it. *Identify key terms* to begin a search. Then search *scholarly literature* using *electronic databases, Boolean operators,* and *wildcard search terms.* Reference librarians can also help determine where and how to search for information on a topic.

Identify Key Terms. Use a preliminary, yet clear, statement of the research topic or question to identify key search terms. For example, Williams, Berthelsen, Nicholson, Walker, and Abad (2012) stated that their study "examines the effectiveness of a group music therapy intervention that addresses the development of positive parenting behaviors" with families with a child with a disability (p. 24). Using the study variables as cues (Dileo, 2005), key search words might be identified as *music therapy, groups, parenting,* and *children.* Key search phrases might be identified as: *group music therapy, positive parenting behaviors,* and *children with disabilities.* Once having established a base of terms such as these, expand that base using synonyms, broader terms, and narrower terms (Dileo, 2005). As the search for related literature progresses, the statement of the research topic and the search terms may shift. New information and understanding may cause

redevelopment of the topic (see Figure 1, Task 1). This is to be expected. The initial identification of search terms is just that: an initial task or, in other words, a place to start.

Scholarly Literature. Scholarly literature is *peer-reviewed,* written by recognized experts in a professional field, and/or advised by experts. Peer review is a process by which a journal article "is checked by a group of experts in the same field to make sure it meets the necessary standards before it is published or accepted" (Peer review, 2016). Scholarly literature can be found in books, scholarly journals, master's theses, dissertations, and conference proceedings. It does not typically include online or print magazine and newspaper articles. Searches, of course, should also include the literature of related disciplines, which increasingly includes articles on music therapy. *Gray literature* is written material that is not published commercially or is not generally accessible. It may be valuable in the development of a research topic. It is important, however, to assess the scholarship of these materials before relying on them.

Electronic Databases. Electronic databases permit scholarly literature to be searched by one or more of several fields (e.g., title, author, publication name, date, keywords). Once a search request has been made, references to journal articles, book chapters, theses, and dissertations related to entered search terms are listed.

Databases of scholarly literature can be found through the Internet and through university libraries. Readily accessible on the Internet, Google Scholar is a simple means of broadly searching for scholarly literature (Google, 2013). Searches result in free access to reference lists of related literature; however, procurement of full-text documents may require payment. Internet searches can also point to *open-access*

	Subject Areas				
Vendors	*Education*	*Psychology*	*Social Sciences*	*Health Science*	*Music*
EBSCOhost	Education Abstracts	PsycINFO	Social Sciences Abstracts	MEDLINE	Music Index
	ERIC	PsychARTICLES	Social Work Abstracts	CINAHL	
		Health and Psychosocial Instruments			
ProQuest	Education Journals	PsycINFO	Social Science Journals		International Music Index to Periodicals
			Social Services Abstracts		
			Sociological Abstracts		

Table 1. Sample of Database Names by Vendors and Subject Areas

literature, which is digital, free of charge, and compatible with features like peer review and copyright (Suber, 2015). To find open-access literature, simply open a Web-based search engine such as Google, Yahoo!, or Bing and enter search terms like *music therapy* and *open-access journals.* University libraries typically provide access to multiple electronic databases of scholarly literature and full-text documents for faculty and registered students. There are many different scholarly databases, and access to them is dependent upon those to which a library subscribes. Visit a reference librarian or a library website to investigate the resources available at a particular library.

Libraries purchase database subscriptions from major database vendors. The different vendors have different databases for different subject areas. Each vendor has also created a unique search engine for its databases. While the search engines all look different, their purpose is the same: to allow a researcher to find literature related to chosen search terms. Learn to make use of the full power of these search engines; online tutorials and reference librarians can help. Common vendors include EBSCOhost, JSTOR, ProQuest, OVID, and Elsevier. Table 1 lists a sample of the different databases provided by EBSCOhost and ProQuest.

Although none of the major database vendors supports a database specific to the music therapy profession, several vendors reference music therapy publications in their education, health science, music, social science, and psychology databases. Select universities and professional associations support a few music therapy–specific databases. The Temple University Music Therapy Program supports a RefWorks database of music therapy journals and books (Temple University, 2016). The World Federation of Music Therapy also supports an archive of full-text articles, conference reports, and information on music therapy (WFMT, 2013; click on the "archive downloads and services" button in the header of the web page). Lastly, the American Music Therapy Association (AMTA) supports digital, full-text archives of their professional journals through a partnership with Oxford University Press. After logging in, current AMTA members can access these archives through the links "*Journal of Music Therapy* Member Access Portal" and "*Music Therapy Perspectives* Member Access Portal" on the AMTA home page (AMTA, 2015a, 2015b).

A database should be chosen relative to a research topic and the scope of a literature review. For example, researchers interested in music therapy with hospitalized adults will, at minimum, want access to health sciences databases, whereas those interested in children with disabilities in educational settings may be more interested in educational and social science databases. A researcher doing a *comprehensive* literature review will need to search literature written not only by Board-Certified Music Therapists, but also by related healthcare professionals (e.g., nurses and social workers) and researchers in related disciplines (e.g., music, neurology, and psychology of music). Literature authored by persons from

related fields has the potential to provide theoretical foundations for research projects and insight into how related health professionals are defining and studying music interventions. Such literature contributes to the context in which a research topic needs to be considered and discussed in a literature review. Additionally, it may provide a basis for discussion and education about the potential use of therapeutic music interventions in a prospective research site. Literature authored by music therapists can provide insight into clinical methods, research methods, and research results. Review of this literature is required to place a research topic into context.

Boolean Operators. Electronic databases are typically searched using the key terms related to a research topic and *Boolean operators*. Boolean operators are simple words (e.g., "or," "and," "not") used as conjunctions to combine or exclude keywords in a search. Their use results in more focused and productive search results (Alliant Libraries, 2016).

The Boolean operator "or" is inclusive and returns the largest number of search results (Internet Tutorials, 2013). Using Williams et al. (2012) as an example, if the research-related terms include *parenting* and *families* and the Boolean operator used is "or," the search request becomes "parenting or families". This search returns all documents that have either *parenting* or *families* in them as well as documents that include both *parenting* and *families.* The white areas in Figure 2 illustrate this search request.

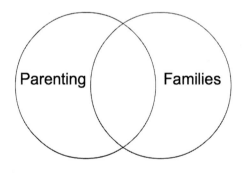

Figure 2. Illustration of the Search Term "Parenting Or Families"

The Boolean operator "and" is exclusive and reduces search results (Internet Tutorials, 2013). For example, if the research-related terms include *parenting* and *music therapy* and the Boolean operator used is "and", the search request becomes "parenting and music therapy". This search returns only documents that have both *parenting* and *music therapy* in them. The light gray, middle section of Figure 3 illustrates this search request.

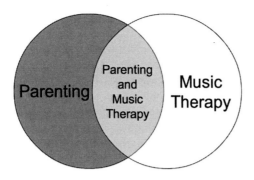

Figure 3. Illustration of the Search Term "Parenting And Music Therapy"

The Boolean operator "not" narrows the scope of a search and can easily eliminate desirable references from search results (Internet Tutorials, 2013). For example, if the research-related terms again include *parenting* and *music therapy* and the Boolean operator used is "not", the search request becomes "parenting not music therapy". This search returns only documents that have *parenting* in them and does not include documents with *music therapy* in them. The dark gray area of Figure 4 illustrates this search request.

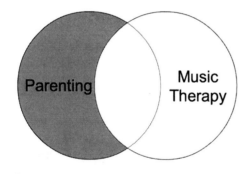

Figure 4. Illustration of the Search Term "Parenting Not Music Therapy"

The Boolean operators can also be combined to create more complex search requests (Internet Tutorials, 2013). For example, the request "(parenting or families) and music therapy" will return any references with the terms *parenting* and *music therapy*, *families* and *music therapy*, and *parenting, families,* and *music therapy* in them. The light gray area of Figure 5 illustrates this search.

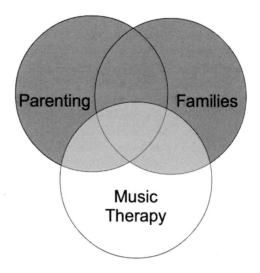

Figure 5. Illustration of the Search Term "(Parenting Or Families) And Music Therapy"

Wildcard Search Terms. Wildcards are truncated words followed by an asterisk. They can be entered as search terms into an electronic database search field. For example, using the wildcard "parent*" in a search will return any reference that includes a word that starts with parent, no matter how the word ends (Landrum, 2012). References with words like parenting, parented, and parent itself would be listed.

Start the Search. Enter initial search terms into the fields of a database search engine. The search engines allow specification of the field type, but if a search term is general, that is, a phrase or word to be found in the title or abstract of an article, there is no need to do so. Figure 6 depicts a search done in the EBSCOhost–PsycINFO search engine using four different terms related to the Williams et al. (2012) research study, including the wildcards "parent*", "child*" and "disab*". The Boolean operators "or" and "and" are used to connect the research-related terms both between and within the search fields. As can be seen in the middle of the figure, the search returned 232 results, the first of which is a reference to the Williams et al. article. The bolded words in the title of the Williams et al. article are search terms. (Note that the wildcard terms returned results with the words "parents", "child", and "disability".) From the resulting reference list, a researcher can click on the title of an article to navigate to a full reference of an article. The full reference will include, among other items, a list of related keywords and an abstract of the article. Throughout a search, create a list of the related keywords and subject terms (seen in Figure 6 below the authors' names) and use them in searches to ensure a *comprehensive* literature review. It can also be helpful to keep track of terms searched in particular databases; doing so may avoid redundant searches.

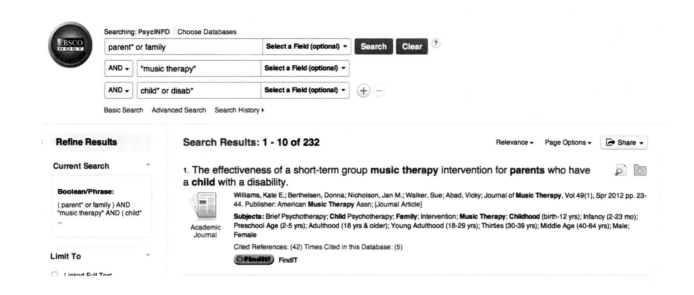

Figure 6. Sample Search in the EBSCOhost-PsycINFO Engine

The PsycINFO® Database screen shot is reproduced with permission of the American Psychological Association, publisher of the PsycINFO database, all rights reserved. No further reproduction or distribution is permitted without written permission from the American Psychological Association. © 2015 EBSCO INDUSTRIES, INC. ALL RIGHTS RESERVED.

Task 3. Select Literature, Develop a Reference List, Retrieve, and File Documents

Once an electronic database search has returned results, begin selecting literature to retrieve while simultaneously developing a reference list and retrieving and filing documents. Read the title and abstract of listed references and use several criteria to select which full-text documents to retrieve. Create a system by which to organize retrieved documents.

Selection Criteria. To select literature to retrieve, first determine the relevance of a paper to a research topic (Dileo, 2005). Some documents are clearly relevant or irrelevant, while others require reading the full text to make a determination. Dismiss those that are clearly irrelevant and add those that are clearly or questionably relevant to a reference list in an electronic document. Second, note whether anything can be ascertained about the quality of the paper from reading the abstract. Retrieval of a full-text document may be required to make a final determination about quality, but initial consideration may determine whether a document is worth retrieving. See Chapter 65, Evaluating Objectivist Research, and Chapter 66, Evaluating Interpretivist Research, for guidelines for evaluating research papers. Third, evaluate the date of publication. Depending on the research topic, it may be important to review literature from several decades past or it may be important

to include only literature published after a certain year (Dileo, 2005). For example, a historical research study would require literature from past decades, whereas research on hospitalized adults would require the most up-to-date understanding of current medical procedures and the ways in which music interventions are useful in modern hospitals. Lastly, determine whether a document is accessible. Untranslated texts in a foreign language will need to be eliminated if they cannot be translated (Dileo, 2005). Additionally, some libraries will be unable access some articles, even through an interlibrary loan department. These documents will also need to be eliminated.

The Reference List. Develop a reference list in some type of electronic document. Use a sortable format so that references can be organized and/or searched. Word processing and spreadsheet tables or *reference managers* can be used for this purpose. As literature is selected, noting which documents are immediately accessible, which require retrieval from the library, and which have been ordered through an interlibrary loan department can save time and effort. Noting what information from the document might be useful can be helpful as well. For example, it might be noted that the reference list from a book chapter contains a document that would be interesting to retrieve or that a journal article describes a clinical method related to the research topic. Lastly, if using a word processing or spreadsheet table to organize references, listing the references in a preferred publishing format can ease the tedium of collating a final reference list for a paper.

Reference managers are software programs that allow references to be saved and organized into folders and to generate bibliographies and citations as papers are written. More than 30 different programs are available. Currently, university library websites commonly refer to four brand names: ProQuest's Refworks and Thomson Reuters' Endnote (available through university libraries or personal purchase), and George Mason University's Zotero and Elsevier's Mendeley (free). Several librarians have published articles on library websites that compare the capabilities of different reference managers. These articles can help determine which program might be most useful to an individual. Search for the most up-to-date information using any Internet search engine using the following keywords: citation, reference, manager, management software, and tools.

Retrieve and File. Most electronic database references will link to an electronic full-text document in PDF format or a way to access a document through the library stacks or an interlibrary loan department. As PDF files and hard copies of documents are gathered, create a system for organizing and searching them. PDF files might be kept in a separate e-folder and titled in the same way they would be cited in the text of a paper, by authors' last name and year. Photocopies might be filed in manila folders and titled as above, by authors' last name and year, and alphabetized. Whatever the organizational system, prepare to easily access documents for repeated review.

Task 4: Read the Literature

As papers are retrieved and read, evaluate them, identify and note information from them that is relevant to the study, and document reference information for citing and quoting in the literature review. Use information from Chapters 65, Evaluating Objectivist Research, and Chapter 66, Evaluating Interpretivist Research, as guidelines to determine whether to include information from a paper in a review. Create a new word processing document for each paper reviewed in which to take notes. Head this document with the reference for the paper and type in relevant research results or conclusions, data collection or analysis methods, clinical methods, or additional references to retrieve. Additionally, in the document, either paraphrase or take direct quotes from papers and create a method for tracking when this is done. This prevents returning to the original article when citing it in a review. To prevent further backtracking, note which papers have been read and which have notes in the reference list. When creating a comprehensive literature review, dedicated notation of what literature has and has not been retrieved, read, and evaluated leaves energy for the higher-order cognitive tasks of organizing, synthesizing, and analyzing information.

Task 5: Develop an Outline

An outline is a living, flexible tool that can be used to *organize* information from diverse literature sources into themes key to a research topic. As this is done, an author can *analyze* the information and *synthesize* a critical discussion about it, while simultaneously building a coherent line of reasoning that provides a rationale for a proposed study. Before beginning an outline, read the chapters "Writing Clearly and Concisely" and "The Mechanics of Style" in the *Publication Manual of the American Psychological Association* (2010). These chapters may further support understanding of the phrase *coherent line of reasoning*. Additionally, read related literature reviews and evaluate the extent to which they are delimited, comprehensive, coherent, synthesized, and well referenced. Quality literature reviews provide excellent examples on which to model work.

Organize. To begin organizing information from literature sources, develop an initial outline. Identify key themes related to the proposed research and the preliminary rationale for it, and install them as first-level headings (see the chapter "Writing Clearly and Concisely" in the *Publication Manual of the American Psychological Association* to learn about headings). Order the headings in alignment with the coherent line of reasoning that develops a rationale for the proposed research. For example, an initial outline for the Williams et al. study (2012) might look like that seen in the first column of Table 2. Note that the search terms identified in Task 2 are apparent in the themes. Additionally, note that the first-level heading number seven is left empty. Empty headings remind a researcher to stay open to new ideas and possibilities as they read literature.

After taking notes on a paper, identify any components from it that are related to the current research topic. Review the initial outline and determine whether the information fits with an already identified theme or whether the creation of a new theme is warranted. Enter information into the outline, ensuring that it is well referenced. When enough information has been gathered to be sorted within first-level headings, theme and gather it under second-level and, if needed, third-level headings. Further development of the Williams et al. outline (2012) might look like that seen in the second column of Table 2.

As the outline develops, consider the rationale for the study and organize information so that it builds a coherent line of reasoning. Gray and Acierno (2003) state:

> The best-written literature reviews adopt a "funnel" approach. That is, they are sufficiently broad in the beginning in order to quickly orient the reader to the subject matter. As the review progresses, it should quickly narrow to the specific focus of your research. ... Once the reader is sufficiently oriented to the larger domain, you

Column 1	Column 2	Column 3
1) Study purpose: To examine "the effectiveness of a group music therapy intervention that addresses the development of positive parenting behaviors with families with a child with a disability" (Williams et al., 2012, p. 24)	1) Introduction to research topic	1) Introduction to research topic & related issues
	2) Parenting children with disabilities: key issues	a) Relationship between parent–child interactions & child development
	a) Early intervention is important (Shonkoff & Meissels, 2000)	b) The impact of disability on parent–child interactions
2) Parenting children with disabilities	b) Exposure to risk areas means parents need mental health and social support (Barnett, Clements, Kaplan-Estrin, & Fialka, 2003)	c) Study purpose
3) Positive parenting and children with disabilities	3) Positive parenting and children with disabilities: current state of research	2) Establish validity of intervention under study
4) Music therapy and parenting children with disabilities	a) Parental responsiveness results in positive outcomes (Mahoney & Perales, 2003)	a) Importance of early intervention
5) Parenting children with disabilities and Sing & Grow	4) Music therapy & parenting children with disabilities: current state of research	b) Importance of mental & social support for parents
6) The proposed research will advance current research in these ways	a) Study result: positive parent satisfaction (Mackenzie & Hamlett, 2005)	c) Importance of program quality
	b) Study result: positive parent satisfaction (Oldfield, Adams, & Bunce, 2003)	d) Intervention has these qualities
	c) Study result: enhanced child developmental skills (Allgood, 2005)	3) Prior related research to MT and families with young children
	5) Parenting children with disabilities & Sing & Grow: current research	a) Variables previously studied with positive results
	a) Nicholson, Berthlsen, Abad, Williams, & Bradley, 2008	b) Analysis of cited studies' methodology
	b) Abad, 2002	4) Prior research related to intervention: Sing & Grow
	c) Williams & Abad, 2005	a) Analysis of Sing & Grow research methodology
	6) Ways the proposed research advances current research	b) Sing & Grow research history
		5) Summary of previous paragraphs
		a) Prior research supports validity of intervention
		b) Delineate current gaps
		6) Ways present study builds upon previous studies
		a) Addressed prior studies' methodological issues
		b) Studied additional outcomes

Table 2. Illustration of Outline Development

must quickly and efficiently focus the review to your specific purposes. (p. 316)

The example outline (see Table 2, Column 1) begins broadly with the theme *parenting children with disabilities* and narrows to *the proposed research will advance current research in these ways.*

Analyze. When information from various literature sources begins coming together under key themes, an author can begin to analyze it. Analysis involves determining what is known about the research topic, identifying gaps in knowledge about the topic, and considering how a proposed study will address gaps. Authors should also compare and contrast information from different sources and determine their similarities and differences. It is important to understand the ways that competing ideas relate to, and could impact, a proposed study. Additionally, it is important to identify methodological weaknesses in previous research and indicate how a proposed study will address them (Gray & Acierno, 2003).

Synthesize. Synthesis is attained in a literature review when well-organized information, and a researcher's analysis of it, are integrated into a coherent line of reasoning that develops a rationale for the proposed research. For example, Williams et al. (2012) wrote:

> The relationship between the quality of parent–child interactions and positive child developmental trajectories is well established (Guralnick, 2006; Shonkoff & Meissels, 2000; Zubrick et al., 2008). A range of parental, family, and socioeconomic risk factors are known to impede parents' capacity to provide responsive parenting for their children. Families with a child with a disability can be considered a special risk case where the atypical developmental characteristics of the child and associated behavioral problems may both add to parental stress (Webster, Majnemer, Platt, & Shevell, 2008) and make positive parental interaction styles more difficult for this group of parents (Guralnick, 2006). Families with a child with a disability are also more likely to experience economic disadvantage (Emerson & Llewellyn, 2008) and social isolation (MacDonald & Callery, 2007). This study examines the effectiveness of a group music therapy intervention that addresses the development of positive parenting behaviors with these families. (p. 24)

In this opening paragraph from the Williams et al. review, the authors introduce key issues related to the research topic and outline an initial rationale for the research. Simplified, the introductory rationale is something like this: (a) parent–child interactions impact child development, (b) there are risk factors that challenge parent–child interactions, (c) when a child has a disability, challenges are even greater, (d) this study will examine the impact of an intervention on parent–child interactions. Previous authors who made statements supporting the ideas were cited, and the current authors' analysis of those ideas led to this coherent line of reasoning.

Later, in the third paragraph of the paper, Williams et al. (2012) write:

> Music therapy with families with young children has a small but growing evidence base. Approaches using music therapy have been associated with positive parent satisfaction (Mackenzie & Hamlett, 2005; Oldfield, Adams, & Bunce, 2003), high levels of parent and child engagement (Lyons, 2000; Oldfield et al., 2003), improved parent–child interactions (Mackenzie & Hamlett, 2005; Oldfield et al., 2003), and enhanced child developmental skills (Allgood, 2005; Archer, 2004; Muller & Warwick, 1993; Oldfield, 2006; Standley, Walworth, & Nguyen, 2009; Walworth, 2009). … However, these findings should be regarded with caution as they are based mainly on descriptive case studies and conducted with small samples. Only a few studies have employed control group designs (Standley et al., 2009; Vlismas & Bowes, 1999; Walworth, 2009) or used previously established measures of outcomes (Muller & Warwick, 1993; Oldfield, 2006). (p. 25)

In this paragraph, information related to the theme *music therapy with families with young children* was organized by positive study outcomes. The paragraph concludes with an analysis of the study methodologies. This paragraph shows how the synthesis of well-organized information and author analysis statements begin to place a study in the context of prior research. As an aside, the analysis statements are later used as part of the complete rationale for the Williams et al. study: The authors acknowledged a need to improve research methodology related to the intervention under study and stated ways in which the present study did so.

In six clear, concise paragraphs, Williams et al. (2012) address related key issues, review previous related research, and lay out a rationale for their study. A final, overview outline of their literature review might look something like that seen in Table 2, Column 3. In the Column 3 outline, it is possible to see how information from the literature is synthesized with the authors' analysis of it to create a coherent rationale for the study. Development from the outline in Column 2 to this outline required significant analysis and synthesis of information from the related literature.

Flexibility in thinking is also required to develop an outline. As understanding of a research topic develops, information can be shifted in the outline. First- and second-level headings can change positions. Information under headings can be moved between headings, organized, and reorganized. Headings can also be renamed; this allows them to become concise and accurately descriptive. This process of change is shown across the three columns of Table 2. It is important to work with information in this manner until a coherent, analytical discussion of the literature is built and a thoughtful, logical rationale for the study becomes clear.

Task 6: Assess

Having read some literature and developed an initial outline, it becomes important to take a moment, step back from the work, and assess what needs to be done next. This is part of the previously described iterative process shown in Figure 1. At this point, new ideas and understanding gleaned from reading and outlining, or a need for further information about a theme, may lead to new database searches. New references may have been found in the bibliographies of reviewed literature, and the associated documents may need to be retrieved. It may be time to reread a document based on insight gained from one more recently reviewed. It may be worthwhile to spend time refining the organization of an outline and analyzing the information in it. In some cases, all of the above may be required. Take time to assess where in the process the work is; do so more than once when creating a comprehensive review. Becoming located in the process can calm nerves and increase patience.

At some point, it is time to assess whether to start writing. Answering a few questions can help with this activity.

- Have all themes related to the research topic included in the initial search terms been addressed? If not, is there a significant rationale to support the decision?
- Has the literature review been successfully held to initial delimitations? If not, is there a significant rationale to support the decision?
- Has the outline settled into a clear, concise, logical discourse that provides a rationale for the purpose of the study?

If the answer is yes to the above questions, it is time to send the outline to others (e.g., a mentor, colleague, or research advisor) for feedback. Additional perspectives on the organization and clarity of the work provide valuable information. Even if they are not experts on the research topic, outside readers should be able to review for flaws in the clarity of the thought process.

Task 7: Write

Scholarly writing should be a deliberate task. Accurate statement of the meaning an author intends typically requires considered use of language, grammar, and punctuation. Learning to write clearly and concisely may take time and patience. A few brief pieces of advice follow on working from an outline, using language, writing introductory and summary paragraphs, writing about core issues and themes, and seeking feedback.[2]

Working from an outline typically indicates that an author's thoughts have been well organized before making any attempt to construct paragraphs and sentences. It may be, however, that the process of writing further clarifies ideas and their organization. Allow an outline to shift even during the writing process. Just a few pages of writing may bring the insight that information under a third-level heading in section two is actually better placed in section one. Additionally, further analysis of information may occur during the writing process, and those new insights will need to be synthesized into the discussion. In sum, retain an attitude of flexibility throughout the writing process.

Before sitting down to write, review the chapters "Writing Clearly and Concisely" and "The Mechanics of Style" in the *Publication Manual of the American Psychological Association* (2010). As stated in the former chapter, "The prime objective of scientific reporting is clear communication. You can achieve this by presenting ideas in an orderly manner and by expressing yourself smoothly and precisely" (p. 65). The chapter covers concepts important to scholarly writing, including: continuity in presentation of ideas, smoothness of expression, tone, economy of expression, precision and clarity, guidelines for reducing bias, and grammar. The latter chapter covers equally important topics such as punctuation, spelling, capitalization, italics, abbreviations, and the use of numbers. While writing, it may be helpful to keep these chapters close.

Introductory paragraphs typically follow each first-level heading and each second-level heading that has third-level headings (notice the organization of the present chapter). Wait to construct these paragraphs only after the information to be discussed under a heading has been gathered, organized, analyzed, and synthesized. These paragraphs are a brief foreshadowing of the information to come and are more easily written when an author is clear about the content of a section. Summary paragraphs may be found at the end of major sections of a paper (the sections under first-level headings). They should be used to reiterate the major findings and/or points of that section.

When synthesized with an author's analysis of them, the core issues and themes related to a research topic become the bulk of a literature review's content. Communicate carefully about them to an audience. When writing about core issues, provide selective examples of them only where appropriate (Gray & Acierno, 2003). The first paragraph of the Williams et al. (2012) study, shown above, provides an example of this technique. Additionally, when writing about a theme, cite only the most prominent examples of it and "be selective and efficient rather than exhaustive" but cover the themes comprehensively (Gray & Acierno, 2003, p. 315). The third paragraph of the Williams et al. work, also shown above, ignores this advice because its purpose was to demonstrate the "small but growing evidence base" for music therapy with families with young children (p. 25). The authors deliberately included as much information as was available and cited many authors to make their point. Typically, however, the advice of Gray and Acierno is appropriate.

Once having determined that a paper is written well enough, ask for feedback on it from an outside reviewer. Be prepared to edit this first draft at small and large levels. Readers may provide feedback on items as specific as word selection and as general as the organization of a major section. Remember, the creation of a scholarly paper often requires input from multiple perspectives. The goal is to create a clear and concise conveyor of information; the more perspectives from which feedback is received, the larger the audience to which the piece will be comprehensible.

Conclusion

Constructing a narrative literature review involves several different types of tasks, which in turn require different types of cognitive skills. Developing the abilities to organize, analyze, and synthesize information is key to writing a quality paper. Retaining the more personal qualities of curiosity, patience, and flexibility will helpful as well.

The iterative process of constructing a review is not always linear. It may require the simultaneous completion of two or more tasks. For example, an author may wait for additional documents to come in from interlibrary loan while gathering and reading those that are immediately available. The process may also require repeating short series of tasks; an author might outline, read more literature, outline again, read more literature, outline again, and then finally turn to the task of writing. Certainly, each researcher's process is uniquely individual and will present unforeseen challenges. The creation and dissemination of quality music therapy literature, however, can be a satisfying and valuable way to contribute to the field.

References

Alliant Libraries. (2016). What is a Boolean Operator? Retrieved from https://library.alliant.edu/screens/boolean.pdf

American Music Therapy Association (AMTA). (2015a). *Journal of Music Therapy* member access portal. Retrieved from http://www.musictherapy.org

American Music Therapy Association (AMTA). (2015b). *Music Therapy Perspectives* member access portal. Retrieved from http://www.musictherapy.org

American Psychological Association. (2010). *Publication manual of the American Psychological Association* (6th ed.). Washington, DC: Author.

Dileo. C. (2005). Reviewing the literature. In B. L. Wheeler (Ed.), *Music therapy research* (2nd ed.; pp. 105–111). Gilsum, NH: Barcelona.

Gray, M.,& Acierno, R. (2003). Reviewing the literature and evaluating existing data. In J. C. Thomas & M. Hersen (Eds.), *Understanding research in clinical and counseling psychology* (pp. 295–317). Mahwah, NJ: Lawrence Erlbaum.

Google. (2013). Google Scholar: About. Retrieved from http://www.google.com/intl/en/scholar/about.html

Internet Tutorials. (2013). Boolean searching on the Internet. Retrieved from http://www.internettutorials.net/boolean.asp

Kucan, L. (2011). Approximating the practice of writing the dissertation literature review. *Literacy Research and Instruction, 50,* 229–240. doi:10.1080/19388071.2010.514037

Landrum, R. (2012). *Undergraduate writing in psychology: Learning to tell the scientific story.* Washington, DC: American Psychological Association.

Magarey, A., Veale, B., & Rogers, W. (2001). A guide to undertaking a literature review. *Australian Family Physician, 30*(10), 1013–1015.

Peer review. (2016). *Merriam-Webster Online.* Retrieved from http://www.merriam-webster.com/dictionary/peer%20review

Suber, P. (2015). Open access overview. Retrieved from http://www.earlham.edu/~peters/fos/overview.htm

Temple University. (2016). Music therapy database. Retrieved from http://www.temple.edu/boyer/academicprograms/music-therapy/#MTDAL

Williams, K. E., Berthelsen, D., Nicholson, J., Walker, S., & Abad, V. (2012).The effectiveness of a short-term group music therapy intervention for parents who have a child with a disability. *Journal of Music Therapy, 49,* 23–44. doi:10.1093/jmt/49.1.23

World Federation of Music Therapy (WFMT). (2013). Music therapy archive. Retrieved from http://www.wfmt.info/Musictherapyworld/

1. Cheryl Dileo wrote this chapter in previous editions of *Music Therapy Research.* Her pioneering work laid the groundwork for the present chapter.
2. Editor's note: Readers can find additional, and more extensive, information on writing in Chapter 68, Reading, Writing, and Submitting Interpretivist Research.

Chapter 5

ETHICAL THINKING IN MUSIC THERAPY RESEARCH[1]

Kathleen M. Murphy

Ethical issues arise in all research, especially in studies that involve human participants (Smith, 2000). Therefore, ethical considerations must be applied to all aspects of the research process, including research design, protocol development, measurement choice, participant recruitment and selection, data analysis, and reporting of results (Seiber, 2000). These considerations may result in tension between ideal research design, required protections of human participants, and reporting of results. A strong foundation in research ethics can assist researchers in making ethical decisions while creating scientifically sound research studies. This chapter will review basic ethical guidelines that should be considered when engaging in research. The reader is encouraged to seek out additional sources of information such as *Ethical Thinking in Music Therapy* (Dileo, 2000) or *Responsible Conduct of Research* (Shamoo & Resnik, 2009).

Ethical Foundations of Research

Research is typically undertaken for the betterment of society and has produced results that have increased the quality of life for many. However, there is a history of unethical research, which may have added to our scientific understanding of illness and disease yet caused extreme suffering and pain in the research participants. The world came to learn of the "atrocities committed by Nazi doctors and scientists on tens of thousands of prisoners held in concentration camps" during the Nuremburg war crimes tribunal (Shamoo & Resnick, 2009, p. 236). The Nuremburg Code, which set standards for informed and voluntary consent by research participants, minimization of harms and risks, validity of research design, and social value, was an outgrowth of the war crimes tribunal. It was the first international code for research using human participants (Shamoo & Resnick, 2009). However, this code did not prevent the conducting of unethical research throughout the world, including research on vulnerable populations such as children, prisoners, economically disadvantaged people, and those with development disabilities or mental health disorders (Egilman, Wallace, Stubbs, & Mora-Corrasco, 1998; Rothman, 1982; Shamoo & Irving, 1993). In response, the National Commission for the Protection of Human Subjects of Biomedical and Behavioral Research was formed in 1974. The commission was charged with identifying basic ethical principles that should underlie research with human participants (National Commission for the Protection of Human Subjects of Biomedical and Behavioral Research,

1979). These principles, set forth in the *Belmont Report* (1979), are (a) respect for persons (protecting the autonomy and privacy of research participants and making provisions for those who are unable to make their own decisions), (b) beneficence and nonmaleficence (maximizing benefits to research participant and society, minimizing harm, ensuring that the harm-to-benefit ratio is reasonable), and (c) justice (benefits and burdens of research are distributed fairly and vulnerable participants are not taken advantage of; Shamoo & Resnick, 2009).

Respect for persons incorporates two fundamental ethical precepts: autonomy and protection. Respecting autonomy means that the researcher must allow individuals who are capable to make their own decision, after personal deliberation and without interference from the researcher, as to whether to participate in a research study. Protection must be afforded to individuals who have impaired or diminished decision-making capabilities to prevent harm or abuse. Potential research participants who have diminished capacity for consent must be appropriately represented and assurance provided that the risk of harmful consequences is minimal (Council for International Organizations of Medical Sciences [CIOMS], 2002; Fischman, 2000).

Beneficence and nonmaleficence mean that researchers should design and carry out studies that will maximize benefits and minimize harm to those involved. Any potential benefit to society must be weighed carefully in light of potential and possibly irreparable harm to the research participant. Additionally, this principle requires the researcher to be competent to conduct the study and safeguard the welfare of the participants (CIOMS, 2000; Smith, 2000).

Justice refers to the ethical obligation to treat individuals with respect and dignity. This principle ensures that no group or class of persons bears more than its fair share of the burdens or is deprived of their fair share of the benefits of the research being conducted (CIOMS, 2000). "These benefits include the direct benefits of participation (if any) as well as the new knowledge that the research is designed to yield" (World Health Organization [WHO], 2011, p. 13). Justice also requires that researchers select the least vulnerable among possible research participants (CIOMS, 2000).

Guidelines for Ethical Research Involving Human Participants

Guidance for research with human participants has been developed and distributed by several organizations at the international, national, and regional levels over the past 50 years (WHO, 2011). A review of each country's laws, regulations, and standards is beyond the scope of this chapter. Therefore, this section will review general ethical guidelines for conducting research with human participants. Readers are referred to the *International Compilation of Human Research Standards* (http://www.hhs.gov/ohrp/international/) for a review of the laws, regulations, and guidelines that govern human subject research in 113 countries (Office for Human Research Protections, 2016).

Current guidelines for ethical research are based on the principles and ideals identified in the *Nuremberg Code* (1949), the *Declaration of Helsinki* (World Medical Association, first adopted in 1964, revised in 2013), and the *Belmont Report* (1979). The Council for International Organizations of Medical Sciences (CIOMS) and the World Health Organization (WHO), using those documents, have developed standards and guidelines for research with human subjects. These documents provide ethical guidance for research involving human participants (CIOMS, 2002) and operational guidance for ethical review of research studies (WHO, 2011). Music therapists should also look to their professional association's code of ethics and institutional review board for additional guidance when conducting research.

All research involving human participants should be carried out in accordance with the three ethical principles cited above, namely *respect for persons, beneficence,* and *justice.* These principles form the basis of the guidelines developed by CIOMS, WHO, and countries around the world. Shamoo and Resnick (2009, pp. 251–252), after a review of relevant literature, have expanded on the principles identified in the *Belmont Report* and have derived the following eight principles that all researchers should consider when developing and carrying out research. These principles been adapted and expanded upon by the author to be applicable to both objectivist and interpretivist music therapy research:

1. *Scientific validity:* Research protocols should be scientifically well designed, meeting established criteria for objectivist and interpretivist research. Additionally, all those involved in the development and implementation of the research study must be competent and qualified (by virtue of education, experience, and training; CIOMS, 2002). Lastly, the research study should "offer a means of developing information not otherwise obtainable" (CIOMS, 2002, p. 23).

2. *Social value:* Researchers should conduct research studies that will benefit society and advance well-being; they should not use human beings in wasteful research. Research studies should be "responsive to the health needs and the priorities of the population or community in which it is to be carried out" (CIOMS, 2002, p. 51).

3. *Informed consent:* Research participants should make an informed choice with regard to participation in research studies. They should be apprised of the risks and benefits and given the option to withdraw from a research study at any time. Safeguards should be put in place for those unable to give informed consent (e.g., obtaining consent from a legally authorized representative).

4. *Respect for persons*: The privacy, confidentiality, and dignity of research participants must be protected. Researchers must respect the decision of individuals to decline an invitation to participate in a research study. They must not attempt to intimidate or use undue influence to entice an individual to participate in a research study.

5. *Beneficence*: Researchers must ensure that the research protocol minimizes harm and maximizes benefits. All risks should be justified in terms of benefits to the individual or society. Research protocols that could cause severe harm (e.g., death or disability) should not be carried out.

6. *Equitable selection of participants:* Benefits and potential harm should be distributed equally among research participants. Individuals should not be excluded from participating in research without a sound justification.

7. *Protection for vulnerable participants:* Safeguards should be put in place to protect vulnerable individuals from harm (e.g., children, prisoners, pregnant women, those unable to give informed consent). Additionally, the researcher must justify the decision to invite vulnerable individuals to participate in a research study (CIOMS, 2002).

8. *Independent review:* All research should be reviewed by an independent body to ensure that the study meets ethical and scientific standards.

The Institutional Review Board

The *institutional review board* (IRB; also called the *research ethics committee* or the *ethical review board*) is a committee that is charged with providing an independent review of all research involving human (or animal) participants at the national, regional, local, or institutional level (WHO, 2011). The IRB is composed of a diverse group of individuals (usually 5 to 20) who are capable of providing a thorough review of a research proposal (CIOMS, 2002). IRB membership should be heterogeneous, with representation from medicine, science, ethics, and other related professions as well as laity in order to ensure scientific rigor and that the cultural/moral values of the community are upheld (CIOMS, 2002; Farrant, Pavlicevic, & Tsiris, 2014). While each country/organization has its own set of specific rules and regulations, there are general principles common to most IRBs that ensure proper research studies. These include requirements to:

- Minimize risk;
- Have a sound design;
- Respect the dignity of the person;
- Benefit the participant and/or society;
- Not unfairly discriminate against any class or cultural group (including but not limited to gender, sexual identity, sexual preference, religion, race, marital status, etc.);
- Meet all national, local, and agency guidelines.

The *International Compilation of Human Research Standards* (Office for Human Research Protections, 2016) specifies the level of review that is required for each country. It is the responsibility of the researcher to be familiar with the rules and regulations that govern research in his or her particular setting.

IRBs typically have the authority to approve/disapprove or require modifications to a research protocol, monitor informed consent, collect information on adverse reactions, identify conflicts of interest, and stop research studies (Shamoo & Resnik, 2009). Researchers are required to submit two documents to the IRB prior to initiating any research study: a research protocol/proposal and a consent form. What follows is a general overview of each document. Readers are encouraged to review the research proposal and consent form guidelines provided by their institution or national agency.

The Research Protocol

The *research protocol* is a document that describes all aspects of a proposed research study, including background information and rationale, research questions, participants, research design, procedures, time frame, associated risks with justification, benefits, and expected outcomes. Additionally, any data collection instruments and participant questionnaires should also be included. It should be a stand-alone document that provides members of the IRB with enough information to approve, disapprove, or request modifications on a given study. Most IRBs will provide researchers with a template for use when preparing a protocol for review. Guidelines for research protocols that have been developed by CIOMS (2002) and the World Health Organization (2015) may be found in the Appendix to this chapter.

Informed Consent

Informed, voluntary consent is an ethical requirement for conducting research with humans. In fact, Guideline 4 from the *International Ethical Guidelines for Biomedical Research Involving Human Subjects* states:

> For all biomedical research involving humans, the investigator must obtain the voluntary consent of the prospective subject or, in the case of an individual who is not capable of giving informed

consent, the permission of a legally authorized representative in accordance with applicable law. Waiver of informed consent is to be regarded as uncommon and exceptional and must in all cases be approved by an ethical review committee. (CIOMS, 2002, p. 32)

So what is informed consent, and why is it important? *Informed consent* is the process by which a decision to participate in research is made by a competent individual after an investigator thoroughly explains the procedure, risks, and benefits of the study. It allows individuals to make a decision to participate in a research study without coercion or fear of retribution. It is important because it upholds the principle of *respect for persons,* which states that "individuals should be treated as autonomous agents" and that "persons with diminished autonomy are entitled to protection" (*Belmont Report,* 1979, n.p.).

The informed consent process begins with the researcher meeting potential research participants prior to the start of a study and continues throughout its entirety. In the initial meeting, the researcher must address the following three points: (a) the purpose of the research, (b) why the individual is being asked to participate, and (c) the nature of the study, including all potential risks (Mazur, 2007). Additionally, the World Medical Association (2013) dictates that researchers disclose sources of funding, potential conflicts of interest, and institutional affiliations. During this meeting, the prospective participant must be allowed to ask questions and given as much time as is needed to reach a decision, including time to seek the advice of family members (CIOMS, 2002). The researcher must make it clear that the participant can withdraw from the study at any time without prejudice. Prior to obtaining consent, which usually involves obtaining the participant's signature on the consent form, the research must ensure that the prospective participant understands all of the information presented. A researcher may ask the prospective participant to state his or her understanding of the expectations, procedure, and risks associated with the investigation. The investigator should seek consent only once he or she is convinced that the potential participant is capable of giving consent, fully understands the expectations, risks and benefits, and is voluntarily agreeing to participate in the study. The informed consent document is usually used as a guide by the researcher for the verbal explanation of the study. This document provides a complete description of the research study, including risks and benefits. Informed consent documents should be written in the native language and at the reading level of the individual being invited to participate in the study. All technical terms should be defined. The exact content for the informed consent document is governed by national law; however, the following elements are common in most jurisdictions (CIOMS, 2002):

1. A statement inviting an individual to participate in the

research study, followed by a description of the exact purpose of the research, duration of participation, explanation of the procedures, and how the research differs from medical care.

2. A description of the risks, including any discomfort or inconvenience the individual may experience.
3. A description of any benefits the individual and others may receive as a result of participation in the research.
4. A description of how confidential information (the individual's identity, protected health information, and data collected in the study) will be protected and how long data will be kept.
5. A description of alternative treatments that may be available in lieu of participation in the research study.
6. A statement explaining how research-related injuries will be treated and if any compensation will be made available.
7. Contact information for the person(s) to contact with any questions about the research study, research participant rights, or research-related injury.
8. A statement that participation in the research study is voluntary and that the participant may withdraw at any time without prejudice. Further, it should be stated that unwillingness to participate in a research study will not result in the withdrawal of treatment or other penalty.

Most IRBs will have templates for the informed consent document that researchers are expected to use. WHO (n.d.) also has several templates that researchers can download and use. These are available at http://www.who.int/rpc/research_ethics/informed_consent/en/ and free of charge.

Consenting Procedures for Vulnerable Participants

During the past decade, more attention has been paid to obtaining informed consent from vulnerable individuals (Verástegui, 2006). Generally, vulnerable participants are those who are considered incapable of making an informed decision due to lack of capacity or circumstances that may influence a decision to participate. The CIOMS (2002) defines vulnerable populations in this way: "Vulnerable persons are those who are relatively (or absolutely) incapable of protecting their own interests. More formally, they may have insufficient power, intelligence, education, resources, strength, or other needed attributes to protect their own interests" (p. 64).

Additionally, the CIOMS provides a comprehensive list of individuals whom they consider as meeting the criteria set forth in the above state definition. For example, CIOMS considers individuals with intellectual disabilities, prisoners, unresponsive patients, residents of nursing homes and other long-term care facilities, and those with fluctuating mental capacity to be vulnerable and in need of special protection of their rights.

Researchers are cautioned against doing research with individuals who are considered to be vulnerable unless there is a clear and compelling reason, and members of the vulnerable population are likely to benefit from the research (CIOMS, 2002; Shamoo & Resnick, 2009). Safeguards to protect those adults considered to be vulnerable include modification of the language used during informed consent, use of a translator, involvement of independent monitors or witnesses during the consent process, and seeking consent from the potential participant's legally authorized representative (Farrant et al., 2014; Shamoo & Resnick, 2009). The WHO (n.d.) notes that "researchers may need to make extra allowance to ensure that the consent is genuine and does not place added risk or stress on the participant" (Section VII).

Consenting and Assenting Procedures for Children

Research involving children should be carried out only when its purpose is to gain knowledge that is relevant to their health needs (CIOMS, 2002). Research with children requires consent from the parent or legal guardian, as most children are not legally deemed to have the mental capacity to make informed decisions, meaning that they are incapable of understanding the nature and possible risks associated with a given research study (Farrant et al., 2014). The age of majority varies from country to country. For example, in the United States, federal law states that children must be at least 18 years of age to consent to participate in research, whereas in some countries children over the age of 16 are considered capable of giving consent (Farrant et al., 2014, pp. 68–69). Parents or legal guardians are required to give consent for those children who legally are not allowed to independently make a decision to participate in a research study.

This does not mean that children should not be asked if they want to participate in a research study. In fact, they, like adults, should be willing participants in any research study. Children who are able to understand the proposed research study, including what they will be asked to do, along with any risks and benefits, have the right to be informed of the research study and make a determination of whether they want to participate. Children have the same rights as adults to ask questions and refuse participation if they choose. The WHO (n.d.) suggests that children over the age of 7 be asked for their *assent*. They should express their desire to participate in a research study on an informed assent form written in age-appropriate language. It is important to remember that the assent form does not replace the parental consent form. Lastly, children who are too young or unable to give their assent may offer expressions of disapproval by crying, screaming, acting out, or failing to comply with an experimental procedure. Researchers must accept their actions as a refusal to participate in the research study and disenroll them from the research study *even if* the parent or guardian has signed a consent form.

Data—Security, Electronic Transfer, Disposal Post-Research

Research data are any information, artifacts, observations, and products related to a research study. Researchers are responsible for safeguarding all study-related data as well as protecting the privacy of research participants and maintaining the confidentiality of their personal information (Farrant et al., 2014; World Medical Association, 2013). This includes information that participants share as well as information collected from medical records or other sources (such as family members). In music therapy research, study-related data may take forms such as numbers, song lyrics, music notation, and audio or audio/visual recordings (Farrant et al., 2014). Researchers must describe how they plan to protect privacy and maintain confidentiality in their research proposal as well as follow through with those plans during the course of the research study. The IRB will make the final determination of whether the participant's privacy and the confidentiality of his/her information will be adequately protected.

"The safest way to protect [the] participant's privacy is to make all data anonymous" (Mazur, 2007, p. 43). Researchers should de-identify all data, that is, remove any personal identifying information from data collection forms or patient records. It is common for researchers to assign participants a "code identifier" (Farrant et al., 2014, p. 98) or a "non-unique identifier" (Mazur, 2007, p. 43) as a means of keeping data confidential. These identifiers do not provide a direct link between data and research participants. Codebooks, if used to record these identifiers, must be treated with the same security as personal information (Mazur, 2007). Researchers may also present quantifiable data in aggregate form, which will protect privacy and maintain confidentiality. Other types of data, such as audio or audio-visual recordings, that are not easily presented in aggregate form can threaten privacy and confidentiality. Researchers can minimize this threat by informing participants of how and where the recordings will be used. Many IRBs require a separate consent for the use of audio or audio-visual forms of data collection.

Researchers have a responsibility to keep data secure and must describe the procedures for data security in their research proposal. Farrant et al. (2014) suggest the following methods for securing data:

- storing data in a locked file cabinet,
- using codes and/or numbers to anonymize the data,
- saving the data in password-protected electronic devices,
- destruction of data at the completion of the research study. (pp. 103–104)

Additional safeguards include limiting who has access to the data and destroying written copies of the data once it has been entered into an electronic database (Coulehan & Wells,

n.d.). Finally, research-related data should be destroyed at the completion of a research project. Hard copies of personal data and code sheets should be shredded. Electronic data should be permanently deleted and recordings destroyed (Farrant et al., 2014).

Protecting Electronic Data

Electronic data may be subject to theft and hacking (Coulehan & Wells, n.d.). Researchers need to take extra care to protect study data that is stored in an electronic format from unauthorized access. This involves protecting access to the actual data by using an encrypted password system for electronic data files, limiting who has access to data files as well as protecting your computer system by keeping antivirus protection on your computer, using firewalls and intrusion detection software, and maintaining current versions of all software (Coulehan & Wells, n.d.).

Use of the Internet for collecting research data is on the rise and is likely to continue to increase. Many online data-gathering programs (such as SurveyMonkey®) purport to offer security features to keep data safe, private, and confidential. Researchers are advised to thoroughly investigate the security features and claims of any online data-gathering software and consult with technology experts before their use (Folkman, 2000). Lastly, data that are shared electronically should be sent only through secure WIFI networks, and all files should be password protected.

Conclusion

This chapter has provided an overview of ethical issues related to music therapy research. Music therapy researchers should always uphold the three ethical principles—autonomy, beneficence, and justice—when designing and carrying out research studies. Additionally, they should seek continued guidance from experienced researchers and monitor changes in laws and regulations in order to maintain the highest ethical standards when conducting research.

References

Belmont Report. (1979). *The Belmont report: Ethical principles and guidelines for the protection of human subjects of research.* Retrieved from hhs.gov/ohrp/humansubjects/guidance/belmont.html

Coulehan, M. B., & Wells, J. F. (n.d.). *Guidelines for responsible data management in scientific research.* Washington, DC: United States Department of Health and Human Services. Retrieved from https://ori.hhs.gov/images/ddblock/data.pdf

Council for International Organizations of Medical Science. (2002). *International guidelines for biomedical research involving human subjects.* Geneva, Switzerland: Author. Retrieved from http://www.cioms.ch/publications/layout_guide2002.pdf

Dileo, C. (2000). *Ethical thinking in music therapy.* Cherry Hill, NJ: Jeffrey Books.

Egilman, D., Wallace, W., Stubbs, C., & Mora-Corrasco, F. (1998). Ethical aerobics: ACHRF's flight from responsibility. *Accountability in Research, 6,* 15–62.

Farrant, C., Pavlicevic, M., & Tsiris, G. (2014). *A guide to research ethics for arts therapists and arts & health practitioners.* Philadelphia: PA: Jessica Kingsley.

Fischman, M. W. (2000). Informed consent. In B. D. Sales & S. Folkman (Eds.), *Ethics in research with human participants* (pp. 35–48). Washington, DC: American Psychological Association.

Folkman, S. (2000). Privacy and confidentiality. In B. D. Sales & S. Folkman (Eds.), *Ethics in research with human participants* (pp. 49–57). Washington, DC: American Psychological Association.

National Commission for the Protection of Human Subjects of Biomedical and Behavioral Research. (1979). *The Belmont report: Ethical principles and guidelines for the protection of human subjects of research.* Retrieved from hhs.gov/ohrp/humansubjects/guidance/belmont.html

Nuremberg Code. (1949). *Trials of war criminals before the Nuremberg Military Tribunals under Control Council Law No. 10* (Vol. 2, pp. 181–182). Washington, DC: U.S. Government Printing Office. Retrieved from http://www.hhs.gov/ohrp/archive/nurcode.html

Office for Human Research Protections. (2016). *International compilation of human research standards.* Washington, DC: U.S. Department of Health and Human Services. Retrieved from http://www.hhs.gov/ohrp/international/index.html

Rothman, D. J. (1982). Were Tuskegee & Willowbrook "studies in nature"? *The Hastings Center Report, 12*(2), 5–7. doi:10.2307/3561798

Shamoo, A. E., & Irving, D. N. (1993). Accountability in research using persons with mental illness. *Accountability in Research, 3,* 1–17.

Shamoo, A. E., & Resnik, D. B. (2009). *Responsible conduct of research* (2nd ed.). New York, NY: Oxford University Press.

Sieber, J. E. (2000). Planning research: Basic ethical decision-making. In B. D. Sales & S. Folkman (Eds.), *Ethics in research with human participants* (pp. 13–26). Washington, DC: American Psychological Association.

Smith, M. B. (2000). Moral foundations in research with human participants. In B. D. Sales & S. Folkman (Eds.), *Ethics in research with human participants* (pp. 3–10). Washington, DC: American Psychological Association.

Verástegui, E. L. (2006). Consenting of the vulnerable: The informed consent procedure in advanced cancer patients in Mexico. *BMC Medical Ethics, 13*(23). doi:10.1186/1472-6939-7-13

World Health Organization (WHO). (2011). *Standards and operational guidance for ethics review of health-related research with human participants.* Geneva, Switzerland: Author. Retrieved from http://apps.who.int/iris/bitstream/10665/44783/1/9789241502948_eng.pdf?ua=1&ua=1

World Medical Association (WHO). (2013). World Medical Association Declaration of Helsinki ethical principles for medical research involving human subjects. *Journal of the American Medical Association, 310,* 2191–2194. doi:10.1001/jama.2013.281053

World Health Organization (WHO). (2015). *Recommended format for a research protocol.* Geneva, Switzerland: Author. Retrieved from http://www.who.int/rpc/research_ethics/format_rp/en/index1.html

World Health Organization (WHO). (no date). *The process of obtaining informed consent.* Retrieved from http://www.who.int/rpc/research_ethics/Process_seeking_IF_printing.pdf

Appendix

Guidelines for Research Protocols, developed by CIOMS (2002) and WHO (2015)

The CIOMS and WHO recommend that the following information be included in all research proposals submitted to IRB or ethical review committee.

General Information

- *General information,* including protocol title, name and contact information of principal investigator; name of the research site, name and contact information for sponsor, and a summary of the study in nontechnical language, should be provided.
- *Rationale and background* information, including a brief review of related research and a clearly stated rationale is needed. The rationale and background should succinctly explain why the research is being done, why the study is needed, and what is hoped to be learned as a result of the study.
- *Research goals and objectives* are required. In objectivist research, this section will include broad statements of what the researcher is hoping to accomplish and the related research questions and hypotheses (see Chapter 12 in this book). In interpretivist research, this section will include the focus and purpose (see Chapter 13 in this book) of the study.

Study Participants

- *Process of recruitment* should be clearly explained. This includes a description of the type of sampling to be used (e.g., convenience, purposive) and rationale, where recruitment will take place, and the means to be used (e.g., flyers, email advertising). Copies of recruitment materials should be included with the proposal.

- *Justification* is needed for (a) including participants with limited or no capacity for consent and (b) excluding any groups on the basis of age, gender, sexual orientation, religion, ethnicity, socioeconomic status, or other reasons.
- *Guidelines for removing participants from a study* should be articulated, including noncompliance or adverse reaction.
- *Compensation for participants* (e.g., gift cards, reimbursement for travel, cash) should be explained.

Research Method

- *Study design* should be clearly outlined and include the following: a description of the research participants (inclusion, exclusion, and withdrawal criteria), the method of selecting participants, and the research design being used (including rationale); if an RCT, the method of randomization and whether the study will be blinded.
- *Study design or methodology* should be thoroughly described and include the following: the process of assigning participants to groups; blinding, pre- and/or posttest measures, instruments used to collect data (including reliability and validity data), and procedures that will be followed. Researchers should include a flowchart in this section of the protocol. Samples of questionnaires, tests, observation forms, and other documents for data collection are included in an appendix.
- *A description of the study site,* including provisions for maintaining participant confidentiality and safety is needed.
- *A description of what type of follow-up* will be provided to the research participants and for how long should be given. This section should also describe reporting mechanisms for adverse reactions/events that occur after data collection has been completed.
- *Quality assurance,* which includes a description of how the research will maintain the integrity of the study and how research assistants will be trained and monitored, should be provided.
- *Timeline* for the study's implementation from recruiting through data analysis should be included.

Data Analysis

- *Data collection tools* should include a description of how data will be collected and recorded. Copies of all tests, scales, and questionnaires should be included with the research proposal.
- *Data management and analysis* should include a

description of how data will be stored and analyzed, and its confidentiality maintained. For objectivist studies, this section includes statistical tests to be used, reasons for sample size, level of significance to be used, and procedures for handling missing data (i.e., use of an intent-to-treat analysis). Interpretivist studies should include a detailed description of how the data will be analyzed (see Chapters 21 & 22). This section should also include a statement of how long the data will be stored and how it will be destroyed.

Risks and Benefits

- *Ethics.* The research proposal should describe any ethical considerations related to the study, including from whom IRB approval will be obtained, reasons for including vulnerable populations, any outcomes that might raise ethical concerns, and the plan for obtaining informed consent (and assent if research participants are minors or have limited capacity). A description of previous submissions and their outcomes should also be included.
- *Expected outcomes* describe how the research findings will contribute to the advancement of knowledge and how the outcomes will impact healthcare, systems, and/or policies.
- *Expected benefits.* Potential benefits that study participants may receive should be explained.
- *Safety consideration* is needed, including a description of any associated risks, how injury (physical or psychological) will be managed, and how adverse events will be recorded and reported. (The WHO, 2015, notes in particular that research questionnaires can have adverse effects on individuals. Therefore, researchers conducting survey research need to address this issue in the protocol.)
- *Dissemination of information related to harm* is required: a detailed plan for contacting study participants if information is made known (e.g., adverse reactions or potential benefits) that could influence their continued participation.
- *Detailed plans of compensation/treatment* that will be offered to participants who suffer injury, disability, or death as a result of research related activities should be provided.

Informed Consent

- *Informed Consent.* The research proposal should include a copy of the informed consent forms (described in detail in the next section) in the language in which they are going to be administered.
- *Procedures for obtaining informed consent (and assent if applicable)* should be fully described, including procedures for obtaining informed consent from those

with limited capacity, who are not at the age of majority, or who are unable to give consent should be completely articulated.

Dissemination

- *Dissemination of results* includes a description of how study results will be disseminated to the scientific community, participants, and the community at large. Circumstances in which it might be inappropriate to disseminate results should also be identified.

Description of the Research Team

- *Name, institutional affiliations, qualifications,* and *curriculum vitae of all investigators* are needed.
- *Project management* describes the roles and responsibilities of each member of the research team.
- *Concurrent research projects.* The proposal should contain a listing of all research projects in which the investigator(s) are currently engaged, along with funding sources and duration.

Financial Information and Conflict of Interest Statement

- *Financing and insurance.* Some IRBs require a separate form for this information; others request it as part of the research protocol. Investigators need to disclose who is funding/sponsoring the research.
- *Financial and conflicts of interests* should be disclosed, and arrangements for addressing these must be described.

1. Cheryl Dileo wrote the chapter on ethics in previous editions of *Music Therapy Research.* Her pioneering work laid the groundwork for the present chapter.

Chapter 6

MULTICULTURAL CONSIDERATIONS IN MUSIC THERAPY RESEARCH

Seung-A Kim • Cochavit Elefant

Our society has become more diverse in the past decade, as evidenced by the influx of immigrants, multiracial and minority groups, and the increasing age gap between generations (Population Reference Bureau, 2015). Consequently, culture has been regarded as a significant construct among researchers. By proposing Culture-Centered Music Therapy, Stige (2002) encourages "all music therapists [to be] more culture-centered in their work and thinking, not by labeling their work as such but integrating cultural perspectives in their thinking" (p. 5). As our own worldviews influence all aspects of music therapy (Dileo, 2000; Wheeler & Baker, 2010), cultural factors provide a significant foundation to all music therapy research. With this perspective, music therapy researchers are essentially multicultural researchers. Moreover, this professional role is not only part of a scholarly endeavor, but also "our ethical and moral obligation" (Vera & Speight, 2003, p. 270).

In response to cultural pluralism (Kallen, 1924), music therapy researchers have attempted to examine the impact of culture in music therapy (Kim & Whitehead-Pleaux, 2015). As the wealth of culture-oriented research increases, the types of questions researchers are asking have evolved through clinical work and training. In addition, music therapists frequently find themselves working in multicultural settings, and engagement in globally collaborative research is on the rise. Moreover, the unique nature of culture becomes an informative and comprehensive access point for music therapists, providing a glimpse of how individuals experience and react to music. Each culture includes a distinct subset of characteristics that defines how groups of people feel, experience, and respond to different musical experiences (Saarikallio, 2012). Despite the growing literature regarding culture and music therapy, resources on multicultural considerations in music therapy research are scarce. Thus, this chapter aims to provide a current review of previous studies, a discussion on culture-related issues and challenges in music therapy research, and recommendations for future studies. To understand how culture affects the research process, it is important to first have a concrete understanding of culture and its nature.

Culture-Related Issues and Challenges in Research

Culture is a multifaceted and dynamic phenomenon that can be interpreted in many different ways. To support further discussion, this chapter adopts the nature of culture as described by Ruud (1998): "Cultural performance is linked to the individual's situatedness, a way of perceiving and giving meaning to the world informed by a certain perspective. This perspective is rooted in the private life world of the person" (p. 54). Culture is fluid and ranges significantly depending on the individual's relationship to various social groups. *Culturally informed research* by definition is concerned with cultural issues involved in music therapy research. More specifically, it is concerned with whether a study is conducted on a specific culture or more than one culture in- and outside the country, or whether a study examines the music and health of the members of marginalized cultural groups in music therapy. Therefore, the culturally informed researcher respects the existence of cultural plurality and promotes social justice, liberation, and community empowerment. *Multicultural* refers to multiple cultures and indicates contrasting identities interacting or relating to one another in some way. This can include the identities of an individual or the identities of many people. Among a wide range of individual identities, multicultural refers to a part of a person's race, ethnicity, age, gender, sexual orientation, language, religious or spiritual affiliation, marital status, ability, education, socioeconomic status, affiliation, and lifestyle. All of the different factors of one's identity coexist and interact with other distinct cultures in a given society. The terms *multicultural* and *cross-cultural* are used interchangeably in this chapter. Multicultural research is complex, contextual, and inclusive of multiple perspectives. In addition, multicultural research includes cultural and musical plurality as well as its own conceptual limitations.

Culture is dynamic and complex in nature, which makes it difficult to describe with respect to one perspective (Ponterotto, Costa, & Werner-Lin, 2002). Due to its multifaceted nature, different schools of thought can interpret culture in various ways. The idea of culture has both implicit and explicit meanings. On the one hand, certain behaviors in culture, such as specific traditions and customs, are observable and explicit. On the other, expectations or hidden norms embody implicit meanings, making a group's cultural nuances subtle. The concept of *implicit meanings* rests on the belief that there are principles that regulate the culture. From an outsider's perspective, many of these implicit traits must be inferred. Culture can also be conceptualized on two levels: internal or external. *Internal culture* relates to a personal variable (e.g., one's values, knowledge, religion), while *external culture* relates to political and organizational aspects in a social and ecological context, including economic status and climate. Therefore, research that includes a cultural perspective must account for the implicit, explicit, internal, and external aspects (Berry, Poortinga, Breugelmans, Chasiotis, & Sam, 2011; Sam & Berry, 2006).

Culture exists within the context of a particular situation permeating social, biological, physical, psychological, historical, and practical effects (Stige, 2002; Stige, Ansdell, Elefant, & Pavlicevic, 2010). Similarly, music is also played within a certain context. For example, in the Venda culture in South Africa, music is an integration of arts and is inseparable from singing, dancing, and other forms of art. Within this context, music is experienced in everyday life as a community act. In contrast, Western culture is more readily displayed in isolated performances at concerts, where music is shared on a physical stage (Saarikallio, 2012).

Social constructivism (Berger & Luckman, 1967; Gergen, 1999) emphasizes multiple realities in society that make interpretations of culture both diverse and individualistic. We actively create our own identities through social and historical constructs. The meaning of reality is fluid and is expressed through the use of language. Ultimately, culture influences how people assign meanings to phenomena such as music and health. From this perspective, a style of music is viewed differently from culture to culture, as is the concept of health and illness (Aigen, 2014; Moreno, 1988; Spector, 2012). In collectivistic societies, integration of body, mind, and spirit is emphasized. These societies also view health as a social concept that embraces community health. For example, Asian clients may believe that an imbalance between yin and yang, rather than a biological cause, causes illness. Traditionally, Western medicine is known to have more of an evidence-based practice that diagnoses and treats patients according to tangible data. Even though many diseases are common across cultures, it is important that translations of any data or pertinent information be accurate and capture the sensitive nuances that exist within a culture.

Moreover, although common symptoms of a disease may be found across cultures, the reaction to a disease may be culture-specific. *Hwabyeong,* anger syndrome, is an example of a culture-bound syndrome that is only found among Koreans (Kim, 2013b). A behavior is considered normal or abnormal depending on the norms of the society (e.g., being thin may be considered healthy or unhealthy depending on the culture; Berry et al., 2011; Zhang & Cross, 2011).

The term *culture* has often been considered to be singular. However, modern anthropologists found the need to refer to cultural plurality to strengthen the value and complexity of cultural diversity (Chiang, 2008; Hall, 1976). Similarly, ethnomusicologists consider music to be plural to emphasize its diverse nature (Mastnak, 1993; Rohrbacher, 2012). There is not one *music,* as had been seen with ethnocentric bias, but there are *musics.* Stige (2002) considers that "although the possibility of universals in music should not be neglected, the traditions of music-making around the world are so diverse that it is meaningful and necessary to talk about musics in

plural" (p. 94). DeNora (2000, 2003), a music sociologist, uses the concept of *affordance* and *appropriation* to look at what music can offer the person in relation to a certain situation. *The potential of musical affordance* is that it affords something specific in relation to the person's perception of it and may offer extra-musical benefits. The idea of musical affordance is relevant when understanding diversity in social and cultural contexts (Stige et al., 2010).

Most conclusions from past research studies on the music therapy profession were based on data drawn from a middle-class, white-male demographic, emphasizing the characteristics of in-group dynamics (Chase, 2003; Dileo, 2000; Saarikallio, 2012). These norms were considered *desirable and typical* (Dileo, 2000; Kim & Whitehead-Pleaux, 2015). Inevitably, this Eurocentric attitude has caused not only conceptual limitations but also possible biases that cannot be applied to a diversifying population (Baker, 2014; Bennett, 2001). For example, fundamental constructs between individualism and collectivism differ drastically, skewing interpretations drawn by researchers. When research is focused on self-concept within the orientation of individualism, the design may not be appropriate in a society where an interdependent self operates through a collectivist construct. For example, Kim (2011) noted in her study of international music therapy students studying in the United States that when personality traits assessments were developed within Western theoretical foundations and examined across cultures, the data became questionable due to the lack of validity and the inability to replicate and compare accurate results. "The fundamental problem remained that when research does not adequately incorporate culture as a central and specific contextual variable, behavior is misidentified and pathologized, and, in some cases, psychologists are at risk of perpetuating harm" (American Psychological Association, 2003, p. 388). Therefore, it becomes important for researchers to be clear on their perspectives regarding the group of interest or study. A researcher's perspective determines how extrinsic factors affect shared psychological functions as a result of different behaviors, and observed behaviors are the results of the interactions between the researcher and the surrounding context.

Multicultural Considerations in Designing Music Therapy Research

Cultural Awareness of the Researcher

When the research process is initiated, a researcher's worldviews inherently influence the types of questions that are asked. Wheeler and Baker (2010) identified how the diverse worldviews of 12 experienced music therapy educators/clinicians representing 16 countries affected their work in multicultural settings. Within a grounded theory framework, they identified multiple cultural factors (e.g., ancestry, childhood musical experiences, family and generational factors, traumas, spirituality) that shaped the participants' worldviews. Their worldviews impacted practice and education.

To minimize cultural biases that may influence a particular study, researchers must thoroughly examine their own cultures, have a good awareness of the similarities and differences between their own cultures and the culture of the participants in the study, and select a culturally appropriate theory-driven inquiry during the phase of conceptualization. Without this process, researchers "may build their cultural biases into the definition and operationalization of constructs. … Language and culture are so intrinsically tied that disentangling the effects of linguistic and cultural biases is not easy" (Sanchez, Spector, & Cooper, 2006, p. 197). Further, it is recommended to reflect on the researcher's process regarding culture. Baker (2014) provides an example of her own reflection during her conceptualization process: "My limited pre-understandings of [therapeutic songwriting] practice with people from older and younger generations, and from non-Christian religious backgrounds, affected the depth with which I could relate to and reflect on the experiences of the research participants and the questions posed to them during their interviews" (p. 148). Just as Baker recognized her biases as a Western-trained music therapist and member of the dominant ethnic group, other researchers must take time to reflect on and analyze their own biases and understandings of potential multicultural impact on a study.

Just as it is important for researchers to be aware of their own values and cultural heritage (Baker, 2014), there is a fundamental necessity for researchers to begin the research process with a comprehensive knowledge about the participants' cultural beliefs and values, as well as to withhold any preconceptions. The most important requirement would be to openly listen to what the participant is saying, doing as much as possible to avoid bias or misinterpretation. Therefore, dialogical interaction among the participants should be a requirement in the study. Member checking and constant reflection will also help ensure the validity of the study. Conducting research with varied cultural groups requires sensitivity to individual as well as social contexts to have a culturally and linguistically unbiased data collection method.

Not only is a lack of diversity and representation in samples problematic, but using a convenience sample is limiting in regard to the usefulness of the findings of the study (Berry, 2006; Worthington, Soth-McNett, & Moreno, 2007). Comparing multiple samples at different locations per country can also minimize the differences between the samples (Wong & Wong, 2006). In addition, when designing studies, samples should reflect the diversity of the study so that the findings can be more representative. Although Public Health Service Act 492B requires that researchers must include women and minority groups as participants in clinical research and to report ethnic and racial data of participants (in the United States; National Institutes of Health, 2014), published studies do not always contain this information.

Measurements

When a researcher designs a data collection method originally developed for a specific culture, cultural considerations must be made before applying findings to other cultures (Saarikallio, 2012). Kim (2011) noted that language is not an exclusive reflection of culture. That is, most assessment tools and instruments are developed in English, but even when participants' primary language is English, they may interpret the questionnaire differently from the author's original intention if their culture is different from the one in which it was created. For example, it would be possible that some participants may try to endure and overcome stress because they may think that they should be able to manage it on their own.

In some cases, researchers still use a research instrument despite reports stating the method to be ineffective due to the lack of instrumentation measuring cultural differences (Berry et al., 2011). When the instrument does not fit the local culture, the findings are questionable. Even if researchers use standardized measures that are widely accepted, culture-related issues still exist. In discussing a current international randomized controlled study of improvisational music therapy's effectiveness for children with autism spectrum disorders (ASD; Geretsegger, Holck, & Gold, 2012), Carpente expressed, "The majority of the assessment/diagnostic tools used to diagnose for ASD were developed and tested in the United States and UK. This may compromise their cultural and linguistic validity in other countries and cultures. In addition, this makes it difficult to acquire the tools and receive adequate training for administration" (J. Carpente, personal communication, October, 2015).

Although there are benefits to using existing instruments, a revised and more comprehensive instrument may be necessary to address potential culture-related issues. Thus, it is crucial that validity for diverse ethnic and racial groups be tested in order to develop culturally oriented measurements (Ip-Winfield & Grocke, 2011) when conducting international research.

Translations

When the same measure is used across cultures, an accurate sample comparison may not be possible if samples interpret the measure differently. Additionally, many texts can be misinterpreted or fail to capture the right nuance when translated, which may lead to cultural and linguistic bias (Sanchez, Spector, & Cooper, 2006). Kim (2011) identified practical challenges that may have occurred in her study when translating the survey for international music therapy students:

While most of the participants primarily use languages other than English, the survey was constructed in English. It is unrealistic that the questionnaires be administered in 25 different languages because the validity of the translations would be questionable. It is also possible that translations may change the structure of the instrument. In order to replicate the study in another language, future work is necessary to provide psychometric evidence in a translated instrument. (p. 88)

There are some inherent issues related to translating an instrument into another language. Even skillful translators may not write comparable questions due to cultural differences between the two languages. Moreover, translations that convert the text to its original language should be carefully considered to ensure that the linguistic integrity and scale value of items are appropriately adjusted and represented (American Psychological Association, 2003; Sanchez, Spector, & Cooper, 2006). This also applies to interpretivist research methods such as an interview that needs to be translated to English. It is recommended that translators be not only linguistically competent but also culturally competent. For this reason, Schwantes (2011) employed a college student rather than a professional interpreter as an interpreter for their study with Mexican migrant farmworkers.

Participants' Responses

The response bias of a participant can influence the results of a study. Sometimes information given by participants in a study may be shared in reporting the results in a way that could reveal their identities (Wheeler & Baker, 2010). Some questions may not be culturally appropriate for a specific group, but be acceptable for another. This may affect how much participants share and how they share their personal information with the researchers. Participants from some countries may prefer extreme responses, while others may avoid them. In some cases, participants may answer in a way they believe is right or the interviewer may unintentionally lead the participants.

Results may also be influenced by how instructions are presented or phrased. Participants may interpret words differently or respond to questions in a unique and unexpected manner. Thus, it is necessary to incorporate the concerns and needs of the target community when selecting the research design and sampling (Marshall & Batten, 2003; Vera & Speight, 2003), as well as acknowledging in-group heterogeneity of the racial/ethnic group sample.

Action research (particularly participatory action research) considers the cultural and social values of the participants, as it includes them as collaborators and owners of the research. Music therapy research often uses action research, in which questions are raised by the participants or negotiated between the participants and the researcher. Because the questions are not determined solely by the researcher, this process is collaborative in nature and can bring a more individualized perspective. Action research can lead to empowerment and the participants' voices being heard within their community or on an international level. Elefant (2010) published her participants' requests for community change, demonstrating how collaborative efforts can address the needs in a target community. Other examples of action research in music therapy are by Stige (2002) and Warner (2005).

Research Design

Researchers need to explore varied options for research designs to examine the complexity of the phenomenon of culture more efficiently. When choosing a research design, they must consider cultural issues and whether they use a certain methodology due to familiarity. In addition, researchers need to consider etic and emic perspectives when doing multicultural research (Berry et al., 2011). The *etic perspective* is the outside view, knowledge, and values that researchers bring with them to the field. The *emic perspective* is the insider view of openness, which will help the researcher to gain the knowledge. Stige (2002) suggests that researchers should apply these two perspectives, since both inform each other in a dialectical manner. A wide range of research methods is recommended (Ponterotto et al., 2002). In addition, this flexibility allows for alternative explanations: "Findings are more convincing when they are based on diverse sources of evidence, multiple sources of data, and different research methods" (Berry et al., 2011, p. 25), as objectivist and interpretivist methods are seen as complementary. When conducting objectivist studies, a longitudinal design is ideal to examine changes between two or more time periods with the same subjects (Berry, 2006). Further, quasi-experimental designs, such as two- or three-group comparisons, are recommended, as it is impossible to obtain information about change with a single-group design. For example, the musical response of counterparts in the home country, immigrants, and non-immigrants may be useful in providing a comprehensive overlook of a certain topic. Action research (Stige, 2002) and mixed methods (Ortiz, Sosulski, & Sherwood, 2012) are also recommended, as these methods include a broad range of perspectives and voices. The mixed methods paradigm contains both objectivist and interpretivist methods. Therefore, this paradigm utilizes multiple types of data and fits well with multicultural views.

Interpretation of Findings Across Cultures

When examining the equivalence of concepts and data throughout the research process, the researcher must take into account three levels of equivalence: structural, metric, and scale equivalence (Berry et al., 2011). *Structural equivalence* is the evidence of conceptual equivalence. *Metric equivalence* can validate changes in scores over measurement occasions. The assessment scores collected from different groups should be comparable maintaining *scale equivalence*. "A lack of comparability, or inequivalence, can be the consequence of many sources of cultural bias. Ultimately, it is the task of a researcher to make it plausible that the interpretation of cross-cultural data is not distorted because of inequivalence. This can be done more easily when different levels of equivalence are distinguished" (Berry et al., 2011, pp. 26–27). When analyzing data, the two levels of analysis (cultural and individual levels of variance) must be taken into account. Statistical techniques examining data at different levels and relationships are available to help researchers test their interpretations or inferences.

Disseminating Findings

Culturally informed researchers are encouraged to think beyond conventional methods of dissemination. Also, they "are encouraged to find ways for the results to be of benefit to the community and to represent the participants' perspectives accurately and authentically" (American Psychological Association, 2003, p. 390). For example, communicating with the participants and communities closely and collaborating with them can help facilitate the research process. Researchers may hire a research assistant or interpreter from their community and consider publishing in magazines or community newsletters to reach research participants, community leaders, and policy makers (Vera & Speight, 2003). In this way, the community can better utilize findings, especially when studies include demographic information regarding age, sex, occupation, ethnic, and racial information.

Ethical Concerns About Power Relationships

There is an inherent power imbalance in the relationship between the researcher and the participant (Marshall & Batten, 2003; Vera & Speight, 2003). If the researcher is from a dominant social group and is studying participants from a minority group, this unequal power relationship can be exacerbated due to sociopolitical factors. Thus, it is important for researchers to be aware of this issue and examine their own assumptions and biases toward the participants, while sensitively executing their study with the participants. Informed consent must be written at their level of comprehension and reviewed with them thoroughly and in a culturally oriented manner.

Doing Research in Different Countries

While conducting research in different countries presents practical and organizational problems, other unforeseen challenges can occur in addition to the cultural and language issues discussed above. These may include the need for funding for long-distance travel and transport of equipment, knowledge regarding foreign administrative structures, and understanding norms and traditions to ensure politically and culturally correct communication (Sarrikalio, 2012, p. 479). It is also important to ensure identical procedures in different locations.

Examples of Culture-Oriented Music Therapy Research

The cultural implications for music therapy research are significant, because culture affects the entire research process. Although there are few publications that focus on the cultural implications for music therapy research, researchers have demonstrated an increasing interest in examining cultural and international issues in music therapy. Unlike other allied professions, research methods in music therapy have been relatively varied, ranging from objectivist to interpretivist to mixed methods. This section discusses multicultural paradigms that can be considered in music therapy research and existing studies. Different research designs that have high utility when exploring music and health in a sociocultural context are presented. The last section will include recommendations for future studies.

Multicultural Research Paradigms

Influenced by postmodernism, there are a few paradigms that influence multicultural research. The following research examples describe how these paradigms are commonly used in multicultural research.

Acculturation. Research based on acculturation theory (Gilboa, Yehuda, & Amir, 2009; Kim, 2011, 2013a; Sam, 2006) offers a foundation for understanding individuals who encounter cultural adjustments. Kim (2011) surveyed international music therapy students to identify predictors of acculturative stress while studying in the United States. Five measurements—demographic information, English proficiency, Acculturative Stress Scale for International Students (ASSIS; Sandhu & Asrabadi, 1994), Neuroticism and Openness to Experience of the Big Five Inventory (John, Donahue, & Kentle, 1991), and Music Therapy Student Academic Stress Inventory (MTSASI; Kim, 2011)—and open-ended questions were used. The findings showed that a larger cultural gap between the host culture and the student's culture might cause a higher level of acculturative stress. English proficiency, neuroticism, and music therapy stress were identified as predictors of acculturative stress. A recommendation from the study was that international students should be aware of their acculturative stress and develop management skills, including early prevention as needed.

Portraiture. Through a constructivist paradigm that employs *portraiture,* the ethnic identity of five Indian men and women were examined through Culturally Centered Music and Imagery (CCMI; Swamy, 2012). The emphasis in portraiture (Davis & Lawrence-Lightfoot, 1997) includes a focus on goodness, social, and cultural context examinations. In her study, Swamy used Indian music to explore identity-based imagery within a globalized context. After considering social, cultural, ethnic, local, and regional influences, Indian music was selected by carefully examining its music theory system, its symbolism, and metaphors within the context of Indian culture and society. The results showed that CCMI was useful in examining cultural or "ethnic unconscious" (p. 230). Furthermore, it is suggested that this approach may be an effective medium for adults during immigration or acculturation.

Critical Theory. Another multicultural paradigm, critical theory (Habermas, 1984), can be found in Hadley's study (2013) of the experience of race in music therapy, where a narrative study is introduced to the field. Within an interpretivist framework, this study provides a way of discovering a narrative of an individual's unique voice. She points out that while a therapist's self-awareness has been emphasized, race or ethnicity has not been explored in music therapy. The subjectivity and bias of the researcher are considered to enrich the work rather than distort the truth. It is commonplace for the researcher's relationship and life experience to influence the study in this way. Hadley explains that with "'thin descriptions,' such narratives misrepresent the complex ways in which identities are actually thick and complex social phenomena. When this happens, the identities of people are in many ways distorted, and they feel oppressed by the dominant narrative and its resultant thin descriptions" (p. 5). Using a purposive sample, the author chose 17 music therapists with diverse racial backgrounds who were located in different countries. They shared their experiences in a therapeutic setting. The conversations were recorded and transcribed. The author and the music therapists collaborated to make the final narrative products, employing narrative techniques in a conversational way. Sharing and reflecting on each person's experiences can bring out unique and authentic voices that would normally be unheard. Thus, some studies use narrative methods to explore multicultural topics.

Community Music Therapy. Community Music Therapy (Stige & Aarø, 2012; Stige et al., 2010) emphasizes cultural and social issues that concern people and practices of health musicking in the community. Community Music Therapy is in line with current discourse on music, culture, and society and areas such as ethnomusicology, music sociology, health promotion, and community psychology (Stige & Aarø, 2012). It expands the boundaries of music therapy practices and considers the social context and the empowerment of the

client. Stige (2002) argues that when working in Community Music Therapy, the community "is not only a context for the work but also a context to be worked with" (p. 113). The use of music and musicking is to help people find their voices and to collaborate and connect with others in and beyond their own community, and it "encourages musical participation and social inclusion, equitable access to resource, and collaborative efforts for health and well-being in contemporary societies" (Stige & Aarø, p. 5).

Musicking is a central foundation of Community Music Therapy (Stige et al., 2010) and can be useful when thinking of music in multicultural research. *Musicking,* a term suggested by Christopher Small (1998), considers music not just as an object (e.g., composition, song) but also as an activity where people participate in a variety of forms. By definition, Small described musicking aptly in his own words: "To music is to take part, in any capacity, in a musical performance, whether by performing, by listening, by rehearsing or practicing, by providing material for performance (what is called composing), or by dancing" (p. 5). Small describes in broad strokes, and implies that participating in musicking can mean to form a relationship with music and to establish meaningful connections by being either passively or actively interacting with the medium. Stige and Aarø (2012) discuss musicking as a social action and interaction and examine musical activities as they involve communal musicking of a group of people. "Communal musicking is an eminent vehicle for collective action, collaboration, and group cohesion. ... Music also allows for social bonding and the expressions of traditions and values" (p. 127).

Research Methods

Participatory Action Research

Through a liberal lens, *participatory action research* (McTaggart, 1997; Stige, 2005) is an appropriate research method for enabling participant expression to produce changes as needed. This methodology encourages participants to gain new perspectives, make personal changes, and initiate changes within their community. This approach was born out of a desire to change and give voice to the voiceless. Using a dialogical approach and negotiations, the academic researcher and the participants are able to go beyond their boundaries and make improvements in their community. Participatory action research "not only involves active lay participation in the research process, it also involves shared ownership of the research ... it is aimed at solving problems as they are experienced by a group or community" (Stige, 2002, p. 277). It empowers participants to be part of the challenge as well as the solution. In Kleive and Stige's study (1988) that incorporated participatory action research, music therapists and Upbeat, a group of adults with developmental disabilities in Norway, brought about social change in the municipality where they lived. Change occurred when the group's musical experiences became more inclusive and was heard by the local community. Similarly, Elefant (2010) conducted a participatory action study with the *Renanim* choir, a group of people with multiple physical disabilities, who also had a significant impact in the local community. Another example is Schwantes' (2011) research with Mexican farmworkers who migrated to the United States.

Phenomenological Inquiry

Kenny (2006) expresses, "Culture is its own unique kind of container with implied signals that are difficult to observe. Culture is lived within a context, but not in a laboratory. So we have thick descriptions to help us find knowledge and truth about the lives lived within these contexts. We have stories" (n.p.). To gain the essence of a multicultural phenomenon and understand common experiences that people may have, music therapists employ *phenomenological* methods to further understand this unique human connection. Gilboa (2015) conducted a multicultural study, interviewing seven former and present leaders of music therapy training programs in Israel. His study investigated multicultural thoughts and considerations in the music therapy training sites. Additionally, Gilboa researched how training courses adapt to the complexity of multicultural issues related to Israeli students. He formulated a model known as *spheres*. This model refers to different fields (spheres) in which multicultural interactions occur in music therapy training, which include the multicultural background of the student, a multicultural mosaic of the students in the program, and cultural and multicultural issues that arise in clinical work (including fieldwork). The results show that multiculturalism in training courses is very complex and that there is a need for dialogue between all spheres.

Kim (2008) employed a phenomenological method to study cross-cultural music therapy supervision. Kim examined the supervisee's experiences in cross-cultural music therapy supervision by interviewing seven music therapy supervisees with diverse cultural backgrounds. The study concluded that a supervisor's ability to have cultural empathy, openness, and nonjudgmental attitudes is an important factor in cross-cultural supervision. Acceptance and acknowledgement of supervisees bring out more effective outcomes. Cross-cultural supervision was explored in a study that examined eight Korean female music therapists' individuation process within a cultural context in the Nordoff-Robbins certification training program in New York (D. M. Kim, 2010). Several important themes were extrapolated from the comprehensive data collected: a tendency to be obedient to authority, fear of self-expression, professional devaluation, being submissive, feeling guilty, and taking leadership. Some themes were related to the participants' common sociocultural factors. D. M. Kim suggests this study should be replicated with trainees from diverse backgrounds and hopes that these findings can help

trainers understand this process to better provide culturally sensitive training.

Ethnographic Interview and Grounded Theory

Utilizing *grounded theory* methodologies, the need for a multicultural perspective in music therapy can be demonstrated. Baker (2014) examined how sociocultural factors impacted the therapeutic songwriting process with 45 experienced music therapists. She identified 26 categories through interviews. These were further analyzed, and seven factors were identified: music's diverse roles in different sociocultural groups; music therapists' knowledge or and skills in playing multicultural music; sociocultural diversity of group members; language; social diversity and the therapeutic relationship; religious beliefs; and gender, generational issues, and ethnicity. Baker concluded that understanding the group membership, the therapeutic relationship, and the therapist's approach affects the songwriting process. Clients' attitudes toward health, treatment, dying, and death are sociocultural. For example, an individual's religious and spiritual beliefs can be expressed through music, and a song does not necessarily "cure but creates the opportunity for the community to seek healthcare advice from the gods" (p. 3).

Mixed Methods

The complexity of a multicultural topic requires varied and flexible research approaches in which both objectivist and interpretivist methods may be appropriate when collecting, analyzing, and interpreting data. Few research studies have used the *mixed methods* approach. In a study by Gilboa et al. (2009), a mixed methods design was used on a musical communal project with a group of 12 university students of various cultural origins living in Israel. Pre- and post-questionnaires were used quantitatively to examine the influences that the group had on a student's feelings and opinions. Interpretivist methods (Alvesson & Sköldberg, 2009) were implemented to explore whether the project enhanced multicultural relations among students of various cultures. The results of the study revealed that students expressed more acceptance and openness toward the *other* from different cultural groups. Music was a major influence in these developments. The researchers avoided bicultural (conflicting) groups and opted for a "diffuse multicultural possibility in which no defined schism exists" (Gilboa, Yehuda, & Amir, 2009, p. 10). Group process enabled most students to identify with their own cultural roots in addition to their overarching Israeli culture.

Another example of a mixed methods study can be found in Schwantes' (2011) research, which explores the effects of culturally appropriate music therapy interventions on 125 Mexican farmworkers' mental health. The research aimed to identify music that was meaningful to the migrant farmworkers and described their relationship with the music therapist. The research, a mixed methods design inspired by participatory action research, utilized a randomized control trial. Schwantes' use of the principles of participatory action research emphasized the value of migrant knowledge, deriving questions from their perspective as well as helping them to reflect on their situation in order to improve their lives, which enabled participants to transform their oppression into empowerment. Although this research was a mixed methods study, the researcher used a flexible protocol, which took into account cultural aspects including idioms and customs, for the objectivist portion. Although the results did not show significant improvement in depression, anxiety, and social isolation scores for the farmworkers who participated in music therapy, those who participated in group music-making between sessions were able to improve their scores in all categories. The participants found focus group interviews helpful and valued their relationship with the researcher.

Conclusion

Engaging in research is ultimately a multicultural act that involves intra- and interpersonal levels of work including individuals and their community within cultural contexts. In this collaborative act, researchers need to come with the authentic intent of wanting to learn from the participants and their community. Therefore, music therapy researchers must continue to be culturally informed in any topic of their study; see beyond the practices, values, and norms of the client's culture; and understand the specific context that may influence the client. Additionally, just as culture permeates through all dimensions of life, it inherently becomes impossible to ignore culture when conducting research. As Kenny (2006) asserts, "We can only function well as global citizens if we embrace the diversity of life, which includes the diversity of standards of practice and research protocols" (n.p.). Research that embeds cultural sensitivity can therefore be achieved through a holistic collaborative effort between researchers and participants, with explicit and well-oriented goals and expectations as well as potential impact for the community being observed.

References

Aigen, K. S. (2014). *The study of music therapy: Current issues and concepts.* New York, NY: Routledge.

Alvesson, M., & Sköldberg, K. (2009). *Reflexive methodology: New vistas for qualitative research* (2nd ed.). London, UK: Sage.

American Psychological Association. (2003). Guidelines on multicultural education, training, research, practice, and organizational change for psychologists. *American Psychologist, 58,* 377–402.

Baker, F. A. (2014). An investigation of the sociocultural factors impacting on the therapeutic songwriting process. *Nordic Journal of Music Therapy, 23*(2), 123–151. doi:10.1080/08098131.2013.783094

Bennett, C. (2001). Genres of research in multicultural education. *Review of Educational Research, 71,* 171–217. doi:10.3102/00346543071002171

Berger, P. L., & Luckman, T. (1967). *The social construction of reality: A treatise in the sociology of knowledge.* London, UK: Penguin.

Berry, J. W. (2006). Design of acculturation studies. In D. L. Sam & J. W. Berry (Eds.), *The Cambridge handbook of acculturation psychology* (pp. 129–141). Cambridge, UK: Cambridge University Press.

Berry, J. W., Poortinga, Y. H., Breugelmans, S. M., Chasiotis, A., & Sam, D. L. (2011). *Cross-cultural psychology research and applications* (3rd ed.). Cambridge, UK: Cambridge University Press.

Chase, K. M. (2003). Multicultural music therapy: A review of literature. *Music Therapy Perspectives, 21,* 84–88. doi:10.1093/mtp/21.2.84

Chiang, M. M. (2008). *Research on music and healing in ethnomusicology and music therapy* (Unpublished master's thesis). University of Maryland, College Park, MD.

Davis, J., & Lawrence-Lightfoot, S. (1997). *The art and science of Portraiture.* San Francisco, CA: Jossey-Bass.

DeNora, T. (2000). *Music in everyday life.* Cambridge, UK: Cambridge University Press.

DeNora, T. (2003). *After Adorno: Rethinking music sociology.* Cambridge, UK: Cambridge University Press.

Dileo, C. (2000). *Ethical thinking in music therapy.* Cherry Hill, NJ: Jeffrey Books.

Elefant, C. (2010). Giving voice. Participatory action research with a marginalized group. In B. Stige, G. Ansdell, C. Elefant, & M. Pavlicevic, *Where music helps: Community Music Therapy in action and reflection* (pp. 199–215). Farnham, UK: Ashgate.

Geretsegger, M., Holck, U., & Gold, C., (2012). Randomised controlled trial of improvisational music therapy's effectiveness for children with autism spectrum disorders (TIME-A): Study protocol. *BMC Pediatrics, 12*(2). doi:10.1186/1471-2431-12-2

Gergen, K. (1999). *An invitation to social construction.* Thousand Oaks, CA: Sage.

Gilboa, A. (2015). Ebony, ivory, and other shades of music therapy training in Israel: Some multicultural thoughts and considerations. In K. D. Goodman (Ed.), *International perspectives in music therapy education and training: Adapting to a changing world* (pp. 130–158). Springfield, IL: Charles C Thomas.

Gilboa, A., Yehuda, N., & Amir, D. (2009). Let's talk music: A musical-communal project for enhancing communication among students of multi-cultural origin. *Nordic Journal of Music Therapy, 18,* 3–31. doi:10.1080/08098130802610999

Habermas, J. (1984). *The theory of communicative action* (Vol.

1). Boston, MA: Beacon Press.

Hadley, S. (2013). *Experiencing race as a music therapist: Personal narratives*. Gilsum, NH: Barcelona.

Hall, E. (1976). *Beyond culture*. New York, NY: Doubleday.

Ip-Winfield, V., & Grocke, D. (2011). Group music therapy methods in cross-cultural aged care practice in Australia. *Australian Journal of Music Therapy, 22*, 59–78.

John, O. P., Donahue, E. M., & Kentle, R. L. (1991). *The big five inventory—Versions 4A and 54*. Berkeley, CA: University of California, Berkeley, Institute of Personality and Social Research.

Kallen, H. M. (1924). *Culture and democracy in the United States*. New York, NY: Boni and Liveright.

Kenny, C. B. (2006). A world of full of voices. *Voices: A World Forum for Music Therapy, 6*, n.p. doi:10.15845/voices.v6i2.248. Retrieved from https://voices.no/index.php/voices/article/view/248

Kim, D. M. (2010). Towards musical individuation: Korean female music therapists' experiences in the Nordoff-Robbins Music Therapy certification training. *Arts in Psychotherapy, 37*, 353–362. doi:10.1016/j.aip.2010.09.005

Kim, S. A. (2008). The supervisee's experience in cross-cultural music therapy supervision. *Qualitative Inquiries in Music Therapy, 4*, 1–44.

Kim, S. A. (2011). Predictors of acculturative stress among international music therapy students in the U.S. *Music Therapy Perspective, 29*, 126–132. doi:10.1093/mtp/29.2.126

Kim, S. A. (2013a). Bringing my Asian identity to light through acculturation. In S. Hadley (Ed.), *Experiencing race as a music therapist: Personal narratives* (pp. 151–162). Gilsum, NH: Barcelona.

Kim, S. A. (2013b). Re-discovering voice: Korean immigrant women in group music therapy. *Arts in Psychotherapy, 40*, 428–435. doi:10.1016/j.aip.2013.05.005

Kim, S. A., & Whitehead-Pleaux, A. (2015). Music therapy and cultural diversity. In B. L. Wheeler (Ed.), *Music therapy handbook* (pp. 51–63). New York, NY: Guilford Press.

Kleive, M., & Stige, B. (1988). *Med lengting liv og song* [With longing, life, and song]. Oslo, Norway: Samlaget.

Marshall, A., & Batten, S. (2003). Ethical issues in cross-cultural research. In W. M. Roth (Ed.), *Connections' 03* (pp. 139–151). Retrieved from http://education2.uvic.ca/Research/conferences/connections2003/10Marshall105.pdf

Mastnak, W. (1993). Non-Western practices of healing-music and applications for modern psychotherapy. *Irasm, 24*, 77–84. doi:10.2307/836990

McTaggart, R. (1997). Guiding principles of participatory action research. In R. McTaggart (Ed.), *Participatory action research: International contexts and consequences* (pp. 25–44). Albany, NY: State University of New York Press.

Moreno, J. (1988). Multicultural music therapy: The world music connection. *Journal of Music Therapy, 25*, 17–27.

doi:10.1093/jmt/25.1.17

National Institutes of Health (NIH). (2014). *Inclusion of women and minorities as participants in research involving human subjects*. Retrieved from http://grants.nih.gov/grants/funding/women_min/women_min.htm

Ortiz, V. D., Sosulski, M. R., & Sherwood, D. A. (2012). Competently mixing: Does a clinical practice cultural competence framework fit in mixed methods research? *Journal of Mixed Methods Research, 6*, 348–363. doi:10.1177/1558689812445196

Ponterotto, J. G., Costa, C. I., & Werner-Lin, A. (2002). Research perspectives in cross-cultural counseling. In P. B. Pedersen, J. G. Draguns, W. J. Lonner, & J. E. Trimble (Eds.), *Counseling across cultures* (5th ed., pp. 395–420). Thousand Oaks, CA: Sage.

Population Reference Bureau. (2015). *2013 world population data sheet*. Retrieved from http://www.prb.org/Publications/Datasheets/2013/2013-world-population-data-sheet.aspx

Rohrbacher, M. (2012). The application of Hood's Nine Levels to the practice of music therapy. In B. D. Koen (Ed.), *The Oxford handbook of medical ethnomusicology* (pp. 265–307). New York, NY: Oxford University Press. doi:10.1093/oxfordhb/9780199756261.013.0012

Ruud, E. (1998). *Music therapy: Improvisation, communication and culture*. Gilsum, NH: Barcelona.

Saarikallio, S. (2012). Cross-cultural approaches to music and health. In R. R. Macdonald, G. Kreutz, & L. Mitchell (Eds.), *Music, health, and wellbeing* (pp. 477–490). Oxford, UK: Oxford University Press.

Sam, D. L. (2006). Acculturation: Conceptual background and core components. In D. L. Sam & J. W. Berry (Eds.), *The Cambridge handbook of acculturation psychology* (pp. 11–26). Cambridge, UK: Cambridge University Press.

Sanchez, J. I., Spector, P. E., & Cooper, C. L. (2006). Frequently ignored methodological issues in cross-cultural stress research. In P. T. P. Wong & L. C. J. Wong (Eds.), *Handbook of multicultural perspectives on stress and coping* (pp. 187–202). New York, NY: Springer.

Sandhu, D. S., & Asrabadi, B. R. (1994). Development of an acculturative stress scale for international students: Preliminary findings. *Psychological Reports, 75*, 435–448. doi:10.2466/pr0.1994.75.1.435

Schwantes, M. (2011). *Music therapy's effects on Mexican Migrant farmworkers' levels of depression, anxiety, and social isolation: A mixed methods randomized control trial utilizing participatory action research* (Unpublished doctoral dissertation). Aalborg University, Aalborg, Denmark.

Small, C. (1998). *Musicking: The meaning of performing and listening*. Middletown, CT: Wesleyan University Press.

Spector, R. E. (2012). *Cultural diversity in health and illness* (8th ed.). Upper Saddle River, NJ: Prentice Hall.

Stige, B. (2002). *Culture-Centered Music Therapy*. Gilsum, NH: Barcelona.

Stige, B. (2005). Participatory action research. In. B. L. Wheeler (Ed.), *Music therapy research* (2nd ed.; pp. 404–415). Gilsum, NH: Barcelona.

Stige, B., & Aarø, L. E. (2012). *Invitation to Community Music Therapy*. New York, NY: Routledge.

Stige, B., Ansdell, G., Elefant, C., & Pavlicevic, M. (2010). *Where music helps: Community Music Therapy in action and reflection*. Farnham, UK: Ashgate.

Swamy, S. (2011). *Temple of ancient knowing: Music therapy portraits of globalized Indian identity* (Unpublished doctoral dissertation). Lesley University, Boston, MA.

Vera, E. M., & Speight, S. L. (2003). Multicultural competence, social justice, and counseling psychology: Expanding our roles. *The Counseling Psychologist, 31*, 253–272. doi:10.1177/0011000003031003001

Warner, C. (2005). *Music therapy with adults with learning difficulties and severe challenging behaviour. An action research inquiry into the benefits of group music therapy within a community home* (Unpublished doctoral dissertation). University of the West of England, Bristol, UK. Retrieved from http://europepmc.org/abstract/ETH/418450/reload=0;jsessionid=UmKJmgVFDAwTA4jKnNtW.4

Wheeler, B. L., & Baker, F. A. (2010). Influences of music therapists' worldviews on work in different countries. *Arts in Psychotherapy, 37*, 215–227. doi:10.1016/jaip.2010.04.006

Wong, P. T. P., & Wong, L. C. J. (Eds.). (2006). *Handbook of multicultural perspectives on stress and coping*. New York, NY: Springer.

Worthington, R. L., Soth-McNett, A. M., & Moreno, M. V. (2007). Multicultural counseling competencies research: A 20-year content analysis. *Journal of Counseling Psychology, 54*, 351–361. doi:10.1037/0022-0167.54.4.351

Zhang, M., & Cross, S. E. (2011). Emotions in memories of success and failure: A cultural perspective. *American Psychological Association, 11*, 866–880. doi:km10.1037/a0024025

Chapter 7

EPISTEMOLOGICAL FOUNDATIONS OF OBJECTIVIST AND INTERPRETIVIST RESEARCH

James Hiller

At the heart of music therapy research, as in any field, is a search for knowledge. For centuries, researchers in a remarkable range of disciplines have conducted research and published findings in a vast array of professional journals and books. It therefore seems reasonable to suppose that we ought to know by now how to go about conducting research and, more importantly, what it means to have gained knowledge. Yet problems have persisted along the way and have at various times proven quite challenging and even inconvenient for researchers and their claims to knowledge (Kuhn, 2012). Of particular significance are philosophical beliefs regarding what actually constitutes legitimate knowledge and how knowledge can be gained or, in other words, beliefs about what can be known and how we can know it (Alvesson & Sköldberg, 2009; Denzin & Lincoln, 2003; Pascale, 2011). These are questions of ontology and epistemology.

Ontology and Epistemology

Ontology is the study of being, of the nature of existence. Said other ways, it is the study of what exists, what is in reality, what is real, or, in Crotty's simplest form, "what is" (1998, p. 10). Ontological beliefs, or assumptions in philosophy parlance, shape the types of questions a researcher might pursue about how the world works or how people act or interact. For example, in the natural sciences, key assumptions about reality fall under the ontology of realism. Realism holds that a reality exists outside of our consciousness of it and that certain fixed laws of nature—that is, given relationships between phenomena—are permanent fixtures of that reality, for instance, the laws of gravity (Madill, 2008). Once discovered, these laws are considered true and reliable toward explaining the natural world. Alternatively, idealist ontology holds that we humans construct experiences of reality in our minds through thoughts and ideas, individually and/or collectively, and that this reality is open to all varieties of interpretation—there are no fixed laws about how reality may be or how it may be experienced. Further, in opposition to the realist perspective, in idealism it is precisely our consciousness that brings reality into being (Alvesson & Sköldberg, 2009; Giacomini, 2010).

Intimately related to ontology (what can be known) is epistemology. An *epistemology* is a theory of knowledge concerning beliefs about "how phenomena [can] come to be known" (Giacomini, 2010, p. 131), that is, how valid knowledge is produced. Pascale (2011) elaborates that epistemology is concerned with "the nature, sources, and limits of knowledge," and that it provides "a *justificatory account* of the scientific production of knowledge" (p. 4, italics original). Said differently yet, epistemology addresses how we come to know that which we believe we know. As with ontology, a researcher might approach the pursuit of knowledge through a range of different epistemologies. Each epistemology rests on its own variety of assumptions (theoretical beliefs) regarding the nature of the relationship between a researcher and the subject(s) of research—between the knower and the known. Therefore, in research with human beings, such as in music therapy treatment studies, there are always dynamics at work between the researcher and those under investigation that result in a researcher's access to different sorts of knowledge, for example, objective versus interpretive knowledge or distantly observed versus relational knowledge. Whether and how such dynamics are accounted for is important for a consumer of research to clearly comprehend the processes that led to the findings and then to most effectively apply the findings to practice.

Epistemological assumptions are reflected in the theoretical perspectives, methodology, and methods of research studies. In other words, depending on a researcher's beliefs about what can be known (ontology) and how to approach coming to know it (epistemology), different decisions will be made toward designing an effective study. These decisions are grounded in a *theoretical perspective*; in essence, an encapsulation of philosophical assumptions that form a cohesive way of viewing relationships between the sorts of knowledge we seek and what must be done to produce it. Thus, a theoretical perspective provides an explanatory stance for our pursuits and our actions. *Methodology* is sometimes referred to as a framework "of logically related means and ends to guide ... research design" (Giacomini, 2010, p. 129) or as the supporting rationale for decisions made in designing methods for data collection and analysis, whereas *methods* are the hands-on procedures or actions used to gather and analyze data (Crotty, 1998).

So, what might be the benefit of bringing the concept of epistemology to our attention in a book about research? Isn't epistemology the realm of philosophy? To be sure, concepts such as epistemology, ontology, axiology (values brought into a study), and methodology are fundamental aspects of philosophical thinking in our never-ending pursuit of knowledge about the world and our place in it. Yet the fact that research is a highly significant avenue of knowledge acquisition means that philosophical foundations are always implicated; every research question, every methodological decision, every procedure, every data analysis has a philosophical and theoretical origin (Crotty, 1998; Pascale, 2011). Understanding the epistemological assumptions that guide a research study means that the reader/consumer of the research either can more deeply understand the findings or can more knowledgably challenge the findings and the processes that led to them. Either situation is beneficial to the nature of the research process itself and to its eventual application to real-life circumstances—which undoubtedly is the hope of all researchers.

As noted above, epistemological assumptions provide justification for research decisions and indicate beliefs regarding the relationship between the knower and the known—that is, between the researcher and those under investigation. Interpretivist researchers tend to include fairly explicit, and sometimes rather elaborate, explanations of their ontological, epistemological, cultural, professional, and personal positions and values with regard to a topic at hand (Aigen, 1995). Such information supports the integrity of the research, reveals motivations and therefore potential biases related to the research project, and assists readers to best understand how they might apply findings in their own contexts (p. 294). Historically in objectivist research, however, the researchers' beliefs and positions relative to a research topic are more often than not left undisclosed, if in fact they receive the researcher's reflection at all (Pascale, 2011, pp. 4–5). Failure to disclose epistemological assumptions in objectivist research is in part due to the fact that researchers are typically trained in data collection methods and analysis techniques without attention to the underlying philosophical foundations for why these might lead to knowledge of a particular sort (Alvesson & Sköldberg, 2009). In essence, students inherit a value of ignorance of the necessity to articulate epistemological assumptions in objectivist research reports (Pascale, 2011, p. 5). For those trained only in objectivist research models (often referred to as quantitative research), realist ontology and objectivist epistemology and methods have come to be considered simply "common sense," requiring no judgment as to their legitimacy as aspects of knowledge and knowledge acquisition processes (Pascale, 2011, p. 4). Consequently, the reasoning behind objectivist approaches to data gathering and analyses is left largely unexplained, and readers are to simply accept that sound philosophical and theoretical foundations were applied. The ethical situation as regards objectivist research, therefore, is one wherein research processes, including method decisions, are rendered unapproachable to critical challenges. How can that which is considered commonsense be challenged as possibly invalid or flawed? Pascale explains:

> Processes of research, which are rendered as matters of common sense, are not easily available to doubt or critique. This is true in part because these assumptions are implicit, but also because common sense prepares one to think about the

world in particular ways by excluding some topics from consideration, while making others appear obvious. (Pascale, 2011, p. 4)

The situation is made more challenging and intractable if the broader community of researchers responsible for holding each other accountable for producing exceptional and creative research (e.g., editorial committees and editors) accepts reports lacking epistemological justification due to shared *commonsense* beliefs (Aigen, 2008; Edwards, 2012). Critical evaluation of situations where traditional methods might actually fail to serve the welfare of participants, either in the moment of research engagement or after the fact in its findings, is obviously essential. As Alvesson and Sköldberg (2009) stress, "Interplay between philosophical ideas and empirical work marks high-quality … research" (p. 10). We might add that a researcher's openness to expanded views of methodologies and methods allows for exercising of greater creativity in the research process, a value that may lead to positive innovations (p. 274).

The purpose of the present chapter is to highlight a small sample of epistemologies from objectivist and interpretivist research paradigms that inform music therapy research. We'll begin, however, with a brief exploration of what has been the dominant epistemology for social and human science researchers as well as for music therapists, namely positivism and its somewhat more liberal revision known as postpositivism. For music therapy, the tenets of positivism continue to shape much of the extant published research literature, at least that produced in the United States. Yet, as will be noted, the tenets of positivism impose serious limitations to knowledge acquisition when applied to the study of human beings and their health promotion via music processes.

Objectivist and Interpretivist Research and the Study of Human Beings

During the past 200 years or so, a variety of epistemologies have evolved in and through the human and social sciences via critiques of positivism and the objectivist stance that is foundational to its assumptions about reality, knowledge, and knowledge production (Denzin & Lincoln, 2005; Madill, 2008). As reviewed below, positivism is the theoretical perspective from which research methods of the natural sciences originate, arguably providing the most well-known processes for apprehending and comprehending the natural world—that is, the world of objects. *Objectivism* as an epistemology assumes a realist ontology, meaning that a reality exists *out there*, whether we are conscious of it or not, and that discovering the truth about that reality is best achieved through an accumulation of carefully planned observations. More basically, objectivism holds that we may come to know the truth about reality through repeated observations of it in highly controlled situations.

Positivism, as an objectivist research perspective, undergirded most human and social science research throughout the 19th century and into the 20th and still has impact in the 21st (Pascale, 2011). Positivism is a philosophical system of knowledge that only accepts observable or measurable (i.e., empirical) experiences of the world as data for analysis, the findings from which are considered positive or absolute truths about reality. Researchers thereby treat persons whom they study no differently than objects, believing that the truth of individuals' experiences, including interpersonal and social experiences, can be studied objectively (p. 8). A long held belief is that particular laws of nature exist—that is, cause–effect statements—regarding the workings of the human psychological and social worlds and that through careful observation these laws could be discovered and truths about humans and how they function thereby explained (Crotty, 1998). Critiques of positivism occurred due to the realization that human beings are by nature vastly different subjects of study than the objects and workings of the natural world in which they live. Humans are beings who possess minds and bodies and who use minds and bodies to exercise will and individual capacities of judgment and action—that which we might refer to as one's agency (Pascale, 2011). Consequently, the meanings of human actions and how these might be understood have created important challenges for researchers. These realizations quite obviously presented very different problems for researchers of human beings than for researchers of the natural world, and therefore called for different approaches to the then dominant positivist–objectivist viewpoint.

Out of severe and unrelenting social science critiques of positivism emerged alternate theoretical perspectives. An alternative that remains anchored securely in much of positivist epistemology and methods, but with a less rigid stance on the veracity of knowledge claims offered, is postpositivism. A *postpositivist* theoretical perspective allows that, regardless of a researcher's faithful adherence to objectivist *scientific* methods, findings are not considered absolute truths but rather are *conjectural* and *circumstantial* (Phillips & Burbules, 2000).

Particularly during the second half of the 20th century, as reevaluations of epistemological views ensued, philosophical and ethical concerns for addressing research participants' capacities for thinking, feeling, and acting—factors unaccounted for in mainstream objectivist social and human sciences research—were stressed (Pascale, 2011). Humans, it was emphasized, make their own meanings both individually and collectively via consciousness, agency, and sociality. Such meanings are valid slices of reality, even if wholly subjective in nature for those experiencing them, and are not simply awaiting observation by an external, objective researcher to be realized. Recognition that these deeply human aspects were unaccounted for in most human science research led to an ongoing search for ways to give voice to meanings belonging to research participants. Even the voices of researchers themselves, who were previously avowed to remain objective and distant from their objects of study, were reconsidered as potentially informative in knowledge production rather than contaminants to the process (pp. 30–32).

Through the ongoing critique of positivism, researchers turned toward interpretive frameworks. *Interpretivism* holds that humans construct knowledge as they interpret their experiences of and in the world, rejecting the objectivist notion that knowledge is simply there to be identified and collected (Constantino, 2008; Pascale, 2011). From an interpretive perspective, all knowledge is grounded in our particular experiences; it is subjective and bound to the natural contexts in which we enact our lives and is thus ontologically *relativist* (Alvesson & Sköldberg, 2009; Denzin & Lincoln, 2005; Greene, 2010). Therefore, interpretive knowledge is also imbued with our values, local and political, and is thus not universal and not generalizable in the sense that it may readily apply to other agents in alternate situations. Pascale (2011) highlights the interpretivist belief that, "In order to understand a situation ... researchers must understand the *meanings* the situation holds for the participants, not just their behaviors" (p. 23, italics original). Schwandt (2003) adds: "From an interpretivist point of view, what distinguishes human (social) action from the movement of physical objects is that the former is inherently meaningful. Thus, to understand a particular social action ... the inquirer must grasp the meanings that constitute that action" (p. 296).

In fact, in contrast to the positivist aim of explanation of causes and effects, *understanding* is the aim of interpretive approaches to knowledge; therefore, an accounting of the meanings ascribed by researchers and participants is required (Crotty, 1998; Schwandt, 2003). Meaningful interpretations of phenomena are considered constructions (also referred to as reconstructions) rather than simply representations of a given experience. Greene (2010) explains:

> Interpretivist knowledge comprises the reconstruction of intersubjective meanings, the interpretive understanding of the meanings humans construct in a given context and how these meanings interrelate to form a whole. Any given interpretive reconstruction is idiographic, time- and place-bound; multiple reconstructions are pluralistic, divergent, even conflictual. (p. 68)

Thus, from the interpretivist perspective, knowledge constructions are understandings from inside the meanings of participants and therefore also embody those persons' contextual meanings. In other words, an interpretivist researcher seeks to gain access to the developed meanings that participants bring to experiences and that entail the broad cultural and experiential worlds from which those individuals' perspectives and beliefs are formed. Yet these understandings also include the same breadth of meanings belonging to the researcher, for the researcher brings her or his own world of beliefs and experiences to the interpretive process. Hence, knowledge is co-created or *intersubjective*—produced through the interactions of the researcher and study participants. Evaluations of understandings are reliant on assumptions of internal consistency and coherence among the various meanings represented rather than through correspondence between a researcher's descriptions of an observed reality and the purported reality itself (Constantino, 2008; Green, 2010).

As indicated above, interpretivist knowledge is idiographic and relative to the situations and persons from which it emerges. No interpretation is privileged over another; no interpretation is a definitive one. The question, then, of how a discipline builds a base of knowledge via interpretivist research will inevitably be posed. In response, Greene (2010) likens interpretive knowledge to "context-specific working hypotheses" rather than absolute or even probabilistic propositions, as in the attempted generalizations of positivism or postpositivism, respectively (p. 68). Greene then introduces Lincoln and Guba's (1985) evaluative notion of *transferability*, which places responsibility for applications of interpretivist knowledge in the hands of practitioners who can most meaningfully use it, given their intimate understandings of the contexts and people with whom they work. The researcher, on the other hand, is charged with providing detailed and well-articulated *(thick)* description of contextual information associated with the study and its participants in order for a practitioner to meaningfully enact transfer. Successful transferability is possible due largely to the fact that interpretivist research is conducted in the natural settings of participants (p. 70). Ways to achieve understanding of meanings—of interpreting—contribute to the various delineations of approaches found in interpretivist research and the philosophies that support them. Examples include grounded theory, constructivism, social constructionism, ethnomethodology, hermeneutics, and variations of phenomenology.

Evolving Music Therapy Research Paradigms

Music therapists in the mid–20th century responded to an ongoing need and responsibility to systematically explore and communicate about the therapeutic benefits of music experiences for human healing, growth, and development. Since its inception, at least in the United States, the organized music therapy profession has sought to gain acceptance from the dominant medical professions. To do so, music therapy researchers embraced the paradigm of the medical establishment, which was and is today dominated by objectivist epistemology and positivist/postpositivist perspectives and methods. Hence, music therapy researchers continue to try to uncover truths about how clients respond to music through repeated, controlled observations in settings that often infuse typical clinical scenarios with laboratory-like

interactions, and, as in earlier social science research that was based on positivist values, music therapy research participants' capacities as human agents with minds and bodies, wills and desires, thoughts, feelings, and individualized meanings have largely been deemphasized in service to an objectivist epistemology. It was not until the 1980s that music therapy researchers with an eye toward more fully accounting for participants' experiences began to explore alternate epistemologies and to apply nonpositivist frameworks and methods for collecting and analyzing data (Aigen, 2008; Wheeler & Kenny, 2005). An interpretivist epistemology (sometimes referred to as the qualitative paradigm) undergirds these alternate approaches that first included grounded theory, naturalistic inquiry, and phenomenology and have since expanded to also include methodologies such as action research, arts-based research, discourse analysis, ethnography, first-person research, hermeneutic inquiry, morphological research, narrative inquiry, participatory action research, and qualitative (interpretivist) case studies (O'Callaghan, 2009; Wheeler, 2005).

Bruscia (2005) clarifies that objectivist and interpretivist research methods are employed to pursue very different sorts of questions. Objectivist research is valuable in pursuing questions wherein generalizable truths are sought via explanations of cause–effect relationships between specific variables. Interpretivist research, on the other hand, is suited to pursuing questions regarding "the lived world of human beings and how that world is subjectively constituted, construed, and made meaningful by individuals and groups" (p. 83). Methodologies and methods brought to bear in both paradigms are founded upon ontological and epistemological beliefs, assumptions, and commitments. When these are reflected upon, enacted through careful decision-making while conducting the study, and clearly articulated in the final document, consumers of research are helped to more fully comprehend the processes undertaken and therefore the potential benefits of the findings.

What follows are descriptions of objectivist and interpretivist research methodologies with explanations of related epistemological assumptions and beliefs. Included are positivism and postpositivism, constructivism and social constructionism, phenomenology, and hermeneutics. For each methodology, a study from the music therapy literature is described and analyzed so as to highlight and explicate how particular epistemological commitments were manifested via the design decisions made and the methods employed and ultimately led to the findings offered.

Objectivist Research Epistemologies

Research methodologies described below adhere to an objectivist epistemological perspective and include positivism and the closely related perspective of postpositivism. These are the primary methodologies that employ objectivist epistemological assumptions and reflect a perspective wherein a researcher controls all possible variables and interactions of those variables in order to explain the nature of the cause–effect relationships witnessed. A realist perspective and objectivity are considered essential aspects of such knowledge pursuits.

Positivism and Postpositivism

For nearly 400 years, positivism has been the dominant perspective for what has been understood to be science and *scientific* investigation (Denzin & Lincoln, 2005). The root of positivism is a belief in objectivity as the cornerstone of knowledge and knowledge acquisition. An *objectivist* stance accepts as ontologically true the notion of a singular reality existing independently of humans' experience of it and that it is possible to increasingly know this extant reality empirically through the senses (or via measurement devices that substitute for observation). Thus, the meanings of observed objects or phenomena are believed to be *in* those objects or phenomena; they exist before a researcher intentionally accesses them through observation methods. For instance, from this viewpoint, a tree in a field is a tree, with all of the understandings of what a tree means that goes with it (e.g., wood for fire and furniture, shade, leaves to rake, the provision of a higher viewpoint than from the ground), regardless of whether a human happens upon it or not.

Positivism is the perspective held in natural science research that has as its focus explanation of cause–effect relationships between inanimate objects (e.g., rocks, trees, and planets) and/or natural phenomena (e.g., gravity, rainstorms, and earthquakes). Positivist research can thus provide glimpses of a reality wherein mechanistic cause-and-effect events occur predictably, relevant variables can be controlled, data are value-neutral, and unequivocal truths may thereby be revealed (Giacomini, 2010). Explanations (theories) that are well warranted by analyzed data are considered general laws about the relationships observed between or among phenomena (Phillips & Burbles, 2000, p. 4). This means that predictions are possible about the nature of how the world and people in it function. A key positivist claim is that the process of objectively and systematically observing, describing, and analyzing specific aspects of reality leads to facts—the way things are—that are value-neutral, that is, research processes and results are uncontaminated by a researcher's values, perspectives, or opinions (Alvesson & Sköldberg, 2009; Fox, 2008).

Findings in positivist and postpositivist research are based on inductive inference or hypothetico-deductive processes. *Inductive inference* entails inferring "general conclusions (e.g., laws, descriptive categories) from particular phenomena (i.e., data observations). Inductive inference involves repeated empirical observations of similar phenomena, to make conclusions about their shared nature" (Giacomini, 2010, p. 131). In contrast, **hypothetico-deductive processes,** also known as *hypothesis testing* or *falsification,* seek to prove or disprove theoretically true statements through controlled experiments. The most typical procedures used to uncover the truths sought by positivist and postpositivist researchers include: establishing hypotheses (theoretically grounded guesses) about the sorts of cause–effect relationships that can be discovered, creating operational definitions to specify precisely what is relevant to observe, controlling variables that might interfere with observing the operationally defined phenomena, gathering relevant observations or measurements (data), and analyzing the data, most often through statistical processes. These procedures, considered classic scientific methods, reveal relationships and the nature of relationships (causes and effects) believed to be present in phenomena and thereby provide explanatory knowledge. Strict control and structure of the process allows for the belief that a researcher's observations do not alter the phenomena observed in any way. Hence, the researcher's identity, values, cultural context, reasons for carrying out the study, and relationship to the phenomena under investigation are believed to have no (or minimal) impact on the data, provided the proper controls are upheld, and therefore the data are a value-free, true representation of reality. Application of statistical procedures for data analysis to determine whether results are likely to have occurred by chance also theoretically removes the possibility of a researcher's values, including speculations or desires about outcomes, having an influence on eventual findings. Conclusions are thus considered factual, accurate, verifiable, *positive,* true knowledge (Crotty, 1998; Ruud, 2005).

As noted above, postpositivism grew out of critiques of positivism and its foundationalist perspective on knowledge. *Foundationalism* holds that knowledge uncovered through research is absolute and securely *founded* (established) in sensorial experience (observation) and/or indisputable reason (Phillips & Burbules, 2000). Postpositivists understood that these sorts of claims, particularly when applied to research with human beings and societies, were faulty and required adaptation. The need for a perspective that accounts for the obvious inconclusiveness of all truth claims was recognized.

Postpositivism retains some established beliefs and values from positivism while altering others. Postpositivism maintains ontological belief in the objective nature of reality but recognizes that undertaking to know objective reality will always be deficient due in part to the limitations of our human capacities. Therefore, what we come to know is considered incomplete and imperfect and will (and should) be revised in light of new evidence (Phillips & Burbules, 2000). Whereas the positivist ideal of seeking absolute truth is worthily maintained, achieving the best-warranted, highly probable explanations of phenomena is the postpositivist agenda (Fox, 2008; Phillips & Burbules, 2000).

In practice, postpositivists maintain belief in the power of the data-gathering methods applied by positivist researchers, but findings are considered conjectural rather than absolute and are admittedly bound to certain conditions rather than comprehensive (Phillips & Burbules, 2000). Clark (1998) explains, "The contextually bound nature of research findings, consequential in acknowledgement of researcher and theoretical biases, warrants that knowledge deemed to be 'truthful' under postpositivistic inquiry is not universally generalizable to all cases and all situations" (p. 1246). Yet the ideal of generalizable truth findings remains the paramount aim of postpositivist research.

Phillips and Burbules (2000) report that critiques of positivism as an epistemological stance from which to conduct meaningful research in the human and social sciences have rendered this position all but abandoned by researchers, yet many of its tenets live on through the postpositivist perspective. Therefore, for the remainder of this chapter we shall refer to postpositivism as the prevalent objectivist methodology.

Below, we will analyze a music therapy study designed according to postpositivist epistemological commitments. The purpose of this review is to make transparent certain choices related to design and enactment relative to postpositivist assumptions, in order to bring attention to issues surrounding their application in research with human beings. As noted earlier, some objectivist epistemological stances and their manifestations in design and implementation are considered *common sense* and thus immune to critique or even explanation (Pascale, 2011). However, philosophical transparency in research reporting may greatly enhance readers' ability to fully comprehend and apply relevant findings in clinical work or future research (Edwards, 2012; Pascale, 2011). This particular analysis is lengthier than the subsequent analyses of interpretivist studies because postpositivist studies draw on a fairly specific and detailed batch of procedural decisions and actions that necessitate explanatory attention, while, in contrast, interpretivist studies tend toward transparency with regard to their epistemological underpinnings and method development and therefore typically require less explanatory detail.

Postpositivist methodological concepts analyzed below include statements of hypotheses, sample characteristics, operational definitions, data collection and analysis, and generalization of findings.

A Music Therapy Research Example. In the selected example (Cevasco 2010), a therapist's nonverbal behavior relative to research participants' affect and participation during music activities was examined. The purpose of the study was to determine cause–effect relationships between four treatment conditions and participants' participation and affect response rates. Research participants were 38 older adult nursing facility residents with Alzheimer's disease and related disorders (ADRD) in five care facilities. The participants were separated into seven distinct groups, each of which underwent a 45-minute session. The treatment conditions were implemented by a single therapist, presumably the researcher. The treatment conditions included when the researcher–therapist (a) altered her affect and physical proximity to the participants while leading varied music activities, (b) altered facial affect only, (c) altered proximity only, and (d) used no altered affect or proximity (that is, stood still and purposely evinced no natural alteration of affect). Music therapy methods used were (a) movement to recorded instrumental music in accordance with modeled movements and verbal instructions, (b) singing of songs with modeled vocalizations and guitar accompaniment, and (c) rhythm imitation exercises wherein participants copied modeled rhythms on handheld percussion instruments. The sequences of music methods presented during the seven singular sessions were predetermined rather than determined in response to participant needs or emergent responses in the moment. Given the predetermination of the researcher–therapist as leader (the researcher was not the residents' usual music therapist), the predetermination of the music therapy methods used and their sequence, and the rigidity of the treatment conditions, the environment in which the research took place does not seem characteristic of an authentic music therapy treatment process but rather has much in common with a laboratory-like situation

Four music activities per method occurred in each session, each facilitated with a different treatment condition. Thus 12 music encounters were undertaken per session. Whereas rationale was provided for choices of music to support movement activities and rhythmic materials for instrumental imitation exercises, rationale for selection of specific song material was not stated except to state that the music was believed to be familiar to the participants. Descriptions were not provided of the character of the live music presented or of the participants' musical responses. Sessions were observed and the rates of participants' affective and participatory responses recorded by student assistants who also rated responses evident in limited videotape footage. Data were collected via a time sample rate of every 15 seconds. Statistical analyses were conducted and conclusions articulated, indicating differences in response rates to the different experimental conditions imposed on the groups.

Analysis of *postpositivist epistemological commitments* in this study reveals that, while not explicitly stated, the study was designed in accordance with these epistemological assumptions. Hypotheses are not explicitly stated, yet the researcher–therapist's predictions can be inferred from the introductory material and subsequent design: specific nonmusical actions by the researcher–therapist will lead to specific participant nonmusical responses (cause–effect relationships). Sampling criteria are not clearly outlined; however, basic criteria can be discerned as male and female older adults with Alzheimer's disease who live in a nursing facility. No mention is made regarding randomization of participants into groups. Participants' individual characteristics are unaccounted for. Providing no information about the individual participants (e.g., cultural contexts and life experiences) infers an assumption that individual differences (e.g., sex, personality, life experiences, cultural background, musical background) were nonconfounding variables and thus were irrelevant to the types of responses sought. Irrespective of the de-emphasis of participants' individual characteristics, according to the postpositivist notion of generalization, findings from this study are assumed to apply to all persons fitting the basic criteria noted above.

The unstated ontological assumptions are foundational and realist. Foundationalism is inferred from the case made in the related literature section supporting possible cause–effect relationships between the independent and dependent variables via predominantly objectivist research findings from music therapy and nonmusic disciplines. A realist view is inferred through the stated belief that persons with Alzheimer's disease respond to particular stimuli in specific ways and that these responses have stable meanings that are embedded in the responses themselves. In other words, given the controlled study design, the meanings of participant responses are believed to be present in the responses themselves and are given; they already exist and are not based on the researcher's interpretations. Hence, the objectivist assumption is that one needs only to observe and track responses in order to gain knowledge about them. Specifically, for this study, enacting *affect* (the act of smiling) and *participation* (exerting effort within music activities) are held to mean that participants are somehow in a greater state of well-being when such behaviors are present than when they are not.

Epistemologically speaking, postpositivist study designs typically develop or identify and report highly specific operational definitions of independent and dependent variables in order to reduce the possibilities of extraneous phenomena interfering with the particular responses under investigation. Operational definitions also focus data collectors' observations on the exclusive responses sought by the researcher and not on other events that might occur, regardless of their potential clinical significance. In this study, procedural aspects of the independent variables (how and when the treatment conditions were enacted) were described in detail, along with brief descriptions of the researcher–therapist's facial affect and relative proximity to the participants demonstrated during each condition. Of significance is that characterizations of the live and recorded music presented—aspects essential to understanding the interpersonal and intermusical context through which the independent variables were experienced by the participants—are conspicuously absent. Neither the attributes of the therapist's musical contributions nor those of the participants appear to have been considered relevant except, perhaps, as potentially confounding variables. The music activities appeared to serve only as environmental contexts for manipulating nonmusical variables. The music itself as a stimulus or as a medium of interaction seems inconsequential.

The four treatment conditions (independent variables) were predetermined and were reportedly not altered in nature or sequence during sessions regardless of the nature of participants' responses in the moment. The condition wherein the researcher–therapist used both affect and proximity seems most similar to actual music therapy engagement processes, whereas the others do not. Precise monitoring of applications of the independent variables was not conducted, potentially compromising the study's internal validity. Regardless, attempting to maximally control for the character of independent variables applied is in this case based on the objectivist assumption that it is possible to add or withdraw certain aspects of natural human interaction processes in order to study those remaining. Further, from a postpositivist perspective, it is believed that the observed responses to the reduced interactions are nonetheless valid representations of participants' interactional functioning. Design decisions that attempt to maintain the most natural environment possible for participants are reportedly valued in postpositivist research (Guba & Lincoln, 2005; Phillips & Burbules, 2000). Yet tightly controlling interaction variables, in essence, introduces contrivances or artificiality into interactional processes. This is a long-standing concern and challenge regarding objectivist research approaches in the human sciences, impacting the balance between internal and external validity (i.e., generalizability; Phillips & Burbules, 2000; Prickett, 2005).

Reducing the independent and dependent variables and their relationships to one or a few concrete behaviors, as in this study, is congruent with the objectivist assumption that discrete human responses can be isolated, manipulated, and explained. From the postpositivist perspective, however, these participants' unique individual and sociohistorical contexts (e.g., personality, emotionality, cultural influences, musical history) are of no relevance to the observed, operationally defined responses sought. Similarly, the researcher–therapist's individual context is believed irrelevant to the interactions between the independent and dependent variables. The unstated postpositivist concept explaining this irrelevance is that the existence of unique human attributes is *controlled for,* accomplished by believing that the participants' unique human contextual factors are spread throughout the groups and are therefore of little or no influence on the findings (a statistical concern) and that the researcher–therapist's unique attributes are minimized in their influence by limiting her or his actions to just those relevant to the treatment conditions (a theoretical concern). Studying humans means studying highly complex beings with unique contexts, aspects that can be considered quite challenging, even inconvenient, when addressing certain types of research questions. Postpositivist researchers deal with this challenge through various design decisions made in service to the methodology and the type of knowledge sought, such as the statistical control just mentioned.

The two dependent variables in this study (alterations of affect and effort exerted to actively participate in music activities) were considered evidence of participants' level of well-being and are representative of the postpositivist concept of construct validity. As is typical in objectivist research, this predetermined meaning was imposed on the participants' responses based on earlier objectivist study findings. Hence, neither participants nor their guardians/agents were consulted regarding alternate viewpoints. Atypical of postpositivist methods, however, operational definitions of the dependent variables were not provided. Nonetheless, incidents of the dependent variables were reportedly observed and numerically accounted for by data collectors; the character or quality of responses, however, was not.

From the postpositivist perspective, reducing data collectors' perceptual focus toward interactions between the stated independent and dependent variables alone—regardless of the nature of the music or of the musical context in which the variables interacted—is intended to provide a level of certainty for capturing the presence of specific nonmusical cause–effect relationships. This also means, however, that other potentially important clinical phenomena are, by methodological necessity, left unaccounted for as factors that might influence the dependent variables or as clinically important events in their own right. This study design also seems to evince the postpositivist belief in the value of ascertaining predictability in cause–effect relationships and that such relationships indeed exist among particular groups and are highly probable clinical truths to be applied to similar contexts. Designs that reduce phenomena quite narrowly are considered unproblematic and, in fact, are favored in objectivist models of research with human beings.

Impartial data collectors tracked their in vivo and videotape observations of participant responses. Data points collected were subsequently turned into numerical units that were analyzed through statistical procedures. Here in the research process, the data points are believed to be true representations of the nature of reality regarding the phenomenon under investigation. The essential belief is that numerical data collection schemes of ostensibly unbiased evaluators (who undoubtedly possess human strengths and fallibilities) are considered unbiased evidence of the reality of another human being's experience. Through statistical procedures, relationships between the frequencies of participants' actions relevant to those of the researcher–therapist were calculated and the resulting numerical relationships submitted in the report. These numerical relationships are believed to accurately reveal the probability that participants' responses are true reflections of ways that older men and women with Alzheimer's disease exhibit or manifest well-being. Consequently, the probability statements from statistical analyses are described in the discussion section as the best currently warranted explanation of the phenomena surrounding these participants' experiences. The article unequivocally states, "The results of this study indicate that a board-certified music

therapist's nonverbal behavior impacts the affect and participation of older adults with ADRD to a significant degree" (Cevasco, 2010, p. 295).

As noted earlier, our analysis of this study is intended to highlight the often unreported yet fundamental beliefs concealed within the process of conducting research with human beings through postpositivist epistemological commitments. A careful reading reveals that the researcher found the topic to be of great interest and believed that benefit would come to participants in a nursing facility and their music therapists from the explanations of cause–effect relationships provided. Not atypically, the way the research question was set forth initially (e.g., "The effects of …") revealed the researcher's postpositivist epistemological stance. These epistemological assumptions subsequently foreshadowed the nature of the methodological procedures that would be undertaken. Pascale (2011) argues that postpositivist researchers tend to simply assume that traditional objectivist research methods, long established in the natural sciences, are the undisputed best ways to gain explanatory knowledge—even of the actions of human beings. Such methods are therefore not questioned but applied without explicitly accounting for their theoretical foundations (p. 46). Concerns about this lack of transparency are what led earlier human and social science researchers to seek alternate perspectives and to account for participants' individuality, experiences, and potential meanings therein. Whereas postpositivist research has value for approaching certain types of questions regarding human action, it is of benefit to readers to have access to explicit information regarding a researcher's epistemological stance. Providing this information in a report also allows readers to hold researchers accountable for their decisions/choices and subsequent truth claims. Further, it allows readers of research to better evaluate the processes and findings reported and thus more carefully scrutinize potential applications of the knowledge gained—a primary reason why such research is conducted in the first place. For the benefit of the music therapy discipline, particularly with the current emphasis on evidence-based practice, objectivist researchers might assist the discipline by providing the most complete picture possible for how they acquired the knowledge they claim as evidence of effective clinical methods, procedures, and techniques.

Interpretivist Research Epistemologies

Research methodologies described below adhere to an interpretivist epistemological perspective and include constructivism/social constructionism, phenomenology, and hermeneutics. These methodologies reflect a perspective wherein an individual or group may ascribe meaning to phenomena or experiences based on encounters with actual objects and people—in other words, meanings that are empirically based encounters but explicitly understood through an individual's or a group's interpretations.

Relativity and subjectivity are considered natural and expedient aspects of such knowledge pursuits.

Constructivism and Social Constructionism

Constructivism is a perspective that views meaningful human reality not as objective—not *out there* to be discovered or uncovered—but rather as *constructed* by individuals through their interactions with and interpretations of the world and each other (Alvesson & Sköldberg, 2009, Crotty, 1998). Crotty emphatically states, "There is no meaning without a mind" (pp. 8–9). However, meanings are not simply created in and from one's mind, for that would indicate a pure form of subjectivism. Meanings emerge, rather, from constructions—or, more accurately, reconstructions of our experiences of an empirical reality. There is a merging of object and subject; of firsthand experiences of reality and contextualized perceptions—"subject and object emerge as partners in the generation of meaning" (p. 9). Meanings are therefore impermanent and change when new experiences bring new perceptual elements and awarenesses (Schwandt, 2003).

Constructivism differs in focus from objectivist research epistemologies in that its aim is *understanding* phenomena through interpretive processes. These processes are intended to explicate meanings rather than explanations of causes and effects identified through distanced observation and subsequent description (Constantino, 2008; Schwandt, 2003). A focus on understanding is particularly relevant for studying human actions and interactions, for unlike in the physical world, these are inherently and essentially meaningful (Schwandt, 2003, p. 296). From a constructivist view, it is the meanings (and meaning-making processes) that people ascribe to their experiences that are of greatest interest, and these are internal processes that are context-bound, unpredictable, and independent of natural laws. In fact, constructivists reject the very notion of natural laws with regard to human agency and meaning-making, believing instead that such processes are idiographic, individualized, and sociohistorically context-specific.

Constructivist research seeks to understand phenomena through the perceptions of those under investigation (Denzin & Lincoln, 2003). According to Guba and Lincoln (1994), constructivist research is epistemologically *transactional* and *subjectivist*: "The investigator and the object of investigation are assumed to be interactively linked so that the 'findings' are *literally created* as the investigation proceeds" (p. 111, italics in original). Meanings are explored between the experiences of a situated research participant and her or his life contexts and those of the researcher. Researchers working from a constructivist stance are interested not just in the experiences of participants but in the ways that participants construct meanings from and about their experiences. Constructivists believe that humans do not simply receive imprints of objects and events encountered in the world

(facts), but instead interpret these through individualized perceptual schemas. In fact, Alvesson and Sköldberg (2009) explain that phenomena are always interpreted in some way: "We never see single-sense data, but always interpreted data, data that are placed in a certain frame of reference" or perspective (p. 6). Thus, meanings ascribed from an individual's interpretations are *relative*—they belong to the *knower* in that time, place, and cultural situation. Knowledge and the knower are thereby inseparable. Schwandt (2003) describes constructivism as a form of *perspectivism*, meaning that an individual sees or experiences a given phenomena through a particular lens, that is, a *conceptual framework* developed through enculturation and socialization processes that inform each individual's personhood and interpretations of the world (p. 306). Accordingly, who I am, based on my life experiences, the contexts in which I live, and the language I use to describe my experiences matters to the potential meanings I construct and communicate about any given phenomenon. And the same goes for everyone else who experiences the same phenomenon (Crotty, 1998). In other words, there exist neither value-neutral perceptions nor singular, permanent truths. Instead, all perceptions are value-laden and truths are multiple and sometimes disparate and conflicting (Pascale, 2011).

Research via the tenets of constructivism seeks understanding of the meanings that human participants ascribe to their experiences of a particular phenomenon. Studies are therefore conducted in the natural environments where phenomena of interest occur. Schwandt (1994) shares that Guba and Lincoln, early proponents of constructivist research methods, initially referred to their conceptions of constructivist methods as "naturalistic inquiry" (p. 128). Data *generation* methods used are those that provide opportunities for participants and researchers to articulate and share their meanings and meaning-making processes. From the constructivist perspective, human science data are not collected since they are not simply in existence and awaiting discovery, but are generated through interactive processes between researchers and participants (Mason, 1998, as cited in Aasgaard, 2005). Participants' and researchers' uses of language are of great import. In fact, constructivist research methods have direct lineages to conceptualizations of hermeneutics and phenomenology, which are highly reliant on linguistic processes of understanding (Constantino, 2008). Consequently, transcriptions of recordings of sessions, open-ended interviews, and narrative-response open-ended questionnaires are often applied methods of data generation. Reconstructions of participant and researcher's meanings are produced for analysis. From interpretive yet systematic analyses emerge varying levels of understanding of a particular phenomenon (Crotty, 1998). Evaluative criteria for the *goodness of fit* of linguistic reconstructions relative to the experiences under investigation are used as means of ascertaining credibility and trustworthiness (Denzin & Lincoln, 2005).

Social constructionism embraces most of the philosophical factors described for the constructivist viewpoint, such as a pursuit of understanding of meanings rather than explanation of phenomena, the notion of knowledge as relative to a particular sociohistorical situation, and the belief that meanings are multiple—that no single interpretation is more authoritative than another. Crotty (1998) clarifies that in social constructionism, *social* has to do with seeking to understand the approaches to meaning-making that are used by groups in constructing knowledge rather than a pursuit of knowledge about social life. A principle difference between constructivism and social constructionism, then, is the belief that interpretations of meaningful reality are intersubjectively co-constructed among persons who share a particular sociohistorical context and language, rather than produced via an individual mind (Crotty, 1998; Pascale, 2011; Schwandt, 1994). Moreover, social constructionist thought holds that it is the transactional and subjective nature of interpersonal relations that bring reality and meanings into being. Thus interaction is essential for understanding both natural and social phenomena, and language is a primary medium through which such meanings are transacted and communicated dialogically (Crotty, 1998; Denzin & Lincoln, 2005; Schwandt, 1994). Even the notion of one's self is believed to be a social construction, emergent through social interactions and subject to ongoing change via new relationships, interactions, and dialogues (Alvesson & Sköldberg, 2009). This means that knowledge about given phenomena not only bears traces from the many layers of culture belonging to human agents, but is in fact emergent from and because of those contextual/cultural attributes and experiences; "Social constructionism emphasizes the hold that culture has on us: it shapes the way in which we see things (even the way in which we feel things!) and gives us a quite definite view of the world" (Crotty, 1998, p. 58).

Guba and Lincoln (2005) characterize social constructionist ontology as "relativism—local and specific co-constructed realities," meaning, as indicated above, that interpretations of meaningful reality are context-specific and multiple and may also be conflicting, but nonetheless are potentially viable (p. 258). Epistemologically, given the transactional and subjective nature of co-constructed meanings, it is believed that the everyday processes involved in situated human living are the very processes that create meaningful realities and are therefore what a researcher must seek to understand in order to be involved in interpreting those emergent realities (Denzin & Lincoln, 2005; Schwandt, 1994). Gergen (1994) emphasizes that language itself, inherent in thought, feeling, and social processes, gains its capacity for meaning-making through the human interactions in which it is used. Therefore, from the social constructivist view, it is believed that we humans are in a constant state of meaning-making. Cultural-contextual influences shape our capacities for experiencing and making sense of our world, and our interactions bring meanings about life into being. Further, the language we use to live out and describe our experiences is shaped by cultural-contextual factors and continues to evolve as we continue to use it. Consequently, our experiences and meanings also continue to evolve individually and collectively. It seems, then, that according to social constructionism, meaning-making through contextually grounded interpretations of our natural and social worlds is simply an occurrence of living in community (Berger & Luckmann, 1966).

Constructivist epistemologies are relevant for music therapy researchers interested in exploring the meanings and meaning-making processes that emerge from clients and therapists during treatment. The very nature of these individualistic processes calls for an approach that is nondeterministic, that is, it does not assume predetermined categories of response. Rather, the approach taken should account for the ways that meanings emerge through the myriad sorts of actions and interactions that unfold during music therapy (Bruscia, 2005).

A Music Therapy Research Example. Aasgaard (2005) explores the meanings that Norwegian children who were hospitalized for cancer treatment ascribe to the songwriting processes that they experienced with the music therapist–researcher as well as the songs composed therein. The study also includes perspectives of others who had any involvement with the song material after the songs had been composed, such as family members, nurses, other patients, teachers, and journalists. This latter part of the study sought to understand the breadth of impact the songs had from years and sometimes great distances beyond the clinical times and spaces of their creation, referred to as the "song histories" (p. 71).

An analysis of *constructivist epistemological commitments* in this example suggests that the researcher decided to conduct the study according to epistemological assumptions of constructivism due to beliefs about the highly individualized character of songwriting as a form of personal and social process for children. The constructivist perspective further lent itself to exploring song histories as these are also social by nature in that song material produced by one person may affect others in numerous and unpredictable ways as the song is presented outside of its context of origin.

In the hospital setting where the children were treated, song composition is a typical music therapy method with which to engage patients. The sample of five pediatric patients chosen for the study was purposefully made in order to acquire information relevant to the research focus. Each of the five children had already written at least one song during hospitalization when the study commenced. Children of a range of ages (4, 7, 7, 13, and 15 years) were chosen as a way to broaden the potential scope of perspectives explored. Nineteen songs in all were written. The sample of research participants was eventually expanded to include others who experienced the children's song material in various ways, as described above. Examples of the numerous data sources accessed by the researcher include dedicated interviews, unplanned conversations, progress notes and case reports, diary entries from parents, music therapy students, the researcher himself, letters from patients, and news media, as well as the artifacts of the songs themselves in written and recorded forms.

In emphasizing the individual nature of the patients' experiences, Aasgaard (2005) notes, "There is no average paediatric cancer patient (as there is no average song). A child who participates in song creations is neither typical nor untypical in relation to anything" (p. 72). Thus, as understood from the constructivist perspective, each individual's interpretations of and meanings ascribed to the songs and related experiences (e.g., composition processes, performances, recordings, presentations on television) are constructed through the influence of sociohistorically evolved contexts. The researcher did not predetermine them, nor are they of a generalizable or universal nature. The meanings described are therefore multiple. While not described explicitly as such, data analyses were carried out continually throughout the research process as new data and sources led to new insights that were accounted for in subsequent analyses. Analyses were thus conducted in a manner reminiscent of techniques applied in grounded theory studies (Amir, 2005). Accordingly, with regard to the meanings that emerged for the children, Aasgaard identified and elaborated on the categories of expression (communicating with others), achievement (optimistic evolution of conceptualizations of self), and pleasure (hedonic value of engaging in creative acts) as highly relevant impacts of engaging in clinical songwriting.

The sorts of relativist, interactional, and interpretive knowledge produced through a constructivist study such as this one honor the perspectives of its many participants. The voices of pediatric cancer patients, their parents and extended family members, related professionals, the researcher, and others are treated inclusively toward understanding the potential impacts of music therapy. Meanings emerged from the interpretive research processes, in contrast to an objectivist, hypothetico-deductive approach that would have imposed limitations on the range of possible response categories available for analysis. Aasgaard's conclusions span a wide range of meanings and meaning-making processes that undoubtedly could not have been foreseen or predicted prior to the study and indeed would not have come to light without the open and inclusive processes allowed for through constructivist epistemological assumptions. Conclusive findings were not sought, but rather the rich range of understandings that emerged over time is one indication of the usefulness of the study. How understandings from the study are applied is an issue of transferability as interested clinicians make use of them in their particular contexts. For certain sorts of questions, therefore, the constructivist perspective is useful as a process that opens a way for expanding possibilities of knowledge generation. Finally, in contrast to social constructionist methods, Aasgaard as the primary researcher was ultimately responsible for the categories constructed and that shaped final interpretations articulated for this study—that is, constructions of meanings. In the spirit of interpretivist research, Aasgaard (2005) reports,

> My role as a researcher includes understanding lay interpretations as well as developing relevant theoretical reflections about the song phenomena. … Interpretive conclusions by this researcher are not necessarily more true than those of other investigators (professional or not) studying the same material; proposing well-founded answers and prolific questions are, however, major (and sufficient) goals here. (p. 80)

Phenomenology

Phenomenology, like the other interpretivist approaches discussed herein, has taken various turns in its evolution as a philosophical and methodological perspective, and therefore its epistemological underpinnings have also transformed over time. Depending on which tenets (which are themselves dependent on the object of study and how best to approach it) a phenomenologist embraces and how these are applied in knowledge production, focus on understandings to be gained may vary from aspects of human consciousness (transcendental phenomenology) to language (linguistic phenomenology) to processes of interpretation (hermeneutic phenomenology) to disciplinary concerns (experiential phenomenology) and to existential and ethical concerns (existential and ethical phenomenology, respectively; van Manen, 2011). At the core, *phenomenological research* seeks understanding of *lived experiences* and the meanings that emerge as individuals experience phenomena in their everyday lives—in the *lifeworld*. The lifeworld may be described as the context wherein an individual has meaning as a person as the result of enculturation and wherein meanings are made through perceptions, cognition, and language surrounding phenomena and experiences (Adams & van Manen, 2008).

From the phenomenological perspective, and in stark contrast to realist and objectivist beliefs, humans are not understood as beings who simply inhabit a world, but rather are understood to be *beings-in-the-world*. One's being-ness is predicated upon the nature of the world in which one lives, and the nature and meaning of the world in which one lives is predicated on the interactions the individual has with that world. Thus, human consciousness is seen as inextricably linked to the experiences one has in the world, and likewise the world is seen as only meaningful through having been encountered by a conscious being who ascribes meaning to it. Consequently, the Cartesian dualist notion of a conscious subject who makes sense of a distantly observed reality *out there* is undermined and the classic subject–object split vanishes (Crotty, 1998). From this phenomenological belief comes a key tenet of phenomenology referred to by Husserl as *intentionality*, referring to the intentional focus an individual exercises toward a phenomenon (Alvesson & Sköldberg, 2009). Crotty (1998) articulates the resulting viewpoint thusly: "Consciousness is always consciousness *of* something. … We are beings-in-the-world. Because of this, we cannot be described apart from our world, just as our world—always a human world—cannot be described apart from us" (p. 79). Therefore, lived experience is the object of study in phenomenology.

Ontologically speaking, early phenomenological researchers sought to go beyond—or more accurately, beneath—descriptions of their own experiential meanings to identify *essences* of experiences—essences being foundational elements undergirding and making experiential meanings recognizable and unique to the experience of a given phenomenon (Adams & van Manen, 2008; Alvesson & Sköldberg, 2009). With regard to identifying a phenomenon's essence, van Manen (1990) adds, "The essence or nature of an experience has been adequately described in language if the description reawakens or shows us the lived quality and significance of the experience in a fuller or deeper manner" (p. 10).

Note that in earlier phenomenological research, the researcher studied her or his own experience—the immediacy of experience therefore being direct between the source of experience and the perceiver. The researcher then described and interpreted her or his own meanings. The process was subjective yet rigorous (Adams & van Manen, 2008). In modern phenomenology, researchers study, with equal rigor, the subjective experiences of others and the meaning-making processes they engage in within the contexts and cultural lifeworlds in which their experiences occur. Forinash and Grocke (2005) clarify different approaches when they refer to *reflexive phenomenology* and *empirical phenomenology* as research methodologies wherein researchers study their own experience of a phenomenon versus the described experiences of others, respectively (p. 323).

Epistemologically, a phenomenological researcher studying experiences and meanings of phenomena believes that by engaging in a crucial process of *bracketing*, that is, setting in abeyance one's own culturally mediated presuppositions and preconceptions regarding a phenomenon, it may be experienced anew—fresh and unadulterated. Behind the concept of bracketing is a theoretical understanding—or, as Crotty describes it, a "suspicion" (1998, pp. 80–81)—that our enculturation, while enriching of our lives and providing us with well-learned and hopefully accurate perspectives on each other and the world, is also limiting with regard to what we see and how we comprehend phenomena. Our cultural foundations, including our language and thought processes, are not inclusive of *all* explanatory and expressive possibilities and perceptual attitudes. What we see and understand regarding phenomena is always filtered through a particular lens, limiting what and how we see, hear, touch, feel about, and

make meaning of experiences. Significantly, the language we use to describe our experiences to ourselves (and to others) influences the character and the very nature of what we experience and share. According to phenomenological thought, then, a good deal of the fullness, completeness, and/or richness of what may be experienced is limited due not only to our fallible human perceptual systems but also to the limitations of our representational systems. By setting aside our prior *taken for granted* meanings and through freshly and openly experiencing phenomena in a theoretically firsthand manner, we may come to new perspectives, or at least to changed perspectives understood as *reinterpretations*, or to new or newer meanings (pp. 82–83). Yet the phenomenological researcher must experience, must be present and available to the phenomenon of interest, for it is from the open, immediate, and subjective orientation to the phenomenon that possibilities for understanding arise: "Subjectivity means that we are *strong* in our orientation to the object of study *in a unique and personal way*—while avoiding the danger of becoming arbitrary, self-indulgent, or of getting captivated and carried away by our unreflected preconceptions" (van Manen, 1990, p. 20; italics original).

Procedurally, various levels of *phenomenological reduction* were developed with regard to a researcher's lived experience and the invariant, universal essences therein. These reductions resulted in interpretations of the nature of how particular essences are constituted (Alvesson & Sköldberg, 2009, p. 77).

Analysis of data generated in a phenomenological study is often closely tied to hermeneutic practices in that the researcher's analyses most often deal with language via descriptions of experiences. Jackson (2016), in Chapter 40 of this book, provides a useful table comparing various approaches to analyzing linguistic data, but note that a common characteristic is "that the interview protocols are distilled to a statement or essence that authentically reflects the experience" (p. 324). It is important to highlight again that, as with all aspects of interpretivist inquiry, analysis processes are not performed with an attitude of objectivity or as inviolate protocols, but remain open and susceptible to variation in technique and sequence as meanings are revealed across analyses. Such is necessary in that not only are the data unique to the individual participants from which they were generated, but also the researcher, too, given her or his humanness and particular lifeworld, provides a unique point from which analysis takes place. Hence, phenomenological analysis procedures are indeed interpretive, but they are also rigorous but not rigid, creative but not arbitrary, and always focused on emergent meanings and the structures that enliven them (essences) rather than predetermined categories.

In addition to analyzing language-based data, music therapy researchers might also seek to understand the meaning potentials of music created by clients or between client and therapist. A variety of analysis procedures are explicated in the music therapy literature for analyzing and/or interpreting music and musical interactions as phenomena of interest. A short list includes Amir (1990), Arnason (2002), Bruscia (1987, 2001), Ferrara (1984), Lee (2000), Pavlicevic (2000), Perry (2003), and Trondalen (2003). The following study by Markworth (2014) focused on the communicative nature of improvised music between client and therapist and is informative for explicating epistemological assumptions revelatory of a phenomenological attitude. The study entailed analyses of both language and music data.

A Music Therapy Research Example. Markworth (2014) investigated the ways that improvised music provides a medium through which a non- or minimally verbal client and therapist communicate. Participants included a purposefully selected sample of three Nordoff-Robbins music therapists whose videotape footage of sessions with three children on the autism spectrum (ages 3–6 years) was analyzed toward identifying essences of communicative meanings experienced between client and therapist.

An analysis of *phenomenological epistemological commitments* reveals that the researcher employed a phenomenological approach due to the nature of the research questions posed, which in turn are based on the nature of the phenomenon of interest. In this case (p. 7): "In what ways do children with autism engage in communicative interactions through the [co-improvised] music?" (a question for description); "How does the music therapist use improvised music to invite or elicit communication?" (a question for description and/or explanation); and finally "What seems to be communicated through the musical interactions?" (a question for interpretation). The sorts of knowledge sought seem inferred through the research questions, as indicated in my parenthetical statements. The first two questions might have been approached through an objectivist methodology wherein the researcher would operationally define what communication in this context looks and sounds like and then would simply note the frequency and/or duration of such events as identified on the videotape footage. But such knowledge would be inadequate toward addressing the researcher's stated true interest. Given the final research question, then, it seems that Markworth ultimately wishes to know what the nature of the communicative musical interactions might be when they occur—that is, the kinds of communication that occur and the essence of these communicative acts. The researcher's decision was to work through an interpretivist methodology more closely aligned with the musical processes undergone by therapist and client and their experiences.

The researcher leaves the reader with no doubt as to whether she believes that communication occurs between client and therapist via improvised music. As articulated in a section titled the *Researcher's Context,* Markworth notes that in her own work with minimally verbal children with autism, she has "experienced the phenomenon of communicative

interactions where music was the primary means for expression," and adds, "I approached this research project with an existing expectation that music can be an effective vehicle for communication …" (p. 2). Description of the researcher's context for pursuing the topic is a methodological procedure known as **bracketing** or **epoché** intended to make explicit the researcher's preconceptions and beliefs about the phenomenon and to thereby consciously hold these perspectives in abeyance during the study, allowing the data to be experienced freshly and hopefully leading to new or deeper knowledge about the phenomenon. By making preconceptions and beliefs explicit, a researcher, in the spirit of the phenomenological attitude, provides the reader the opportunity to judge whether the findings have been influenced by the researcher's biases or not, thereby enhancing the trustworthiness of any eventual knowledge claims.

Data were generated via analysis procedures adapted from Lee's (2000) approach to analyzing clinical music improvisations and included the verbalized perspectives of both the researcher and the participant music therapists about the music and the interactions. Procedurally, Markworth first reviewed the videotape footage alone, "listening, writing out music transcriptions, and documenting observations and personal perceptions of the communicative interactions between the client and therapist" (p. 9). The initial review also included indexing (with time markers) meaningful events in the sessions. In the second stage, a preliminary analysis of the researcher's impressions from the music transcriptions and written documentation led to identification of emergent themes revelatory of meaningful groups of musical interactions. In the third stage, semi-structured interviews with the music therapists while reviewing their respective videotape footage were conducted, guided in part by the researcher's initial discoveries from the music transcriptions and themes. The interviews were audio-recorded and transcribed. In the fourth stage, direct quotes from participants specifically linked to indexed events on the videotapes were charted, as were themes that emerged from these statements. As the analysis process unfolded, a chart was created that included indexed events, the researcher's observations, initial themes, participant therapists' statements, and themes relevant to therapist quotes. Thus it became possible to compare perspectives of both researcher and therapists across meaningful events. In the last stage of analysis, a comprehensive list of themes was created and synthesized into categories.

A careful examination of the synthesized list of categories relevant to the question of communication through clinically improvised music led to identification of two general perspectives surrounding method (musical techniques used) and meaning (communicative content) of communication, but these essential aspects required greater specificity in order to integrate all of the data. A subsequent return to the raw data allowed for more useful coding of thematic ideas into the interrelated themes of Music Language, Musical

Expression, and Music as Shared Experience, for which the earlier identified perspectives of method and meaning are described as essential (p. 13). After providing a detailed account of the nature of these themes along with narrative descriptions linking the musical transcriptions and verbal data that support their inherent relationships to the processes of communication, Markworth follows through by further connecting prior research and theoretical conceptions that are coherent with her findings.

From an interpretivist epistemological perspective, Markworth drew on a particular set of assumptions and beliefs to guide the research process, as well as to enhance the trustworthiness of the data and emergent understandings. For example, understandings emerged for the researcher from experiences in interacting with the videotape footage rather than attempting to fit observations into predetermined categories; multiple perspectives were clearly valued in that a synthesis of researcher's and therapists' views was embraced rather than relying on the researcher's or the therapists' meanings alone; and analysis of data was an ongoing endeavor, revealing openness to new or alternative interpretations (meanings) that were allowed to inform both the process and the findings. It is also important to emphasize that knowledge gained through this phenomenological study was heavily reliant on concepts drawn from hermeneutics, wherein interpretations of the *texts* of both verbal and musical natures figure prominently due to the experiential phenomena under investigation. As noted previously, hermeneutics and phenomenology have long-standing ties. It might also be noted that, whereas Markworth classified her study as related to transcendental phenomenology (study of consciousness), we might also relate it to reflexive phenomenology (study of researcher's own experiences) as well as to empirical phenomenology (study of the experiences of others), as both sources of data and meaning-making were relevant. Such borrowing across varied related areas of research is not at all uncommon in interpretivist research, particularly in light of the fact that it is the research question (supported by ontological and epistemological beliefs) that determines the methods used in pursuit of understandings.

Hermeneutics

The world of hermeneutic study is enormous and far-ranging. Therefore, the topic is here considerably delimited in order to work within the length and scope of the present book. The form of hermeneutics examined below for its epistemological assumptions is referred to by Alvesson and Sköldberg (2009) as alethic hermeneutics in reference to the notion that this type of research seeks to reveal something that is hidden in a given phenomenon. Such an approach leads to deeper understanding than meets the eye during our typical daily routines of interpreting and making meaning of our worlds (p. 96).

Hermeneutics has had a long history and complex

evolutionary process among interpretivist approaches. Its origins reach back to ancient Greece (Crotty, 1998). What follows, therefore, are some general concepts relevant to understanding basic epistemological assumptions foundational to current hermeneutic research practices. *Hermeneutics* as "the art and science of interpretation" (Kenny, Jahn-Langenberg, & Loewy, 2005, p. 335) was developed by early Protestant scholars for interpreting ancient religious texts and by early humanists to study *classic* texts (Alvesson & Sköldberg, 2009). Thus, from the beginning, language, linguistic meanings, and interpretive processes were and have continued to be of great import. In current hermeneutic thought, the ways that humans use language to describe experiences influence the ways that such experiences are perceived and understood. Our language, as a system of symbols, thus shapes what we see and how we see our realities and interpret their meanings (Crotty, 1998, p. 88). Expanded perspectives of what constitutes a *text* occurred mostly during the 20th century, leading to a perspective that construes human actions, artworks, and speech as forms of texts and therefore susceptible to interpretive hermeneutic inquiry (Kenny, Jahn-Langenberg, & Loewy, 2005). Modern hermeneutic studies, therefore, take as objects human experience(s) and the individual and collective meanings that humans ascribe to these. More broadly, Crotty tells us that hermeneutics has been applied toward "human practices, human events, and human situations—in an attempt to 'read' these in ways that bring understanding" (p. 87). Such human practices, events, and situations are believed to be meaningful symbols available for interpretation. Hermeneutics joins other interpretive perspectives in rejecting the objectivist and foundationalist tenets of positivism, seeing them as unsuitable to address questions outside of the natural sciences and wholly inappropriate for inquiry into human affairs (Alvesson & Sköldberg, 2009; Freeman, 2008).

Hermeneutics has as its aim understanding meanings underlying human experiences, in contrast to, for instance, postpositivist explanations of causal relationships regarding phenomena or phenomenological pursuits of essences of objects, events, and experiences (Alvesson & Sköldberg, 2009; Forinash & Grocke, 2005). Moreover, rather than seeking to establish lawlike statements of causes and effects between phenomena, hermeneutics rejects the existence of such laws (Freeman, 2008). And, although hermeneutic practices (like phenomenological studies) are retrospective in nature (meaning that researchers and participants reflect back upon events, experiences, and texts that have already transpired or come to be), rather than seeking essences (invariant/universal structures extant at the core of given experiences), hermeneutics seek to interpret *meanings* regarding these phenomena. From a hermeneutic perspective, understanding itself is even a process of continually coming closer to true understandings, although fully incontrovertible under-standings or truths are not achievable for many reasons, not the least of which is the imprecise and ever-changing nature of the language with which we represent experiences and meanings to ourselves and others.

Current hermeneutic practices, as might be applied in music therapy research, seek to understand the processes whereby humans ascribe meanings to their experiences. Foci are on the linguistically described experiences of those who are studied, their actions, and the products of their actions (e.g., creations of art or music), as well as the experience of the researcher in the process—and, significantly, the confluence of all of these (Crotty, 1998; Freeman, 2008). To gain understanding of another's experience requires comprehending and empathizing with the contexts (historical and present) in which the other lives and through which their meanings emerge and are shaped. But such comprehension is not enough. The researcher needs also to draw from her or his own self-understandings and contexts in order to interpret the contexts, actions, artifacts, and meanings of the other. These various *parts*—that is, the people studied, their historical and cultural contexts, their actions, artworks, and linguistic descriptions of their experiences, as well as the researcher's contexts, experiences, artworks, and language—are perceived as a *whole*. These contextual aspects (the parts), as constitutive of the totality of a given experience of interest (the whole), form the elements for the methodological analysis process known as the *hermeneutic circle*. Understandings are achieved and transformed into new and deeper understandings through engaging in an ongoing cycle of analytic movement between the parts and the whole and back again. The parts can be understood only in their relation to the whole, and the whole can be understood only in its relation to the parts. Knowledge gained from working back and forth via the hermeneutic circle was earlier believed to close the gap between explanation and understanding (Crotty, 1998). More current conceptualizations emphasize a gap between pre-understanding (those understandings that are already in place for us through the processes of living; that is, *being in the world* [Alvesson & Sköldberg, 2009, p. 117]) and new understandings, meaning the gap between what a researcher brings to a study in terms of tacit knowledge and beliefs about a phenomenon and those that emerge through analysis processes. Of consequence is the fact that through the process of back-and-forth movement between one's pre-understandings and new understandings, one's *horizon of meanings* (that is, one's perceptual context) is also changed. Therefore, how one comes to understand also continually changes—and the same goes for research participants' horizons of meaning. A *fusion of horizons* thus occurs through interactions between the researcher's meanings and those of participants, thereby enriching potential interpretations and understandings of each (Alvesson & Sköldberg, 2009, pp. 120–121).

Epistemologically speaking, the processes of hermeneutic knowledge production, then, are recollective (recalling of experience), self-reflective (researcher's and participants' awarenesses of *self* at various levels regarding the focus of a study), sociohistorical (meanings are time-, place-, and cultural context–specific), collective (attempts are made to integrate meanings), empathic (attempts are made to understand the experience of the other), intuitive (applications of tacit and imaginative ways of knowing), and ultimately interpretive (Alvesson & Sköldberg, 2009). Alvesson and Sköldberg stress the importance of intuition and empathy in the interpretive process:

> The idea is that in the last instance the mind of one individual—especially its more creative, non–rule-bound aspects—is not accessible to the reason of another individual, trying to analyze it from the outside; only intuition can fully assimilate the mental universe of another human being. In so far as this empathy is complemented by the interpreter's broader or at least different stock of knowledge, is it possible—and this constitutes one of the main theses of hermeneutics—for interpreters to understand agents better than the agents understand themselves. (p. 93)

For music therapy, hermeneutic inquiries might, for example, seek understanding of how clients make meaning of their experiences of music, of musical processes (e.g., improvising, composing, re-creating, listening), of the therapist, or of aspects of the therapy situation itself. The researchers in the study example below sought to understand meanings ascribed by independent listeners exposed to recordings of piano improvisations that were created during therapy by abandoned and traumatized children. The children were living in residential care away from their families. Understanding was also sought of the children's verbalizations about their improvisations, as well as those of the researcher–therapist. In this case, the *texts* analyzed included recordings, verbal descriptions, and transcriptions of the improvisations. In a contrasting way, the researchers might have used hermeneutic inquiry as a way to study the actual processes of improvising that the children experienced or the experiences of the independent listeners as they learned of the true life histories of the children whose improvisations they heard and what the music may therefore have meant in treatment. In any of these situations, it is the texts—in whatever form they might take—that a researcher analyzes through her or his particular horizon of meaning, alongside that of the participants, toward uncovering potential meanings.

A Music Therapy Research Example. Amir and Yair (2008) used hermeneutic processes to analyze the following data: (a) three recorded piano improvisations, one each from three Israeli children living in a residential care setting (two females and one male, ages 5.5, 7, and 8 years, respectively); (b) verbal descriptions of the improvisations provided by independent listeners/describers (a math student, a business student, and a music student interested in attending a music therapy graduate program), a professional pianist who transcribed and musically analyzed and commented on the improvisations, the researcher–therapist, and the children themselves; and (c) the analysis of the music transcriptions. The authors noted that they drew from phenomenological as well as hermeneutic methodologies in designing and carrying out the study, and the close relationship (historically and methodologically) of phenomenological and hermeneutic approaches to research. However, the primary emphasis of the study was on analyzing the verbal descriptions provided by the various participants and the meanings to be potentially uncovered through these textual materials. Further, the researchers drew transparently from their own intuitions and pre-understandings regarding the children and clinical musicing prior to formal analyses of the various texts rather than attempting to suspend their beliefs about the phenomenon under investigation as in a phenomenological study (Forinash & Grocke, 2005). Therefore, the study is considered principally hermeneutic in nature, drawing on interpretive data that lends itself to hermeneutic analysis as well as pursuing the uncovering or discovering of hidden meanings.

An analysis of *hermeneutic epistemological commitments* in this study suggests that the researchers' epistemological assumptions, which in part guided research design decisions, are themselves uncovered through analyzing the text of this article. The researchers state clearly the assumption that the children possess continuously developing *inner worlds* that are shaped through life experiences and that these inner worlds can be accessed in part via interpreting the children's words (albeit this aspect—the *texts* of the children's verbalizations—was found to be limited in these particular children). The researchers state the assumption that the children's improvisations also provide a form of text or "musical narrative" (Amir & Yair, 2008, p. 134) for analysis:

> Based on the assumption that a musical improvisation represents the client's inner world (Amir, 2004), and that one can find meanings in musical improvisations via verbal language and the use of images, metaphors, and stories, it can be said that in the present study, the three improvisations tell the clients' stories. (Amir & Yair, 2008, p. 133)

Acquiring knowledge about the children's inner worlds transpired by studying the children's verbal descriptions of their experiences while listening to their improvisations, as well as on revelations from interpretations of the improvisations themselves. It is apparent in the report that interpretations of the improvisations are based on the belief that the music can symbolically transmit meanings relevant to the children's experiences and therefore to their inner (hidden) worlds: "We can conclude that the analysis showed the ability of the music to mirror the clients' inner experiences and represent the clients' clinical profiles" (Amir & Yair, 2008, p. 133).

The researchers based procedures for collecting the independent listeners' interpretations of the improvisations on an interesting assumption steeped in valuing interpretive (hermeneutic) processes. The explicitly stated assumption is that the listeners' verbalized interpretations could, in essence, *serve as* or *be* the voices of/for the children whose own interpretive statements were considered by the researchers to be limited to *richly* describing their experiences (Amir & Yair, 2008, p. 120). Hence an additional, apparently unexpected level of meaning was inferred in the analysis—the meaning reflected in the listeners' voices as surrogates for the children's voices. The listeners' interpretations included words and phrases characterized as *qualities* of different sorts to describe evoked scenes and images, emotions heard in the music, and emotions evoked from the music listening. The listeners' verbalizations included many metaphors that were considered coherent with the ways that the improvisations unfolded musically and were found to be quite consistent between all participants. Rather than seeking some form of *evidence* that might *correspond* to the words or music as a means of justifying findings (as in objectivist research), the notion of *coherence* among the various interpretations guided the analyses. The idea of coherence among interpretations of the meaning-makers (participants) leaves open the possibilities of many and varied interpretations that may lead to new insights and deeper understandings, but never to deterministic and/or validated truths. The notion of coherence also speaks to the epistemological belief in the value of shared or collective meanings. The researchers applied analysis procedures to all of the participants' interpretations toward uncovering potential meanings rather than predetermining the sorts of categorical meanings that might be discovered. The researchers explain:

> Our intention was not to generalize the findings. … We believe that this kind of qualitative inquiry allowed us to discover a more holistic picture which was composed of the meanings derived while listening to the improvisations of these children. Our interest was to look for shared meanings and not to examine which factors affected which other factors. (Amir & Yair, 2008, pp. 135–136)

Research findings relevant to the epistemological assumptions noted were supported in the report by other researchers' findings from the literature but also significantly by Amir's and Yair's past experiences and intuitions about these children and the value of clinical music improvisation. As noted above, making transparent how one's pre-understandings and intuitions shape decisions regarding methodology and analysis and lead to deeper understandings is fundamental to modern hermeneutic research and clearly distinguishes it epistemologically from the objectivist–positivistic approaches previously described.

In this instance, the authors report in their discussion of the findings: "Although the general picture confirmed what we already knew based on our intuition and experience, we found some of the findings to be meaningful" (Amir & Yair, 2008, p. 132).

Conclusion

Objectivist epistemological beliefs regarding knowledge and knowledge acquisition through research have been fundamental for centuries. Researchers of music therapy embraced these beliefs during much of the 20th century. Methods of data gathering and analyses in objectivist research have in some sense become ubiquitous in terms of their application toward explanatory knowledge—simply common sense, as emphasized by Pascale (2011). Thus the nature of how objectivist research is carried out changes very little from study to study. Predictability of method, it is believed, begets a high level of predictability that a realist and objective sort of knowledge will be discovered. Interpretivist epistemological beliefs, on the other hand, support research processes that are intentionally malleable and subject to numerous changes within a study as emergent findings come to light. Recall that in interpretivist research, data analysis is often an ongoing process from the initial point of data generation through to the end. Researchers are free to draw ideas and methods from alternate frameworks as the researcher's experience and understanding of the data suggests. As an interpretivist researcher's understandings grow within a study, alterations in how subsequent data are generated and analyzed may change as well in order to more fully understand the phenomenon of interest. In fact, analysis might lead a researcher to draw from a different methodology from the one in which the study began. Hermeneutic researchers may draw from grounded theorists, constructivist researchers may draw from phenomenologists, and so on. Thus a form of cross-methodology sharing may and often does occur, potentially leading not only to a deeper understanding of the particular phenomenon under investigation, but perhaps also to development of new comprehensive methodologies (Alvesson & Sköldberg, 2009). Hence, interpretivist research continues to grow as humans continue to pursue more useful ways of understanding each other and how we all experience the world in which we live.

Emphasized repeatedly in this chapter is the notion that epistemology matters in the process of undertaking and understanding research. For the music therapy researcher, understanding one's epistemological beliefs as they relate to the myriad forms of phenomena that occur in music therapy is essential to formulating the most appropriate research questions, determining the most useful approach or methodology through which to study a phenomenon, and designing the most useful methods and analysis procedures to answer one's questions. For just as there are different types of knowledge one might wish to gain, there are different ways of coming to know each. Objectivist and interpretivist epistemologies provide the foundations from which varying pursuits of knowledge occur. Yet researchers are often not educated about the foundational facets undergirding research work. Researchers are taught *how to,* but not *why*—the methods, but not the supporting philosophical and theoretical bases for them (Pascale, 2011).

> Academic institutions tend to offer research courses that are focused on techniques for data collection—often without significant philosophical consideration. Yet research paradigms offer scholars and students more than simple orientations for data collection and analysis. They provide frameworks for recognizing what we see, as well as for understanding the relevance and importance of what we see. Without understanding the theoretical underpinnings of social research methods, we are reduced to taking what is often referred to as a "cookbook approach" (Hesse-Biber & Leavy, 2006) to research that inevitably precludes a deeply critical stance. (Pascale, 2011, pp. 24–25)

A lack of reporting philosophical foundations is often more prevalent in objectivist research for reasons articulated previously, but the issue is one that should be of concern to interpretivist researchers as well. Consumers of music therapy research who seek to learn from and apply findings in real-life music therapy treatment (as called for in the current climate of evidence-based practice) deserve to have the full picture when examining a study—not just how the study was conducted but, equally as important, why each step was taken. It is with this contextual knowledge that clinicians are best able to evaluate and apply findings to benefit clients.

By understanding and embracing the now greatly expanded range of valuable epistemologies and methodological frameworks available, music therapy researchers can expand the possibilities for the types of questions they pursue and the approaches they apply. Undoubtedly, such expansion will lead to much more clinically relevant and useful research to fill our journals and texts and thereby the minds of present and future music therapists.

References

Aasgaard, T. (2005). Song creations by children with cancer—process and meaning. In D. Aldridge (Ed.), *Case study designs in music therapy* (pp. 67–96). London, UK: Jessica Kingsley.

Aigen, K. (1995). Principles of qualitative research. In B. L. Wheeler (Ed.), *Music therapy research: Quantitative and qualitative perspectives* (pp. 283–311). Gilsum, NH: Barcelona.

Aigen, K. (2008). An analysis of qualitative music therapy research reports, 1987–2006: Articles and book chapters. *Arts in Psychotherapy, 35*(4), 251–261. doi:10.1016/j.aip.2008.06.001

Adams, C., & van Manen, M. (2008). Phenomenology. In L. Given (Ed.), *Sage encyclopedia of qualitative research* (pp. 614–619) [electronic resource]. Thousand Oaks, CA: Sage.

Alvesson, M., & Sköldberg, K. (2009). *Reflexive methodology: New vistas for qualitative research* (2nd ed.). Thousand Oaks, CA: Sage.

Amir, D. (1990). A song is born: Discovering meaning in improvised songs through phenomenological analysis of two music therapy sessions with a traumatic spinal-cord injured adult. *Music Therapy, 9*, 62–81. doi:10.1093/mt/9.1.62

Amir, D. (2005). Grounded theory. In B. L. Wheeler (Ed.), *Music therapy research* (2nd ed.; pp. 365–378). Gilsum, NH: Barcelona.

Amir, D., & Yair, M. (2008). When the piano talks: Finding meaning in piano improvisations created by three children at risk who live in residential care. *Qualitative Inquiries in Music Therapy, 4*, 113–166.

Arnason, C. (2002). An eclectic approach to the analysis of improvisations in music therapy sessions. *Music Therapy Perspectives, 20*(1), 4–12. doi:10.1093/mtp/20.1.4

Berger, P. L., & Luckmann, T. (1966). *The social construction of reality: A treatise in the sociology of knowledge.* Norwell, MA: Anchor.

Bruscia, K. (1987). *Improvisational models of music therapy.* Springfield, IL: Charles C Thomas.

Bruscia, K. (2001). A qualitative approach to analyzing client improvisations. *Music Therapy Perspectives, 19*(1), 7–21. doi:10.1093/mtp/19.1.7

Bruscia, K. (2005). Research topics and questions in music therapy. In B. L. Wheeler (Ed.), *Music therapy research* (2nd ed.; pp. 81–93). Gilsum, NH: Barcelona.

Cevasco, A. (2010). Effects of the therapist's nonverbal behavior on participation and affect of individuals with Alzheimer's disease during group music therapy sessions. *Journal of Music Therapy, 47*(3), 282–299. doi:10.1093/jmt/47.3.282

Clark, A. (1998). The qualitative-quantitative debate: Moving from positivism and confrontation to postpositivism and reconciliation. *Journal of Advanced Nursing, 27*(6), 1242–1249. doi:10.1046/j.1365-2648.1998.00651.x

Constantino, T. E. (2008). Constructivism. In L. Given (Ed.), *Sage encyclopedia of qualitative research* (pp. 116–120) [electronic resource]. Thousand Oaks, CA: Sage.

Crotty, M. J. (1998). *The foundations of social research: Meaning and perspective in the research process.* Thousand Oaks, CA: Sage.

Denzin, N. K., & Lincoln, Y. S. (2003). *The landscape of qualitative research* (2nd ed.). Thousand Oaks, CA: Sage.

Denzin, N. K., & Lincoln, Y. S. (2005). *Sage handbook of qualitative research* (3rd ed.). Thousand Oaks, CA: Sage.

Ferrara, L. (1984). Phenomenology as a tool for musical analysis. *Musical Quarterly, 70*(3), 355–373. doi:10.1093/mq/LXX.3.355

Forinash, M., & Grocke, D. (2005). Phenomenological inquiry. In B. L. Wheeler (Ed.), *Music therapy research* (2nd ed.; pp. 321–334). Gilsum, NH: Barcelona.

Fox, N. J. (2008). Positivism. In L. Given (Ed.), *Sage encyclopedia of qualitative research* (pp. 646–650) [electronic resource]. Thousand Oaks, CA: Sage.

Freeman, M. (2008). Hermeneutics. In L. Given (Ed.), *Sage encyclopedia of qualitative research* (pp. 386–388) [electronic resource]. Thousand Oaks, CA: Sage.

Gergen, K. J. (1994). *Realities and relationships: Soundings in social construction.* Cambridge, MA: Harvard University Press.

Giacomini, M. (2010). Theory matters in qualitative health research. In I. Bourgeault, R. Dingwall, & R. de Vries (Eds.), *Sage handbook of qualitative methods in health research* (pp. 125–156). Thousand Oaks, CA: Sage.

Greene, J. (2010). Knowledge accumulation: Three views on the nature and role of knowledge in social science. In W. Luttrell (Ed.), *Qualitative educational research: Readings in reflexive methodology and transformative practice* (pp. 63–77). New York, NY: Routledge.

Guba, E. G., & Lincoln, Y. S. (1994). Competing paradigms in qualitative research. In N. K. Denzin & Y. S. Lincoln (Eds.), *Handbook of qualitative research* (pp. 105–117). Thousand Oaks, CA: Sage.

Guba, E. G., & Lincoln, Y. S. (2005). Paradigmatic controversies, contradictions, and emerging confluences. In N. K. Denzin & Y. S. Lincoln (Eds.), *Sage handbook of qualitative research* (3rd ed.; pp. 191–216). Thousand Oaks, CA: Sage.

Kenny, C., Jahn-Langenberg, M., & Loewy, J. (2005). Hermeneutic inquiry. In B. L. Wheeler (Ed.), *Music therapy research* (2nd ed.; pp. 335–351). Gilsum, NH: Barcelona.

Kuhn, T. (2012). The structure of scientific revolutions. Chicago, IL: University of Chicago Press.

Lee, C. (2000). A method of analyzing improvisations in music therapy. *Journal of Music Therapy, 37*(2), 147–167. doi:10.1093/jmt/37.2.147

Lincoln, Y. S., & Guba, E. G. (1985). *Naturalistic inquiry.* Newbury Park, CA: Sage.

Luttrell, W. (2010). *Qualitative educational research: Readings in reflexive methodology and transformative practice.* New York, NY: Routledge.

Madill, A. (2008). Realism. In L. Given (Ed.), *The encyclopedia of qualitative research* (pp. 731–735) [electronic resource]. Thousand Oaks, CA: Sage.

Markworth, L. (2014). Without words: Music as communication for children with autism. *Qualitative Inquiries in Music Therapy, 9*, 1–42.

O'Callaghan, C. (2009). Objectivist and constructivist music therapy research in oncology and palliative care. *Music and Medicine, 1,* 41–60.

Pascale, C. (2011). *Cartographies of knowledge: Exploring qualitative epistemologies.* Thousand Oaks, CA: Sage.

Pavlicevic, M. (2000). Improvisations in music therapy: Human communication in sound. *Journal of Music Therapy, 37*(4), 269–285. doi:10.1093/jmt/37.4.269

Perry, M. M. R. (2003). Relating improvisational music therapy with severely and multiply disabled children to communication development. *Journal of Music Therapy, 40*(3), 227–246. doi:10.1093/jmt/40.3.227

Phillips, D. C., & Burbules, N. C. (2000). *Postpositivism and educational research.* Washington, DC: Rowman and Littlefield.

Prickett, C. (2005). Principles of quantitative research. In B. L. Wheeler (Ed.), *Music therapy research* (2nd ed.; pp. 45–58). Gilsum, NH: Barcelona.

Ruud, E. (2005). Philosophy and theory of science. In B. L. Wheeler (Ed.), *Music therapy research* (2nd ed.; pp. 33–44). Gilsum, NH: Barcelona.

Schwandt, T. A. (1994). Constructivist, interpretivist approaches to human inquiry. In N. K. Denzin & Y. S. Lincoln (Eds.), *Sage handbook of qualitative research* (pp. 118–137). Thousand Oaks, CA: Sage.

Schwandt, T. A. (2003). Three epistemological stances for qualitative inquiry: Interpretivism, hermeneutics, and social constructionism. In N. Denzin & Y. Lincoln (Eds.), *The landscape of qualitative research* (pp. 292–331). Thousand Oaks, CA: Sage.

Trondalen, G. (2003). "Self-Listening" in music therapy with a young woman suffering from anorexia nervosa. *Nordic Journal of Music Therapy, 12*(1), 3–17. doi:10.1080/08098130309478069

Wheeler, B. L. (Ed.) (2005). *Music therapy research* (2nd ed.). Gilsum, NH: Barcelona.

Wheeler, B. L., & Kenny, C. (2005). Principles of qualitative research. In B. L. Wheeler (Ed.), *Music therapy research* (2nd ed.; pp. 59–71). Gilsum, NH: Barcelona.

van Manen, M. (1990). *Researching lived experience: Human science for an action sensitive pedagogy.* Albany, NY: State University of New York Press.

van Manen, M. (2011). *Orientations in phenomenology.* Retrieved from http://www.phenomenologyonline.com

Chapter 8

PRINCIPLES OF OBJECTIVIST RESEARCH

Nicki S. Cohen

At this point in the text, the reader has been introduced to the relationship between music therapy research, theory, and practice; the pertinent decisions one must make when in the preparatory stages of determining a research study; and the epistemological foundations of objectivist and interpretivist research. The purpose of this chapter is to focus on objectivist research: attitudes, principles and concepts, historical development, designs, steps for planning an objectivist study, and risks of bias. This chapter addresses the following questions: (a) What is objectivist research? (b) What is an objectivist attitude? (c) What types of topics and questions are typically addressed through objectivist research? (d) What are the beliefs of objectivist researchers regarding how knowledge can be acquired? (e) How did objectivist research develop, including publications and its development in music therapy? (f) What major concepts and terms are associated with objectivist research? (g) What are the most common objectivist research designs? (h) What are the steps for designing an objectivist study? (i) What are the risks of bias, and how can they be controlled for when conducting music therapy objectivist research?

What Is Objectivist Research?

When attempting to define objectivist research in music therapy, a simple approach might be to liken it to the scientific method, which begins with empirical observation. *Empirical* is defined as "originating in or based on observation or experience" ("Empirical," 2015). Gravetter and Forzano (2006) take this definition a step further by linking empirical observation to knowledge: "the use of observation or direct sensory experience to obtain knowledge" (p. 14). For example, a music therapist working in a university-affiliated facility with preschool-age students in a special needs classroom may make an empirical observation that the children with cerebral palsy demonstrated less muscular rigidity and facial grimacing during the time that they were listening to live children's songs sung by the therapist. In this case, the direct sensory experience was the music therapist's visual observation of the children's responses.

Inherent in this definition is the understanding that a research guess or hypothesis should be based upon the simplest explanation of a client's behavior, rather than something more esoteric or complicated (Prickett, 2005). In this case, the music therapist would attribute either the presence of the live music, the songs themselves, or the presence of the therapist as possible reasons for the changes in the children's muscle tension.

The *scientific method* involves formulating specific questions based on one's empirical observations and then systematically finding answers to those questions (Gravetter & Forzano, 2006). The scientific method begins when an individual observes an event or behavior, formulates an educated guess about the observation, and sets about attempting to substantiate the guess through a series of systematic, repeatable, and measurable observations (O'Callaghan, 2009).

To continue with the example begun above, the music therapist may hypothesize that listening to live children's songs sung by the therapist may cause a decrease in muscle tension in the children with cerebral palsy. The researcher can identify, collect, and analyze data representing the children's motoric responses, and the results will either verify or not verify the educated guess. The scientific method was the primary basis for research until other forms of inquiry, such as those created for sociological or anthropological inquiry, began to emerge at the end of the 19th century (O'Callaghan, 2009). Today, the scientific method still dominates research practices, as evidenced in published literature from most disciplines (Böhme, Childerhouse, Deakens, & Towill, 2012). It is important to point out that the example given above about live music and muscle tension, although representing the scientific method, should not be confused with research. It takes much more than that to make a research study.

Although the scientific method served as the basis for the predominant form of inquiry until the 20th century, it is not the keystone of objectivist research. The scientific method and objectivist research do share two beliefs (Kuper, Reeves, & Levinson, 2008): (a) that an absolute truth or reality exists that can be discovered, and (b) that this discovery results in a type of knowledge that is both objective and neutral. Table 1 lists basic characteristics of objectivist research, all of which will be discussed in this chapter.

Topics and Questions

What types of questions are typically answered by conducting objectivist research? Researchers must learn to select the best objectivist methods to most appropriately answer their research questions. Bruscia (2005) identified eight categories of music therapy research questions that are often proposed in objectivistic research:

- *Incidence Questions:* How much or how often? The most basic type of research questions; answers are typically reported as frequency distributions, measurements of

Common Methodologies	Descriptive, small *n* research, pre-experimental, experimental, meta-analysis
Common Tools	Standardized measures, statistical analyses; surveys; scientific or medical instrumentation
Data Analysis	Deductive
Fundamental Questions	What, how much, why (cause)?
Generalizability	Predictive
How Quality Established	Internal and external validity; reliability; statistical significance
Knowledge Accumulation	Accretion, cumulative, establishing causality
Meaning	External to the knower
Questions	Specific, fixed, causal, effect
Reality	Structured in a way that is shared similarly by all who perceive it; can be modeled and shared with others
Research Context	External to what is being studied
Researcher's Stance	Detached from what is being studied
Researcher's Values	Knowledge is value-free, context-free, neutral
Sampling Techniques	Random, controlled, cluster, systematic, stratified

Table 1. Characteristics of Objectivist Research

Modified from Cronjé, 2006; Crotty, 1998; Kuper, Reeves, & Levinson, 2008; O'Callaghan, 2009

central tendency, and variability; often associated with survey, content analysis, or small *n* studies.

- *Measurement Questions:* What is the most accurate method to evaluate and measure what is being researched? Includes procedures to determine reliability and validity of a measurement tool; associated with research designed to create a replicable assessment, treatment, or evaluation protocol.

- *Correlation Questions:* To what extent are variables related? To define the extent to which one variable fluctuates in relation to another; to determine if a change in one variable can predict a change in another or how multiple variables can be related; associated with nonexperimental designs.

- *Factor Questions:* What additional factors influence or predict the research results? To identify factors that may coexist along with the treatment (e.g., additional independent variables, participant characteristics, research protocol) and their relative impact on the research findings; associated with nonexperimental methods such as causal–comparative or predictive studies.

- *Development Questions:* What is the impact of time, generation, or age on a particular dependent variable? To determine changes that occur due to the influence of time, cohort, or age and the nature (i.e., sequence, timing) of these changes; associated with nonexperimental methods such as longitudinal or cross-sectional studies (Gravetter & Forzano, 2006).

- *Static Comparison Questions:* What is the natural state of the participant group responses prior to the introduction of an intervention? Associated with conducting small *n* studies that include baseline phases or avoiding biases when choosing respondents for more than one participant group.

- *Treatment Questions:* What is the effect of the treatment on the variable being studied? The most common question associated with experimental research.

- *Interaction Questions:* How do individual factors or levels of factors interact, and how do these influence the variable being studied? Associated with factorial design studies (Gravetter & Forzano, 2006).

Epistemology: Positivism and Postpositivism

Objectivist research is based on the belief in an absolute truth that is both context- and value-free and that results in objective and neutral knowledge (Kuper, et al. 2008). This belief was previously associated with the *positivistic* stance (O'Callaghan, 2009). In contrast, qualitative research was considered *nonpositivistic*. These two positions were often represented as a polarized relationship, with each being mutually exclusive of the other.

However, the term *positivistic* is dated and is not synonymous with objectivist research. Objectivist research is better associated with the term *postpositivistic*, a perspective that recognizes an objective truth but also acknowledges that the biases of the researcher may influence what is being observed (Robson, 2011). Edwards (1999) describes post-positivism as possessing the knowledge that a natural order exists, but also understanding that there are unknowable dimensions to the *truth* that can be revealed only though investigation. Multiple perspectives, repetitions, or methods are required to glimpse or approximate the entire truth of an experience or event (p. 75). Edwards further clarifies that, while the positivist approach is committed to research conducted in a laboratory, post-positivistic research takes place in real or natural settings where the findings are not meant to be generalized from laboratory to natural setting, but from natural setting to natural setting (p. 75).

Objectivist research is also referred to as quantitative research. The major difference between this new term and the previous ones is that objectivist research cannot be fully understood without its counterpart, interpretivist (or qualitative) research. Objectivistic and interpretivist research are not found to be mutually exclusive (e.g., one is objective and the other is subjective), nor do they exist separately along a continuum between objectivity and subjectivity (Cronjé, 2006).

Historical Roots

How did objectivist research develop? This section will present the historical development of objectivist research, landmark publications documenting the development of specific vernacular for this research, and a review of music therapy objectivist research published in English in peer-reviewed journals.

Historical Development. The earliest references to objectivist research can be traced back to the Middle Ages (Daston & Lunbeck, 2011). In the 13th century, people thought that knowledge could be gained only through direct, sensory engagement with animals, plants, or minerals (Park, 2011). At the heart of the earliest research lay the concept of *experimentum,* which was a written set of directions, usually formulaic in nature, which included both direct experimentation and trial-and-error allowances (Park, 2011). In the mid–13th century, the Holy Roman Emperor, Frederick II, described experimentum as "a form of knowledge intermediate between the raw sensation of phenomena and the higher reaches of practical knowledge" (as cited in Park, 2011, p. 17). Frederick was an avid falconer and studied his birds with a staunch desire to understand their behavioral and flying patterns. In this early contribution, he hoped to contribute what he learned into the building of a pool of knowledge regarding falconry. This first systematic practice was, in fact, a portion of what would later be called the scientific method. What was missing at that point was the emphasis on empirical observation, which is based solely on the senses.

Throughout the 15th and 16th centuries, the meaning and usage of terms relating to research remained inconsistent. More disciplines became involved in *obsertavio* and *experimentum* (e.g., medicine, alchemy, and natural history) as a means of explaining truth and knowledge. In the 1540s, Johannes Shöner published a text in which he defined obsertavio as not just observing, but an "act guided by a rule, protocol, or code of behavior" (as cited in Pomata, 2011, p. 47). At this point, the meaning of obsertavio shifted dramatically from mere observation to empirical observation.

During the 17th through to 19th centuries, researchers began to perceive the terms *obsertavio* and *experimentum* differently. Whereas previously the terms had represented different concepts, now they became "complementary and interlocking parts of a single method of inquiry" (Daston, 2011, p. 82). It was at the beginning of the 19th century that scientific reasoning and the scientific method began to dominate all modes of inquiry ("Scientific Method," 2015). The scientific method, as explained earlier in this chapter, is grounded in the concepts of empirical observation, or the early obsertavio, and systematic examination, or the early experimentum.

Landmark Publications. What earlier publications have provided the foundation for what is now labeled objectivistic research? Most of the landmark books about objectivist methodology were published in the 20th century. Previously, this type of research was labeled as experiment, experimental, quasi-experimental, quantitative, or empirical. One of the earliest texts was *How to Experiment in Education* by W. A. McCall (1923). McCall was the first author to introduce the concepts of random sampling, counterbalancing, and quasi-experimental research, although his claims regarding the rate and degree of progress that would result from experimentation were highly exaggerated and his descriptions of statistical calculations were limited (Campbell & Stanley, 1963, p. 2).

Known as the *bible* of objectivist research, *Experimental and Quasi-Experimental Designs for Research* was coauthored by Donald Campbell and Julian Stanley (1963). This text introduced experimental and quasi-experimental research designs and defined factors that influenced the researcher's perception of internal and external validity. Although published in the mid–20th century, it remains a critical reference on what was then referred to as quantitative research designs; however, many students find the language in the text to be oblique and confusing. Perhaps for this reason, Stephen Isaac and William Michael published the *Handbook in Research and Evaluation* in 1971 to translate Campbell and Stanley's designs into more accessible language. They also added sections about planning evaluation studies and research studies, topics that were not found in the original Campbell and Stanley text. Another text, by Cook and Campbell (1979), soon followed, focusing on conducting quasi-experimental research in natural, rather than laboratory, settings. In the 21st century, *Experimental and Quasi-Experimental Designs for Generalized Causal Inference* (Shadish, Cook, & Campbell, 2002) was published; it is regarded today as a leading reference on experimental causation.

Objectivist Research in Music Therapy. Since its origin, the profession of music therapy in the United States has valued the scientific and medical recognition of the documentation of outcomes resulting from music therapy interventions and has supported the efforts of its members to conduct objectivist research. Since the late 1990s, the American Music Therapy Association (AMTA) has been working from a strategic plan that reinforces the development of a "robust portfolio of evidence supporting the effectiveness of music therapy through documentation in research" (American Music Therapy Association, 2015). Also in support of music therapy research, since 1999, AMTA has awarded the annual Arthur Flagler Fultz Research award to a member who is conducting research. To date, this award has most often been presented to music therapy researchers conducting objectivist studies (musictherapy.org; Arthur Flagler Fultz Research Award).

The *Journal of Music Therapy (JMT)*, a research journal, was first published in 1964. A number of content analyses have been conducted, examining research methodologies, topics, credentials of authors, names of journals, and categories of articles found in published music therapy literature (Brooks, 2003; Codding, 1987; DeCuir, 1987; Gfeller, 1987; Gilbert, 1979; Heal & Wigram, 1993; Jellison, 1973; Wheeler, 1988). Although the authors may not have used exactly the same variables or journals in their content analyses, enough similarities exist to be able to draw conclusions about the status of objectivist research in the field of music therapy (Brooks, 2003).

As an example, Brooks (2003) conducted an extensive review of music therapy periodicals and discovered that out of 1,521 research articles that had been published in nine English language music therapy journals between 1964 and 2001, 524 were categorized as objectivist research. It is relevant to point out that at the time this article was published, objectivist research, which was still labeled as quantitative, included all descriptive, applied behavioral analysis, and experimental modes of inquiry. Taking that into consideration, objectivist research was by far the most predominant method of inquiry in all of the music therapy research publications. Brooks determined that a sharp increase occurred in the publication of objectivist research between 1964 and 1989, which then leveled off to an average of 11 to 16 articles per year. The *Journal of Music Therapy*, which remains the research-based journal for AMTA, has published 78.6% of all the objectivist studies since 1964. This reinforces the strong emphasis placed on research documentation, as reinforced by AMTA's Strategic Priority on Research and the Arthur Flagler Fultz Award.

Objectivist Concepts and Terms

Concepts

What major concepts are associated with objectivist research? The following statements represent fundamental objectivist research concepts and their related sources:

- Objectivist research is based on the premise that an absolute truth exists that can be discovered (Bernstein, 1983; Kuper et al., 2008);
- Objectivist research results in knowledge that is both objective and neutral (Kuper et al., 2008);
- Objectivist research results in knowledge that is both context- and value-free (Kuper et al., 2008);
- Objectivist research is sometimes associated with a postpositivist perspective (Robson, 2011);

- Researchers attempt to answer questions by ascribing numbers to empirical observations (O'Callaghan, 2009);
- Objectivist research results are generalizable (Rainbow & Froelich, 1987; Shadish et al., 2002);
- Objectivist research results are replicable and predictable (O'Callaghan, 2009);
- Results from objectivist research, although replicable and generalizable, must always be open to verification through replication and newer forms of research methodology (Prickett, 2005).

To clarify these concepts, let us return to the scenario of the music therapist working with a classroom of preschool-age children with cerebral palsy who seem to demonstrate decreased muscular rigidity and facial grimacing during the time when they are listening to live children's songs sung by the therapist. Let's say that the music therapist decides to conduct a study to determine the effects of live children's songs on the muscular tension of children with cerebral palsy. As the music therapist sets about to plan the study, it would be with the understanding, perhaps not conscious, that the results would reveal a truth—not yet known—regarding the research hypothesis. The truth would emerge from the formation of the hypothesis followed by the resultant answers, just as in the scientific method. The results of the study, in addition, would be objective, neutral, value-free, and context-free, as long as the researcher took the necessary steps to control for biases and for other factors that might influence the outcome of the study. The collected data would take a numerical form. The researcher would analyze the data with some form of statistical test. Whatever knowledge was gained from this study could be generalized to other music therapists working in similar settings with a similar population, and other therapists could replicate the research procedures.

Terms

For objectivist research to be used by different disciplines, it needs to own a common vocabulary and set of concepts that can be shared by all who are studying or undertaking the research. This section will answer the question: What major terms are associated with objectivist research? The terms and their definition appear below in alphabetical order. All are covered in more detail in other chapters of this book.

Assessment. Prior to beginning a study, the researcher must determine the method for gathering the numerical data that represents the observations. The *assessment* is the formal or informal tool used to gather the data. Examples of assessments include a published assessment, scientific equipment, or a self-constructed behavioral checklist. In objectivist research, published assessment tools with adequate psychometric properties are recommended whenever possible, as the validity and reliability of these tools will have been established. If the researcher must construct an original tool, the elements of the tool should be selected from published literature on the topic and reviewed by experts before use. Assessments can range from a standardized psychological profile to a self-constructed behavioral checklist to an electromyogram (EMG) connected to a PC that is operating a software program. Often, more than one assessment is used to quantify the dependent variables.

Causal Relationship. According to Shadish et al. (2002), a *causal relationship* occurs whenever these three criteria are met: (a) the cause precedes the effect; (b) the cause is related to the effect; and (c) no plausible alternative explanation exists for the effect other than the cause. When conducting experimental research studies, a causal relationship may be established; however, descriptive, or applied, behavioral analysis research cannot establish causal relationships. A reader can usually identify an attempt at a causal relationship when the title of a research article contains the terms "the effect of X on Y." Authors disagree on whether causation can be established via quasi-experimental research (Shadish et al., p. 14).

Control. *Control* refers to how clearly the results of a study are based on the effect of the independent variable on the dependent variable, and not on other reasons. It can be described as the extent to which a research study produces a single, clear explanation for the relationship between the independent and the dependent variables (Gravetter & Forzano, 2006).

Delimitations. *Delimitations* are internal limitations established by the researcher that limit the focus of a study. According to Wheeler (2005), delimitations are statements of what will and will not be included in a study. Delimitations allow a researcher to limit a study beyond those limitations already implied by the research purpose and hypotheses. Examples of delimitations include restricting the years of publication in a literature review, identifying which journals will be reviewed in a content analysis, or deciding to use only one group as study participants in an experimental study. Delimitations need to be identified in the text during the proposal stage of a research study; this helps the researcher to better define the boundaries of the study and the specific context and situation (Prickett, 2005).

Dependent Variable. The *dependent variable* is the variable that is observed for changes in order to assess the effects of manipulating the independent variable (Gravetter & Forzano, 2006). The dependent variable is often a human behavior or a response that yields outcome information for analysis (Prickett, 2005).

Design. The way that a research study is set up in order to investigate what is intended, including the independent and dependent variables and various aspects of the procedures, is the *design*. Although this term is not specific to objectivist research, it is generally associated with objectivist research, with the researcher having determined in advance exactly what will be done rather than changing it as the study proceeds. A variety of designs can be used in objectivist research. Those presented in this book include single-subject and small *n* research (case study, withdrawal, multiple baseline, changing criterion, multiple treatment), survey research, research that employs correlation and regression analytic techniques, economic analysis, the Delphi technique, longitudinal, pre-experimental (one-sample), quasi-experimental (static group comparison), and experimental (parallel group, crossover, factorial) designs. These are covered in Unit 6, Objectivist Designs.

External Validity. *External validity* addresses the question of generalizability. It asks to what extent one can generalize the results of the research study to other populations, settings, times, measurements, and characteristics (Gravetter & Forzano, 2006).

Hypothesis. A *hypothesis* is an educated guess. According to the scientific method, it is the idea that will be tested in the study (Prickett, 2005). Moreover, it identifies a tentative relationship between the independent and dependent variables (Gravetter & Forzano, 2006). A hypothesis can be in the form of a statement or a question.

Independent Variable. This is the variable over which the researcher has control. The researcher can choose and manipulate the *independent variable*. In certain types of objectivist research, the independent variable stands alone and is not changed by the other variables that are being examined. In experimental research, the independent variable often consists of two or more specific treatments or conditions to which the participants are exposed (Gravetter & Forzano, 2006).

Internal Validity. See *Control.*

Limitations. *Limitations* are external conditions placed on the researcher that limit the focus of a study. Limitations may be caused by a number of factors, including a lack of financial resources, a small sample pool, a disruption that occurs while the study is being conducted (e.g., an unexpected event), or limited time to complete the study.

Measurement. In objectivist research, data are represented as numbers ascribed to empirical observations. *Measurement* occurs whenever numbers are assigned to any unit or variable as a way of representing that property. The measurements are classified into four levels: nominal, ordinal, interval, and ratio. These are covered in several chapters in Unit 4. Data that are based on nominal and ordinal levels of measurement are usually calculated with nonparametric statistical tests, while data that are based on interval or ratio levels of measurement are usually calculated with parametric statistical tests.

Operational Definition. This is a set of operations used to define and measure the variables in objectivist research (Gravetter & Forzano, 2006). The measurements, in turn, define the hypothetical constructs being measured. One common example of an *operational definition* is an IQ test, which is used to measure intelligence. In this example, the test measures external, observable behaviors in the form of responses to questions. The resultant IQ scores serve as both a definition of intelligence and a measurement of it.

Population. In objectivist research, the term *population* refers to the entire group of objects or people in whom the researcher is interested (Gravetter & Forzano, 2006). Typically, a sampling of the population participates in an objectivist study, but the findings can be generalized to the entire population if the study is conducted correctly. For that reason, the population must be defined very precisely in regard to the information that the researcher is hoping to gain (Rainbow & Froelich, 1987).

Reliability. A score is said to be *reliable* if the same measurement, repeated under the same conditions, produces identical, or nearly identical, results. Several types of reliability exist. Researchers estimate reliability by calculating an appropriate statistical procedure using one of several possible tests of reliability.

Sample. Just as the population is the entire group of objects or people about which information is sought by the researcher, the *sample* is a part of the population that is used to gather information about and to represent the entire population. A recommendation coming from Improving Access and Quality: Music Therapy Research 2025, a research symposium sponsored by the American Music Therapy Association, is that researchers list the ICD-10 diagnoses of the research participants. This will help to link the benefit of a particular intervention for a particular diagnosis (Else & Farbman, 2015, p. 94).

Significance. This common word has a very specific meaning in objectivist research. It means that the effect caused by or related to the independent variable is large enough that it would be extremely unlikely to have been observed by chance (Gravetter & Forzano, 2006). For example, if the researcher who is conducting an experimental study chooses the probability level of $p = 0.05$ during the planning of the study, this means that there would be only a 5% chance that the results of the study were due to chance and a 95% chance that the results of the study were due to the effect of the independent variable on the dependent variable. *Significance* is determined by the statistical tests that were used to analyze the data.

Designing Objectivist Research

This final section will present how to design an objectivist study. The part of the process that deals with designing research refers to what is usually contained in the Method section of a research proposal or report, the part that is created after the researcher has identified a research topic, reviewed the literature, determined the feasibility, formulated and then stated a research problem, asked the research questions, and formulated one or more hypotheses. For additional information on how to design

Year	Type	Author	Title	Journal
2006	Exp	Ceccato, Caneva, & Lamonaca	Music therapy and cognitive rehabilitation in schizophrenic patients	*Nordic Journal of Music Therapy*
2006	Sm n	Lesta & Petocz	Familiar group singing: Addressing mood and social behavior of residents displaying sundowning	*Australian Journal of Music Therapy*
2008	Des	Baker, Wigram, Stott, & McFerran	Therapeutic songwriting in music therapy	*Nordic Journal of Music Therapy*
2011	Des	Hahna & Schwantes	Feminist music therapy pedagogy: A survey of music therapy educators	*Journal of Music Therapy*
2011	Sm n	Hanser, Butterfield-Whitcomb, & Kawata	Home-based music strategies with individuals who have dementia and their family caregivers	*Journal of Music Therapy*
2013	Exp	Ghetti	Effect of music therapy with emotional approach coping on preprocedural anxiety in cardiac catheterization: A randomized controlled trial	*Journal of Music Therapy*

Des = Descriptive   Exp = Experimental   Sm n = Small n study

Table 2. Music Therapy Objectivist Research Examples

and implement a research study, please consult the *Publication Manual of the American Psychological Association* (6th ed., 2009) or refer to information on designing studies using various objectivist methods contained in Unit 6 of this book. Table 2 contains six recently published music therapy research articles that will be used as examples in this section of the chapter. They were chosen from journals published in several countries and based solely on specific characteristics that will help clarify the steps in designing an objectivist study. Many other suitable articles exist that could also have served this purpose.

Selecting the Design

The nature of the research topic, problem, and questions will guide the researcher to choose an appropriate design for the study. The main purpose for selecting a design is to answer the research questions in the most appropriate and efficient manner possible. Wheeler (2005) reinforces this idea by describing the research design as the way that the researcher structures the study to best answer the questions posed. Factors that must be considered before choosing a research design include, but are not limited to, the estimated number of participants, whether the participants will be randomly selected from the population, whether the participants will be divided into groups, whether the groups will be randomly assigned or matched, the time allotted for the entire study, and the resources (e.g., financial, statistical, equipment) available to the researcher.

Choosing the Participants

A number of factors must be taken into consideration when selecting participants for a study. These factors are discussed below.

Assumptions. When choosing a research sample, the participants need to be representative not only of the population, but also of those individuals to whom the results will be generalized (Wheeler, 2005). That is why one of the assumptions for conducting some objectivist research (specifically that which will be analyzed using parametric statistics) is that the *population be normally distributed.* In most situations, researchers do not have the opportunity to study the entire research population. The sheer number of research participants within most identified populations would be too staggering to study. In addition, if too many participants are involved in a study, the results, although statistically significant, might lack practical applications. To counter these potential problems, researchers try to ensure that the sample taken from the population is also normally distributed.

A second assumption for conducting some objectivist research is that *every person in the population has an equal chance of being selected to participate in the study.* As stated above, it is rarely the case that researchers have access to the entire population from which to choose a sample. More than likely, an investigator will have access to only a discrete number of individuals from the identified population, and those individuals become the research sample.

Sampling Techniques. *Random sampling* is by far the best technique a researcher can use to create a representative group from the identified population. If random selection from the population to the sample is not possible, the investigator should strive to randomly assign the subjects to the research groups. This occurred in Mohammadi, Shahabi, and Panah's study (2011) and Ghetti's (2013) study, in which the researchers could not randomly select patients from the available population, so they made sure to randomly assign them to either the treatment or the control groups. *Matched sampling* occurs when the investigator attempts to create matched groups of participants with characteristics that are typical of individuals in the desired population (Wheeler, 2005). Ceccato et al. (2006) placed 16 patients who were diagnosed with schizophrenia in two groups of eight that were matched for clinical characteristics. *Purposive sampling* occurs when individuals are recruited to participate in a study because they resemble the characteristics of the intended population (Wheeler, 2005). Lesta and Petocz (2006) used *volunteer sampling* to recruit four patients who were diagnosed with dementia to determine if music therapy had an effect on sundowning behaviors. Realistically, music therapists often work with small numbers of clients, so it may not be possible to find enough participants to create matched groups. In this case, already-existing samples may be available to a music therapist. When naturally occurring groups are chosen to form control and treatment groups, the procedure is called *cluster sampling* (Gravetter & Forzano, 2006).

Certain sampling procedures are used primarily when conducting survey research. *Stratified sampling* involves the identification of specific subgroups (strata) in the sample, followed by the selection of equal random samples from each pre-identified subgroup (Gravetter & Forzano, 2006). *Systematic sampling* represents a probability sampling technique in which, after a random start, a sample is chosen by selecting every nth participant from a list containing the total population (Gravetter & Forzano, 2006). Baker et al. (2008) used systematic sampling in their two-part survey study of music therapy songwriting practices.

Determining the Sample Size. The number of participants in a study needs to be large enough that the variability caused by individual differences does not outweigh the variability caused by the effect of the independent variable on the dependent variable (Wheeler, 2005). The first consideration is to calculate the *power* that is needed. Power is a statistical procedure that helps to determine how large a sample size is needed for an experiment.

When choosing a sample group, the researcher has to allow for the fact that not all potential participants will agree to participate. Even if they do agree to participate at first, they always have the right to withdraw from the study at any time without penalty. It is typical for the number of subjects to shrink by the end of a study period. The term *subject mortality* refers to the loss of participants from the study groups (Campbell & Stanley, 1963). Because subject mortality occurs, it is best to recruit a larger sample than what you predict you will probably end up with. In general, the size of the participant sample needs to be large enough to allow for generalizability.

Along with mortality, investigators often encounter other challenges when attempting to begin a study. For example, if the potential subjects are under the age of 18, informed consent must be obtained from the subjects' parents or legal guardians; in addition, *assent* is often obtained from minors or any individual who is legally is unable to give informed consent. In addition, a researcher may experience challenges when attempting to gain access to a desired setting or permission from an agency to conduct research on-site. In the research examples listed in Table 2, the number of participants ranged from four nursing home residents in the Lesta and Petocz small *n* study (2006) to 477 professional music therapists representing 29 different countries in the Baker et al. (2008) survey study about songwriting practices (2008). As expected, the small *n* studies by Lesta and Petocz (2006) and Hanser, Butterfield-Whitcomb, and Kawata (2011) had the smallest participant samples. The two descriptive studies by Baker et al. (2008) and Hahna and Schwantes (2011) contained the largest participant samples. The two experimental studies both featured multiple groups in their designs; the Ghetti study had 37 participants divided into three groups, and the Ceccato et al. (2006) study contained 16 participants divided into two groups. Out of the given examples, Ghetti (2013) was the only researcher to employ power calculations to determine adequate sampling sizes.

Setting

Choosing the optimal setting in which to conduct research is paramount. Keeping the setting exactly the same across all conditions eliminates the probability that *confounding*, or nuisance, variables will interfere with the results of the research (Wheeler, 2005). Due to the nature of music therapy research, which primarily contains some form of music as the treatment, the research setting needs to be free from extraneous noises, distractions, and the risk of outside interruptions. All participants, trainers, and researchers will need to silence their electronic devices prior to the beginning of the treatment or measurement procedures. Every participant in the experimental group must experience the independent variable in the same setting, and the measurement of the dependent variables must take place in an identical setting for both the experimental and control groups. This eliminates the chance that differences in the settings will impact the results of the study. For example,

Lesta and Petocz (2006) held their music therapy sessions for four consecutive days in the late afternoon, immediately before the evening hours, when sundowning behaviors are the most prevalent. In the Mohammadi et al. study (2011), the two groups of participants met in the music therapy clinic of the long-term care center where they resided, whereas the settings for the two descriptive studies (Baker et al., 2008; Hahna & Schwantes, 2011) were chosen at the convenience of the research participants who completed the surveys.

Music therapy research often occurs in institutions of higher learning, where faculty and graduate students are encouraged to conduct research. In these settings, there is increased access to equipment, financial support, larger sample sizes, and physical resources (Edwards, 2005). Universities also more commonly have laboratory spaces where soundproof rooms may be available.

Independent and Dependent Variables

For a research protocol to be replicable, the researcher must follow and write up the procedures very clearly. For an experimental study: (a) the independent variable must be precisely defined so that anyone reading the research report will be able to understand it; (b) the implementation of the independent variable must be carefully explained so that any reader can replicate the procedure; (c) the procedure for what will occur with the control group while the treatment group is receiving the independent variable must be clearly explained; and (d) how the dependent variable(s) will be measured must be clearly defined so that any reader can replicate the measurement of the dependent variable(s). Not only should the treatment intervention be defined in detail, but also the time allotment per treatment session or measurement session should be clarified (e.g., how long each treatment session will last, how many treatment sessions will occur, the total amount of treatment time each subject will be expected to participate). An important point for music therapy researchers is a recommendation from the research symposium sponsored by the American Music Therapy Association, Improving Access and Quality: Music Therapy Research 2025: "Define and describe the intervention using accepted standards in published research and as part of research planning. When planning a research study, the music therapy intervention needs to be identified and specified by intervention and not just by the term 'music therapy'" (Else & Farbman, 2015, p. 93).

In certain types of descriptive studies (e.g., survey, content analysis), an independent variable is not applicable. These types of inquiries focus on the present status of an event, behavior, or practice. The two survey studies included in this section do not base their protocols on an independent variable. Instead, they pose questions about the current status of a phenomenon and then set about trying to recruit participants to answer the questions. As shown in Table 3, Hanna and Schwantes (2008) adapted an already existing assessment tool to answer their research questions about feminist music therapy pedagogy, while Baker et al. (2011) constructed their own concerning songwriting practices across clinical settings and populations.

Protocol, Measurement, and Research Apparatus

The *protocol* is the plan for a scientific experiment ("Protocol," 2015). It is the set of complete and systematic procedures followed during the implementation of the independent variable (Wheeler, 2005). Protocols identify which trainers or administrators will present the independent variable during the course of the study, along with what will be presented. Ceccato et al. (2006) used the *Sound Training for Attention and Memory* (STAM) method as the treatment protocol. The STAM protocol consisted of a progressive series of sound tracks and music sessions recorded on a CD, which provided a sequence of step-by-step exercises aimed at stimulating and checking attention and memory. A section of the STAM protocol follows:

- Phase 1: Association of stimuli and movements. The music therapist instructs the subjects to link particular sound stimuli with specific body movements.
- Phase 2: Reaction to acoustic stimuli. This task consists of reacting to previously heard acoustic stimuli. The sound stimuli of the previous exercise are used. The reaction consists in recognizing the type of stimulus and counting how many times it occurs in a recording with background noise.
- Phase 3: Shifting attention. This task consists of reacting to a drum by clapping hands after the stimulus is heard and not clapping when the drum sound is preceded by a cymbal. (p. 115)

Music therapy researchers are encouraged to use *standardized tests, assessments, and scales* when measuring dependent variable(s) to ensure high content validity and reliability. In the Ceccato et al. study described above (2006), the measurements for memory and attention included the *Paced Auditory Serial Addition Test*, the *Wechsler Memory Scale*, and the *Life Skills Profile*. In this research, the subjects who received the STAM protocol significantly improved their performance on the WMS ($p = 0.01$) and the LSP ($p = 0.01$), when compared with the control group. Other standardized measurements in the music therapy research examples in this chapter were the *Depression Anxiety Stress Scale* (Mohammadi et al., 2011), the *Positive and Negative Affect Schedule* (Ghetti, 2013), and the *Visual Analog Scale* (Hanser et al., 2011).

Research apparatus are any additional objects (e.g., visual props, musical instruments, audio recordings, audio devices, digital equipment, software, hardware) used during the administration of the independent variable(s) or the measurement of the dependent variable(s). All equipment used in a research study needs to be sturdy and of high quality. For example, musical resources (e.g., digital players or musical instruments) must be inspected in advance to ensure a good and consistent-quality audio sound (Wheeler, 2005). Akin to the research setting, the protocol and apparatus must be maintained carefully throughout the entire research process to avoid other confounding variables that might impact the results of the study.

Below is an example of a carefully chosen protocol, assessments, and apparatus. The treatment protocol used by Mohammadi et al. (2011) consisted of 10 weeks of daily music-based sessions (i.e., listening to music, singing, and playing percussion instruments) with 11 nursing home residents (each session was 90 minutes). The eight control participants who received no music participated in regular activities at the same time. More specifically, the music treatment used in this study included rhythmic instrument playing, lyric and folk Persian singing, music and rhythmic movement, improvisation, and reminiscing associated with song listening. The researchers used both classic and traditional Persian instruments (e.g., *daf, tombak, santur, maracas, tambourine*). The 21-item *Depression Anxiety Stress Scale* (DASS-21, 1995) was used to measure the dependent variables of depression, anxiety, and stress. The pretest to posttest results indicated significant reductions in mean scores of anxiety ($p = .004$), stress ($p = .001$), and depression ($p < .001$) in the intervention group (music) as compared with the control group (no music; Mohammadi et al., 2011).

Not all music therapists have the financial resources or administrative support to purchase expensive measurement equipment. Many types of accessible tools are available free or at low cost, including software programs, electronic monitors, standardized assessment tools, adapted assessment tools, visual analog scales, self-report forms, and observational recording methods. Table 3 represents the independent variables, dependent variables, and types of measurements used in the eight sample research studies.

Data Collection and Analysis

When using self-constructed observation checklists to measure research participants' behavior, it is important to use more than one observer to take data and to establish a high interrater reliability between the observers. When using multiple observers, the researcher will probably need to train the observers with practice sessions prior to beginning the study. Self-constructed checklists or surveys usually need to go through a level of review by experts prior to adopting the assessment as the research instrument. This also helps to establish better content validity for the self-constructed assessment.

If the researcher finds an assessment that seems perfectly suited to measure the dependent variable, the first step is to determine if the assessment requires training to administer. If training is required, the music therapy researcher needs to determine if he or she meets the qualifications to be trained.

If the music therapist does not meet the qualifications, then collaboration with an expert who is qualified to administer and score the test may be the only option. If a music therapist finds an assessment that seems ideal for the research that is published in a journal, the researcher will need to contact the author(s) of the article for written permission to use the tool for the music therapy study.

The electronic equipment employed to take data on dependent variables must demonstrate calibrated precision. Wheeler (2005) agrees that the best data collection instrument is of no use if it is not properly operated. Electronic data can easily be stored on computer hard drives, Internet cloud programs, or flash drives for easy accessibility and analysis, and researchers should be prudent about backing up their data on a regular basis and keeping it password-protected. Internet survey programs like *SurveyMonkey*® provide not only the resources to create multiple types of survey questions, but also data analysis features and data security.

Once the data have been collected, the analysis can take place. In the case of experimental studies, the data analysis must be tied directly to the research questions and design (Wheeler, 2005). In other words, the type of research analysis and the level of confidence must be chosen *a priori* or before the beginning of the study. The specific statistical tests used to compare between or within groups must also match the data's level of measurement. For example, ordinal data need to be analyzed using nonparametric tests. Most survey results are represented as the percentages of respondents who answered a question in a certain way. Small n results are often represented in visual form, such as tables or graphs. Statistical tests can be used in small n studies, but the tests must be well suited for smaller samples. Experimental studies may use inferential statistical tests to compare the results between groups. Ghetti (2013) provides an excellent example of systematically planning the data analysis to measure multiple dependent variables through randomization and a two-group a priori design.

An essential point to remember is that once the research study has been planned, the independent and dependent variables chosen, the design selected, the participant criteria determined, the treatment protocol developed, the instrumentation selected, and the data collection methods and analyses chosen, any research study that involves human participants must go through an ethical review. Most healthcare facilities and academic institutions have ethical review boards on site that meet regularly to review proposed research applications. These committees determine that the benefits the researcher is offering to the potential human

Year	Type	Author	Independent Variable	Dependent Variable	Measurements
2006	Exp	Ceccato, Caneva, & Lamonaca	STAM	Attention & memory in patients with schizophrenia	*PASAT, LSP, WMS*
2006	Sm n	Lesta & Petocz	Small group singing	Negative mood Nonsocial behavior	Self-constructed mood-behavioral checklist
2008	Des	Baker, Wigram, Stott, & McFerran	N/A	Songwriting: Most frequently applied goal areas across clinical populations	21-question online survey
2011	Des	Hahna & Schwantes	N/A	Views of/use of feminist music therapy & feminist pedagogy by music therapy educators	Adapted *Feminist Pedagogy Survey* (Stake & Hoffman, 2000)
2011	Sm n	Hanser, Butterfield-Whitcomb, & Kawata	Caregiver-administered music program	Mood & psychological state in persons with dementia; Distress & satisfaction in caregivers	*Visual Analog Scale* Self-report
2013	Exp	Ghetti	MT/EAC	Affective state; systolic blood pressure; procedural length; amount of analgesia	*Positive and Negative Affect Schedule; Visual Analog Scale;* heart rate, respiratory rate, oxygen saturation, & blood pressure; length of procedure, amount of sedative, & amount of analgesic

Des = Descriptive   Exp = Experimental   Sm n = Small n study

Table 3. Independent Variables, Dependent Variables, and Measurements: Sample Studies

participants far outweigh the risks and that informed consent is guaranteed. Only after the board approves the proposal can the study be implemented.

Risk of Bias

Evidence-based practice (EBP) is "the conscientious, explicit, and judicious use of current best evidence in making decisions about the care of individual patients" (Sackett, Rosenberg, Gray, & Richardson, 1996, p. 71). EBP is important in music therapy and many types of healthcare, as well as related services such as education and special education. Because of the emphasis on evidence and to ensure the highest quality of music therapy services, it is essential that music therapists produce multiple kinds of evidence, including various client populations and types of interventions to add to the overall knowledge base. In addition, high-quality research is essential as music therapists strive for recognition from third-party providers, state legislators, and others. Much of this evidence comes through objectivist research and, in particular, randomized controlled trials.

A *randomized controlled trial (RCT)* is an experimental study that consists of at least two groups of participants, or conditions, with each participant having been randomly assigned to one of the groups. One of these groups, known as the treatment group, receives the independent or treatment variable, and the other group, the control group, receives a different treatment or no special treatment. The groups are treated identically (or with no systematic differences between them) with the exception of the addition of the independent variable for the treatment group(s). RCTs are often considered the *gold standard* of research studies. RCTs are discussed more fully in Chapter 34 and other chapters in Unit 6 of this book.

High-quality RCTs have a low *risk of bias,* the assessment of which is based on several criteria. Yinger and Gooding (2015) assessed risk of bias in music-based interventions for procedural support according to five criteria (adapted from the "Checklist to Evaluate a Report of a Nonpharmacological Trial"; Boutron et al., 2005, as cited in Yinger & Gooding, 2005): "(a) adequate generation of allocation sequences; (b) treatment allocation concealment; (c) blinding of care providers; (d) blinding of outcome assessors; and (e) whether outcomes were analyzed according to the intention-to-treat principle" (p. 10). These criteria are similar to other tools used to assess the quality of research (e.g., the *Cochrane Collaboration's Tool for Assessing Risk of Bias*; Higgins & Green, 2011).

The first of these, adequate generation of allocation sequences, often referred to as *method of randomization*, refers to the system used to allocate participants to groups so that each participant has an equal chance of being assigned to each condition. Bradt (2012) describes simple, block, and stratified randomization methods that can be used to randomly assign people to conditions. Most smart phones and tablets and many Internet sites now have number-generating applications that can be used to create random assignment schedules. Methods of assignment that are *not* random and should not be used include alternate assignment to groups, using odd or even birth dates, date of admission, hospital or clinic record number, or allocation by availability of intervention (Bradt, 2012).

The second criterion, *treatment allocation concealment,* requires that participants are assigned to study conditions in such a way that the assigned treatment is not known to those recruiting participants prior to the participants' entering the study (Bradt, 2012). One of the better ways to protect allocation concealment is the *SNOSE method*, in which group assignment labels (e.g., *treatment* or *control*) are written on pieces of paper that are then slipped into sealed "sequentially numbered, opaque, sealed envelopes" (SNOSE; Bradt, 2012, p. 129). In the presence of each participant, the researcher will select the subsequent envelope, open it, and read aloud the participant's assignment, thus avoiding bias in assigning participants to conditions on the part of the researcher.

Blinding helps to control for performance bias and detection bias (Bradt, 2012). Blinding refers to the concealment of assigned treatments from all parties who are involved with data collection, data analysis, and the patients' treatment, including the participants, the music therapy researcher, research assistants, facility or agency assessors, and statisticians. The third and fourth criteria used by Yinger and Gooding (2015), blinding of care providers and blinding of outcome assessors, are both part of this category. Blinding is common in pharmaceutical studies, and the participants do not know whether they are receiving the treatment medication or the placebo medication. Placebo capsules can even be produced to look identical to the treatment capsule. In music therapy, however, it is virtually impossible to blind the participants. Participants assigned to a treatment group will know that they are receiving the treatment, especially if it is an active one, and that may influence their attitude toward the treatment, the investigator, and any self-report measures they may be asked to complete (e.g., anxiety or depression self-report scales). Since the music therapist is usually the one administering the treatment, it would also be next to impossible to blind the interventionist. However, the music therapist should not distribute or collect the assessments, data sheets, or anything else related to the research outcomes from the participants. Research assistants or third parties blinded to the conditions should do these kinds of tasks.

The final criterion considered by Yinger and Gooding (2015) in assessing the risk of bias is called *intention to treat.* This is a method used to correct for differential dropout rates between patients in the treatment and control groups by analyzing the data with the intent to treat (Stolberg, Norman, & Trop, 2004). Using intent to treat, the data are analyzed in the same way that the participants were randomized and assigned to groups, even if they did not receive the correct intervention or not all treatment sessions. (For example, it is possible that one participant may have decided to attend the other group instead of the group to which he or she was allocated.) As Bradt (2012) summarizes, "It is recommended that all randomized patients be included in the analysis and kept in the groups to which they were originally assigned, regardless of their adherence to the treatment protocol" (p. 144).

The risk of bias in music therapy studies is often moderate to high. This may be due to the fact that blinding of participants and interventionist is not possible. Unfortunately, the risk of bias in music therapy studies is often higher than it should be because of lack of attention to sources of bias such as allocation concealment. Systematic reviews have repeatedly indicated that the majority of music therapy RCTs do not use allocation concealment and that a large percentage use inadequate forms of randomization (see Bradt, 2012, for more information on this; also refer to specific Cochrane reviews). Yinger and Gooding (2015) found that "across all intervention studies (music therapy and music medicine), the majority were at high risk of bias" (p. 61). Bradt (2012) says, "Reviews of the music therapy research literature indicate a need for increased scientific rigor in the design and conduct of RCTs" (p. 146). These statements highlight the need for music therapy educators to place more emphasis upon risk of bias in their teaching, for reviewers to be more aware of it when reviewing articles, and, of course, for music therapy researchers to be more aware of risk of bias in designing and carrying out research.

Conclusion

The purpose of this chapter was to give the reader an overview of objectivist research, including an exploration of the following questions: (a) What is objectivist research? (b) What is an objectivist attitude? (c) What types of topics and questions are typically addressed through objectivist research? (d) What are the beliefs of objectivist researchers regarding how knowledge can be acquired? (e) How did objectivist research develop, including publications and its development in music therapy? (f) What major concepts and terms are associated with objectivist research? (g) What are the most common objectivist research designs? (h) What are the steps for designing an objectivist study? (i) What are the risks of bias and how can they be controlled for when conducting music therapy objectivist research? Additional chapters in this textbook will explain objectivist research in more detail.

References

American Music Therapy Association. (2015). Strategic priority on research. Retrieved from http://www.musictherapy.org/research/strategic_prior ity_on_research/overview

Baker, F., Wigram, T., Stott, D., & McFerran, K. (2008). Therapeutic songwriting in music therapy. Part I: Who are the therapists, who are the clients, and why is songwriting used? *Nordic Journal of Music Therapy, 17,* 105–123. doi:10.1080/08098130809478203

Bernstein, R. J. (1983). *Beyond objectivism and realism: Science, hermeneutics, and praxis.* Philadelphia, PA: University of Pennsylvania Press.

Böhme, T., Childerhouse, P., Deakens, E., & Towill, D. (2012). A method for reconciling subjectivity and objectivist assumptions in management research. *Journal of Leadership & Organizational Studies, 19,* 369–377. doi:10.1177/1548051812442965

Bradt, J. (2012). Randomized control trials in music therapy: Guidelines for design and implementation. *Journal of Music Therapy, 49,* 120–149. doi:10.1093/jmt/49.2.120

Brooks, D. (2003). A history of music therapy journal articles published in the English language. *Journal of Music Therapy, 15,* 151–168. doi:10.1093/jmt/40.2.151

Bruscia, K. (2005). Research topics and questions in music therapy. In B. Wheeler (Ed.), *Music therapy research* (2nd ed.; pp. 81–93). Gilsum, NH: Barcelona.

Campbell, D. T., & Stanley, J. C. (1963*). Experimental and quasi-experimental designs for research.* Chicago, IL: Rand McNally College.

Ceccato, E., Caneva, P., & Lamonaca, D. (2006). Music therapy and cognitive rehabilitation in schizophrenic patients: A controlled study. *Nordic Journal of Music Therapy, 15,* 111–120. doi:10.1080/08098130609478158

Codding, P. A. (1987). A content analysis of the *Journal of Music Therapy, 1977–85. Journal of Music Therapy, 24,* 195–202. doi:10.1093/jmt/24.4.195

Cook, T. D., & Campbell, D. T. (1979). *Quasi-experimentation: Design and analysis issues for field settings.* Chicago, IL: Rand McNally.

Cronjé, J. (2006). Paradigms regained: Toward integrating objectivism and constructivism in instructional design and the learning sciences. *Educational Technology Research and Development, 54*(4), 387–416. doi:10.1007/S11423-006-9605-1

Crotty, M. (1998). *The foundations of social research: Meaning and perspective in the research process.* Sydney, Australia: Allen & Unwin.

Daston, L. (2011). The empire of observation: 1600–1800. In L. Daston & E. Lunbek (Eds.), *Histories of scientific observation* (pp. 82–114). Chicago, IL: University of Chicago Press.

Daston, L., & Lunbeck, E. (2011). *Histories of scientific observation.* Chicago, IL: University of Chicago Press.

DeCuir, A. (1987). Readings for music therapy students: An analysis of clinical research literature from the *Journal of Music Therapy.* In C. D. Maranto & K. E. Bruscia (Eds.), *Perspectives on music therapy education and training* (pp. 57–70). Philadelphia, PA: Temple University Esther Boyer College of Music.

Edwards, J. (1999). Considering the paradigmatic frame: Social science research approaches relevant to research in music therapy. *Arts in Psychotherapy, 26,* 73–80.

doi:10.1016/S0197-4556(98)00049-5

Edwards, J. (2005). Developments and issues in music therapy research. In B. L. Wheeler (Ed.), *Music therapy research* (2nd ed.; pp. 20–32). Gilsum, NH: Barcelona.

Else, B., & Farbman, A. (2015). *Improving access and quality: Music Therapy Research 2025 proceedings.* Silver Spring, MD: American Music Therapy Association.

Empirical. (2015). In *Merriam-Webster online dictionary.* Retrieved from http://www.merriam-webster.com/dictionary/empirical

Gfeller, K. (1987). Music therapy theory and practice as reflected in research literature. *Journal of Music Therapy, 24,* 178–194. doi:10.1093/jmt/24.4.178

Ghetti, C. (2013). Effect of music therapy with emotional-approach coping on preprocedural anxiety in cardiac catheterization: A randomized control trial. *Journal of Music Therapy, 50,* 93–122. doi:10.1093/jmt/50.2.93

Gilbert, J. P. (1979). Published research in music therapy, 1973–1978: Content, focus, and implications for future research. *Journal of Music Therapy, 16,* 102–110. doi:10.1093/jmt/16.3.102

Gravetter, F. J., & Forzano, L. B. (2006). *Research methods for the behavioral sciences* (2nd ed.). Belmont, CA: Wadsworth.

Hahna, N. D., & Schwantes, M. (2011). Feminist music therapy pedagogy: A survey of music therapy educators. *Journal of Music Therapy, 48,* 289–316. doi:10.1093/jmt/48.3.289

Hanser, S. B., Butterfield-Whitcomb, J., & Kawata, M. (2011). Home-based music strategies with individuals who have dementia and their family caregivers. *Journal of Music Therapy, 48,* 2–27. doi:10.1093/jmt/48.1.2

Heal, M., & Wigram, T. (1993). *Music therapy in health and education.* London, UK: Jessica Kingsley.

Higgins, J. P. T., & Green, S. (Eds.). (2011). *Cochrane handbook for systematic reviews of interventions, version 5.1.0.* The Cochrane Collaboration. Retrieved from www.cochrane-handbook.org

Isaac, S., & Michael, W. (1991). *Handbook in research and evaluation* (3rd ed.). San Diego, CA: Edits.

Jellison, J. A. (1973). The frequency and general mode of inquiry of research in music therapy, 1952–1972. *Council for Research in Music Education, 35,* 1–8.

Kuper, A., Reeves, S., & Levinson, W. (2008). An introduction to reading and appraising qualitative research. *British Medical Journal, 337,* 404–407. doi:10.1136/bmj.a288

Lesta, B., & Petocz, P. (2006). Familiar group singing: Addressing mood and social behaviour of residents with dementia displaying sundowning. *Australian Journal of Music Therapy, 17,* 2–17. doi:10.1186/1471-2458-11-142

McCall, W. A. (1923). *How to experiment in education.* New York, NY: Macmillan.

Mohammadi, A. Z., Shahabi, T., & Paha, F. M. (2011). An evaluation of the effect of group music therapy on stress, anxiety, and depression levels in nursing home residents. *Canadian Journal of Music Therapy, 17*(1), 55–68. doi:10.1080/10911359.2013.766147

O'Callaghan, C. (2009). Objectivist and constructivist music therapy research in oncology and palliative care: An overview and reflection. *Music and Medicine, 1,* 41–60. doi:10.1177/1943862109337135

Park, K. (2011). Observation in the margins: 500–1500. In L. Daston & E. Lunbeck (Eds.), *Histories of scientific observation* (pp. 15–44). Chicago, IL: University of Chicago Press.

Pomata. G. (2011). Observation rising: Birth of an epistemic genre, 1500–1650. In L. Daston & E. Lunbeck (Eds.), *Histories of scientific observation* (pp. 45–80). Chicago, IL: University of Chicago Press.

Prickett, C. (2005). Principles of quantitative research. In B. L. Wheeler (Ed.), *Music therapy research* (2nd ed.; pp. 45–58). Gilsum, NH: Barcelona.

Protocol. (2015). In *Merriam-Webster online dictionary.* Retrieved from http://www.merriam-webster.com/dictionary/protocol

Rainbow, E. L., & Froelich, H. C. (1987). *Research in music education.* New York, NY: Schirmer.

Robson, C. (2011). *Real world research.* West Sussex, UK: Wiley.

Sackett, D. L., Rosenberg, W. M. C., Gray, J. A. M., Haynes, R. B., & Richardson, W. D. (1996, Jan. 13). Evidence-based medicine: What it is and what it isn't. *British Medical Journal, 312,* 71–72. doi:10.1136/bmj.312.7023.71

Scientific method. (2015). In *Merriam-Webster online dictionary.* Retrieved from http://www.merriam-webster.com/dictionary/scientificmethod

Shadish, W. R., Cook, T. D., & Campbell, D. T. (2002). *Experimental and quasi-experimental designs for generalized causal inference.* New York, NY: Houghton Mifflin.

Stolberg, H. O., Norman, G., & Trop, I. (2004). Randomized control trials. *American Journal of Roentgenology, 183,* 1539–1544. doi:10.2214/ajr.183.6.01831539.PMID/15547188

Wheeler, B. (1988). An analysis of literature from selected music therapy journals. *Music Therapy Perspectives, 5,* 94–101. doi:10.1093/mtp/5.1.94

Wheeler, B. L. (2005). Developing a topic. In B. L. Wheeler (Ed.), *Music therapy research* (2nd ed.; pp. 94–111). Gilsum, NH: Barcelona.

Yinger, O. S., & Gooding, L. F. (2015). A systematic review of music-based interventions for procedural support. *Journal of Music Therapy, 52,* 1–77. doi:10.1093/jmt/thv004

Chapter 9

PRINCIPLES OF INTERPRETIVIST RESEARCH[1]

Barbara L. Wheeler

The terms *interpretivist research* and *qualitative research* refer to a variety of methodologies. Qualitative research is an older term, but interpretivist research emphasizes interpretation, a primary feature of this type of research. The terms will be used interchangeably in this chapter, with qualitative research used primarily when referring to what others have written about qualitative research and providing historical information and interpretivist research used when speaking of current issues and applications.

What Is Interpretivist Research?

Interpretivist, or qualitative, research has been defined in many ways by music therapists and those in the larger research community. According to music therapist Kenneth Bruscia (personal communication, 2014):

Qualitative research is a collection of research practices that have evolved in different disciplines, variously sharing the following premises:
- Focus: A primary interest in the subjective world of human beings—as it unfolds naturally in the "lived" world.
- Purpose: To gain an understanding of how human beings create, discover, and communicate meaning—as individually and collectively constructed through actions, interactions, experience, language, and art.
- Method: The use of data collection strategies that encourage the participants and phenomena under inquiry to reveal themselves in their own way, unencumbered by the researcher.
- Reflexivity: Continuous efforts of the researcher to bring into awareness, evaluate, and when necessary modify the research process so as to ensure the integrity of the data and its interpretation and to monitor the researcher's personal contributions to all aspects of the research.
- Interpretation: A belief that findings of one's research are constructed, value-laden, context-bound, and time-bound and a continual concern for the epistemology underlying the interpretation of data.

Denzin and Lincoln (2011), in *The Sage Handbook of*

Qualitative Research (4th ed.), provide a generic definition of qualitative research:

Qualitative research is a situated activity that locates the observer in the world. Qualitative research consists of a set of interpretive, material practices that make the world visible. These practices transform the world. They turn the world into a series of representations, including field notes, interviews, conversations, photographs, recordings, and memos to the self. At this level, qualitative research involves an interpretive, naturalistic approach to the world. This means that qualitative researchers study things in their natural settings, attempting to make sense of or interpret phenomena in terms of the meanings people bring to them. (p. 3)

These authors go on to paraphrase a definition from Nelson, Treichler, and Grossberg (1992, p. 4):

Qualitative research is an interdisciplinary, transdisciplinary, and sometimes counterdisciplinary field. It crosscuts the humanities, as well as the social and the physical sciences. Qualitative research is many things at the same time. It is multiparadigmatic in focus. Its practitioners are sensitive to the value of the multimethod approach. They are committed to the naturalistic perspective and to the interpretive understanding of human experience. At the same time, the field is inherently political and shaped by multiple ethical and political positions.

Qualitative research embraces two tensions at the same time. On the one hand, it is drawn to a broad, interpretive, postexperimental, postmodern, feminist, and critical sensibility. On the other hand, it is drawn to more narrowly defined positivist, postpositivist, humanistic, and naturalistic conceptions of human experience and its analysis. Furthermore, these tensions can be combined in the same project, bringing both postmodern and naturalistic, or both critical and humanistic, perspectives to bear. (Denzin & Lincoln, 2011, p. 6)

Some have found it more useful to refer to *interpretivist* or *interpretive research* rather than to *qualitative research*. The use of these terms acknowledges that interpretation by the researcher is a primary characteristic of all forms of this type of research. Referring to qualitative research, as contrasted with quantitative research, sometimes leads to a simplistic understanding of both, for instance, that qualitative research focuses only on the qualities of what is studied while quantitative research deals only with numbers. A dichotomy between qualitative and quantitative research, which is also sometimes perceived as a conflict, is another problem. These are among the reasons that the term *interpretivist research* is used by many and is the term used throughout this book.

Focuses, Topics, and Questions

Interpretivist research methodologies may be classified in numerous ways. These vary over time, and different authors use different classifications.[2] Marshall and Rossman (2011) divide qualitative research into genres providing:

- A focus on society and culture: ethnographic approaches, including traditional ethnography and also more recent types of ethnography such as Internet ethnography and critical ethnography;
- A focus on individual lived experience: phenomenological approaches;
- A focus on talk and text: sociolinguistic approaches, where analyzing talk is a central focus for discourse analysis and critical discourse analysis.

These authors suggest a fourth category, critical approaches, that has research goals that are "openly ideological and have empowering and democratizing goals" (Marshall & Rossman, 2011, p. 21). These include the following qualitative research genres: critical ethnography, autoethnography, queer analysis, critical race analysis, feminist research methods, cultural studies, multimodal studies, and Internet ethnography (p. 21).

Interpretivist research can be done in any of the three broad topical areas suggested by Bruscia—discipline, profession, or foundational—and can focus on events, actions, and interactions; experiences; written and spoken language; artworks; and persons (individuals, groups, communities, or cultures; Bruscia, 2005b).

Most interpretivist research in music therapy has focused on Marshall and Rossman's (2011) second area, individual lived experience, and used phenomenological, grounded theory, or naturalistic methodologies (Aigen, 2008a), all of which are very useful for understanding many of the things in which music therapists are interested. There has been increasing interest in methodologies that focus on society and culture (Marshall & Rossman), such as ethnographic and action research. This is due in part to interest in Community Music Therapy, which has as one of its tenets involvement and participation of all as part of the community. Music therapists have used few methods that focus on talk and text or critical approaches (Marshall & Rossman, 2011), although some of what these approaches can investigate can be of value for music therapists and are included in this book (see Chapters 42 through 45, labeled as Meaning-Focused Approaches, and Chapters 46 through 48, labeled as Language-Focused Approaches, in Unit 7, Interpretivist Designs).

Philosophical Bases and Epistemology

Interpretivist research can be contrasted with objectivist research by the beliefs of those who engage in it. By examining these beliefs, it becomes clear that the differences are deeper than the research methods used or the type of data (quantitative or qualitative) collected.

An understanding of ontology and epistemology is important for interpretivist research. *Ontology* refers to assumptions or beliefs about the nature of reality and the nature of truth. The fundamental questions concern what is real and what is not real and what conditions must be used to determine the difference. Similarly, is there such a thing as truth? If so, what conditions must be used to determine what is true and not true? A person's ontological beliefs help to determine the kinds of questions that he or she asks.

One's ontology is then connected with epistemology, which asks what are the ways in which knowing can be achieved within the frame of this reality? *Epistemology* is concerned with "the nature, sources, and limits of knowledge" (Pascale, 2011, p. 4). One's view of reality, or ontological perspective, is basic to how one will then understand how this reality can be studied, or epistemological perspective.

Crotty (1998) speaks of epistemology as "the theory of knowledge embedded in [a] theoretical perspective and thereby in the methodology" (p. 3) and connects epistemology, theoretical perspective, methodology, and methods. He distinguishes between *methodology*, which refers to the "strategy, plan of action, process or design lying behind the choice and use of particular methods and linking the choice and use of methods to the desired outcomes" (p. 3), while *methods* are the procedures used to gather and analyze data.

The research methodology that one chooses to use reflects one's ontological and epistemological assumptions. The researcher will design a study based upon his or her beliefs about the nature of truth and reality, as well as what can be known and how to approach getting to know it. Various research methodologies have very different ontologies and epistemologies, and these differences have an impact on interpretivist research. These will be illustrated for phenomenological, hermeneutic, constructivism, and social constructivism, four epistemologies utilized by interpretivist researchers.[3]

One of the areas influenced by one's epistemological beliefs is *what* is studied. In modern phenomenology, the researcher studies *experience*—most often the experience of research participants—with the belief that the researcher's preconceived notions about the experience can be suspended (bracketed) so as not to unduly influence interpretation and understanding. The phenomenological researcher seeks to discern essences and underlying structures. In hermeneutics, *representations* are studied in the form, for example, of verbal descriptions or of music representative of situations, events, or meanings. The hermeneutic researcher seeks hidden meanings. Researchers following constructivism and social constructivism study the *ways that meanings are produced*. In constructivism, these are sought through interactions between the researcher and the object of study, and in social constructionism, they are sought through studying intersubjective processes, accounting for participants' contexts and cultural influences. Each of these focuses or topics of research also depends upon the researcher's ontological beliefs. Are experiences real, and can experiences hold or reveal the truth about what is real? Similarly, are representations and meanings real, and can they be regarded as reflecting the truth about what is real?

A second area impacted by one's epistemology is *who* does the interpreting. Is it done by an individual, or is the process shared or negotiated? An individual interpreter draws from his or her own world of experiences, knowledge, and theoretical beliefs, so the interpretations are from a single mind, with its own context and cultural influences. Phenomenology and constructivism are of this type (with the caveat that the phenomenological researcher intends to hold his or her context in abeyance). Hermeneutics and social constructionism, on the other hand, are collectivist in the interpretative process: Both the researcher's and the *others'* context and culture undeniably manifest in the interpretive process, so multiple minds influence interpretations.

The third consideration, then, is *how* the interpretive process is undertaken. In phenomenology, the researcher, interpreting alone, seeks underlying structures or essences and does so through processes that might draw from empathy, relational knowledge, embodied knowledge, situational awareness, and intuition. In hermeneutics, the interpretive process occurs through the hermeneutic circle, which involves returning to the other as a source of input and therefore employing a collective process. In constructivism, meanings emerge from interaction between the researcher and the object of study, and it is believed that the one who studies and the object of study have meaning only in relation to each other in the particular instances of the research process. In social constructionism, interactions and transactions between participants (including the researcher) are necessary sources from which meanings emerge and are recognized.

Historical Roots

Qualitative research has a long history. Its development in anthropology, psychology, and other areas is documented, and preceded its development in music therapy. The general history is presented here to put the music therapy history, which occurred later and follows the more general development in some ways, into a broader context.

General Development

Denzin and Lincoln (2000) divide the history of qualitative research in North America since 1900 into a number of periods or moments. The first, the *traditional period*, began in the early 1900s and continued until World War II. At this time, they say, "Qualitative researchers wrote 'objective,' colonializing accounts of field experiences that were reflective of the positivist scientist paradigm. … The 'other' who was studied was alien, foreign, and strange" (p. 12). Ethnographic researchers from this time include Bronislaw Malinowski, Margaret Mead, and Gregory Bateson, and the Chicago School, which focused on studying urban social phenomena through qualitative methodologies and was influential in sociology.

The second period was the *modernist phase*, which lasted until the 1970s (Denzin & Lincoln, 2000). Attempts were made during this stage to formalize qualitative research and to make qualitative research as rigorous as quantitative research. Many texts attempted to formalize qualitative research, and new interpretive theories, such as ethnomethodology, critical theory, feminism, and phenomenology, emerged. The work of Glaser and Strauss (1967) characterizes research in this tradition.

The third period, from 1970 to 1986, is labeled the moment of *blurred genres*, the term used by Geertz (1983) to suggest that the boundaries between the social sciences and the humanities had become blurred (Denzin & Lincoln, 2000). During this time, qualitative researchers utilized many paradigms, theories, and strategies and many ways of reporting their findings. Naturalistic, postpositivist, and constructionist paradigms "gained power" (Denzin & Lincoln, 2000, p. 15) during this period, particularly in education, with Eisner, Guba, Lincoln, Stake, and Wolcott as influential figures. Several qualitative journals were also published during this phase.

The fourth period, the *crisis of representation*, occurred in the mid-1980s, when several exposés about the flawed results and skewed interpretations of prominent anthropologists brought scrutiny from other scholars to anthropological writings (Denzin & Lincoln, 2000). As a result of this crisis, "research and writing became more reflexive and led to questions about issues of gender, race, and class; new models of truth, representation, and method were sought; issues such as validity, reliability, and objectivity re-emerged as being problematic" (Onwuegbuzie, Leech, & Collins, 2010, p. 698). Researchers focused on the difficulty or impossibility of adequately describing experience. Questions about how to evaluate qualitative research also became important at this time (Morrow, 2005).

In the fifth period, called the *postmodern moment* (1990–

1995), qualitative researchers found new ways of reporting and writing research (Denzin & Lincoln, 2000). This period was characterized by further shifts from the suggestion that a research paper reflected the reality of a particular context to the idea of the research paper as narrative and storytelling and the realization that different qualitative methods tell different stories. Another feature was an abandonment of the researcher as an aloof, privileged person who can decide what is true.

The sixth period, or the *postexperimental inquiry moment* (1995–2000), was characterized by high levels of excitement, new publishing options for qualitative scholars, and the encouragement of new ways of communicating qualitative research that did not distinguish clearly between social science and the humanities (Denzin & Lincoln, 2000). Publication outlets for social science scholarship were expressed in poetry, drama, performative, visual, multimedia, and conversational modes.

The seventh period, labeled (in 2008) as the *methodologically contested present* (2000–2004), was a period of conflict, tension, and retrenchment. The body of literature on paradigms, approaches, and methods grew. Lincoln and Denzin (2008) suggest that the seventh moment revealed a mature sophistication that characterized the choices that qualitative researchers could make, apparent with the "growing body of literature on specific methods, theoretical lenses, and paradigms" (p. 539).

The eighth period is one of two phases that began in 2005. Lincoln and Denzin (2008) suggest that this was a time of confronting the methodological ramifications of the evidence-based social movement. They suggest that social scientists and policymakers who were part of the U.S. government promoted both a narrowing of the focus of research and other changes in the research environment, including funding priorities. This period was not given a name (Onwuegbuzie, Leech, & Collins, 2010).

In the ninth period of qualitative research, which also began in 2005, Lincoln and Denzin (2008) suggest that qualitative research had entered a *fractured future* where methodologists had formed two opposing camps, one promoting the *gold standard* of scientific research (e.g., using randomized field trials) and the other advocating socially, culturally, ethnically, and racially responsive, communitarian, and justice-oriented research.

Onwuegbuzie et al. (2010) consider the tenth period, which they say "is what we hope will emerge" (p. 699), to be that of *methodological innovation*. During this period, they say that qualitative researchers will "go beyond the traditional ways of collecting primary and reflexive data" (p. 697) and that researchers are using "innovative approaches to reflexivity and the latest technology and computer-mediated communication" (p. 698).

With these periods in the development of qualitative research in mind, we can look at how qualitative—or interpretivist—research has developed in music therapy.

Development in Music Therapy

Elements of interpretivist research in music therapy have existed since music therapists working in clinical settings created descriptions of music therapy sessions by writing in charts or keeping case notes. These descriptions, in the broadest sense, were a form of interpretivist research, even though they usually did not become formalized into research texts. Case notes were and still are a way of monitoring treatment, sharing specific therapeutic events with therapeutic teams, and, generally, observing and assessing the effectiveness of music therapy sessions. It is the observing and interpreting aspects of case note writing that are particularly relevant in tracing the history of interpretivist music therapy research.

Many music therapists choose qualitative methods precisely because these descriptive means of gathering data relate directly to their experiences with patients and clients. They become a type of field note, a method used in ethnographic research that easily translates into the more general qualitative practice of research, which includes both observing and interpreting.

Some of the early articles on music therapy were case studies, another descriptive method that is qualitative in nature. These include case studies written by Paul Nordoff and Clive Robbins (1971, 1977), by numerous authors in *Music in Therapy* (Gaston, 1968), and by many contributors to the *Books of Proceedings* of the National Association for Music Therapy, published under the title *Music Therapy* between the years 1951 and 1963.

Although the clinically based notes were qualitative, much of music therapy clinical practice in the early years of music therapy as a profession in the United States was based on a behavioral approach. It was natural that the research would have been congruent with that philosophy, and music therapists adopted quantitative methods in their research practices.

According to Aigen (2008a, 2008b), qualitative research in music therapy emerged in the 1980s due in large part to music therapists' identification of a need for research that was directly relevant to clinical practice. This history will be presented here as a three-stage process which, of course, is still in the process of developing[4]: (a) exploration of qualitative methods for music therapy research; (b) qualitative or interpretivist research as a defined means of inquiry in music therapy; and (c) rapprochement and working together of research methods.

Exploration of Qualitative Methods for Music Therapy Research. In the mid-1980s, music therapists in the United States were looking for a means of studying music therapy that could capture important aspects of the music therapy experience. They searched for means of doing research that were congruent with clinical work and could capture and explore important aspects of music therapy clinical work. An early study took place in 1982, when Kenneth Bruscia used his own autobiography as the primary source of data for a study called "Music in the Life of One Man: Ontogenetic Foundations for Music Therapy" (Forinash & Kenny, 2015). Carolyn Kenny's (1987) doctoral dissertation, *The Field of Play: A Theoretical Study of Music Therapy Process,* was an early major qualitative investigation, and Kenneth Aigen's (1991) doctoral dissertation, *The Roots of Music Therapy: Towards an Indigenous Research Paradigm,* provided a comprehensive exploration of the need for a new approach and how it fit with music therapy clinical practice. In his dissertation, Aigen considers historical influences on music therapy research from the philosophy and theory of science and describes the critique of what he calls *the received view* from a position of process, clinical realities, creativity, and research methodologies.

An international symposium titled *Music in the Life of Man* was organized by Barbara Hesser at New York University in 1982 (Forinash & Kenny, 2015). This symposium brought music therapists from around the world together, according to the invitation, to "probe deeply into the musical experience and its effects on our bodies, minds, and spirits." This symposium was an important to the development of qualitative research in music therapy, as it provided an opportunity for those attending to consider how to study music in the life of man, including the use of qualitative methods. As a participant in the symposium, I (Barbara Wheeler) can attest to the excitement of exploring these *new* approaches to research, which few of us in the United States had previously considered. According to Even Ruud, Norwegian music therapy leader (personal communication, April 22, 2014), "To my knowledge, we [Europeans] had no qualitative research prior to 1982. This concept was as far as I know not introduced to music therapy. However, we had a lot of theoretical/historical/philosophical writing, but it was not socially or empirically based." An additional outcome of the symposium was that the communication between U.S. music therapists and their European colleagues expanded greatly after this time.

Qualitative Research as a Defined Means of Inquiry in Music Therapy. Following the events and writing that brought qualitative research to the attention of music therapists, a period of activity in music therapy qualitative research ensued. The advantages of qualitative research in speaking to clinical practice and reflecting the experience of music therapists and clients, and the additional ways of investigating music therapy that this research opened up, helped to nurture this development. This occurred due to several developments, including the increased international communication among researchers after the 1982 NYU symposium described above. One of these was a series of symposia organized by Mechtild Jahn-Langenberg, beginning with The First International Symposium for Qualitative Research in Music Therapy in Düsseldorf, Germany, in 1994, which brought qualitative researchers together. An outgrowth

of this symposium was *Qualitative Music Therapy Research: Beginning Dialogues,* edited by Langenberg, Aigen, and Frommer (1996). Several other symposia, organized by Dr. Langenberg after she had moved to the Berlin University of the Arts (Universität der Künste Berlin), that brought qualitative researchers together played an important role in the communication about qualitative research in music therapy and its development. These occurred every few years until 2007 and were important in increasing communication among music therapy qualitative researchers as well as helping them to work out issues surrounding the research (see Merrill, 2002, and Edwards, 2004, for reports on the 2002 and 2004 symposia, respectively).

This period also brought increasing venues for the publication of qualitative music therapy research. Several content analyses of journal articles shed light on where interpretivist research is published and on other aspects of its publication. Brooks (2003) examined articles from nine music therapy journals over a 37-year period, from the time that they were first published until 2001, looking for trends and types of article and comparing them across journals. The number of articles published in each of these journals was, of course, related to the length of time that the journal had been published and the number of issues a year. She said:

> The publication rate of qualitative ... articles has grown fairly steadily and significantly since about 1985. Ninety-eight (98) qualitative research articles were included in this study. Qualitative research publications were most prevalent in the *Nordic Journal of Music Therapy* (21), the *British Journal of Music Therapy* (18), *Music Therapy: Journal of the American Association for Music Therapy* (17), and the *Journal of the Association for Music and Imagery* (11). (p. 159)

To examine more recent trends in the publication of qualitative research, I counted qualitative/interpretivist research articles in music therapy journals from 2010 through 2015. The results are summarized in Table 1, with a total of 107 interpretivist research articles. This is a large increase from Brooks' (2003) tally, which covered many more years for a total of 98 qualitative articles. Some of the articles were classified as mixed methods; they are included in the tallies of interpretivist articles. (In addition to studies that I determined to be interpretivist, studies labeled by the authors as either qualitative or mixed methods were included in these numbers; I did not make any judgment as to whether I agreed with those classifications.)

A special issue of the *Journal of Music Therapy,* published in Fall 1998 and edited by Michele Forinash and Colin Lee, focused on qualitative research, with additional qualitative research articles in succeeding issues of the journal. This was intended to increase awareness of qualitative research, although there was continued concern that not enough

Journal Name (journals are listed in order of total number of articles published per year)	Total number of articles	Number of interpretivist research articles	Percentage of interpretivist research articles (from total articles in journal, excluding editorials and book reviews)	Number and percentage of mixed methods studies (included in number and percentages of interpretivist articles)
Journal of Music Therapy	110	12	11%	2 (2%)
Music Therapy Perspectives	99	12	12%	1 (1%)
Arts in Psychotherapy*	76	21	28%	7 (9%)
Nordic Journal of Music Therapy	73	26	36%	1 (1%)
British Journal of Music Therapy	34	8	24%	1 (3%)
Australian Journal of Music Therapy	32	11	34%	3 (9%)
Canadian Journal of Music Therapy	31	10	32%	3 (9%)
NZ Journal of Music Therapy	19	8	42%	1 (5%)

* Only music therapy articles in *Arts in Psychotherapy* were counted; articles about other disciplines were not included.

Table 1. Qualitative/Interpretivist Research Published, 2010–2015

qualitative research was published in the *Journal of Music Therapy.*

A monograph series published by Barcelona Publishers since 2004, *Qualitative Monographs in Music Therapy,* focuses exclusively on qualitative research and has included a total of 38 qualitative monographs as of Volume 10, published in 2015.

Aigen examined qualitative articles and chapters (2008a) and qualitative dissertations (2008b) published from 1987–2006. He found 92 articles and book chapters, 55 doctoral studies, and six books to have been published during that period. In the period from 1987–1990, two articles and chapters and two dissertations (or doctoral theses) were published; from 1991–1994, five articles and chapters and seven dissertations; from 1995–1998, 20 articles and chapters and seven dissertations; from 1999–2002, 31 articles and chapters and 13 dissertations; and from 2003–2006, 34 articles and chapters and 23 dissertations. This clearly represents a large increase in qualitative research in music therapy, beginning in the mid-1990s. Aigen (2008a) found grounded theory, phenomenology, and naturalistic inquiry to be the most frequently used qualitative research methods in music therapy. Most of the dissertations done by students in the Doctor of Arts (DA) program at New York University were of qualitative research while, at the same time, a number of qualitative research studies were done at Temple University and Aalborg University. Students from some other universities also produced qualitative research dissertations and theses.

Some of the growth of interpretivist research in music therapy is reflected in changes in the current book. The first edition of this book, *Music Therapy Research: Quantitative and Qualitative Perspectives* (Wheeler, 1995), was one of the first

music therapy sources to classify quantitative and qualitative research as two distinct types of research. That book included an overview of qualitative research, chapters on topics and several chapters on the process of doing qualitative research, and two chapters on methods of qualitative research: interpretational and phenomenological. The second edition, *Music Therapy Research* (Wheeler, 2005), also included an overview and chapters on topics and methods, plus 12 chapters on methods: phenomenological, hermeneutic, naturalistic, first-person, ethnography and ethnographically informed, participatory action, morphological, qualitative case study, and arts-based research; grounded theory; narrative inquiry; and personal construct psychology and the repertory-grid technique. Clearly, these changes reflect decisions by the editor and authors as well as changes in the landscape of qualitative research, but they provide indications of its evolution in music therapy. This edition of *Music Therapy Research,* the third, focuses on interpretivist research (closely related to qualitative research but with some changes, as discussed in this chapter) and includes 17 methods: ethnographic research, naturalistic inquiry, action research, phenomenological inquiry, first-person research, hermeneutic inquiry, critical inquiries: feminist perspectives and transformative research, arts-based research, morphological research, discourse analysis, qualitative content analysis, narrative inquiry, grounded theory, personal construct psychology and the Repertory Grid Technique, consensual qualitative resaerch, thematic analysis, and interpretivist case study research.

Rapprochement and Working Together of Research Methods. As interpretivist music therapy research continues to develop, researchers are also grappling with emerging challenges of how interpretivist research can or should be included as part of evidence-based practice (EBP). Because of this issue and other developments, reflexive synthesis is being explored and developed and is providing one avenue of contributing to EBP. Reflexive synthesis systematically reviews and formally integrates findings and reports from various qualitative studies (Sandelowski & Barroso, 2007). It makes it possible for these studies to be considered and integrated into systematic reviews, thus contributing to EBP. Qualitative or interpretivist researchers are also joining with quantitative researchers to develop mixed methods designs to study problems using both perspectives. These developments in the way that music therapy research is viewed and used will continue to change interpretivist music therapy research.

Features of Interpretivist Research

Patton (2002) has described design strategies, data collection and field characteristics, and analysis strategies of qualitative inquiry. These all apply to music therapy research, with a reminder from Bruscia (2005a):

> Qualitative research is intrinsically a developmental process … a complex process that unfolds moment to moment, proceeding one step at a time with each step flowing unpredictably from the previous one and leading just as unpredictably to the next step. While such a process can appear to the outsider as rather serendipitous or arbitrary, in reality, qualitative research unfolds in quite an orderly, developmental way. … The real challenge of doing qualitative research is not so much in the *doing* as it is in the *being*. To do qualitative research, one must be a qualitative researcher. Qualitative research is not a method to be mastered—it is an approach to human inquiry and discovery that can only emerge from a particular way of being in the world. (pp. 136–137)

Design Strategies

Several general characteristics apply to the design of interpretivist research. These include naturalistic inquiry, an emergent design flexibility, and purposeful sampling.

Naturalistic Inquiry. Much interpretivist research takes place in natural or real-world settings, where the researcher does not attempt to manipulate or change the situation or phenomenon of interest. By occurring in a natural setting, the research is done on the same events and interactions that the researcher wishes to study. This is in contrast to some types of quantitative or objectivist research in which the variables of interest are manipulated and which must be done outside of the natural setting. Even interpretivist research that does not occur in a completely natural setting, such as interviews about one's experience of a phenomenon, attempts to capture the normally occurring thoughts, feelings, and interactions of the participants.

This means that music therapy clients and sessions may be studied as they are occurring and in the places where they naturally occur, rather than being re-created in a laboratory or experimental session. Interpretivist researchers in music therapy believe that this ability to study music therapy as it occurs makes the research relevant to what music therapists actually do. One of many examples of naturalistic inquiry is Turry's (2010) account of the naturalistic inquiry process in his study of song improvisations co-created with a female adult client who had been diagnosed with non-Hodgkin's lymphoma within the context of a Nordoff-Robbins music therapy session.

Emergent Design Flexibility. An important aspect of interpretivist research is that its design is not set and inflexible and may change based on the information that emerges and what the researcher learns during the research process. The researcher pursues new areas as they emerge so that the research evolves, taking advantage of what is learned in its earlier stages.

In music therapy research, this means that the researcher can take into account client and therapist responses as the research progresses and adjust the design accordingly. There may be an instance, for example, in which client responses that were unexpected emerge during the research process, and the researcher will therefore decide to move the research in the direction of the new material, either in addition to or in place of the previous focus. Aigen (1995) describes a time in his research on the process of a music therapy group in which he decided to add interviews with the music therapists as an additional means of gathering data for his research; this decision was made partway through the research in response to the needs of the research.

Purposeful Sampling. In purposeful sampling, research participants are selected because of what their study may bring to the research question, not because they are necessarily typical of the group being studied. The purpose of selecting participants is not, therefore, so that the results may be generalized (as in quantitative experimental studies), but instead because there are things that can be learned from studying them.

Rather than using typical music therapy clients in a study, the interpretivist music therapy researcher may select clients who have shown particular benefits from the music therapy. Similarly, the choice might be made to study a therapist who brings a unique perspective or specific strengths to the therapy situation, even though this person is not considered to be a typical therapist. The information gleaned from the research is not expected to apply to all similar situations, but instead is valued for what it can show about the instance under study. Two examples of from the music therapy literature are Wheeler and Baker's (2010) selection of participants from a variety of countries, all of whom had both practiced clinically and taught music therapy in at least two different countries, and Zanders' (2012) selection of participants using a "purposive approach in order to (a) maximize heterogeneity in the sample with regard to presenting problems and past experiences (e.g., trauma, abuse, bereavement, etc.) and (b) create clusters of similar presenting problems and past experiences with foster care placements" (p. 79).

Data Collection and Fieldwork Strategies

Data collection and fieldwork strategies commonly used in interpretivist research include the use of qualitative data, the importance of personal experience and engagement, reliance upon empathic neutrality and mindfulness, and an acknowledgment that systems are dynamic.

Qualitative Data. Patton (2002) summarized qualitative data as "observations that yield detailed, thick description; inquiry in depth; interviews that capture direct quotations about people's personal perspectives and experiences; case studies; careful document review" (p. 40). There are many examples of detailed descriptions of the situation under investigation and quotations from the participants in music therapy interpretivist research. One is from *Playin' in the Band* (Aigen, 2002), a case study of a 7½-year music therapy experience with an adult who had developmental delays and was nonverbal, through which Aigen illustrates the use of improvisation in popular music styles. Aigen includes video segments of many musical examples, coordinated with descriptions in the book, one of which follows:

> The improvisation based on *Get Back* begins to near a musical climax unusual in Lloyd's sessions. Lloyd stops, looks at Alan, who also stops, then looks down at his guitar and resumes strumming as Alan resumes playing. One minute and twenty seconds into the excerpt, we attempt to establish a "stop" rhythm. This rhythmic feel is stylistically related to the stop accents, but adds syncopation to them and builds a novel rhythmic feel based on these stops. This music is too jarring for Lloyd and he leaves the therapy room. (p. 41)

Personal Experience and Engagement. The interpretivist researcher conducts the research largely through personal experience and engagement. Topics, areas of focus, and data for the research come largely from personal experiences. The researcher conducting the study becomes engaged with the participants, often going into the setting where they live or work and actually participating with them. These features,

personal involvement and engagement, are part of the essence of interpretivist research, which is intended to involve participants as fully and humanly as possible.

There are many examples of personal experience and engagement in the music therapy research. One is the statement by Jackson and Gardstrom (2012):

> Our interest in this research topic stems from our own experiences as students in experiential learning exercises during undergraduate and graduate music therapy training and as clients in individual and group verbal and music psychotherapy. Both of these types of experiences have assisted in the development [of] our skills, but personal therapy has helped us to understand clinical processes more clearly, trust musical processes more deeply, develop greater insight into our own and others' emotional lives, and expand our capacity for empathy. Our ability to practice effectively and ethically is, in large measure, connected to our engagement as clients in personal therapy. (p. 66)

Empathic Neutrality and Mindfulness. The interpretivist researcher works to be empathic but not judgmental while conducting the research. In addition, the researcher strives to be fully present when observing or interviewing. These help in conducting research in an intentional, thoughtful manner that builds upon the researcher's relationship with the participants, while still allowing him or her to maintain the distance necessary to conduct the research in a trustworthy manner.

This was important in Wheeler's (2002) study of music therapy students' experiences of music therapy practicums. As she interviewed music therapy students to learn their perceptions, it was important to be able to listen, without judging, to what the students said. Since some of the students' perceptions were quite different from what Wheeler, as a faculty member, had anticipated, this ability to be empathic but not judgmental was important.

Dynamic Systems. Interpretivist researchers acknowledge the ever-changing nature of systems and attempt to build protocols into the research design that monitor these dynamics, enabling a shift in protocols as required. Interpretivist research does not assume that things can remain static long enough to predict the continuing relevance of a set of protocols throughout the research, hence the research process must constantly adjust to these changes.

Aigen (1991, 1993) advocated for qualitative research as most appropriate for studying music therapy because it allows the researcher to examine *process*, which Aigen suggests is important in music therapy practice and cannot be studied through quantitative methods. The process that Bullard (2011) employed in her study of music therapy as an intervention for inpatient treatment of suicidal ideation is an example of this. She says, "Due to high turnover rates and often sudden discharge of patients, the sampling emerged as the study progressed and was not preselected" (p. 84). Grounded theory studies in which recruitment takes place until saturation of the data occurs are another example of taking account of changing dynamics. O'Callaghan et al. (2014) recruited 52 patients for a study examining adult cancer patients' views of the role of music before and after diagnosis. O'Callaghan reports recruiting a diverse range of people, but that the data are still not saturated (C. O'Callaghan, personal communication, June 10, 2014).

Analysis Strategies

Some analysis strategies are important in interpretivist research. These include treating each case as unique, employing inductive analysis and creative synthesis, taking a holistic perspective, being sensitive to context, and being mindful of the researcher's voice and perspective and the need for reflexivity in the research. These are all connected, as the findings are based on what emerges based on the researcher's reflection.

Unique Case Orientation. Each case is unique and important in interpretivist research, and thus the interpretivist researcher analyzes and strives to understand each case. Comparisons are made only after careful understanding of the individual cases.

There are many examples of this in the music therapy research, where the researcher begins by understanding the individuals in the study and then later makes comparisons in an effort to form categories or draw conclusions. One example of this is Jackson's (2010) study of models of response to client anger in music therapy. She had collected data through questionnaires from 29 participants. Each of these "was examined as a single case with the intent of developing a phenomenological description that allowed for deeper understanding of the individual experiences and responses of the participant" (p. 48). Jackson read each participant's responses many times, and notes were made. She then formed the responses of each participant into a descriptive narrative, "using as many of the participant's own words as possible and reflecting my understanding of the event" (p. 48). She then received feedback from the participants and incorporated any changes into the narrative. She continued this process until each participant felt that the narrative fully represented his or her experience of the event that had been described. Jackson followed additional steps to make further sense of the data, but all were based on this initial understanding of the individual responses of each participant.

Inductive Analysis and Creative Synthesis. The process of analyzing data for interpretivist research generally requires the researcher to immerse him- or herself in the data, looking for patterns, themes, and relationships. There are few rules for this process, and the researcher must depend largely on his or her own ability to see these patterns. The process is guided by the principles underlying the research approach being used.

There are numerous examples of researchers' use of these strategies in interpretivist music therapy research. One example is Bruscia's (1995) study in which he sought to understand the music therapist's experience of *being there* for his client. Through his analysis of a Guided Imagery and Music (GIM) session, Bruscia discovered three experiential spaces and four levels of experience through which he moved his consciousness in the process of guiding a session. The procedures that he used in the research, and which he outlines in his article, involved inductive analysis and creative synthesis, as described here.

Holistic Perspective. Interpretivist research studies its subjects from a holistic perspective. Interpretivist researchers are skeptical about laboratory studies that attempt to isolate variables in human experience and reason that it is virtually impossible to account for all potential variables because of the complexity of the referential totality of contexts. Although the phenomenon under study may be observed in pieces for some aspects of study and analysis, "the whole phenomenon under study is understood as a complex system that is more than the sum of its parts" (Patton, 2002, p. 41). This emphasis on the whole is an important feature of interpretivist research.

Music therapy researchers who have specifically focused on gaining a holistic perspective include Murphy (2007), who studied experiential learning using a case study approach, which "was taken in order provide an 'intensive, holistic description and analysis of a single entity, phenomenon or social unit'" (p. 34) and Wheeler (1999), who studied the experience of pleasure when working with children with multiple severe disabilities and "wanted to get as broad and holistic a description of this experience as possible, then look for underlying themes" (p. 61).

Context Sensitivity. One of the principles of interpretive research is that each situation is unique, and there is no possibility of generalization from one setting to another. When the results of interpretivist research are applied to other areas, it is because of an understanding of the case that was presented, and thus an ability to apply it to a similar setting. Because of this, interpretivist researchers are very sensitive to the context in which the observations and research occur.

In Wheeler and Baker's (2010) study of how people's worldviews influence their clinical work and teaching, one participant cautioned that her perceptions should not be applied to others from her country. This participant's reminder reinforced the understanding in interpretivist research that each situation is unique.

Voice, Perspective, and Reflexivity. The interpretivist researcher recognizes that the experiences being investigated are seen through the researcher's eyes and heard through the researcher's ears, and thus are shared in the researcher's voice. Through reflexivity, the researcher maintains an awareness of these issues and takes steps to present the research fairly and as reflecting the researcher's perspective. One of the ways that interpretivist researchers own their research is by what may be called the *stance of the researcher,* an *epoché,* or a *self-hermeneutic,* in which the researcher shares who he or she is in relation to the research, including the motivation for the research, prior ideas about probable results, and other things that might affect his or her perspective on the research. It is hoped that by stating these aspects clearly, the researcher can work to keep them from unduly influencing the research.

Reflexivity is central to the conception of interpretivist research. The researcher must reflect on all aspects of the process, and the findings emerge based on the data, context, and analytic strategy. The information from Jackson and Gardstrom's (2012) study presented earlier, in which they shared past experiences that had led to their interest in experiential music therapy training, is an example of sharing information as part of this process of reflection. The material that was described there was labeled as an epoché.

Conclusion

Interpretivist research aims to explore a phenomenon as it unfolds and reveals itself during a study. Interpretivist researchers assume that there are multiple realities and that people construct reality as they interpret their experiences of and in the world, so that our knowledge is grounded in our unique experiences.

Although music therapists have used elements of interpretivist research since the early years of music therapy, it emerged with specific methods in the 1980s, and music therapists find it useful in investigating aspects of music therapy that cannot be studied satisfactorily through other means. It is now a recognized means of investigation in music therapy, and the number of interpretivist studies in journals worldwide is increasing. Some recent publications use mixed methods, combining interpretivist and objectivist methods.

Acknowledgments

The author thanks Carolyn Kenny for her contribution through the chapter "Principles of Qualitative Research" by B. L. Wheeler and C. Kenny in the previous edition of this book and Anthony Meadows, Kenneth Bruscia, and James Hiller for feedback on the current chapter.

References

Aigen, K. (1991). The roots of music therapy: Towards an indigenous research paradigm (Doctoral dissertation, New York University, 1990). *Dissertation Abstracts International, 52*(6), 1933A. (UMI No. DEY91–34717)

Aigen, K. (1993). The music therapist as qualitative researcher. *Music Therapy, 12,* 16–39. doi:10.1093/mt/12.1.16

Aigen, K. (1995). Principles of qualitative research. In B. L. Wheeler (Ed.), *Music therapy research: Quantitative and qualitative perspectives* (pp. 283–311). Gilsum, NH: Barcelona.

Aigen, K. (2002). *Playin' in the band: A qualitative study of popular music styles as clinical improvisation.* New York, NY: Nordoff-Robbins Center for Music Therapy.

Aigen, K. (2008a). An analysis of qualitative music therapy research reports 1987–2006: Articles and book chapters. *Arts in Psychotherapy, 35*(4), 251–261. doi:10.1016/j.aip.2008.06.001

Aigen, K. (2008b). An analysis of qualitative music therapy research reports 1987–2006: Doctoral studies. *Arts in Psychotherapy, 35*(5), 307–319. doi:10.1016/j.aip.2008.06.001

Brooks, D. (2003). A history of music therapy journal articles published in the English language. *Journal of Music Therapy, 40*(2), 151–168. doi:10.1093/jmt/40.2.151

Bruscia, K. E. (1995). Modes of consciousness in Guided Imagery and Music (GIM): A therapist's experience of the guiding process. In C. B. Kenny (Ed.), *Listening, playing, creating: Essays on the power of sound* (pp. 165–197). Albany, NY: State University of New York Press.

Bruscia, K. E. (2005a). Designing qualitative research. In B. L. Wheeler (Ed.), *Music therapy research* (pp. 129–137). Gilsum, NH: Barcelona.

Bruscia, K. E. (2005b). Research topics and questions in music therapy. In B. L. Wheeler (Ed.), *Music therapy research* (pp. 81–93). Gilsum, NH: Barcelona.

Bullard, E. (2011). Music therapy as an intervention for inpatient treatment of suicidal ideation. *Qualitative Inquiries in Music Therapy, 6,* 75–121.

Creswell, J. (2013). *Qualitative inquiry & research design: Choosing among five approaches* (3rd ed.). Los Angeles, CA: Sage.

Crotty, M. (1998). *The foundations of social research.* Thousand Oaks, CA: Sage.

Denzin, N. K., & Lincoln, Y. S. (2000). Introduction: The discipline and practice of qualitative research. In N. K. Denzin & Y. S. Lincoln (Eds.), *Sage handbook of qualitative research* (2nd ed., pp. 1–28). Thousand Oaks, CA: Sage.

Denzin, N. K., & Lincoln, Y. S. (2011). Introduction: The discipline and practice of qualitative research. In N. K. Denzin & Y. S. Lincoln (Eds.), *Sage handbook of qualitative research* (4th ed., pp. 1–19). Thousand Oaks, CA: Sage.

Edwards, J. (2004). Report of the 5th International Symposium for Qualitative Music Therapy Research. *Music Therapy Perspectives, 22*(2), 116–117. doi:10.1093/mtp/22.2.116

Forinash, M., & Kenny, C. (2015). *The 1982 Symposium on "Music in the Life of Man": The beginnings of music therapy theory.* Dallas, TX: Barcelona.

Gaston, E. T. (1968). (Ed.). *Music in therapy.* New York, NY: Macmillan.

Geertz, C. (1983). Blurred genres: The reconfiguration of social thought. In C. Geertz, *Local knowledge: Further essays in interpretive anthropology* (pp. 19–35). New York, NY: Basic Books.

Glaser, B., & Strauss, A. (1967). *The discovery of grounded theory.* Chicago, IL: Aldine.

Jackson, N. A. (2010). Models of response to client anger in music therapy. *Arts in Psychotherapy, 37*(1), 46–55. doi:10.1016/j.aip.2009.09.006

Jackson, N. A., & Gardstrom, S. C. (2012). Undergraduate music therapy students' experiences as clients in short-term group music therapy. *Music Therapy Perspectives, 30*(1), 65–82. doi:10.1093/mtp/30.1.65

Kenny, C. (1987). The field of play: A theoretical study of music therapy process. (Doctoral dissertation, The Fielding Institute, 1987). *Dissertation Abstracts International, 48*(12), 3067A. (UMI No. DEV88–02367)

Langenberg, M., Aigen, K., & Frommer, J. (Eds.). (1996). *Qualitative music therapy research: Beginning dialogues.* Gilsum, NH: Barcelona.

Lincoln, Y. S., & Denzin, N. K. (2008). Epilogue: The Eighth and Ninth Moments—Qualitative research in/and the fractured future. In N. K. Denzin & Y. S. Lincoln (Eds.), *The landscape of qualitative research* (pp. 539–554). Thousand Oaks, CA: Sage.

Marshall, C., & Rossman, G. B. (2011). *Designing qualitative research* (5th ed.). Thousand Oaks, CA: Sage.

Merrill, T. R. (2002). Beginner's mind: Personal reflections on the Fourth International Symposium on Qualitative Music Therapy Research. *Nordic Journal of Music Therapy, 11,* 61–64. doi:10.1080/08098130209478-47.

Morrow, S. L. (2005). Quality and trustworthiness in qualitative research in counseling psychology. *Journal of Counseling Psychology, 52*(2), 250–260. doi:10.1037/0022-0167.52.2.250

Murphy, K. (2007). Experiential learning in music therapy: Faculty and student perspectives. *Qualitative Inquiries in Music Therapy, 3,* 31–61.

Nelson, C., Treichler, P. A., & Grossberg, L. (1992). Cultural studies. In L. Grossberg, C. Nelson, & P. A. Treichler (Eds.), *Cultural studies* (pp. 1–16). New York, NY: Routledge.

Nordoff, P., & Robbins, C. (1971). *Therapy in music for handicapped children.* New York, NY: St. Martin's Press.

Nordoff, P., & Robbins, C. (1977). *Creative Music Therapy.* New York: John Day.

O'Callaghan, C., McDermott, F., Michael, N., Daveson, B. A., Hudson, P. L., & Zalcberg, J. R. (2014). "A quiet still voice that just touches": Music's relevance for adults living with life-threatening cancer diagnoses. *Support Care Cancer, 22*(4), 1037–1047. doi:10.1007/S00520–013–2059–1

Onwuegbuzie, A. J., Leech, N. L., & Collins, K. M. T. (2010). Innovative data collection strategies in qualitative research. *The Qualitative Report, 15*(3), 696–726.

Pascale, C. M. (2011). *Cartographies of knowledge.* Thousand Oaks, CA: Sage.

Patton, M. Q. (2002). *Qualitative research and evaluation methods* (3rd ed.). Thousand Oaks, CA: Sage.

Sandelowski, M., & Barroso, J. (2007). *Handbook for synthesizing qualitative research.* New York, NY: Springer.

Turry, A. (2010). Integrating musical and psychotherapeutic thinking: Research on the relationship between words and music in clinically improvised songs. *Qualitative Inquiries in Music Therapy, 5,* 116–172.

Wheeler, B. L. (1995). (Ed.). *Music therapy research: Quantitative and qualitative perspectives.* Gilsum, NH: Barcelona.

Wheeler, B. L. (1999). Experiencing pleasure in working with severely disabled children. *Journal of Music Therapy, 36*(1), 56–80. doi:10.1093/jmt/36.1.56

Wheeler, B. L. (2002). Experiences and concerns of students during music therapy practica. *Journal of Music Therapy, 39*(4), 274–304. doi:10.1093/jmt/39.4.274

Wheeler, B. L. (Ed.). (2005). *Music therapy research* (2nd ed.). Gilsum, NH: Barcelona.

Wheeler, B. L., & Baker, F. (2010). Influences of music therapists' worldviews on work in different countries. *Arts in Psychotherapy, 37*(3), 215–227. doi:10.1016/j.aip.2010.04.006

Zanders, M. (2012). The musical and personal biographies of adolescents with foster care experience. *Qualitative Inquiries in Music Therapy, 7,* 71–109.

1. Portions of this chapter are based on "Principles of Qualitative Research" by B. L. Wheeler & C. Kenny, in B. L. Wheeler (Ed.), *Music Therapy Research* (2nd ed.; pp. 59–71). Gilsum, NH: Barcelona.

2. Creswell (2013) provides an overview of what he calls a "baffling number of choices of approaches" (p. 7).

3. The author is grateful to James Hiller for sharing his work and writing on epistemology and its relationship to music therapy interpretivist research. The material presented here is based on what he wrote and has kindly shared.

4. The perspective on the development of qualitative research in music therapy that is presented here is based on the author's experience as an attendee at the *Music in the Life of Man* Symposium and involvement in developments of qualitative music therapy research that followed. It is also influenced by feedback from Anthony Meadows, who suggested the three stages in the development of music therapy qualitative research that are presented here.

Chapter 10

OVERVIEW OF MEASUREMENT ISSUES IN OBJECTIVIST RESEARCH

Eric G. Waldon

While all research involves some form of data collection, objectivist approaches employ methods, instruments, or devices to obtain a quantitative index of the characteristics under investigation. Because results and subsequent conclusions are based on these numeric outcomes, it becomes particularly important to consider the nature and overall quality of measures used in data collection. The purpose of this chapter is to assist in identifying relevant, quality measures that can address objectivist research questions. After defining key terms involved in objectivist measurement, general principles regarding the selection of measures will be presented. The technical adequacy of measures will follow and will include discussion on reliability, validity, and helpful resources for identifying appropriate research measures. Levels of measurement (nominal, ordinal, interval, and ratio) and commonly encountered measurement items in music therapy research will conclude this chapter. After reading this chapter, you should be better equipped to select, evaluate, and ultimately employ multiple methods of data collection within an objectivist paradigm.

Key Measurement Terms

According to Stevens (1946), "*measurement* [emphasis added], in the broadest sense, is defined as the assignment of numerals to objects or events according to rules" (p. 677). Given this definition, when encountering the term *measure*, one can assume that a quantity (number) has been recorded that represents the construct under investigation.

A *construct* is a hypothetical concept or phenomenon (e.g., intelligence, depression, ability, or dysfunction) that cannot be observed directly. Therefore, one must infer the relative presence or absence of the construct through a measurable and observable event (e.g., a test score, questionnaire response, participant verbalization, or behavior observation). For example, while one cannot directly observe musical aptitude (a concept referring to a person's musical potential), one may use a specific test (e.g., Gordon's Musical Aptitude Profile [MAP]) as a means of inferring the extent to which one possesses the construct of musical aptitude. Similarly, an investigator may be interested in studying the effects of a music-based intervention on disruptive behavior. In this case, a researcher would need to clearly define the construct (disruptive behavior) in a specific, observable, and measurable manner (e.g., frequency of speaking without permission, amount of time out of seat when directed to

remain in the seat) to precisely quantify the relative presence or absence of the phenomenon. The process of defining the ways in which a construct is measured, whether it is a test or behavioral observation, is called *operationalization*. An *operational definition* (the product of operationalization) is a description of a specific event, process, or behavior in a manner allowing others to independently measure, test, or observe it consistently.

Instrument is a general term used to describe the methods (e.g., observational techniques or interviews) or devices (e.g., tests or questionnaires) used in objectivist data collection. The term *instrumentation* is commonly used in research reports to describe the measurement procedures employed in objectivist research studies, including the technical aspects (e.g., reliability and validity) of those measurement methods. Frequently, instrumentation sections in a research summary will describe the procedures or tools used to collect data or, in the case of behavioral observations, response definitions that delineate the behavior being studied.

Test refers to "any device used to evaluate behavior or performance of a person" (Aiken, 1997, p. 474). All tests employ a structured format, examination, or performance situation from which a measurement is obtained to make inferences about the extent to which the examinee (research participant) evidences that particular characteristic. There are several types of psychological and educational tests (aptitude, personality, and achievement tests), the titles of which usually include a descriptor alluding to the constructs they purport to measure (e.g., the aforementioned MAP). Medical and physiological tests may also fall under this category, although the titles of these tests do not as clearly allude to the phenomena being measured (e.g., positron emission tomography [PET]). It is important to note that the demarcations between the terms *measure*, *instrument*, and *test* are negligible, and, in practice, they may be used interchangeably in research reports.

Measurement: Evaluating Technical Adequacy

One of the responsibilities in objectivist research is assuring the technical adequacy of measures used in data collection. In short, optimal objectivist measures are those that yield reliable measurements from which valid inferences are drawn. This is an important consideration for researchers because high-quality measurement is more likely to lend credibility to any field's body of scientific evidence.

Fortunately, there are a variety of ways in which the adequacy of measures can be gauged or evaluated.

Reliability

Reliability is the extent to which a measurement consistently measures a given construct on multiple occasions, assuming that there is no change in the underlying phenomenon being studied. Taking a straightforward example, suppose a researcher administered a measure of cognitive ability (a construct considered relatively constant) on two occasions, 1 week apart. If that measure were reliable, one would expect to receive similar (if not identical) scores on those two testing occasions. However, if those scores were radically different, then the presence of *measurement error* (that which the researcher does not intend to measure) is suspected. Therefore, reliability is a gauge of how free a measure is from error: The higher the reliability, the lower the error.

According to classical measurement theory, whenever a measurement is taken, that *obtained score* contains an amount of *true score* variance and *error score* variance (Coleman, 2009). According to Geisinger (2013), psychometricians define true score as "the score an individual would theoretically achieve on a perfectly accurate test" (p. 22). Conceptually, the obtained score, true score, and error score are explained by the following:

$$\text{Obtained Score} = \text{True Score} + \text{Error Score}$$

Geisinger goes on to explain that perfect measurement is not possible because all measurement is subject to some amount of error variance. Error score variance originates from: fluctuating participant characteristics (e.g., inattentiveness, guessing, or motivation), measurement characteristics (e.g., ambiguous test items, confusing directions), and administration or scoring irregularities (e.g., nonstandard administration of the measure, computational errors). Psychometrically speaking, the objective of determining reliability is to minimize error, thereby raising the overall precision of measurement.

Reliability coefficients are used to describe the degree to which a set of scores is reliable and, therefore, free from error. Typically, reliability is calculated using a simple regression (r) whereby one set of scores is correlated with another set of scores obtained from the same group. (Note: Not all reliability coefficients are based on correlation; an example of one that is not is interrater reliability.) These coefficients range in value from 0.00 to 1.00 and represent the ratio of true score variance to total (observed) score variance:

$$\text{Reliability } (r) = \frac{\text{True Score Variance}}{\text{Total (Observed) Score Variance}}$$

The closer a reliability coefficient approaches 1.00, the higher the reliability; the closer a value approaches 0.00, the lower the reliability. Pragmatically, one can interpret the amount of true score present in a variable simply by looking at the reliability coefficient. For example, a reliability coefficient of $r = 0.80$ indicates that 80% of a measure is due to true score variability, with the residual variance attributed to error.

Test–Retest Reliability. There are several methods for evaluating the reliability (or precision) of a given measure. The first, *test–retest reliability,* involves administering the same measure on two occasions in order to obtain an estimate of stability. Test–retest reliability is appropriate when examining the consistency of traits that are relatively stable over time. The cognitive ability example discussed previously is an example of this type of reliability.

Alternate Forms Reliability. The next estimate of reliability uses the *alternate forms* method (sometimes referred to as *parallel forms* method), which provides an estimate of equivalence. This approach to reliability is important in situations when two forms (e.g., Form A and Form B) of the same measure are used. For example, a researcher wanting to administer a measure on two occasions may be interested in using a test with alternate, yet equivalent, forms to reduce the deleterious consequences of pretesting or practice effects. In this case, the researcher would want to be confident that the scores yielded from the two forms of the test are equivalent.

Internal Consistency. *Internal consistency* methods are important when multiple items within a single measure are used to measure a particular construct. These methods estimate the extent to which responses measuring one trait are consistent with other items purportedly measuring the same trait. Unlike the previous two methods of reliability, internal consistency approaches require only a single test administration, because the specific techniques used to judge consistency (e.g., Kuder-Richardson formula, Cronbach's α, and split-half techniques) compare all possible combinations of a single measure's items. This approach to reliability can be particularly useful when researchers develop surveys or questionnaires for their studies, as it allows them to retain, revise, or remove test items that reduce the instrument's overall precision (see Fishman & Galguera, 2003).

Interrater Reliability. The last approach to reliability discussed here, *interrater reliability,* involves reliability based on agreement (although Geisinger [2003] argues that reliability based on agreement is another form of internal consistency). Other names commonly associated with this form of reliability include interscorer agreement, concordance, and interobserver reliability. Unlike other methods, interrater reliability estimates can be computed using either correlation (e.g., intraclass correlation, Pearson's r, Spearman's ρ) or percentage of agreement. The following is an example of the latter (see Araujo & Born, 1985):

$$\% \text{ Agreement} = \frac{\text{Agreements}}{\text{Agreements} + \text{Diagreements}} \times 100\%$$

This form of reliability is relevant for measurements involving subjective ratings of a phenomenon (e.g., the absence, presence, or quality of a behavior) among two (Cohen's κ) or more judges (Fleiss' κ).

Reliability is an important concept when considering measurement in objectivist research. First, if measures are to be credible, they should evidence acceptable reliability. Next, if measures of variables are not reliable, then the scores produced will be composed largely of error, which would bring into question the quality of the data collected. It should be noted that the type of reliability evidence needed depends on the measure and how it is interpreted. Measures that represent phenomena that show little change over time (i.e., stability) should evidence high test–retest reliability. Equivalent forms of an inventory used in a research study would need to evince alternate forms reliability, while measures consisting of multiple items representing a single trait should have good internal consistency. Finally, in situations where subjectively derived scores are used, interrater reliability is needed. For a discipline like music therapy, it would seem important to ensure that any conclusions drawn are based on measures or observations that are free from error. Finally, measurement reliability is a necessary condition for the next parameter of technical adequacy: validity.

Validity

Fishman and Galguera (2003) argue that "validity is the ultimate goal of all test construction for research purposes" (p. 19). *Measurement validity* is the extent to which a data collection procedure (e.g., test, questionnaire, or observation) assesses what it purportedly measures, and there are two ways to examine it: internally and externally. Internally, we may examine the appearance of a measure's procedures (*face validity*) or the content of its items (*content validity*). One may also examine the underlying structure and evaluate the extent to which it reflects theory or research (*construct validity*, based on internal structure) or how the measure relates to other substantive variables (*criterion-related validity*).

Externally, validity is concerned with the interpretations, conclusions, or decisions derived from data. First, one may ask whether a measurement was appropriate for the given situation. For example, administering a childhood depression inventory to a child would be a valid use of a measure, but administering the same inventory to an adult would not be a valid use. Secondly, an external examination of validity can be used to determine whether accurate conclusions were drawn from the measure. For instance, using a bathroom scale to draw conclusions about someone's weight may be valid, while using the same measure to draw conclusions about someone's overall health status is not. Therefore, validity refers not only to the measurement itself (internal) but also to the appropriate use of and inferences derived from the data (external).

When selecting a measurement approach in objectivist research, there are generally three avenues of evidence that are used to argue whether the score yielded from a data collection procedure is valid: *content validity, criterion validity,* and *construct validity.* Within these there are subtypes of validity as well as multiple approaches for obtaining evidence of validity.

Content Validity. Evidence based on *content validity* rests on how well a measurement's procedures or a test's items accurately reflect the domain being measured. For example, in assessing students' knowledge of research design in music, exam scores would evidence content validity to the extent that the test's items cover the material covered in the course. Typically, a measure's content validity is determined using a panel of *content experts* capable of judging the relevance of items or procedures regarding the domain being assessed. In the example about assessing students' knowledge of research design in music, the course instructor would be considered the content expert. As another example, Darsie (2009) adapted a survey originally use in child life research to measure allied health professionals' perceptions of music therapy in pediatrics. Because Darsie modified the original instrument, she submitted her revised survey to a panel of content experts (pediatric music therapists) before using it in her study.

It should be pointed out that content validity should not be confused with *face validity*. Evidence of face validity is based on the perspective of the one being subjected to the measure (the research participant or test taker) as opposed to the judgment of a panel of content experts (as in content validity). Put another way, face validity refers to what appears to be measured and not what is actually measured. Sattler (2001) states that "[High] Face validity is important because if the test does not appear to measure what it is supposed to measure, examinees may become skeptical and not perform adequately" (p. 115). But there may be situations where concealing the purpose of a test's items (low face validity) helps to reduce bias due to *demand characteristics* (i.e., cues that influence participants to behave or respond differently because they know the purpose of a study) or *pretesting effects* (i.e., when having taken a pretest unduly influences participant responses on a dependent measure). In both of these situations, the researcher may find it important to obscure the purpose of measurement procedures, as doing so may reduce the chances of participants responding differently based on a feature of the study itself (e.g., the questionnaire being used) as opposed to how they respond to the experimental or other research conditions.

Criterion Validity. Sometimes referred to as *criterion-related validity*, this type of evidence is based on the extent to which a measure relates to an independent (or external) measure or benchmark. Criterion validity is important in situations where the purpose is to establish either current or future performance and there are two sources of evidence used to draw conclusions about each: concurrent validity and predictive validity.

Concurrent validity (also called *concurrent criterion validity*) is the degree to which a measure relates to a criterion (e.g., another measure or performance standard) established at the same time. Returning to the research class example above, if student scores on the instructor-designed exam positively correlate with scores obtained from a different test of research design knowledge (administered at the same time), one may say that concurrent validity is present. In their analysis of measures of disorders of consciousness, O'Kelly and Magee (2013) found that both the Sensory Modality Assessment and Rehabilitation Technique (SMART) and the Music Therapy Assessment Tool for Awareness in Disorders of Consciousness (MATADOC) evidenced a high degree of concordance. Although the correlation between the two was not perfect (as each measure tended to show more sensitivity to certain sensory modalities), the high level of agreement between the two measures suggests that both the SMART and MATADOC would result in similar diagnostic decisions.

The second source of evidence, called *predictive validity* (and sometimes *predictive criterion validity*), is based on a measure's ability to predict a future outcome or performance. Examples of this type of evidence are found in the ways that college entrance scores or high school grade point averages are used to predict college success. This type of evidence can also be based on the extent to which a measure matches a standard or judgment by a panel of observers. As an example, Waldon and Wolfe (2006) generated evidence of *predictive utility*, a type of evidence related to predictive criterion validity, by examining the extent to which test data from the Computer-Based Music Perception Assessment for Children (CMPAC) assisted music therapists in a making referral decisions in the pediatric setting. After administering CMPAC to a group of pediatric patients, Waldon and Wolfe distributed the assessment data to music therapists with expertise in pediatrics and asked them to make one of three referral decisions: accept for services, do not accept for services, or cannot make a decision. The judgment of validity, in this case, was based on how well CMPAC data assisted the music therapists in assigning a referral disposition.

Construct Validity. Construct-related evidence, or *construct validity*, involves the degree to which a measure captures, or approximates, the phenomenon (i.e., the construct) under investigation. Some argue that all evidence of validity impacts construct validity because a measurement procedure's ability to quantify that which is intended is based on both the content of the measure (i.e., the test's items and procedures) and external criteria (i.e., the conclusions drawn or inferences made). Arguments for a measure's construct validity usually consist of evidence from multiple sources; occasionally, content and criterion-related evidence are used. More commonly researchers use evidence of a measure's relationship with other measures or its internal structure when drawing conclusions about construct validity.

When building an argument for the construct validity of a measure by examining its relationship to similar measures, two general approaches are used: obtaining evidence of convergent validity and/or divergent (or discriminant) validity. *Convergent validity* relates to a measure's similarity to another measure, both of which purport to sample the same (or a similar) construct. As an example, Lipe, York, and Jensen (2007) compared scores from the Residual Music Skills Test and the Music-Based Evaluation of Cognitive Functioning with those obtained from the Mini-Mental State Exam (MMSE). They found that both music-based measures correlated strongly with the MMSE, suggesting that the tools measure similar constructs. Similarly, Waldon and Broadhurst (2014) set out to establish the extent to which the Music Attentiveness Screening Assessment (MASA) sampled the construct of auditory attention. After administering MASA and a comparator instrument of auditory attention to a sample of children ages 5 to 9 years, they determined that MASA measured, at least partially, a construct similar to that of auditory attention.

Contrastingly, measures of different constructs correlate poorly with each other and evidence *divergent* (or *discriminant*) *validity*. Generally obtained in conjunction with convergent evidence, average inter-item correlations are usually calculated between measures that are both similar to and different from the construct being explored. Afterward, formulae are used to discern whether the measures investigated represent either similar or separate constructs. Divergent validity may be important to investigators when selecting instruments for use in a study because it provides some assurance that the construct measured is fairly circumscribed, thus eliminating doubt when interpreting results.

When basing construct validity on internal structure, multivariate statistical methods such as factor analysis or dimensional modeling are used to substantiate whether a measure's items or procedures represent the hypothesized construct. With regard to test development, Jeong (2013) utilized exploratory factor analysis to identify underlying constructs for a music-based measure of attention. Jeong's analysis evidenced a five-factor structure for various types of attention (including sustained, selective, and divided) underlying the assessment. In other situations, it is important to demonstrate that a measure has assessed the construct it was intended to measure before valid conclusions can be drawn. In assessing music therapists' perceptions about integrating research into clinical practice, Waldon (2015) implemented the BARRIERS to Research Utilization Scale

(Funk, Champagne, Wiese, & Tornquist, 1991), a tool originally designed for use in nursing research. To ensure that the BARRIERS measure adequately sampled the construct of interest, Waldon carried out a principle components analysis, which verified a factor structure similar to that yielded by Funk et al. (1991), suggesting that the tool measured the same phenomenon in both studies.

In summary, one type of validity is no more important than another; instead, certain types of validity may be of more importance in one instance than another. For example, content validity would be more important for a teacher-designed exam in terms of how well the test covers the material reviewed in a course (e.g., assessing a graduate student's knowledge of research design). Criterion-related validity is more important in situations where a measurement approach is used to predict future or current performance (e.g., passing a Board Certification exam and successful practice as a music therapist). Finally, construct validity is needed when a researcher chooses to measure an abstract concept or trait (e.g., cognitive functioning) following intervention.

The Relationship Between Reliability and Validity

The terms reliability and validity are easily confused—in part because the two terms are conceptually and statistically related (see Figure 1). Reliability refers to the precision of measurement and its freedom from error. This means that a measure obtained on multiple occasions would yield similar,

if not identical, measurements if found to be reliable. Validity refers to a measure's *accuracy* and the extent to which the target construct has been sampled. This implies that a measure can be precise in its measurement but evidence low validity if it does not capture the intended construct; in other words, it would be *precisely wrong* (Figure 2a). Therefore, a measure evidencing sufficient validity would also need to have acceptable reliability to hit the desired target (see Figure 2b). This means that reliability is a necessary, but not a sufficient, requirement for validity.

Resources for Finding and Evaluating Measures

Numerous resources are available to researchers with regard to finding tests and measures as well as evaluating the technical adequacy of research measures.

Databases and Clearinghouses. Published by the Buros Institute of Mental Measurement, *Tests in Print* (and, more recently, *Test Reviews Online*, https://marketplace.unl.edu/buros/) provides comprehensive information about the methodological quality, cost, and user qualifications of various educational and psychological measures. Similarly, the American Psychological Association (apa.org/science/faq-findtests.html) and the Educational Testing Service (ets.org/test_link/about) provide online reviews and purchasing information for over 20,000 tests and measures

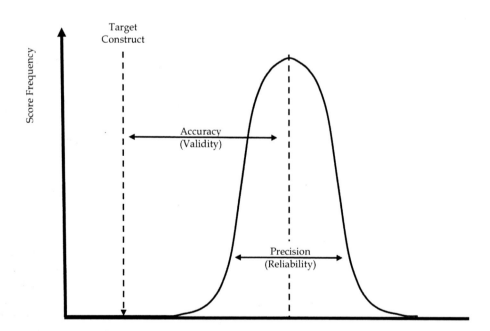

Figure 1. Relationship Between Measurement Precision and Accuracy for a Given Target Construct

Note. Precision is represented by the dispersion of scores across the horizontal axis with a narrower dispersion representing less error and higher reliability. The accuracy of the measure is seen in the relative distance to the target construct. The closer the measurement is to the target construct, the higher the validity.

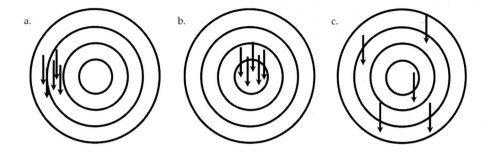

Figures 2a, 2b, and 2c. Illustration of the Relationship Between Reliability and Validity

Note. The measure (a) appears to evidence reliability as the scores (arrows) land closely (consistently) together; however, validity is not evident as the target (bull's-eye) was not *hit*. The measure (b) appears to evidence reliability, because the scores are landing closely together, and validity, because scores are landing at the target. The measure (c) appears to have low reliability (score inconsistency) and, therefore, does not evidence validity (scores do not land at the target).

used in clinical and research settings. Full access to these resources is usually available through institutional (e.g., college and university) affiliations, but individual subscriptions can be obtained for a fee.

COSMIN. Driven by the need to improve the quality of measurement tools in healthcare research, the *COSMIN* (*COnsensus-Based Standards for the Selection of Health Measurement INstruments*; www.cosmin.nl) Initiative Group established guidelines to evaluate the technical adequacy of research measures. The guidelines include a checklist of methodological measurement qualities (including reliability, content validity, criterion-related validity, construct validity, measurement error, and responsiveness) as well as procedures for selecting and rating those qualities. Although initially established to evaluate health outcome measures, the checklist may be helpful when selecting measures in educational, social science, or other allied health professions research.

Levels of Measurement

Objectivist measurement involves assigning numbers or quantities to those phenomena under investigation: participants, constructs, conditions, and events. Assigning values in this way allows researchers to differentiate one entity from another, thereby allowing comparison or detecting relationships. Statisticians generally recognize four levels (or scales) of measurement, each distinguished from the next in terms of (a) their mathematical characteristics, (b) their interpretative properties, and (c) the types of statistical procedures that can be applied. First identified by Stevens (1946), the four levels of measurement are (a) nominal, (b) ordinal, (c) interval, and (d) ratio. Each is described in more detail below. In addition to the information presented here, these levels of measurement are summarized in Table 1, Summary of Data Characteristics, in Chapter 18 in this book.

Nominal

The most rudimentary scale of measurement is *nominal,* and at this level, as the name suggests, numbers simply name or label; therefore, the numbers (or codes) do not represent quantities. The only mathematical characteristic present in the nominal scale is numeric distinctiveness, which assists the researcher in assigning numbers to mutually exclusive categories to distinguish participant characteristics or conditions from each another. As a result, some may refer to this measurement scale as *categorical, classificatory,* or *discontinuous*. Data at the nominal level yield categorical variables, which are reported as frequencies and analyzed using certain nonparametric statistical tests (e.g., chi square [x^2] or proportion tests).

At the nominal level, numbers can be assigned to differentiate between naturally occurring participant characteristics like gender, wherein male participants may be assigned a value of 1 and females a value of 2. This does not imply a sense of order (i.e., males precede females) or quantity (i.e., females are somehow greater than males). Instead, the numeric assignment distinguishes one group (males) from another (females). In other situations, the researcher may define *artificial* categories, which represent multiple dimensions of a construct. Examples may include height (tall versus short), anxiety (high versus low anxiety), or musical aptitude (high versus low musical potential). One may wonder about the value of this numerical coding over simply using *M* for male and *F* for female. In response, Boslaugh (2013) states that assigning numeric codes using a nominal approach simplifies data management, because many statistical packages prohibit entry of nonnumeric characters.

Nominal assignment is not, however, restricted to dichotomous (two) categories. A nominal scale may be used to demarcate multiple aspects of participant characteristics (e.g., high, low, and middle income) or identify treatment conditions (e.g., music treatment, standard treatment, and no-treatment control conditions); this allows investigators to compare participant responses between various participant groups. For example, Wolfe, O'Connell, and Waldon (2002) used a nominal scale of measurement to represent two participant groups (musicians and nonmusicians) in their investigation of relaxing music characteristics. In another study, Wolfe and Noguchi (2009) randomly assigned participants to one of four listening conditions (spoken story without distraction, spoken story with auditory distraction, musical story without distraction, and musical story with distraction) to compare performance on a sustained attention task. In this case, numbers (codes) were assigned to distinguish one participant listening condition from another.

Ordinal

The next level of measurement is *ordinal,* which, as the name suggests, implies the presence of order, that is, that higher numeric values represent more of a particular construct than lower values. This allows researchers to rank characteristics so that values can be compared to others as being equal to, less than, or greater than them. Mathematically, numeric assignment at the ordinal level provides quantitative meaning, unlike at the nominal level. The ordinal scale also represents what some statisticians term the first of the *continuous* (as opposed to categorical) scales of measurement. It should be noted that while numeric magnitude is assumed at the ordinal level (i.e., that one value is equal to, less than, or greater than another), distances between points along an ordinal dimension are not. For example, research participants may be ordered in terms of height (from shortest to highest) and assigned a number representing their rank. This does not, however, suggest that the difference in height between participants 4 and 5 is equivalent to that between participants 9 and 10. As a result, data at the ordinal level is statistically analyzed using certain nonparametric tests suitable for use with ordinal data (e.g., Mann-Whitney U or Kruskal-Wallis one-way analysis of variance).

Ordinal measurement typically involves ranking or rating events, concepts, or opinions along a dimension of some importance. Examples include ranking participants by illness severity (e.g., most to least severe), obtaining opinion or preference ratings (e.g., highly agree to disagree, most to least preferred), or ordering the importance of an important attribute (e.g., most to least importance). Multiple examples of ordinal measurement are found in Wolfe et al. (2002). First, the researchers asked participants to rate the relaxation potential of multiple recorded music selections using 4-point Likert scale items. Next, rank ordering of songs (in terms of relaxation potential) was compared between the musicians and nonmusicians (using Mann-Whitney U). In both cases, the numeric assignment (either the 4-point rating or the rank ordering of music selections) holds quantitative meaning, allowing comparison along an underlying continuum.

Interval

The second of the continuous scales is found at the *interval* level of measurement. Interval level measurement possesses the mathematic characteristic of order, in addition to the assumption of equal distances (interval equivalence) between all points along a continuum. In a previous (ordinal) example using height, one could not assume that distances between ranks are equal. However, a standard score of 100 on a standardized intelligence test (e.g., the Wechsler Adult Intelligence Scale, 4th Edition [WAIS-IV]) is 10 points higher than a score of 90 and 10 points lower than a score of 110. This means that distances between all points along a given continuum are equal, permitting the mathematical operations of addition and subtraction. However, interval level measurement does not have a true zero point (unlike the ratio level, discussed below); therefore, multiplication and division are not appropriate. Therefore, one could not claim that a person with a standard score of 140 on the WAIS-IV is *twice* as intelligent as someone achieving a standard score of 70. Although not equivalent to a ratio scale of measurement, interval and ratio data are treated statistically the same and are analyzed using a variety of parametric statistical tests (e.g., *t* test and ANOVA).

Examples of interval measurement include temperature (on the Fahrenheit or Celsius scales), calendar time, and standardized test scores. The use of interval levels of measurement can be found throughout the music therapy research literature. For example, in a study examining the impact of songwriting with patients undergoing substance use treatment, Silverman (2012) employed a standardized test (the Circumstance, Motivation, and Readiness Scales for Substance Abuse Treatment) that measured motivation, readiness, and treatment retention potential. Yinger and Standley (2011) examined patient satisfaction scores among patients receiving music therapy in a hospital setting. Their instrument (the Press Ganey Inpatient Survey [PGIS]) consisted of 38 scale items, from which 10 subscores and a total score are derived. Single scale items should be treated as ordinal; however, when scale items are combined into cumulative scores (as with the PGIS), data can be treated as interval level measurement (Norman, 2010).

Ratio

Representing the fourth, and most sophisticated, level of measurement is the *ratio* scale. It shares mathematical characteristics with the other continuous scales (i.e., numeric order with ordinal and equality of measured intervals with interval) in addition to possessing an absolute zero point. This means that one can measure the relative presence or absence of a characteristic as well as compare measurements proportionately. This also means that multiplication and division can be applied to ratio scales in a meaningful and appropriate way. Consider again the example of height: One can rank order participants *by* height (an ordinal characteristic); one can assume that the difference in height between someone who is 5' 7" and 5' 10" is the same as the difference between someone who is 6' 3" and 6' 6" (an interval characteristic); and one can accept that an adult who is 6' is twice as tall as child who is 3' (a ratio characteristic). As mentioned previously, ratio data are treated statistically in the same manner as interval data.

Many physical measurements (e.g., height, weight, strength), acoustic properties (e.g., using stroboscopic tuning instruments), time, speed, distance, monetary cost, and number of events or behaviors are considered at the ratio scale. Ratio-level measurement is present throughout the music therapy literature. Thaut and colleagues (2007) used a number of ratio-level measurements to examine the effects of rhythmic auditory stimulation with patients following hemiparetic stroke. Those measures included velocity, stride length, and cadence (steps per minute). In a series of studies examining the use of music therapy–based social skills training, Gooding (2011) conducted event recordings of on-task, prompted, and off-task social behaviors among adolescents with social skills deficits. Similarly, Kennedy and Kua-Walker (2006) used a combination of frequency recording and time sampling to measure correct motor responses, articulations, and instrument playing in a 10-year-old male with myotonic dystrophy.

Types of Measurement Items

Standardized tests, observation systems, and researcher-designed questionnaires or surveys can consist of a variety of measurement items. *Standardized tests* involve a collection of measurement items that are written, administered, scored, and interpreted in a consistent manner to yield a score representing a factor, ability, or trait in an examinee (or research participant). Quantitative *observation systems* involve measuring the frequency, duration, content (using checklists), and quality (using ratings) of examinee behaviors. Researcher-designed *questionnaires* and *surveys* are one of the most frequently used techniques for obtaining information from research participants and often contain a combination of measurement items. While an exhaustive list would extend beyond the confines of this chapter, what follows is a parsimonious taxonomy of *measurement items* most commonly encountered in the music therapy research literature.

Open-Format Items

Open-format items allow the research participant to answer in an unrestricted manner because their responses are not constrained by predetermined choices or closed response modes (e.g., numeric responses). Both written and verbal (interview) item approaches are discussed below.

Written. The first type of open response format requires participants to write in their desired responses. For example, in the study by Wolfe et al. (2002), participants responded to open-ended items questions (e.g., "What did you rate as highly relaxing?" [p. 54]) by identifying musical characteristics that enhanced or detracted from the relaxing potential of a given music selection. From an objectivist perspective, open formats provide wider response options to participants than closed formats (e.g., checklists, scales, or ranks) but should be carefully considered before being used as an alternative to closed-ended formats. Consider the following open-ended item: "How long have you been practicing as a music therapist?" The researcher may intend to obtain a numeric value for use in the analysis. However, should a participant respond with "10 to 11 years," measurement precision is lost, which may impact the quality of the analysis. Therefore, McMillan and Schumacher (2006) suggest using "open-ended questions first with a small group of subjects in order to generate salient factors and then use close-ended items, based on the open-ended responses, with a larger group" (p. 198).

Verbal. Another open format option involves the administration of items verbally; this essentially embeds the measurement questions within the context of a conversation or interview. According to McMillan and Schumacher (2006), when used within an objectivist context, "Interview schedules are essentially vocal questionnaires" (p. 203). This method of measurement may be helpful for researchers working with respondents who are unable to read, need clarification of test items, or require motivation from the examiner to respond. Disadvantages include increased time or cost associated with administration, the potential introduction of bias on the part of the examiner, the need to train interviewers, or unwillingness on the part of participants to provide truthful responses because of the intimate nature of the interview process.

Closed-Format Items

Undoubtedly constituting the majority of objectivist measure items, a variety of closed-ended approaches are available to researchers. Sometimes referred to as *paper and pencil* items (McMillan & Schumacher, 2006), most of these limit respondents to a single response. Many are discussed in more depth below.

Checklist Items. *Checklist items* provide a number of choices from which participants choose; multiple choices items (as on tests of learning comprehension, competency, or achievement) would fall under this category. Depending on the format and the purpose of the item, respondents may have the option to choose one or multiple options. Both response formats are present in Wolfe et al. (2002). First, participants were asked to select one response option to questions related to age group, years of education, and the frequency of music listening. Later in the questionnaire, the authors employed a multiple response format when asking about music listening preferences (e.g., rock, pop, country). This type of response format usually falls under the nominal scale of measurement.

Scaled Items. Response options arranged along a dimension are usually called *scaled items* (Colman, 2009). This response format allows research participants to express their opinions, beliefs, or perceptions in a straightforward manner that is easily quantified and analyzed. In general, there are two types of scaled items: Likert scale items and analog scales items (Figure 3). Before proceeding further, it is important to note the difference between a scale and a scale item. All scales have multiple items from which one can calculate composite scores. A scale item is just that—a *single* item that can employ either a Likert or analog format (both of which are discussed in more detail below). The distinction is important from a measurement and statistical perspective: the composite score from a scale (made of multiple items) can be considered interval level measurement while single scale items should be treated at the ordinal level.

First introduced by Rensis Likert (1932), **Likert** (pronounced *lick-ert*) **scale** items represent a dimensional construct (e.g., attitude, preference) requiring respondents to choose a value along that continuum representing the magnitude of their perception. All Likert-type items have a written or pictorial descriptor at each *degree* along the scale. While there is no consensus as to the number of choices required to qualify as Likert item (i.e., an even versus odd number of choices), Likert's original examples contained an odd number (three or five) of response options. Others prefer an even number of response choices, thereby avoiding a middle response (e.g., neither agree nor disagree). An example of this is the four-point Likert item used in Wolfe et al. (2002), which assessed participants' perceptions of relaxing music recordings: "1 = not at all

relaxing; 2 = somewhat relaxing; 3 = relaxing; 4 = very relaxing" (p. 43).

Unlike Likert items, *analog* (or *semantic differential*) scale items provide a range of response options that are not restricted by the designation of descriptors for each response choice. While formats may vary, music therapy researchers frequently use *visual analog scale (VAS)* items consisting of a single line (typically horizontal with or without numbers) that have anchoring descriptors at both ends; this provides the dimensional quality along which participants respond. Scoring is usually calculated by measuring the distance (using either millimeters or predesignated degrees) between the participant's mark on the line and one of the ends. Robb (2000) used VAS items to gauge participants' perceptions of relaxation. Walworth, Rumana, Nguyen, and Jarred (2008) used a number of VAS items (100-millimeter horizontal lines) in their study investigating the use of music therapy for those undergoing elective surgical brain procedures. In their study, participants marked their perceived levels of relaxation, anxiety, mood, pain, and stress with each variable represented on a separate horizontal line.

The challenge inherent in using Likert or analog items and scales lies in establishing their technical adequacy. Ideally, when designing a study, one would choose a scale or scale item for which reliability and validity is already available. Frequently, though, researchers simply create their own scale or items, assuming that the technical properties of the measure are sufficient. Without fully exploring the technical characteristics of any scaled measure, however, one risks the overall interpretability of the data. The use of pilot testing of scales and items is recommended, at a minimum, to determine whether the measure approximates the desired construct (construct validity) and whether it does so consistently (refer to the different forms of reliability). Additionally, many experts (Fishman & Galguera, 2003; Jameison, 2004; Norman, 2010; Wewers & Lowe, 1990) argue against the use of inferential interpretation of single scale items that have not been subjected to rigorous psychometric

How do you rate the relaxation potential of the music selection?

(a) Check one of the following:

| Not at all relaxing | Not relaxing | Neutral | Relaxing | Significantly relaxing |

(b) Mark your response on the line provided:

Not at all relaxing   Significantly relaxing

Figure 3. Example of (a) Likert Scale Item and (b) Analog Scale Item (both measuring the relaxation potential of a music selection)

analyses. Instead, descriptive interpretation on a single item would seem more prudent.

A final point about the use and analysis of scaled items is relevant to the current discussion. A single Likert or analog scale item does not constitute a *scale* and should (at the most conservative level) be treated statistically at the ordinal level (Jameison, 2004). Conceptually, a scaled item does not represent an evenly distributed array of numbers along a continuum, a mathematic characteristic of the interval scale. However, when multiple scaled items are scored or summed together, one can identify the combination of items as a *scale* that can be treated as interval data (Norman, 2010).

Ranked Items. One of the limitations of scale items is that respondents can rate any number of items as *equally* important or preferred, which may reduce systematic variance and affect the ability to detect differences or relationships. Ranked items, however, compel respondents to prioritize an array of objects from most to least important or preferred. As an example, Kennelly, Baker, Morgan, and Daveson (2012) asked respondents to rank (from 1 to 5) the theoretical models used most frequently during music therapy supervision. Ranked items are also considered ordinal level measures.

Conclusion

From an objectivist perspective, it can be challenging to measure things that are valued but somehow evade direct observation. In order to interpret research results confidently, one needs to ensure that the measures used are free from error (an issue of reliability) and accurately represent the phenomenon being investigated (an issue of validity). The four types of reliability discussed here (test–retest, alternate forms, internal consistency, and interrater) are used to judge the consistency with which research instrumentation (e.g., tests, questionnaires, surveys, or observations) measure. Researchers should also review different types of validity evidence to gauge the extent to which measures cover the intended domain (content validity), relate to other measures or independent criteria (criterion validity), and quantify the desired construct or phenomenon (construct validity). Following data collection, researchers must carefully consider the type of data represented (nominal, ordinal, interval, and ratio) so that appropriate statistical analyses and interpretation may be applied.

Luckily, music therapy researchers have a number of measures at their disposal, including standardized tests, questionnaires, interviews, and observations. In addition to those measurement procedures used in previous research, music therapy researchers are encouraged to consult with their multidisciplinary colleagues or use the databases mentioned here. Furthermore, if researchers choose to design their own measures, a number of resources have been cited in this chapter to help them pursue that endeavor.

References

Aiken, L. R. (1997). *Psychological testing and assessment* (9th ed.). Needham Heights, MA: Allyn and Bacon.

Araujo, J., & Born, D. G. (1985). Calculating percentage agreement correctly but writing its formula incorrectly. *Behavior Analyst, 8,* 207–208.

Boslaugh, S. (2013). *Statistics in a nutshell: A desktop quick reference* (2nd ed.). Sebastopol, CA: O'Reilly.

Colman, A. M. (2009). *Oxford dictionary of psychology* (3rd ed.). New York, NY: Oxford University Press.

Darsie, E. (2009). Interdisciplinary team members' perceptions of the role of music therapy in a pediatric outpatient clinic. *Music Therapy Perspectives, 27,* 48–27. doi:10.1093/mtp/27.1.48

Fishman, J. A., & Galguera, T. (2003). *Introduction to test construction in the social and behavioral sciences: A practical guide.* Lanham, MD: Rowman & Littlefield.

Funk, S. G., Champagne, M. T., Wiese, R. A., & Tornquist, E. M. (1991). BARRIERS: The barriers to research utilization scale. *Applied Nursing Research, 4,* 39–45.

Geisinger, K. F. (2013). Reliability. In K. F. Geisinger (Ed.), *APA handbook of testing and assessment in psychology* (Vol. 1; pp. 21–42). Washington, DC: American Psychological Association. doi:10.1037/14047-002

Gooding, L. F. (2011). The effect of a music therapy social skills training program on improving social competence in children and adolescents with social skills deficits. *Journal of Music Therapy, 48,* 440–462. doi:10.1093/jmt/48.4.440

Jameison, S. (2004). Likert scales: How to (ab)use them. *Medical Education, 38,* 1212–1218. doi:10.1111/j.1365-2929.2004.02012.x

Jeong, E. (2013). Psychometric validation of a music-based attention assessment: Revised for patients with traumatic brain injury. *Journal of Music Therapy, 50,* 66–92. doi:10.1093/jmt/50.2.66

Kennedy, R., & Kua-Walker, Y. (2006). Movement, singing, and instrument playing strategies for a child with myotonic dystrophy. *Music Therapy Perspectives, 21,* 39–51. doi:10.1093/mtp/24.1.39

Kennelly, J. D., Baker, F. A., Morgan, K. A., & Daveson, B. A. (2012). Supervision for music therapists: An Australian cross-sectional survey regarding views and practices. *Australian Journal of Music Therapy, 23,* 41–56.

Likert, R. (1932). A technique for the measurement of attitudes. *Archives of Psychology, 22*(140), 5–55.

Lipe, A. W., York, E., & Jensen, E. (2007). Construct validation of two music-based assessments for people with dementia. *Journal of Music Therapy, 44,* 369–387. doi:10.1093/jmt/44.4.369

McMillan, J. H., & Schumacher, S. (2006). *Research in education: Evidence-based inquiry* (6th ed.). Boston, MA: Allyn and Bacon.

Norman, G. (2010). Likert scales, measurement, and the

"laws" of statistics. *Advances in Health Science Education, 15*, 625–632. doi:10.1007/S10459-010-9222-y

O'Kelly, J., & Magee, W. L. (2013). The complementary role of music therapy in the detection of awareness in disorders of consciousness: An audit of concurrent SMART and MATADOC assessments. *Neuropsychological Rehabilitation, 23*, 287–298. doi:10.1080/09602011.2012.753395

Robb, S. L. (2000). Music-assisted progressive muscle relaxation, progressive muscle relaxation, music listening, and silence: A comparison of relaxation techniques. *Journal of Music Therapy, 37*, 2–21. doi:10.1093/jmt/37.1.2

Sattler, J. M. (2001). *Assessment of children: Cognitive applications* (4th ed.). San Diego, CA: Jerome M. Sattler.

Silverman, M. J. (2012). Effects of group songwriting on motivation and readiness for treatment on patients in detoxification: A randomized wait-list effectiveness study. *Journal of Music Therapy, 49*, 414–429. doi:10.1093/jmt/49.4.414

Stevens, S. S. (1946). On the theory of scales of measurement. *Science, 103*, 677–680.

Thaut, M. H., Leins, A. K., Rice, R. R., Argstatter, H., Kenyon, G. P., McIntosh, G. C., …Fetter, M. (2007). Rhythmic auditory stimulation improves gait more than NDT/Bobath training in near-ambulatory patients early poststroke: A single-blind, randomized trial. *Neurorehabilitation and Neural Repair, 21*, 455–459. doi:10.1177/1545968307300523

Waldon, E. G. (2015). Music therapists' research activity and utilization barriers: A survey of the membership. *Journal of Music Therapy, 52*, 168–194. doi:10.1093/jmt/thv001

Waldon, E. G., & Broadhurst, E. H. (2014). Construct validity and reliability of the Music Attentiveness Screening Assessment (MASA). *Journal of Music Therapy, 51*, 154–170. doi:10.1093/jmt/thu008

Waldon, E. G., & Wolfe, D. E. (2006). Predictive utility of the Computer-Based Music Perception Assessment for Children (CMPAC). *Journal of Music Therapy, 43*, 356–371. doi:10.1093/jmt/43.4.356

Walworth, D. D., Rumana, C. S., Nguyen, J., & Jarred, J. (2008). Effects of live music therapy sessions on quality of life indicators, medications administered and hospital length of stay for patients undergoing elective surgical procedures for brain. *Journal of Music Therapy, 45*, 349–359. doi:10.1093/jmt/45.3.349

Wewers, M. E., & Lowe, N. K. (1990). A critical review of visual analog scales in the measurement of clinical phenomena. *Research in Nursing and Health, 13*, 227–236.

Wolfe, D. E., O'Connell, A. S., & Waldon, E. G. (2002). Music for relaxation: A comparison of musicians and nonmusicians on ratings of selected musical recordings. *Journal of Music Therapy, 39*, 40–55. doi:10.1093/jmt/39.1.40

Wolfe, D. E., & Noguchi, L. K. (2009). The use of music with young children to improve sustained attention during a vigilance task in the presence of auditory distractors. *Journal of Music Therapy, 46*, 69–82. doi:10.1093/jmt/46.1.69

Yinger, O. S., & Standley, J. M. (2011). The effects of medical music therapy on patient satisfaction as measured by the Press Ganey Inpatient Survey. *Music Therapy Perspectives, 29*, 149–156. doi:10.1093/mtp/29.2.149

Chapter 11

POTENTIAL PROBLEMS IN OBJECTIVIST RESEARCH

Arthur P. Sullivan • John A. Sullivan

It can be disheartening for a music therapist to experience the effects of therapy in the clinic, yet fail to find significant effects when a research trial is performed. Many real effects remain unsubstantiated, even in apparently well-designed studies. This can divert music therapy in unproductive directions. Further, when research is in preliminary stages, any finding that indicates the investigation is on the right track is valuable (e.g., Nayak, Wheeler, Shiflett, & Agostinelli, 2000). But as findings accumulate and are surveyed and reviewed, as they have been in music therapy research (e.g., a number of Cochrane reviews that have been done on music and music therapy, www.cochranelibrary.com), more is at stake for the researchers and ultimately for the patients and clients who will be affected by what is learned or could have been learned. For these reasons, music therapy researchers are encouraged to seek more than just a match among the parts of the research project. Seeking an excellent or at least a best-possible match is proposed.

Pursuing the anatomy of a best possible match starts by identifying the problems that remain after a reasonable match has been made. The breadth of coverage of objectivist research in music therapy presented in this volume assures the careful reader the procedural knowledge required to create a good research design. Since music therapy research has reached a maturity where vulnerability to pitfalls has become important, a competent overview must attempt to blend the several parts of the research process while focusing on any potential pitfalls and how they can be remedied or their damage attenuated.

Potential Problems

Some of the problems that can occur will be raised here. Possible solutions will be presented in the next section.

Failing to detect a real effect can occur when the researcher has not paid attention to sometimes enormous **Type II error** probabilities. Validating the success of a procedure in the clinic can keep researchers focused on **Type I error** alone. Each researcher wishes to deliver therapeutic effectiveness which cannot reasonably be attributed to chance, so the goal is an error probability of less than .05; better still less than .01 or .001. These low probabilities provide increasing likelihood that findings are not measurement artifacts and that the client improvements observed are actually present.

Yet the related question is typically not addressed and often not even considered. What is the likelihood that there was real client improvement which the research failed to detect? This is the Type II error question. In many research projects, this probability is between 40% and 60%. Because this probability was not calculated, the researcher proceeded with an experiment wherein the effect was quite unlikely to be found and then discarded the procedure being tested as useless because the effect was not found, or was *not significant.*

Correcting this problem is not so easy as adjusting a Type I error probability, but Type II error probability can be reduced. Indeed, it often must be reduced if there is to be any hope of finding the effect.

Type II error neglect is not the only potential pitfall. It can also be frustrating for a music therapist who has done some preliminary research and found client improvement to then be *unable to demonstrate a causal link* between client improvement and music therapy. This often happens in research projects because of the small number of participants available, but more typically because of the therapist's being unable or unwilling—for compassionate, practical, or ethical reasons—to construct a true, randomly assigned control group. There are fixes: Causality can be demonstrated without using a randomized control group, for example, with a regression–discontinuity design as discussed below.

Regression to the mean, either unnoticed or inadequately addressed, is another potential problem. The most obvious scenario plays out frequently because treatments are created for extreme groups, specifically for clients with problems. Posttesting is doomed to show improvement because of regression to the mean, and true effects can be lost among the artifactual ones.

The situation is greatly exacerbated when clients are selected for the study by administering a selection test at random. The probability that randomly administered tests correctly find the clients in need of therapy is quite surprisingly low, even when the percentage of suitable clients in the sampled population is relatively high and the test has reasonably good psychometric properties. For example, in a patient population of 100 where 10 are in reality suited for music therapy, a screening test with .90 sensitivity and .90 selectivity can be expected to identify 9 of those 10 patients. But it will also identify 8 patients incorrectly, giving the researcher a treatment group of 17 in which almost half are unsuitable. Getting a more accurate screening test barely helps: Fewer patients will be identified, but still only around 50% of them will actually be suitable. These inappropriately selected clients can sharply increase the posttest regression effect, particularly in otherwise suitable, even posttest-only designs.

Researchers who are not also statisticians can underestimate the damage done by *violating statistical assumptions.* The statistical assumptions are made to allow solving of the mathematical equations that underlie the statistical procedure. Even small violations can do unexpectedly large damage and cause misleading results, for example, finding random fluctuations to be significant or failing to find an effect that is actually present. These problems are often correctible by minor changes in the statistical analysis or by changes in the research design.

Finding a statistically significant result is invariably encouraging. But pursuing it without estimating the *effect size* or confusing the level of significance with the size of the effect may leave the therapist expending far too much effort in therapy for very little gain for the client. A businessperson would take a cost–benefit approach to the situation to determine whether the effect found was worth pursuing. While no researcher wants to abandon a significant finding, perhaps a hint of the cost–benefit approach is useful.

Cautions are not all provided by statisticians. Some decision theorists (Kahneman, 2011) report a tendency for people in general to *answer easier questions than those that were asked*. A school principal trying to inhibit behavior asks himself the question, "What punishment does this student deserve for what he did?" That is not precisely the right question, but may be sufficiently close. However, the principal might inadvertently answer that question, "How much does what the student did make my job more difficult?" Researchers, ever oriented to the actual questions they wish to ask and answer, can still pursue easier questions and inadvertently predicate the answers they find for the easier questions as answers to the real research questions. This can be the unnoticed by-product of the piecemeal topography of the research process, or it can occur unobtrusively when operational definitions are being decided.

These are considerations that rise to the level of concern in music therapy research and, in fact, in all research. This overview undertakes to set them in useful context and point to possible solutions.

Recognizing and Ameliorating Problems

Although insight about any part of the research project can occur to the researcher at any time, the process has a structured flow. Specifying the flow is not intended to impede the researcher's thought process, but to organize the results of it. A new insight typically causes an important change to one part of the project, but also causes secondary changes in other parts. Keeping the overall picture in focus helps to adjust all parts of the process for an improvement made in any one part.

In general, the sequence of the superordinate elements that form the spine of the research project is: (a) research questions, (b) creation of research design, (c) adoption of measurement instruments, (d) statistical analysis, and (e) translation to clinical practice. The problems that plague the researcher, often enough without being noticed, can appear differently in different parts of the research process. Some problems occur exclusively at certain points in a research project. The following sections organize the problems within the part of the research process where they are likely to occur, and managing them is addressed in that context.

In the Research Questions

The research question begins with the researcher's curiosity and contains comparisons. When the comparison is not explicit, it is there anyway, implicitly, even in phenomenological research. Although there might seem to be no comparison involved when determining if, when, to what degree, and how often an event occurs, or whether an event is predictable, comparison exists, to a standard or at the very least to a background against which the observation is made. Total lack of contrast prevents a figure from being discernible from the ground. The first formalization of the researcher's curiosity is to make the comparison clear.

Whether the comparison is to a standard norm or metric, between groups of persons, or between persons and themselves at a different time will trigger a cascade of decisions. The nature of the comparison narrows the possible choices of research design, which then affects the choices in every part of the research process.

This book includes a taxonomy of research questions (see Figures 1 and 2 in Chapter 19, Introduction to SPSS), and it is very probable that the reader will find the form of the desired research question on this list. After selecting the most similar question, the reader can then use the decision tree there to see which statistical methods and associated research designs are useful for that type of comparison.

Problem: Answering an Easier Question. It is at this point, while specifying the research questions, that the researcher is encouraged to become watchful about inadvertently substituting an easier question. It is easier to determine whether patients enjoyed the therapy than it is to determine whether it attenuated their dysphoria. Measures of anxiety and depression, for example, can devolve into measurements of enjoyment of the sessions or appreciation of the therapist if the research elements are not selected with a view to preventing such substitutions.

In the Creation of the Research Design

Choice of research design is often merged with considerations of the statistical analyses to be performed. This is a useful approach and is reflected in the structure of the decision tree from Chapter 19 in this book, referred to above, which omits separate mention of the research design because the statistics are often closely wedded to the specific designs. In overview, however, the quality of the match between statistics and research question can be inspected for possible improvements that can assist in avoiding research problems.

Useful research designs include those to which chapters

of this book are devoted: case study; AB, ABA, ABAB, and other withdrawal designs; multiple baseline, changing criterion, and multiple treatment designs; survey research; longitudinal designs; one-sample designs; static group comparisons; parallel group designs; crossover designs; and factorial designs. Other designs that may be useful are time series/repeated measures, counterbalanced, Solomon four group, and Latin square; information about these designs is also found in this book.

The connection between design and statistical analysis is evident. Some of the above designs (e.g., case study, withdrawal, multiple baseline, changing criterion, and multiple treatment) do not require statistics, although they may be used in some cases. Estimation of population parameters requires descriptive statistics and graphics only. Parallel group, crossover, and factorial designs, among others, call for *t* tests and various ANOVAs, and ANCOVAs when covariates are present. Several designs, such as repeated measures and Solomon four group, are often overlooked even when the researcher has designed a near equivalent (Creswell, 2012). These designs are useful alternatives that change procedure only but do not disrupt the connection between research question and statistical analysis. Using these alternative designs can facilitate the research effort and avoid some of the problems under consideration.

Problem: Attributing Causality Without a Control Group. The *regression-discontinuity* design is used when random assignment to a control group is not practical, is not desirable, or is unethical. A review of the capabilities and limitations of the regression-discontinuity design is presented by Imbens and Lemieux (2007). This design can be used when the participants are screened for severity of symptoms so that those with the most severe symptoms, for example, in the worst pain, will receive the treatment first, while those with less severe symptoms will be placed on a wait list and receive treatment later. The screening has a cutoff point for severity. Those very near the cutoff point on either side of it have very similar symptom severity, and the probability is high that they fell on one or other side of the cutoff by chance arising from *measurement error.* The essence of this design is in comparing the near-the-cutoff participants who were barely included for treatment (those just above the cutoff) to those who were barely excluded from treatment (just below the cutoff point).

Statistically, this subgroup of patients near the cutoff can be treated as if they were randomly assigned to treatment or control groups, and the ordinary least-squares procedures such as ANOVA, ANCOVA, and the whole range of linear and multiple regression methods may be used. The conclusions are causal provided that the researcher did not disturb the cutoff process, for example, by compassionate inclusions of patients in the treatment group who fell below the cutoff but whom the researcher felt should get treatment without delay. The group assignment to experimental and control was not perfectly random but rather *as good as random*

and further disturbance of the process may invalidate it.

The drawback to this design is that only a fraction of the patients treated can be viewed as near the cutoff point and included in the study, so a number of cycles may have to be run before a sufficient sample size is attained.

Problem: Failing to Detect a Real Effect—Too Few Participants. Not finding an effect that is actually present is discussed under the headings of *Type II error* or *low power* when it is discussed or noticed at all. Researchers can think that if they have a large enough sample size, this is not a concern, and, to a point, they are correct. But considering the time and effort spent in providing music therapy treatment, the number of participants a researcher can include in a reasonable period of time is often well below what the researcher would desire. In this event, specialized designs might be worth considering.

One method for increasing the power of research with few participants is through the use of a repeated measures design (Ellis, 1999). The researcher using this design measures client change repeatedly, often beginning with a pretest. In a study where the music therapy procedures are intended to reduce client distress, the pretest measurement establishes the baseline level of distress for all participants. The researcher then repeats the measurement, perhaps five times over 15 therapy sessions. This has the effect of increasing the power of the experiment to the level of one with almost five times as many participants, thus greatly reducing the likelihood of missing a real improvement in the clients if an improvement actually happens.

Where very few clients are available, a **Latin square design** can be adopted under certain conditions. Latin squares have been popularized among the general public in the Sudoku puzzles. Like these puzzles in which a number must appear only once in each row or column, each research subject must appear once and only once in each condition and level. Using this design, a music therapy researcher wishing to study, for example, the effects of music therapy and anxiety medication on patient distress could use a Latin square design requiring only three clients yet have the statistical power of a three-way ANOVA design requiring at least 15 times as many client participants.

To do this, the researcher would define three levels of music therapy (perhaps number of sessions or variations in the therapy procedure) and three levels of prescription anxiolytics (perhaps zero plus two other dosage levels). Each client's distress, the dependent measure, is assessed in each of the three conditions he or she experienced.

There are restrictions. Factor levels must be randomly assignable. Thus levels of patient pain, illness, or gender cannot be used, but levels of exposure to treatment, therapist, or procedures can be used. Like the rows, columns, and numbers in Sudoku puzzles, the number of clients, levels of treatment, and levels of medication must all be equal. Also like Sudoku, each client will appear once only in each row (level of therapy) and column (medication dose), and these must be randomly assigned: That is, for the research, each of the three participants is assigned to a level of therapy and medication three times, at random. The excellent leverage in this procedure can be attractive to patients who desire to make a personal contribution to scientific knowledge and prefer participating in this type of study rather than in a conventionally designed, large-scale study where they are only one of very many participants.

Note that the design has additional advantages beyond requiring so few participants. The conclusions are causal, with effective control of extraneous error sources. Conclusions about treatment versus no treatment can be made, as in the example here, by including a zero level in the treatment factor. The statistical analysis is ANOVA and can be done with SPSS, though the guidance of a statistician is suggested.

Problem: Failing to Detect a Real Effect—Treatment Is Lengthy or Patients Are Treated Sequentially. Obtaining a treatment effect in music therapy may take many sessions that extend over months. Additionally, the music therapist conducting the research can provide therapy to only a few clients at a time. Aggregating enough clients this way could take years, even with cooperating therapists including their patients in the study by using the experimental procedures.

In an instance like this where both time and number of clients are issues, *acceptance sampling* may be considered. Typically seen only in business and industry, the expense of providing treatment to each music therapy client amply motivates the straightforward adaptation of the procedure to music therapy research. The statistical analyses can be performed after every few clients have completed the treatment (or placebo treatment if they were assigned to the control group) as if the full planned number of participants had been reached. The experiment is halted when a significant result is obtained, or when the planned number of clients has completed it, whichever comes first. A significant result that will have a large effect size can emerge early, after relatively few clients have been treated, conserving resources. When no significant result occurs, it may become obvious that this will happen before all the planned clients have been treated. This is a disappointing outcome, but again, it will conserve resources for other research leads. Note that the need for random inclusion of additional clients for successive analyses is critical.

Problem: Failing to Detect a Real Effect—Variables Are Related Nonlinearly. The relationship between anxiety and performance is a well-studied example of this. As anxiety increases, the client's performance tends to improve, to a point. After that point, further increases in anxiety tend to deteriorate performance. Anxiety is thus both positively and negatively related to performance, so an experimental procedure effectively reducing a client's anxiety will improve the performance of some of the clients and worsen the

performance of others, yielding a net finding that reducing anxiety has not occurred or has little or no desirable effect.

This problem is usually addressed statistically. The data analysis should routinely include scatterplots of each *independent variable* with each dependent variable. If the shape of the scatter departs markedly from a roughly oval-shaped grouping, research results from statistical methods that assume linearity are being reduced by nonlinearity of relationship between the variables. This can be avoided by *curve fitting* (finding mathematical lines, curves, and surfaces that fit the data well and both elucidate and display its meaning) or corrected by *transforming* the nonlinear variables to near-linear to facilitate both analysis and interpretation or by using *separate statistical analyses* for different segments of the data range. In this example relating anxiety to performance, *separate statistical analysis* would involve merely performing separate analyses for the parts of the range in which the variables are positively related and the parts where they are negatively related. In the case of anxiety, really all three of these methods are viable candidates for fixing the problem.

One further note on scatterplots: If the scatter is roughly oval-shaped, but the oval is angled markedly different from 45 degrees, research results will be attenuated because of *restriction of range*. This is typically corrected by changing the metric of the variables or by increasing the sample size in the hope of increasing the range of values for the variable with the restricted range.

Problem: Regression to the Mean—Extreme Groups Are Being Studied. The very-worst-case scenario is when a researcher uses a measure to find the clients who need the treatment, provides the treatment to these clients, and then uses the same measure to detect treatment success. Measurement error, which is larger in extreme scores, will virtually guarantee that the researcher will find a significant client improvement, and possibly a quite large one. This research was doomed to seemingly succeed; how much of the improvement is regression to the mean artifact is unknown. This seriously compromised design is sometimes used when a researcher is working on a new method or an improvement on an existing method of therapy. The researcher tries it out on a small group of clients with difficult or treatment-resistant problems, and it seems to work because of regression artifact. The researcher may then spend scarce resources pursuing the development of a method that really does not work. When studying extreme groups, using a randomly assigned control group is essential. Analyzing the outcome data with ANCOVA, using the selection test as the covariate, further reduces error fluctuations and improves the likelihood of research findings that prove to be veridical.

Problem: Failing to Detect a Real Effect—Clients Are Found by Screening Tests. When researchers find study participants by random screening or by screening the entire population of a facility, 40%–60% of the participants found to be eligible are not actually eligible. Even if the screening test has excellent psychometric properties, this happens. The cause is in the baseline percentage of eligible clients in the group screened. The lower the percentage, the greater the number of ineligible clients who will be incorrectly identified. And the ineligible participants can prevent any true treatment effect from being detected by dilution.

One approach to avoiding this problem is to restrict screening to potential clients who have already been identified in some other way as likely to be eligible. For example, instead of screening an entire facility to find eligible candidates, only those who have been found appropriate by clinical examination would be screened. This approach reduces inappropriate participants to statistically manageable levels.

Problem: Attributing Causality—Concerns About the Effect of the Pretest and Other Persistent Concerns About Validity Threats. Concerns about *pretest sensitization* affecting posttest outcomes independently of treatment is the most common of this class of problems, but other concerns about pretest effects or alternative causes for posttest outcomes can concern the researcher. The *Solomon four group design* allows the researcher to test for the presence of these flaws in the research outcome.

This design is actually a fully randomized pretest/posttest control group design together with a fully randomized posttest-only control group design combined. The multiple comparisons possible among the two pretests and four posttests with this design make the concerns that might otherwise have been study flaws directly testable and possibly correctable if present. This design has excellent statistical power and is very robust in the face of challenges to internal and external validity. It can, however, be expensive and difficult to administer because of the strict randomization and the number of groups. Consequently, weaker designs are typically selected.

In the Adoption of Measurement Instruments

Research questions typically permit a number of possible dependent variables, and the researcher chooses among them to find an optimal fit: one that most closely expresses the central intent of the research question, while remaining practical. For example, a researcher testing the clinical effectiveness of music therapy in reducing client distress might select depression, anxiety, or any other dysphoric state as the dependent variable, and in doing so, define *distress* for the study. The precise operational definition of the selected variable will be the method by which it is measured. In the instance of anxiety, the method could be the client's score on an existing research measurement, such as an existing test for severity of anxiety, or on a commercially available test of anxiety. It could also be predetermined observations and measurements made by the researchers, as in the example above on priming research. Or it could be a test authored by

the researchers built to their own exact needs.

An example of the value of a good operational definition of the dependent variable concerns the priming effect (Bargh, Chen, & Burrows, 1996), in which students primed with stereotypes of older adults in an apparently unrelated word task walked significantly more slowly down the corridor to the next task than did controls. The contents of pre- and postinterviews and careful experimental design protected the conclusion from alternative explanations, and the study is a compelling demonstration of the aspect of priming known as the *Florida Effect*. Operationally defining *aging* as *slower walking speed* enabled the study.

Problems appear in the selection of variables and creating their operational definitions, as in other parts of the research process which merit researcher attention and adjusting. Operational definitions work best if they are intuitive, compelling, and minimally technical, as in this example.

Problem: Answering an Easier Question—Selecting an Existing Test. Many tests exist in the research literature and are available through the author or commercial channels, and it is likely that a good enough test already exists for most clinical studies. Any selection will have advantages and disadvantages. The disadvantages that make the test a measure of something even slightly different from what the research question asks must be weighed carefully. If the match is not precise, the researcher might wish to consider a different mode of measuring the variable of interest or creating a test exactly suited to the research purpose.

Problem: Answering an Easier Question—Authoring or Customizing a Test for the Research Project. In creating a test instrument or observation procedure to operationally measure the variable of interest, the researcher might follow the following steps to validate a test for use in research: (a) specify the construct; (b) review the related literature; (c) specify the need for the new measure and how it differs from what is available; (d) specify the domain; (e) specify the structure (unidimensional scale, subscales, etc.); (f) create initial items; (g) conduct an initial pilot test on a convenient sample; (h) conduct a reliability analysis and repair problems; (i) perform an initial validity procedure using structural exploration with factor analysis; (j) perform a second validity procedure (the gold standard is the Multitrait-Multimethod Matrix [MTMMM; Campbell & Fiske, 1959; Cronbach & Meehl, 1955], but consider other appropriate demonstrations of validity suited to your measurement); (k) perform a second pilot test on a representative but small sample; and (l) when still working with small pilot samples and having improved/added/deleted items to improve psychometric properties (benchmark), hold on to the best reliability and validity estimates for your plans to validate the test on an appropriately sized validation and norming sample. Watch for deviations from these benchmark values by ongoing recalculations as you collect data.

These steps include iterations. If, for example, the statistical properties of the initial test items are not adequate, some rewriting is needed, followed by a trial of the new item set. The factor analysis should reveal a structure anticipated by the test author or one congruent with the researcher's purpose. It is important to select *display* of the correlation matrix determinant. Some programs, including some versions of SPSS, do not automatically display this quantity, even when it is exactly equal to zero, which happens frequently enough. A true solution with a zero determinant cannot exist because it includes division by zero, and the program may create potentially irrelevant output without warning.

Once discovered, the zero-determinant problem can usually be remedied, depending on its cause. One cause of a zero determinant is one item being a linear combination of other items. Two perfectly correlated items is an obvious case of this. Drop one of the items, since it adds no information. Less obvious is when two or more items exactly predict another item. This happens when scale scores or the total score of the test have inadvertently been included in the analysis. These scores are summations of items, which predict the total and scale scores perfectly. Eliminate these and rerun the analysis. Even less obvious is when some items predict other items perfectly in a given sample because of the nature of the content. Watch for lack of error variance or negative error variance and repair or remove the problematic items. If the problematic items are difficult to find, stepwise linear regression can be useful. These hints are not exhaustive, and researchers validating their own tests will soon learn to check for many other causes when the determinant is exactly zero.

Problem: Failing to Detect a Real Effect—Scaling Level of Measure Too Low. While almost any type of measurement will lend itself to statistical analysis, higher levels of scaling will provide incrementally more statistical power. Select instruments at the highest scaling level the content permits, typically interval or ratio levels. When the researcher decides to author an instrument to meet the research needs more precisely, it is worthwhile to design it to provide measurements at the highest levels of scaling possible. Many variables in psychology and sociology are not demonstrably measured with interval-level scales, and treating them as interval scales when they are in reality ordinal-level introduces additional error. If a fully interval-level measure cannot be fitted to a research variable, a strong alternative that may require some help from a statistician is a Thurstone scaling. Ordinal processes in general can be measured at interval level or better by techniques like Thurstone scaling, particularly Case V scaling, which depends on the law of comparative judgment (Thurstone, 1927), an intrinsically ordinal process. Even lower-level scaling can be analyzed by powerful interval-level statistics: Nominal data can be converted to binary variables, which can then be used for some least squares statistics, such as regression, by employing

a system such as dummy coding. Consulting with a statistician or someone with experience in psychometrics would also be advisable for help in dealing with this problem.

Problem: Failing to Detect a Real Effect—Inadequacy of the Dependent Variable. Some of the applications of music therapy can be viewed as influencing a developmental trajectory, rather than producing a fixed effect. Children who are developing normally but achieve developmental milestones more slowly than desired are exposed to interventions to accelerate the developmental process, thereby reducing distress and the sequelae of being routinely behind their peers. Complete development likely would have occurred anyway, and it is only the speed that was affected.

A typical outcome variable in the social sciences can be insensitive to this type of change. The application of music therapy may have measurable effects over time whereby the trajectory (i.e., the dependent variable) is significantly altered despite the final outcome remaining unchanged. Music therapy employed to bring relief to clients in the final stages of degenerative processes which will result in death would seem to be better studied by defining variables designed to detect this change in the trajectory of the degenerative process. In addition to the specific sensitivity of variables like this to the effect of music therapy as applied to certain clients, this method brings the added advantage of requiring very few research participants.

To apply this remedy, the researcher would define the dependent variable as a change in *slopes* of a line's tangent to the developmental curve at the testing point times. For example, despite medical interventions, dementia has an insidious degenerative course ultimately resulting in death. Interventions used to slow the rate of degeneration must look at variables that alter the course of the disease, but not necessarily the endpoint. The application of music therapy in dementia patients could slow the rate of disease progression without influencing survival time, a change reflected in change or rate or slope.

Alternatively, if the researcher hypothesizes that survival time is influenced, *Kaplan–Meier estimation* may be useful. These procedures are currently more widely used in the biological and other-than-social sciences but may find useful application in music therapy. For researchers unfamiliar with recent developments in *latent curve analysis* and related procedures, consultation with a statistician is suggested.

In the Statistical Analysis

The use of particular statistical procedures to investigate research questions within various research designs allows considerably more creative leeway than usually may be supposed. The most conservative and widely accepted coupling of statistical procedures to designs and research questions has been well expounded in other chapters (e.g., Chapters 18 and 19). When a complex or creative statistical approach may be needed, a consultation with a statistician is suggested.

Table 1. Primary Statistical Tools

	Factor analysis
r, τ, ρ, ϕ	Correlations
f	Discriminant function
f	ANOVA, rANOVA, MANOVA, ANCOVA
z	z-test, percentiles
t	t test
$\hat{y}, \beta$	Multiple regression, polynomial regression
μ, σ	Descriptives & estimation
z, t	Confidence intervals
Z	Linear programming
p	Simple probability
f	Repeated measures
χ^2	Chi square
U	Mann–Whitney
R^2, D, η^2, ω^2	Size of effect, % variability accounted for
K-S	Kolmogorov–Smirnov goodness of fit
W	Wilcoxon signed-rank test
	Runs test for randomness

The researcher's basic statistical toolkit should include at least the tools listed in Table 1 (see Chapter 18 for additional information). Each has underlying assumptions, depending upon its application, and violation of these assumptions can greatly increase the probability of an erroneous outcome. Before employing a statistical procedure, it is useful to check what **assumptions** must be made. Many procedures are *robust* with respect to assumption violations. Robust, however, is not a synonym for impervious. The greater the violation of assumptions, the greater the likelihood that the statistic will not perform properly.

Problem: Assumption Violations—Unequal Variances. Many statistics assume that the variances within different groups are equal, and each statistic has a margin of tolerance for violation of this assumption. ANOVA is one of the most tolerant. Rather than ignoring unequal variances and relying on robustness or using a *rule of thumb,* a simple statistical test such as Levene's or Bartlett's will determine if the violation is excessive. If the test is failed, Welch's ANOVA is an option. Alternatively, transforming data to z values will correct for the unequal variances, also termed *heteroscedascity,* and any non-normality at the same time. Before using a correction, be sure to plot the data and determine whether the cause could be incorrectly coded data, or, more importantly, if the existence of outliers reveals important information about the research question, procedures, or sample.

Problem: Effect Size. A significant result is not necessarily an important or useful one. Depending on the selection of alpha, the sample size, and the power of procedures, a certain number of significant results will occur by chance alone. These results are quite unlikely to replicate. Legitimately significant results, however, may still not be important. A significant change in therapeutic procedure yielding only a 1% improvement in outcome will have its main value in improving understanding of the procedure or pointing the researcher in a useful direction. The change in and of itself will hardly be worth the time and effort in clinical application. Resources are usually limited or scarce in research, so they need to be allocated to the most important gains or the most promising leads. To manage these concerns, a statistic that estimates the *effect size* is calculated whenever a significant result has been found, to give the researchers a grasp on the magnitude of the effect that has been found.

The size of the improvement is a useful indicator of importance. The size can be viewed as a mean change (How much improvement, on average, was there in clients' outcomes?) or a percent of variability (Of all the variability in the clients' outcomes, what percent is attributable to this change in therapy procedure?). It is simple to calculate, readily available in SPSS, and provides an essential context for evaluating any significant outcomes of research.

Problem: Failing to Detect a Real Effect—Low Statistical Power. The power of a statistical procedure is the probability that it will find a treatment effect, if one exists. The power depends primarily on sample size, alpha, and the size of the anticipated effect. The population mean and variance need to be known, but they can be estimated from a sample. The sample size and alpha are chosen by the researcher. The size of the anticipated effect can be derived theoretically (this therapy should alter client response to this many items and therefore lower the dysphoria score 10 points or more) or estimated from the sample in the pilot study. Thus all quantities are known, or estimable. From these, the power can be calculated with a t test.

The power should be calculated before the research is begun, as soon as the quantities above can be estimated. There are two reasons for this. First, if the power was 42%, for example, it is doubtful that any researcher who knew this would undertake to do the research. There would be less than a 50/50 chance of detecting whether the therapy worked. Changes would have to be made if this research were to be done at all, but calculating the power in advance is the only way to know this. Software that assists in estimating power (e.g., PASS, G*POWER) could also be useful.

Second, the calculation can be used a different way. By the researcher's deciding that the minimum acceptable power is, for example, 90% (in effect deciding that there must be a 90% chance of finding the effect if it exists), the researcher can then calculate how large a sample size would be required to achieve this power. Knowing the resources of time, money, etc., required per client, the cost can then be estimated and a determination made whether the study is worth the cost.

Problem: Failing to Detect a Real Effect—Insensitive Dependent Measure. A dependent variable defining a fixed effect may be insensitive to a treatment that modifies a developmental process, as described above. Defining variables that quantify rate of change rather than magnitude of change either continuously or from one measurement point to another may find usefulness in music therapy research. The statistical power of repeated measures is attractive for music therapy research for reasons discussed above. Adding the statistical power of use of slope as a dependent variable might enable a more sophisticated examination of the effects of music therapy and a finer attuning of its use to client needs.

In Translation to Clinical Practice

Once the research has been carried out and the results are known, along with their effect sizes, the findings are reported in both statistical terms and in the parlance of scientist/researchers. The significant and important findings reside thenceforth in a filed report or a scientific journal article. In both places, it will be read but probably not acted on.

It is well established in research literature and academic discussion (Kahneman, 2011) that statistical arguments, however compelling, convince people cognitively but do not routinely influence their decisions. It is conjectured that readers acknowledge scientific findings while exempting themselves and those in contact with them from their applicability. However, it is also known to those studying availability heuristics that a single anecdotal tale, especially one with emotional connection, will influence decision-making and behavior, even if the anecdote is about a very rare instance.

Therefore, the communication of the research results, if they are to be incorporated into clinical practice by nonprofessional caregivers, includes more than reporting. It includes a separate task of communicating them to potential users in a manner that will affect their decision-making, that is, cause them to believe the research results so that they will be able to accept the findings and act on them. Ironies abound here. Research suggests that the most sophisticated findings might most effectively be translated to practice when framed as a case study. But case study is a research design thought by many to be a less sophisticated type of research than what may have led to the findings, an amusing irony in reporting the results of research.

Conclusion

This chapter has outlined potential problems that may occur in the design of an objectivist research study and means of ameliorating them. Problems addressed in the chapter are divided into those that occur in the research questions, in the creation of the research design, in the adoption of measurement instruments, in the statistical analysis, and in translation to clinical practice.

References

Bargh, J. A., Chen, M., & Burrows, L. (1996). Automaticity of social behavior: Direct effects of trait construct and stereotype priming on action. *Journal of Personality and Social Psychology, 71,* 230–244. doi:10.1037//0022-3514.71.2.230

Campbell, D. T., & Fiske, D. W. (1959). Convergent and discriminant validation by the multitrait–multimethod matrix. *Psychological Bulletin, 56,* 81–105. doi:10.1037/h0046016

Creswell, J. (2012). *Educational research: Planning, conducting, and evaluating quantitative and qualitative research* (4th ed.). Boston, MA: Pearson.

Cronbach, L. J., & Meehl, P. E. (1955). Construct validity in psychological tests. *Psychological Bulletin, 52,* 281–302. doi:10.1037/h0040957

Ellis, M. V. (1999). Repeated measures designs. *The Counseling Psychologist, 27,* 552–578. doi:10.1177/0011000099274004

Imbens, G., & Lemieux, T. (2007). *Regression-discontinuity designs: A guide to practice.* Retrieved from http://www.nber.org/papers/w13039. Cambridge, MA: National Bureau of Economic Research. doi:10.3386/w13039

Kahneman, D. (2011). *Thinking, fast and slow.* New York, NY: Farrar, Straus, and Giroux. doi:10.1086/674372

Nayak, S., Wheeler, B., Shiflett, S., & Agostinelli, S. (2000). Effect of music therapy on mood and social interaction among individuals with acute traumatic brain injury and stroke. *Rehabilitation Psychology, 45,* 274–283. doi:10.1037//0090-5550.45.3.274

Thurstone, L. L. (1927). A law of comparative judgment. *Psychological Review, 34,* 273–286. doi:10.1037/h0070288

Chapter 12
INTRODUCTION TO STATISTICAL CONCEPTS

Anthony Meadows

Statistics is a general term used for a variety of mathematical procedures that have been found to be helpful, even essential, in fields such as medicine, psychology, nursing, and economics. We turn to statistics to understand how often things occur, how likely they are to occur, and how common they are. More complicated forms of statistical analyses can look at relationships, causal factors, and even the relative strength and importance of one variable in relationship to others. Music therapy researchers have, for decades, used a range of statistical procedures to further their understanding of clinical practice, particularly the effectiveness of interventions on client's skills and behavior. This chapter serves as an overview of these approaches, including the procedures undertaken when using statistical methods. Where possible, specific examples from the music therapy literature are used to demonstrate the particular method, including several examples that parallel the SPSS examples provided by Behrens in Chapter 19.

Purposes of Statistical Analysis

In the field of music therapy, there is a range of attitudes and feelings about the uses of statistics in research. Some researchers, educators, and clinicians feel that statistics are very important in understanding clinical work; the beliefs, attitudes, and attributes of music therapists; and the relative effectiveness of our work when research is examined as a whole (e.g., meta-analysis). Others feel that statistical methods, along with corresponding methodological procedures, reduce, limit, or otherwise obscure the complexities of clinical processes, thereby reducing something complex and organic to causal relationships among isolated, simplified variables. From this perspective, variability, diversity, and uniqueness are valued more than predictability, homogeneity, and replicability.

The arguments of both positions are relevant to music therapists, and, equally importantly, both have their place. While, historically, statistical findings were often seen as *proof* that something in the field worked and was therefore the truth about an intervention, the majority of researchers who use statistical methods do not hold this belief. Statistics are ways of representing people, events, relations, and effects as averages and/or tendencies and, when handled with care, serve a valuable role in communicating the impact and benefits of music therapy.

Further, while our research is often directed toward ourselves, to further our understanding of clinical practice (or even education and training), we are increasingly being asked to speak to others outside the field, such as a medical doctor, school administrator, or health insurance company. When we are asked to speak to others, we need to do so in the same language, and that language is most often statistics. A medical team wants to know whether improvising music with a patient experiencing pain can help to reduce her pain experience and, if it does, wants proof of this. The proof most commonly asked for is statistical information.

Finally, we are, and will always be required to be, consumers of research. Whether we are clinicians, educators, students, or fellow researchers, we are required to read and integrate research findings into clinical practice, educational programs, classes, and/or future research. This is a responsibility we have to our clients and to each other. Part of this responsibility is to be able to read critically, to consume and integrate the work of others into our own work (whether it be work with clients, work with students, etc.), and to think about how current research informs and even changes our work. Understanding what statistical analyses mean (e.g., what ANOVA is) is an important part of this process, not only in understanding concepts such as statistical significance or effect size, but also in being able to translate statistical information into the practicalities of everyday work.

This chapter serves as a starting point for these endeavors. Statistics are *ways of seeing*. Sometimes these ways are very important, and sometimes less so. Their relative importance, though, is your responsibility, as reader, to consume, analyze, and integrate. Doing so requires an understanding of what each statistical analysis means.

Types of Statistics and Levels of Data

There are two basic types of statistics: descriptive and inferential. *Descriptive statistics* use mathematical methods to summarize sets of numbers. This can include things like totals (number of patients), averages (average age of patients), distributions (types of disabilities), and so forth. *Inferential statistics* are mathematical methods that employ probability theory to ascertain relationships between and among variables. For example, this can include methods for evaluating whether an intervention affects a client (e.g., does songwriting improve mood?) or what set of elements in an intervention combine for greatest effectiveness in addressing a patient's symptoms. An overview of common statistics employed in music therapy research will be described in the following sections, but readers are encouraged to consult Reid (2014) and Nolan and Heinzen

(2010) for detailed explanations of statistical concepts and procedures (among a range of texts discussing statistics).

Remember, numbers are simply symbols. They can represent the amount of time a patient does something, how often it is done, or how regularly. They can also represent changes a patient undergoes during music therapy, and even predict the extent to which other patients might be changed by music therapy interventions. For example, Ghetti (2012) examined the effectiveness of a music therapy intervention (music therapy with emotion-approach coping) on the emotions of patients waiting for cardiac catheterization. Prior to and after a single music therapy session, she asked patients to complete a 20-item questionnaire (Positive and Negative Affect Schedule), from which she undertook a statistical procedure known as an ANOVA (analysis of variance) to compare the two questionnaires. In so doing, she found that patients who participated in the music therapy group felt more positive in preparation for the catheterization procedure, suggesting that the music therapy intervention might be helpful to other patients with similar characteristics, as a more positive emotional state impacts the patient's emotional and physiological experience of catheterization.

There are four basic types of numbers, which are commonly referred to as *levels* or *scales of measurement*: nominal, ordinal, interval, and ratio. These are described in Chapter 14, Overview of Measurement Systems in Objectivist Research. To review, nominal variables are used to *name* or label a series of values. Ordinal scales provide good information about the *order* of events. Interval scales give us the order of values and the ability to quantify *the difference between each one*. Finally, ratio scales give us the ultimate—order, interval values, and the *ability to calculate ratios* since a *true zero* can be defined. Table 1 provides a summary.

Table 1. Summary of Data Characteristics

Characteristics	Nominal	Ordinal	Interval	Ratio
Categories and frequencies of distribution	Yes	Yes	Yes	Yes
Mode, median		Yes	Yes	Yes
Order of values is known		Yes	Yes	Yes
Can quantify the difference between each value			Yes	Yes
Can add or subtract			Yes	Yes
Can multiply or divide				Yes
Has absolute zero				Yes

Descriptive Statistics

Measures of Central Tendency

The mean, median, and mode are three commonly used descriptive statistics that use simple computational methods to summarize data. The *mean* is an average of scores, calculated by adding all the scores together and dividing by the total number of scores. The median is the measure of central tendency, that is, the score that splits all the scores into equal parts. The mode is the most common score. Each will be briefly explained using the example in Table 2.

Let's begin with an example of calculating an average score. This would be possible for columns two, three, and four (age, number of verbalizations, and number of minutes participating). To calculate the average age, we will add all the ages (7, 5, 6, 5, 6, 6, 8 = 43) and divide by the total number of children (43 ÷ 7), which equals 6.14 years. We could use the same procedure to calculate the average number of verbalizations (9.57 verbalizations) and the average number of minutes participating in sessions (18.86 minutes). The symbol for mean is m, x, or M.

The *median*, or central tendency, is calculated by arranging all the scores in order and identifying the middle score. For example, when viewing age (5, 5, 6, **6**, 6, 7, 8), the median is 6. When there is an even number of data in a set, then the median is calculated by locating the middle two scores and calculating the average between them.

Finally, to calculate the *mode*, simply examine all the scores together and find the score that occurs most often. In the case of age, that is 6.

Table 2. Descriptive Data Used to Summarize a Music Therapy Session

Child	Age (in years)	Number of verbalizations during the session	Number of minutes participating in the 30 min. session
1	7	8	18
2	5	3	22
3	6	7	14
4	5	11	18
5	6	4	23
6	6	15	26
7	8	6	11

Notice that different kinds of data are used in Table 2. Column 1, *Child*, uses nominal data, where each number represents a child, whereas columns 2, 3, and 4 are ratio data.

Normal Distribution and Variance

Statistical procedures, particularly inferential statistics, are built on the premise that the group of people researchers are collecting data from/about are reflective of the population they are from. Thus, a *sample* is the group of people in the study (from which data are collected), whereas the *population* is the total number of people possible in the group. For example, in the United States there were approximately 232,340 new cases of breast cancer in 2013 (www.cancer.gov). If we are interested in researching the benefits of a music therapy intervention to improve mood for women with breast cancer undergoing chemotherapy for the first time (new cases), then the population for the study is 232,340. If there are 100 women in the study, then this is the sample. Researchers hope that the sample is representative of the population, so that findings from the research can be *generalized.*

The next element important to understand in relation to populations is the concept of *normal distribution.* It is sometimes called the *bell curve* or the *Gaussian curve.* Normal distributions are symmetric around their mean, and the mean, median, and mode are equal. All members of a population are distributed under the bell curve, and 68% of the area of a normal distribution is within one standard deviation of the mean (95% of the area of a normal distribution is within two standard deviations of the mean). Understanding that a population's (e.g., first-time cancer patients) scores will be distributed *normally* helps us to know what kinds of calculations (parametric or nonparametric) can be undertaken using inferential statistics, discussed further in the following section.

Another important element of samples and populations is variability. Both standard deviation and variance measure variability. *Standard deviation* is the average deviation of scores within a sample, with the symbol σ. *Variance* is the average of the sum of the squared deviations for a population, with the symbol σ^2. Variance (σ^2 is pronounced "sigma squared") is just another way of saying that we are dealing with a variance in population. For example, if we look at the a measure commonly examined in the music therapy literature, namely the number of social interactions completed by children with autism in a music therapy session, we might find that in a single session, there are 8, 10, 11, 15, and 7 observable interactions for each of five children. The mean number of social interactions is (8 + 10 + 11 + 15 + 7 / 5) = 10.2. The variance is calculated by looking at the difference between each score and then computing the average amount of difference between the mean score and each score. Thus, for the child who interacted 8 times in the session, his score deviates 2.2 interactions from the mean score, and when all the scores are examined together using the formula above, the total variance is 7.76.

Standard deviation is a related measure of variability. Whereas the variance calculates variability of the scores of a population (all members of a group), standard deviation, , is the square root of the variance. Thus, for the example just given, the standard deviation of the children's social interaction scores is 2.78.

Inferential Statistics

Inferential statistics are used when making data-based decisions and in essence look at relationships among and/or between variables (Reid, 2014). These are particularly important when examining relationships that are observed in a sample and determining the extent to which these relationships can be generalized to a population representative of the sample. Before discussing inferential statistics in more detail, several concepts are important to introduce: experiment, independent and dependent variable, experimental and control group, effect size, confidence intervals, and power. Each will be briefly discussed below.

As previously mentioned, a *sample* is simply the group of people selected to participate in the research. Samples can be chosen in two primary ways: random or convenience. A *convenience sample* is generally drawn from an existing group or setting in which a music therapist is working. For example, if a music therapist is working with children who have cerebral palsy and wants to investigate the effects of a music-movement program on range of movement, he/she may find it more convenient and appropriate to work with the children in his/her school setting. The disadvantage of a convenience sample is that it may be biased, that is, not representative of the population as a whole. For example, if the school in which the music therapist works only works with children with spastic quadriplegia, then the results of the intervention may not apply to children with diplegia or paraplegia. *A random sample* is one in which, technically, every member of a specific *population* (e.g., men with prostate cancer) has an equal chance of being chosen to participate in the research, thereby increasing the potential generalizability of any study outcomes. In general, when clients consent to participate in an intervention, they are randomly assigned to either a treatment or control group, thereby increasing the likelihood that the sample is unbiased and reflective of the population as a whole.

The *scientific method* seeks to identify relationships that can be expressed mathematically and is built upon a foundation of rigorous logic and careful observation (Reid, 2014). The scientific method is also built upon *hypothesis testing.* Here researchers refer to two kinds of hypotheses. The *null hypothesis,* or H_0, posits that an intervention (also called the treatment) will not have an effect, whereas the *alternative hypothesis,* H_1, posits that the intervention will have an effect. Thus, the goal of an experiment is to evaluate the extent to which the null hypothesis is rejected or the alternative hypothesis accepted.

How is this achieved? Hypothesis testing always involves probability, which is where inferential statistics become essential. These procedures test the researcher's hypotheses and determine the extent to which any changes in data reflect the effectiveness of the intervention or occur just by chance. There is no absolute answer as to how to calculate this, but in general, if the probability is that the outcome occurs less than one time in 20, then we reject the null hypothesis and accept the alternative hypothesis. One time in 20 is 5%, or 0.05. Thus a commonly used measure to reject the null hypothesis, known as the *alpha level*, is α = 0.05.

While alpha gives researchers an indication of probability, there is always the possibility of being wrong. Setting alpha to .05 simply allows researchers to conclude that the odds of any observed differences are less than 5% and that these differences occurred by chance. However, this also means that there is a 1 in 20 chance that the null hypothesis will be rejected when it is in fact true. This is called a *Type I error* (signified by α). No one likes to make mistakes, so researchers will often set the alpha value to .01, thereby increasing the likelihood of a Type I error to 1 in 100. While this increases the probability of a treatment effect, or relationship between variables, it may have an unintended negative consequence. By decreasing alpha, you inadvertently increase the likelihood of failing to reject the null hypothesis when it is in fact false. This is known as a *Type II error* (signified by β). Thus, as the probability of making a Type I error decreases, and the probability of making a Type II error increases.

Accounting for Type I and Type II errors is important as part of the research process, and one way of addressing this is by including an analysis of *power*. Power is simply the probability of correctly rejecting a null hypothesis, and, fundamentally, the goal of an experiment is to conduct as powerful a study as possible. Although power is calculated as 1 − β, and a power analysis is often included in study results, several steps are taken to ensure adequate power. These include considering:

- *The statistical test being performed.* Some statistical tests are inherently more powerful than others.
- *The sample size.* In general, the larger the sample size, the larger the power. However, generally increasing sample size involves tangible costs in time, money, and effort. Consequently, it is important to make sample size *large enough*, but not wastefully large.
- *The size of experimental effects.* If the null hypothesis is rejected by a substantial amount, power will be higher than if it is rejected by a small amount.
- *The level of error in experimental measurements.* Measurement error acts like *noise* that can bury the *signal* of real experimental effects. Consequently, anything that enhances the accuracy and consistency of measurement can increase statistical power.

Effect size is the next concept of importance to understand when using inferential statistics. It is a numerical way of expressing the strength or magnitude of a reported relationship between variables, be it causal or not. The basic formula to calculate the effect size is to subtract the mean of the control group from that of the experimental group and then divide the numerator by the standard deviation of the scores for the control group. Effect size is expressed as a decimal number and, while numbers greater and 1.00 are possible, they do not occur very often. Thus, an effect size near .00 means that, on average, experimental and control groups performed the same; a positive effect size means that, on average, the experimental group performed better than the control group; and a negative effect size means that, on average, the control group performed better than the experimental group did. For positive effect sizes, a larger number indicates that the experimental treatment is more effective. As a general rule of thumb, an effect size in the .20s (e.g., .27) indicates a treatment that produces a relatively small effect, whereas an effect size in the .80s (e.g., .88) indicates a large treatment effect (Cohen, 1988).

Finally, *confidence intervals* are also important to understand when examining a data set. As defined by Reid (2014), a confidence interval is "the range of values that has a known probability of including the population parameter, usually the mean" (p. 217). Put in another way, it is a range of values that describes the uncertainty surrounding an estimate. For example, if the mean (*M*) score is 14.2 verbalizations during music therapy for a group of six children with autism, and the standard deviation (*SD*) is 2, then the following formula calculates the confidence interval (for a *t* test), where t_c is the critical value of *t* and s_m the estimate of the standard error from the sample.

$$M - t_c (s_m) < \mu > M + t_c (s_m)$$

Thus, when calculated, the confidence interval is 9.26 < μ > 19.54, which means that with sample size of 6, we are 95% confident that the population mean will fall between 9.26 and 19.54.

To summarize, the scientific method moves through a series of stages or steps, summarized below:

1. The researcher begins by asking a question,
2. The literature is then consulted to understand what is already known about the phenomenon,
3. Based upon this, a hypothesis is developed,
4. The hypothesis is tested with an experiment,
5. The data are analyzed and conclusions drawn,
6. The results become the basis for new experiments, developing new hypotheses built upon these analyses and conclusions,
7. There is, hypothetically, never an endpoint to this process, as data are used to develop ever more complex and integrated theories that generate new questions and hypotheses.

The scientific method is a self-correcting process. Even if a conclusion is incorrect, or partially correct, as an evidence base is built, clearer, more robust findings, captured over time, will clarify and confirm existing research, thereby developing our understanding of the relationships between variables.

Inferential Statistical Methods

Inferential statistics are used when making data-based (or data-driven) decisions and are concerned with whether there is sufficient evidence for a relationship or pattern that is observed in a sample to be generalized to the population it represents. There are fundamentally two types of research designs, difference designs and association designs (Reid, 2014), which are summarized in Table 3.

Difference designs examine whether an observed difference is likely to be the result of chance or, instead, provide evidence for a real or systematic effect. These include statistical procedures such as chi square, z-score, Kruskal-Wallis *H*, and analysis of variance (ANOVA). *Association designs* examine whether an association between variables is likely to have been the result of chance or, instead, provide evidence of systematic effect. These include statistical procedures such as Spearman *r*, Pearson *r*, and linear and multiple regressions.

These designs also help us to understand another important difference in inferential statistics, that is, the difference between parametric and nonparametric tests. Parametric tests include the independent samples *t* test,

paired samples *t* test, and one-way ANOVA, whereas nonparametric tests include the Mann-Whitney test, the Wilcoxon signed-rank test, and the Kruskal-Wallis *H* test. Each category (parametric and nonparametric) draws from different *assumptions* about research data. Parametric tests are based upon three assumptions about the population (Nolan & Heinzen, 2010): (a) that the dependent variable is assessed using a scale measure (e.g., interval or ratio data), (b) that participants are randomly selected, and (c) the distribution of the population of interest is normal (or close to normal). By contrast, nonparametric tests are not based upon a test of assumptions about the population. While parametric and nonparametric tests are of equal value in understanding differences, given the specific data set under review, parametric tests are generally seen as having more power, whereas nonparametric tests are generally seen as being more *conservative* (i.e., more likely to make a Type II Error) and having less statistical power.

A Music Therapy Example: Framing Questions and Statistical Methods

In the forthcoming example (Figure 1), provided by Behrens (Chapter 19), some music therapy researchers are interested in understanding the ways in which song discussion experiences influence the frequency and quality of emotion-related statements made and words used by adolescents in an inpatient facility. They are interested in both association

Type of Data				
Nominal (Frequency)		**Ordinal** (Ranked)	**Interval/Ratio** (Continuous Measure)	
Inferential Statistics (Finding Relationships)				
Statistical procedures for difference and interaction designs				
One variable with at least two outcomes	Goodness-of-fit chi-square	**One IV with one sample—one DV**		One sample z score or one-sample t test
		One IV with two or more independent samples—one DV	*Kruskal-Wallis H*	One-way between subjects ANOVA (only two independent samples—independent samples t test)
		One IV with one sample having two or more repeated measures—one DV		One-way within-subjects ANOVA (only two repeated measures—dependent samples t test)
Two variables, each with at least two outcomes	Chi-square test of independence	**Two IV each with two or more independent samples—one DV**		Two-way between subjects ANOVA
Statistical procedures for association designs				
Correlation	Phi		*Spearman r*	Pearson r
Regression				Linear Regression *Multiple Regression*

Table 3. An Overview of Inferential Statistics

From Reid (2014, p. 109). Reprinted with permission

and prediction questions, and their associated designs, which are summarized in Table 4. This table also identifies the independent variable (IV), the dependent variable (DV), and the level of measurement. Each will be explained in more detail in the following sections, under the headings "Difference Questions, Designs, and Statistics" and "Association Questions, Designs, and Statistics."

Examples of the questions of interest, devised from the vignette in Figure 1, are outlined in Table 4, along with the IV, DV, and statistical analysis appropriate for the question. As you can see, these are divided into difference questions and relationship questions, which will be elaborated below.

Chris and a group of music therapists were interested in the influence of song discussion experiences on the frequency and quality of emotion-related statements. They all work in a facility for adolescents, ages 14 to 21, with emotional/ behavioral needs and were observing differences in how the adolescents talked during song discussions based on their type of performing arts background, age, and gender. All of the adolescents had been through groups that taught them the nuances of using the five most common emotions, happy, mad, sad, scared, and proud. Because of the number of music therapists, they each had slightly different questions that they wanted to answer based on their observations in sessions:

1. Are the standardized emotion-coping scores for the adolescents at the facility significantly different than the national average for their age group?
2. Do the male and female adolescents significantly differ in their frequency of emotion-related statements during song discussion experiences?
3. Do adolescents verbalize significantly more emotion-related statements during song discussion experiences or verbal processing groups?
4. Does the frequency of emotion-related statements for the adolescents significantly differ depending upon their performing arts background, music, visual arts, and no art-related background?
5. Do adolescents verbalize significantly more emotion-related statements during a song discussion experience, a verbal processing group or an informal social group time?
6. Do adolescents with a music or no performing arts background verbalize significantly more emotion-related statements during song discussion experiences or verbal processing groups, and does this difference vary depending upon whether they have a music or no performing arts background?
7. Do adolescents with a background in music or no performing arts significantly differ in whether they do or do not use the five emotion words on which they were trained?
8. Do adolescents with a background in music or no performing arts significantly differ in a ranking of how soon they use three emotion words during a song discussion experience?
9. During song discussion experiences, do adolescents who have high emotion-coping scores tend to verbalize a high frequency of emotion-related statements and those who have low emotion-coping scores tend to verbalize a low frequency of emotion-related statements?
10. During song discussion experiences, do adolescents who have high quality ratings for their emotion-related statements tend to be ranked as quickly using three emotion words and those who have low quality ratings for their emotion-related statements tend to be ranked as taking a long time to use three emotion words?
11. During song discussion experiences, is there a relationship between adolescents' use and nonuse of five emotion words and their emotion coping score?
12. How accurately can age and a measure of the number of emotion-related statements predict emotion-coping skills?

Chris designed a study to accommodate all the questions where the group of music therapists first recorded information on 60 randomly selected adolescents: age; gender; whether they had a music, visual art, or no performing arts background; and their emotion-coping score from a standardized measure given to all adolescents by the facility. The music therapists were surprised and delighted when they found that the type of performing arts background formed three equal groups of 10 adolescents across the three types, music, visual arts, and no arts backgrounds; and that an equal number of males and females existed in each group. A one-way between-subject ANOVA indicated that age also was randomly distributed across the groups, as there was no significant difference across the three groups.

The music therapists then conducted the study. They first randomly assigned the 60 adolescents to three treatment groups. They devised three equivalent conditions: a song discussion experience, a verbal processing group, and an informal social group time. They collected the following data on the adolescents in each of the three groups during the three conditions that were randomly ordered in their presentation.

Figure 1. Scenario, Research Questions, Methods, and Variables.
From Behrens, Chapter 19

Difference Questions, Designs, and Statistics

The first kinds of questions asked by these researchers are concerned with understanding whether any of the therapy groups affected the use of emotion-related statements or five emotion words (happy, sad, mad, proud, scared). In other words, the researchers are interested in knowing whether music therapy sessions made a positive difference in each of these areas, but want to compare the adolescents' responses across groups to see if music therapy is more effective than verbal therapy and recreational activities. Before considering this in more detail, let's looks at some of the key elements, based upon some of the earlier concepts outlined in the chapter.

This first element of importance is to identify the independent (IV) and dependent (DV) variables and to identify the type of statistical analysis associated with the question. In this example, there is one IV (type of intervention) and two DVs (1: emotional-related statements, 2: emotion words). Note that as there are three types of interventions, there are three levels of the IV: music therapy, verbal therapy, and recreation group.

Because of the way the researchers gathered the data, we also have an additional independent variable that may be included in analyses, based on the questions asked: sex (male and female). We also have an additional dependent variable, which is the scores on the standardized emotional-coping scale given to all teens when they entered the facility. Thus, the researchers can use these IVs and DVs in various combinations to answer their questions of interest, applying the appropriate statistical analysis when doing so.

Let us look briefly at some of the other elements discussed so far in this chapter. You'll notice that the use of IVs, DVs, and random assignment are all characteristics of the scientific method. Because of the number of participants and way they were selected and assigned to the different therapy groups, we can also assume that this sample is representative of the population of adolescents with emotional/behavioral needs, and any results can be generalized. There are also different levels of data. We have nominal data (sex: male and female), interval data (emotion-coping scores) and ratio data (emotion-related statements). Each of these data types can be used in the forthcoming analyses, as each serves a different kind of purpose.

When we look at the questions in Figure 1, we notice that each is asked in a way that reflects the curiosity of the researcher: Does it make a difference? Is it related or connected? Can it predict something—where *it* is an intervention or characteristic of the adolescents? If we apply these questions and move them into hypothesis testing, then we can create a null (H_0) or alternate (H_1) hypothesis for each question. For example, if we take the first question, "Are the standardized emotion-coping scores for the adolescents at the facility significantly different than the national average?," then we can restate these as follows:

H_0: There are no differences between adolescents' scores on a standardized emotion-coping scale when compared with the national average.

H_1: Adolescents will score lower than the national average on a standardized measure of emotional coping.

Similarly, Research Question 3, "Do adolescents verbalize significantly more emotion-related statements during song discussion or verbal processing groups?" can be stated as:

H_0: There are no differences in emotion-related statements between the song discussion and verbal processing groups.

H_1: The song discussion group will produce significantly more emotion-related statements than the verbal processing group.

Notice that the null hypothesis always suggests no differences between groups, whereas the alternate hypothesis always suggests a difference, be it positive or negative.

The next stage is to choose the statistical analysis, probability level, and direction of the difference (positive or negative). While the type of analysis always guides these three questions, these three elements are usually undertaken simultaneously. As discussed earlier, in general, researchers choose a probability level of $p = 0.05$, which means that fewer than 5 times out of 100 these results would be due to chance alone, or, putting it another way, there is less than a 1 in 20 probability that any differences are the result of chance but rather can be attributed to the intervention. Sometimes, researchers will choose a value of $p = 0.01$, but as the *p value* decreases (gets smaller), the likelihood of a Type II error increases. Similarly, researchers will commonly use a ***two-tailed prediction,*** which is connected to the null hypothesis. The null hypothesis assumes that any differences could be positive or negative—and are simply not known. Thus, a two-tailed prediction allows for either a positive or negative effect, whereas a ***directional prediction,*** or ***one-tailed prediction***, assumes that the direction of the effect is known and can be expected based upon previous research. Because we are still building our research base in music therapy, most researchers use two-tailed prediction. The main difference, from a statistical point of view, is that the numerical value of the statistical analysis is different based upon the direction.

Once the statistical analysis, p value, and direction (one-tailed or two-tailed) have been determined, then the actual analysis is undertaken and the value of the analysis found (this is the actual statistic). This number is compared with the ***critical value*** needed to determine whether the finding is significant or not. For example, in the first analysis undertaken in this chapter, the t value calculated was $t = 28.16$, which indicates a significant difference. In order for the difference to be significant, thereby rejecting the null hypothesis, the number must be greater than 2.045. Significance is important because it tells us whether the

Research Questions from the Scenario	Variable/s*	Level of Measurement	Difference or Relationship Question	Statistical Analysis (Parametric/ Nonparametric)
1. Are the standardized Emotion Coping Scores for the adolescents at the facility significantly different than the national average for their age group?	DV—Emotion Coping Score	IV—N/A DV—Interval	Difference	One-sample *t* test—Parametric
2. (a) Do the male and female adolescents significantly differ in their frequency of emotion-related statements during song discussion experiences? or (b) Do female adolescents verbalize significantly more emotion-related statements than male adolescents during song discussion experiences?	IV—Sex (male/female) DV—Frequency of emotion- related statements	IV—Nominal DV—Ratio	Difference Difference	Independent *t* test – Parametric (a) two-tailed test (b) one-tailed test
3. Do adolescents verbalize significantly more emotion-related statements during song discussion experiences or verbal processing experiences?	IV—Treatment (music/verbal) DV—Frequency of emotion- related statements	IV—Nominal DV—Ratio	Difference	Dependent or Paired-sample *t* test—Parametric
4. Does the frequency of emotion-related statements for the adolescents significantly differ depending upon their performing arts background: music, visual arts, and no arts-related background?	IV—Type of background (music/art/none) DV—Frequency of emotion-related statements	IV—Nominal DV—Ratio	Difference	One-way between-subject ANOVA— Parametric
5. Do adolescents verbalize significantly more emotion-related statements during a song discussion experience, a verbal processing experience, or an informal social group experience?	IV—Treatment (none/music/verbal) DV—Frequency of emotion-related statements	IV—Nominal DV—Ratio	Difference	One-way within-subject ANOVA— Parametric
6. Do adolescents verbalize significantly more emotion-related statements during song discussion experiences or verbal processing experiences, and does this difference vary depending upon whether they have a background in music or no performing arts background?	IV—Treatment (music/verbal) IV—Type of background (music/none) DV—Frequency of emotion-related statements	IV—Treatment —Nominal IV—Type of background— Nominal DV—Ratio	Difference	2 x 2 mixed ANOVA— Parametric
7. Do adolescents with a background in music or no performing arts background significantly differ in whether they do or do not use the five emotion words on which they were trained?	IV—Type of background— (music/none) DV—Used five emotions— yes/no	IV—Nominal DV—Nominal	Difference	Chi square— Nonparametric
8. Do adolescents with a background in music or no performing arts background significantly differ in their ranking of how soon they use three emotion words during a song discussion experience?	IV—Type of background— (music/none) DV—Ranking —number of minutes to use three emotion words (1 = fewest)	IV—Nominal DV—Ordinal	Difference	Mann-Whitney *U*— Nonparametric

9. (a) During song discussion experiences, do adolescents who have high Emotion-Coping Scores tend to verbalize a high frequency of emotion-related statements and those who have low emotion-coping scores tend to verbalize a low frequency of emotion-related statements? (b) During song discussion experiences, is there a relationship between adolescents' Emotion-Coping Scores and their frequency of emotion-related statements verbalized during song discussion experiences? CV—Frequency of emotion-related statements	PV—Standardized Emotion-Coping Score	PV—Interval CV—Ratio	Relationship Relationship	Inferential test of Pearson product-moment correlation coefficient (r)— Parametric (a) one-tailed test (b) two-tailed test
10. During song discussion experiences, do adolescents who receive high quality ratings for their emotion-related statements tend to also receive high rankings for quickly using three emotion words and those who receive low quality ratings for their emotion-related statements tend to also receive low rankings for taking an extended time to use three emotion words?	PV—Reverse rank of number of minutes to use three emotion words (1 = fewest) CV—Quality rating for emotion-related statements	PV—Ordinal CV—Ordinal	Relationship	Spearman rho—Nonparametric
11. During song discussion experiences, is there a relationship between adolescents use and nonuse of five emotion words and the emotion-coping score?	CV—Emotion-coping score (emotional coping skills) PV—Yes/no use of five taught emotion words	CV—Interval PV—Nominal (discrete categories)	Relationship	Point–biserial Nonparametric
12. How accurately can age and a measure of the number of emotion-related statements predict emotion coping skills?	PV—Age, Frequency of emotion-related statements CV—Emotion-Coping Score	PV—Age— Frequency statements— Ratio CV—Interval	Relationship	Multiple regression— Parametric

Table 4. Summary of Research Questions, Types of Variables, and Statistical Analyses
* Abbreviations: IV = independent variable; DV = dependent variable; CV = criterion variable; PV = predictor variable
From Behrens, Chapter 19, Introduction to SPSS

findings from the data analysis (the statistic) lead us to accept or reject the null hypothesis.

Critical values and significance are sometimes the hardest things to understand. Where, after all, does the significant level come from? How is that number calculated? Simply put, these numbers come from distribution tables and show the minimum number needed to confidently predict that the statistic calculated is greater than, less than, or equal to the average number for a particular group. This, in turn, is affected by the number of people in the research group. You calculate the level of significance by subtracting 1 from the actual number of people in the group. This is called the **degrees of freedom** and helps researchers to calculate the significant t (or F, etc.) value. Continuing the above example, as there were 30 adolescents in the group, the degrees of freedom (df) is 29 and the related t value 2.045. Using the

same tables, if there were only 15 adolescents in the group, then the df would be 14 and the critical t (the value at which the null hypothesis is rejected) is 2.145. So as the group size decreases, the critical t value increases—meaning that the smaller the group gets, the larger the t statistic needed to indicate a treatment effect. This is a common problem in music therapy research, as researchers often have small sample sizes and thereby have to have larger treatment effects in order to suggest intervention effectiveness at a statistically significant level.

Let us move now to discussing a number of these statistical analyses (which are often colloquially called *statistical tests* or *tests*). We will focus on three tests here: the t test, ANOVA, and chi square.

T Test. The t test is one of the most commonly used

statistical analyses and is used to compare two means. There are several types of *t* tests, of which the most commonly used are: one-sample *t* test, independent samples *t* test, and dependent or paired-samples *t* test. The one-sample *t* test is used to compare a sample and population mean, the independent samples *t* test is used to compare two independent means (the means from two different samples: e.g., an experimental and control group), and the paired samples *t* test is used to compare two groups that are thought to be equivalent in some way. Let's look at the first three research questions in the adolescent study to clarify this further, identifying the IV, DV, and data types when doing so.

1. Are the standardized emotion-coping scores for the adolescents at the facility significantly different than the national average for their age group?
   a. IV: none
   b. DV: emotion-coping score (interval data)
2. Do male and female adolescents significantly differ in their frequency of emotion-related statements during song discussion experiences?
   a. IV: sex (male/female) (nominal data)
   b. DV: frequency of emotion-related statements (ratio data)
3. Do adolescents verbalize significantly more emotion-related statements during song discussion experiences or verbal processing experiences?
   a. IV: treatment (music/verbal) (nominal data)
   b. DV: frequency of emotion-related statements (ratio data)

Question 1 is analyzed using a one-sample *t* test, because it considers all the adolescents as a group, and compares them to the national average (the average of all possible adolescents). Question 2 uses an independent-sample *t* test, because it treats the male and female adolescents as two different groups, separated by sex, and asks whether they are different from each other in the use of emotion-related statements. Question 3 requires a paired-sample *t* test (also called a dependent-sample *t* test), because the two adolescent groups are thought to be equivalent (because of random assignment to each group) and therefore any differences between the frequency of emotion-related statements is assumed to be because of the intervention and not any *a priori* differences in the groups.

ANOVA. Perhaps the most commonly used analyses cited in the literature are analyses of variance (ANOVA; DeCuir, 2005). ANOVAs are, in many ways, an extension of *t* tests in that they compare means. ANOVAs go beyond *t* tests, though, in that they allow researchers to compare the means of three or more groups simultaneously. Like *t* tests, there are within groups and between groups ANOVAs, as well as mixed ANOVAs. The statistic calculated for an ANOVA is the *F* value, so an ANOVA can also be called the *F test*.

The one-way ANOVA is used with one nominal independent variable and one interval or ratio variable. The independent variable can consist of any number of groups (levels). Let's use research Question 5 to frame this discussion:

1. Do adolescents verbalize significantly more emotion-related statements during a song discussion experience, a verbal processing experience, or an informal social group experience?
   a. IV: treatment (music/verbal/social group; nominal data)
   b. DV: emotion coping score (interval data)

For this question, the researchers are interested in knowing whether there are differences in the emotion-related statements between the three treatment groups: song discussion, verbal processing and informal social group. As you know, students were randomly assigned to each of these three groups. Note that this is a within-subjects design since it can be assumed that each of the groups is equivalent and any differences in emotion-related statements can be accounted for by the intervention, not group makeup. Second, notice that instead of two groups (i.e., levels) of the independent variable, we now have three. The *t* test, which is often used in similar experiments with two groups, is only appropriate for situations where there are only two levels of one independent variable. When there is a nominal independent variable and a ratio dependent variable and there are more than two levels of the independent variable and/or there is more than one independent variable (a case that would require a two-way or three-way ANOVA), then the appropriate analysis is an analysis of variance.

When there are more than two levels of the independent variable, the analysis goes through two steps. First, we carry out an *F* test to determine if there are any differences among any of the means. If the *F* value is statistically significant, then we carry out a second step in which we compare sets of two means (e.g., song discussion and verbal group, song discussion and recreation group) at a time in order to determine specifically where the significant difference lies. Let's say that we have run the experiment and conducted the within-subjects one-way analysis of variance. We use a statistical program and analyze the data with treatment as the independent variable and emotion-related statements as the dependent variable.

When the statistical analysis is conducted, the resulting *F* value $F(2, 58) = 12.32$, $p = 0.000$, suggesting a significant main effect. Let's look at what this means. The numbers in the parentheses (2, 58) are the degrees of freedom (df_1, df_2). As you know, degrees of freedom give an estimation of the amount of error in the sample in relation to a population mean for the same sample. In other words, it just provides researchers with a way of accounting for measurement error. In this example, 2 represents the number of treatment groups minus 1 (3–1), and the second value is the number of participants minus df_1(60–2), or 58. Thus, the degrees of freedom are 2 and 58. Once the degrees of freedom are calculated, the researcher can evaluate the F statistic against the critical F value tables to determine whether the F value is statistically significant—larger than the critical F value.

In this ANOVA analysis, the F value was 12.32, which is significantly higher than the critical F of 2.76 required to support a statistically significant finding. The p value (0.000) suggests that there is less than 1 chance in 1,000 that the result occurred by chance!

What we don't yet know is where the differences lie (which groups produced more emotion-related statements?)—we know only that there is a difference. To answer this question, the researchers ran a series of Tukey's post hoc tests, which are like a series of t tests. These post hoc tests are more stringent than the regular t tests, however, due to the fact that the more tests you perform, the more likely it is that you will find a significant difference just by chance. These analyses showed that the largest number of emotion-related statements occurred in the song discussion group ($\bar{x}$ = 6.80, SD = 1.75), and that this was significantly different from the verbal processing group (p = 0.022; x = 4.60, SD = 2.12) and the recreation group ($\bar{x}$ = 3.00, SD = 1.16). When taken as a whole, the findings can be stated as follows: There were significant differences in the number of emotion-related statements between the three treatment groups $F(2, 58)$ = 12.32, p = 0.000. Adolescents in the song discussion group produced more emotion-related statements than those in the verbal processing or recreation group, suggesting that the song discussion group is the most effective in eliciting emotion-related statements and may further suggest that the intervention is effective in engaging adolescents in discussions related to feelings.

Chi Square. A chi-square test, also labeled χ^2, is a statistical test commonly used for testing independence and goodness of fit. Testing independence determines whether two or more observations across two populations are dependent on each other (that is, whether one variable helps to estimate the other).

$$\chi^2 = \frac{\sum (O-E)^2}{E}$$

Testing for goodness of fit determines if an observed frequency distribution matches a theoretical frequency distribution. In both cases, the equation to calculate the chi-square statistic is presented above, where O equals the observed frequency and E the expected frequency. The results of a chi-square test, along with the degrees of freedom, are used with a previously calculated table of chi-square distributions to find a p value. The p value can then be used to determine the significance of the statistic. Whereas t tests use interval or ratio data and are therefore understood as

parametric tests, chi square uses nominal data and is understood as a nonparametric test.

If we return to the adolescent research, Question 7 is an excellent example of a chi-square analysis because it asks whether there are any differences between groups and uses nominal data for both the IV and DV. This can be further understood as a 2 x 2 chi square, as there are two levels of the IV (music/no arts) and two levels of the DV (did or did not use emotion words):

1. Do adolescents with a background in music or no performing arts background significantly differ in whether they do or do not use the five emotion words on which they were trained?
   a. IV: type of background (music/no arts; nominal data)
   b. DV: use of emotion words: did, or did not use them (nominal data)

When undertaking this analysis, the formula evaluates any differences in the proportions of the two nominal variables arcoss the two groups. When calculated using the above formula, the chi-square value is χ^2 = 5.05, p = 0.025, and can be stated as follows: The proportion of adolescents with music backgrounds who used the five taught emotion words during music experience discussions was significantly higher than the proportion of adolescents with no performing arts background who used the five taught emotion words.

Relationship Questions, Designs, and Statistics

While difference questions tend to focus on evaluating the extent to which an intervention is effective (e.g., t test) or more effective than another intervention (e.g., ANOVA), association questions are about relationships. Specially, we are asking if two variables *covary*. This means that changes in one variable help us to predict changes in another, and when we see a relationship, we say there is a *correlation*. Table 5 provides a summary of statistical procedures based upon the type of data. Specifically, if both variables are nominal (e.g., sex: male, female) then you would use *phi;* if both are ordinal, then you use Spearman *r;* and if both variables are interval or ratio, then you employ Pearson *r*. Table 5 provides an overview.

Table 5. Statistical Procedures According to Type of Data

	Nominal	Ordinal	Interval or Ratio
Correlation	Phi	Spearman *r*	Pearson *r*
Regression			Linear regression
			Multiple regression

Each of these correlations can vary from –1 to +1, where a correlation of 0 indicates no association and a correlation of 1 indicates a perfect association. The –/+ values are important because they tell is the direction of the relationhip. A positive correlation means that as one value increases so does another. For example, the longer a child participates in music therapy, the higher their social skills scores. Conversely, a negative correlation suggests that as one variable increases, the other decreases. For example, the larger the number of individual music therapy sessions, the lower the depression score for patients undergoing chemotherapy. In general, a correlation of 0–0.3 suggests a lower or small relationship; 0.31–0.69, a modest correlation, and above 0.7, a high correlation. Thus, the –/+ sign indicates the direction of the relationship, and the number the degree of relationship.

Let us return once again to the adolescent study and review Question 9a (Table 4):

1. During song discussion experiences, do adolescents who have high emotion-coping scores tend to verbalize a high frequency of emotion-related statements and those who have low emotion-coping scores tend to verbalize a low frequency of emotion-related statements?
   a. PV: emotion-coping scores (ratio data)
   b. CV: emotion-related statements (ratio data)

The first thing to recognize is that there is no traditional IV-DV when asking correlation questions. We are looking for relationhsips, not differences. Rather, the terms *predictor variable* and *criterion variable* are used. The predictor variable (in IV-DV thinking, this would be the IV) is the one used to predict the criterian variable (in IV-DV thinking, this would be the DV). The researchers are interested in predicting the adolescents' emotion-coping scores from the frequency of their emotion-related statements. The formula for the Pearson *r is:*

$$r = \frac{\sum xy}{\sqrt{\sum x^2 \sum y^2}}$$

Using the above formula, the *Pearson r* = 0.63, with a significance of 0.000, suggesting that the relationship is significant and modestly strong. The results would be reported as follows: $r(28) = 0.63$, $p = 0.000$. The number 28 refers to the degrees of freedom, which is calculated by subtracting the total number of groups (2) from the number of adolescents: 30 – 2 = 28.

Multiple regression (along with linear regression) takes the basic concepts of the Pearson *r* and extends it to situations in which there is more than one predictor variable for a criterian variable, aiming for prediction. In other words, in our previous example, the researchers found that high emotion-related statements predicted high scores on an emotional-coping scale. In many situations, though, there can be more than one variable that predicts another—for example, sex, age, years of education, number of music therapy sessions, scores on a depression scale, and so forth, could all be predictors of emotional coping.

Multiple regression looks at all the predictor variables simultaneously, using the following formula, and through this process drops any that do not significantly enhance the overall prediction.

$$F = B_1X_1 + B_2X_2 + B_3X_3 + B_0$$

B_1 is the regression weight associated with variable 1, B_2 the regression weight associated with variable 2, and so forth. B_0 is a constant, associated with the value of the Y intercept that reflects the relationship between the predictor and criterian variables. Question 12 from the adolescent study reflects a multiple regression question:

1. How accurately can age and a measure of the number of emotion-related statements predict emotion-coping skills?
   a. PV: emotion-related statements (ratio data)
   b. PV: age (ratio data)
   c. CV: emotion-coping scores (interval data)

When the multiple regression is computed, the following statistic emerges: adjusted $R^2 = 0.59$, $F(2, 27) = 21.78$, $p = 0.000$. The R^2 value indicates the amount of variance for emotion coping that is accounted for by the combination of age and frequency of emotion-related statements, 59%, and that the variance contributes significantly to predicting emotion-related statements: $F(2, 27) = 21.78$, $p = 0.000$. This can be stated as an equation, using additional elements of the regression analysis:

Emotion coping scores = 0.48 age + 0.36 emotion-related statements + 1.58

This suggests, overall, that these two predictor variables account for a signifcant portion of the variance of scores associated with emotional coping.

Conclusion

Statistics is a general term used for a variety of mathematical procedures that help us to understand differences and relationships. They help us to understand the extent to which an intervention is effective and is influenced by the characteristics of group members, and whether one skill or attribute changes in relation to another. Descriptive statistics help us to describe sets of numbers, whereas inferential statistics use probability theory to ascertain relationships among variables. Traditionally, four kinds of data can be identified (nominal, ordinal, interval, and ratio), although this can also be understood as categorical (nominal) and continuous (ordinal, interval, ratio).

The scientific method underpins statistics, wherein independent and dependent variables are identified, controlled, and analysed in relation to the types of questions of interest to the researcher. Null hypotheses always assume there is no difference between any groups compared according to levels of the IV, whereas the alternatre hypothesis always assumes there is a difference and attempts to predict the direction of the difference. Sampling is important to any statistic procedure, as this helps researchers to conclude whether they can transfer the findings from their sample to the larger population they represent. Random sampling is a key element of this endeavor.

Power analyses and effect sizes, although only briefly discussed, are important when understanding the extent to which statistical significance has practical significance. A small effect size suggests that any significant change may have limited clinical application, whereas a large effect size suggests that the finding may be an important clarifier or addition to our understanding of a music therapy intervention and could thereby shape future practice.

Inferential statistics can be divided into two basic types: difference designs and association designs. Difference designs include the t test, chi square, and ANOVA, while association designs include the Pearson r and Spearman r. A subcategory of association designs is prediction designs, in which variables are linked together to show how they influence or change another variable. Linear regression and multiple regression are examples of prediction designs.

While providing an overiew of core components of statistics, this chapter is a start to such endeavors, rather than an end. Working with, understanding, and mastering statistics is an ongoing journey, one best undertaken through mentorship and education. Readers are also strongly encouraged to read Behrens' (2016) SPSS chapter, especially while reading the examples provided in this chapter, as the concepts and methods parallel one another and enrich our understanding of statistics while doing so.

References

Cohen, J. (1988). *Statistical power analysis for the behavioral sciences* (2nd ed.). Hillsdale, NJ: Lawrence Erlbaum.

DeCuir, A. (2005). Statistical methods of analysis. In B. L. Wheeler (Ed.). *Music therapy research* (2nd ed.; pp. 138–167). Gilsum, NH: Barcelona.

Ghetti, C. (2012). Music therapy as procedural support for invasive medical procedures: Toward the development of music therapy theory. *Nordic Journal of Music Therapy*, *21*(1), 3–36. doi:10.1080/08098131.2011.571278

Nolan, S., & Heinzen, T. (2010). *Essentials of statistics for the behavioral sciences.* New York, NY: Worth.

Reid, H. (2014). *Introduction to statistics: Fundamental concepts and procedures of data analysis.* Thousand Oaks, CA: Sage.

Chapter 13
DATA COLLECTION IN INTERPRETIVIST RESEARCH

Douglas R. Keith

While I was preparing to write this chapter, I undertook a pilgrimage on the *Camino de Santiago,* or the Way of St. James. The history of this pilgrimage is too long for this context, but suffice it to say that there are many routes coming from all across Europe and the Iberian Peninsula, all ending in the city of Santiago de Compostela, in northwestern Spain. There, according to legend, lie the remains of St. James (Santiago), the patron saint of Spain. I walked for 3 weeks, approximately 300 miles. During this time, I fell in with a community of pilgrims, all of whom were on the same path as I was, at the same time, and moving along at approximately the same speed. Many of them had begun much farther from Santiago than I had; some of them had started in their home countries, and some had started elsewhere in Spain. Many of them were younger than I, and quite a few were older. Some carried symbols of the pilgrimage on their backpacks, while others did not. Some were very slow, deliberate walkers, while others really sped along very quickly. During the first few days, I found myself becoming very interested in these other pilgrims and in the experience of pilgrimage. Without intending to, I was starting to act like an interpretivist researcher, practicing fieldwork.

During the weeks of my pilgrimage, I found myself collecting data in all sorts of ways: doing participant observation, interviewing people, holding informal group interviews, and even in some small ways examining artifacts of the pilgrimage. I found myself moving among steps of data collection, analysis, and reflection, even in this informal setting. I began to focus on particular questions. Some of these were: What constitutes a pilgrimage? How does this kind of pilgrimage work? What is it like to be a pilgrim? What helps pilgrims succeed, and what are barriers to their success? What meanings do the symbols have for the pilgrims?

While I did not complete a full research study based on my pilgrimage, it became a helpful metaphor for planning and conducting interpretivist research for me. And it all started with a sense of purpose: I wanted to know about the experience of walking the Camino.

When researchers collect data, their method flows from a purpose. This is true, irrespective of the theoretical orientation of the researcher. The purpose may be in the form of a *problem statement,* as in objectivist research, or in the form of a *focus,* as in interpretivist research. Each purpose is rooted in a particular epistemology and theoretical perspective.

In objectivist research, problem statements lead to clearly defined research questions, because objectivist research focuses on specific, defined, and measurable phenomena or constructs. By contrast, the focus in interpretivist research does not typically lead directly and unambiguously to a specific question and methodology, because interpretivist research is an emergent process. Instead, interpretivist researchers must observe the phenomenon of interest and then decide the best way to proceed to allow the phenomenon to reveal itself (Bruscia, 2005). When they write about their work, some interpretivist researchers state the purpose only, such as, "The purpose … was to understand how changes in images, life, events, and music unfold in the course of [Analytical Music Therapy]" (Eyre, 2007, p. 5). Other researchers state research questions, such as, "How is intuition experienced and used by music therapists within a music therapy session?" (Brescia, 2005, p. 67). In any case, the process of conducting interpretivist research is markedly different from the process of conducting objectivist research; the former is open-ended, while the latter is closed-ended. The practical steps and implications of collecting data in interpretivist research are the focus of this chapter.

Considerations in Data Collection

As discussed in the second edition of this text, it is difficult if not impossible to differentiate between the processes of designing and conducting interpretivist research (Bruscia, 2005). Interpretivist research involves multiple steps that are not necessarily related linearly to one another. Researchers must consider several things when making decisions on the process of data collection, and it is useful to think carefully about the type of data to be collected; the level on which the researchers wish to engage with data; and the role of reflexivity, user perspectives, and sampling. Consideration of these issues may help to orient the researcher in the cyclical process that is interpretivist research.

Type of Data to Be Collected

The researcher must consider the type of data to be collected. Interpretivist studies focus on several sources and types of data, including events, experiences, language (written and spoken), art, artifacts, and persons (Bruscia, 2005). Researchers may collect these types of data using a variety of methods, including conducting interviews, observing, and collecting and studying documents and artifacts (Patton, 2006). For example, to collect data on events, a researcher might observe interactions between clients and therapists

(Holck, 2007); another might make video recordings of clients performing original works (Snow, Snow, & D'Amico, 2008). To collect data on experiences, a music therapy researcher might interview people who have gone through a shared experience in the past (Day, Baker, & Darlington, 2009); another might engage individuals in a musical experience and ask them to talk about that experience. To collect spoken language, a music therapy researcher might transcribe a conversation in a GIM session. See Bruscia (1991) for an example. It is not always easy to distinguish between research sources, methods, and types of data. For example, O'Grady (2011) studied the process of a group of incarcerated women who created and performed a musical. O'Grady used a number of data collection methods (observation of clients and of self, collection of song lyrics), resulting in various types of written documents.

Level of Engagement with Data Sources

Bruscia (2005) notes three levels of researcher engagement with data sources: experimental, naturalistic, and retrospective. In interpretivist research, *experimental engagement* means that the researcher sets up specific tasks or situations in order to engage participants in the phenomenon of interest, while *naturalistic engagement* means that the researcher can observe the phenomenon of interest in a natural, lived world, and *retrospective engagement* means that the participants have already encountered the phenomenon of interest, and the researcher gathers data that are already available. These levels have several practical implications for data collection.

Researchers engaging with data on the *experimental level* typically engage participants in a specific activity in order to collect data. Engagement with data on the experimental level can result in numerous types of data and data collection, including interviews, text, music, and other artifacts. The researcher's involvement is substantial, and reflexivity becomes very important. Adjustments to the data collection process are likely to impact the results. It is likely that the researcher will need to reach some point where she or he is no longer adjusting the procedures. Having relatively consistent data collection procedures can contribute to this. Engaging with data on the experimental level, even in interpretivist research, exhibits some postpositivist leanings; that is, it is based in the belief that the results can be interpreted in a way that can lead toward some kinds of truth statements.

Researchers engaging with data on the *naturalistic level* collect data in a natural setting. This means that the researcher may have a less prominent role and thus have less personal impact on the research. Although researchers may engage with data in a natural setting, they may have a personal impact on the research in a number of ways. For example, researchers must make choices about what they observe and analyze; they cannot analyze everything. Also, researchers observing human phenomena may affect those

phenomena. Engagement with data on the naturalistic level may lead to different types of data and data collection, including field notes, interviews, text, music, artifacts, and persons. It may also include participant observation.

Researchers engaging with data on the *retrospective level* collect data from sources that already exist. This shifts the role of the researcher slightly. Instead of creating the situation for data collection or observing a phenomenon as it happens, the researcher makes decisions about what data to collect from what already exists.

It is very common for interpretivist researchers to use multiple methods of data collection to facilitate engagement with data on more than one level (e.g., retrospectively and naturalistically) and to incorporate multiple types of data in a given study. This is called *triangulation* (Patton, 2006, pp. 247–257). Each method of engaging with data produces different types of raw data. Interviews typically produce verbal data, which is then transcribed. Observation usually produces written notes, and various types of processes can produce documents or artifacts. While data collection with all of these is an emergent process, interviews are typically discrete events, while other methods may be ongoing, allowing researchers to develop their methods gradually. Interviews are emergent in at least two ways: (a) within interviews, researchers can naturally follow topics as they develop; and (b) between interviews, researchers can change their interview strategies (e.g., question sequence). By contrast, observations are typically ongoing (unless video-recorded), and researchers may have to develop their methods on the go; events are usually unpredictable and do not repeat themselves. Documents and artifacts are usually studied retrospectively, but their selection can be an emergent process, related closely to the process of analysis. When using multiple methods, researchers have a seemingly endless stream of options. Patton (2006) offers useful questions to help guide the decision-making process, some of which are:

- What is the primary purpose of the research?
- What is the focus of the study?
- What are the units of analysis?
- What will be the sampling strategies?
- What types of data will be collected?
- What type and degree of control will be exercised?
- What analytical approach(es) will be used?
- How will the validity of and confidence in the findings be addressed? (p. 254)

Reflecting on these questions can help researchers to make better decisions about their data collection processes.

These multiple methods can also affect one another, similar to what occurs when an object is reflected in multiple mirrors and the appearance of the object changes, depending on how many mirrors reflect it and on the quality of the mirrors themselves. Researchers who use multiple methods of data collection and collect multiple types of data are engaging in hermeneutics, which is concerned with interpreting meaning, typically from various sources of data.

The Practice of Reflexivity

Interpretivist researchers practice *reflexivity* throughout the research process. At the start, the researcher needs to begin with the phenomenon of interest and the basic question: "What does it say to me?" While many reflexive practices are part of data analysis rather than data collection, the emergent design that is central to interpretivist research is characterized by alternating phases of data collection and analysis, with reflexivity interspersed throughout this cycle. In practical terms, this means that as researchers determine how to analyze the data they have collected, they may journal or write memos about the process, leading to insights of various kinds. Reflexive practices may lead to insights about data collection, such as the need to refocus. It is easy to get lost when interviewing or observing, and researchers are well advised to consider the need to stay focused on the phenomenon at hand.

Reflexive practices may lead to insights about the research participants and the responsibilities toward them, such as their roles in the research process, protecting sensitive information, and their potential reactions to the results (Watt, 2007). Or they may lead to insights about the data, such as undiscovered patterns or interesting dimensions of a particular case. Perhaps most prominently, reflexive practices may lead to insights about oneself and one's role in the research study; this is to be expected and valued in interpretivist research, because the researcher him- or herself is the main research instrument. Thorough reflexivity can take any number of things into account, including the researcher's own history with the phenomenon. Common reflexive tasks include journaling, writing memos, and composing an epoché, or statement of self-inquiry. In any case, it is common for interpretivist researchers to adjust significant phases of their research procedures as a result of reflexive practices. In doing so, they demonstrate the relationship of reflexivity to emergent design.

User Perspectives

Much of interpretivist research focuses on human experience, and since music therapists do their work with humans, often with various conditions or disorders that lead to disabilities, the experience of these individuals is an important focus for clinical work and research. Only relatively recently have music therapy researchers begun to incorporate the experiences of clients in their studies. Hibben's (1999) book on client perspectives in music therapy might be considered a pioneering example. The current preferred term is *user perspectives* and is closely related to the concepts of mental health recovery, Community Music Therapy, and Resource-Oriented Music Therapy (Solli & Rolvsjord, 2014), all of

which reflect the belief that people who use music therapy have the right to influence its further development. Incorporation of user perspectives is thus another consideration when planning research. Music therapy researchers may be ideally poised to conduct interpretivist research with individuals who have disabilities or health problems because music therapists come to the whole research process with an education and work history focused on improving health, broadly defined (Bruscia, 1998). Music therapists are accustomed to taking the characteristics of widely varying people into account and can bring a great deal of awareness of individual needs to the research process.

Sampling

In interpretivist research, both the quality and the size of the sample deserve serious attention. *Purposive sampling,* which allows researchers to choose participants (or other data sources) that they believe will provide useful data, is often used in interpretivist research. The basis for purposive sampling is that social processes, typically the focus of interpretivist research, have a particular logic and coherence that would be destroyed by random sampling (Miles & Huberman, 1994, p. 27). Within the broad category of purposive sampling are other subcategories, such as snowball, confirming case, disconfirming case, criterion case (Miles & Huberman, 1994), extreme or deviant case (Patton, 2006), and theoretical sampling (Corbin & Strauss, 2015, p. 134).

In *snowball sampling,* also called *chain sampling,* the researcher asks a research participant to put him or her in contact with similar people who might provide rich data. The sampling strategy known as a *confirming case* can help researchers elaborate on an initial analysis. By contrast, a *disconfirming case* can reveal variations. Both of these specific strategies help refine theory. A *criterion case* looks at all cases that meet a certain criterion (Miles & Huberman, 1994, p. 28). *Extreme* or *deviant case sampling* can provide data about special or unusual cases that may be troublesome or enlightening (Patton, 2006). *Theoretical sampling* maximizes opportunities to develop concepts in terms of properties and dimensions and helps uncover variations and identify relationships between concepts (Corbin & Strauss, 2015, p. 134).

This is not an exhaustive list, but music therapy researchers are wise to think carefully about the theoretical implications of their sampling procedures. For example, if a music therapist is seeking to develop theory about when clients are likely to benefit from a particular approach, it would be advisable to employ sampling strategies that lead to data sources that lead to both confirming and disconfirming cases.

As data collection proceeds, usually alternating with data analysis, it is common for interpretivist researchers to wonder how large a sample is needed. Are the data that have been gathered sufficient, or are more needed? This likely depends on the purpose of the study, but the concept of *theoretical saturation* can be helpful. Theoretical saturation (Morse, 2004) is a phase or theoretical point where a researcher, after continuous sampling and analysis, finds no new data and where no new concepts appear in the analysis. Theoretical saturation, derived from grounded theory, is useful in many forms of interpretivist research that attempt to develop theory. In other types of interpretivist research, such as interpretivist case studies, the researcher may be working within previously defined boundaries (e.g., a single client or group in music therapy). This may seem to simplify issues of sampling, but the researcher must still make choices about what raw data to collect, and these are sampling choices. For example, observing interactions between music therapists and their clients can potentially yield unmanageable amounts of data. Wheeler (1999) examined video recordings of her work with clients and, after considerable reflection, selected specific examples for further analysis. This sampling strategy, like any sampling strategy, includes certain data and excludes other data. By communicating clearly about sampling strategies, researchers contribute to the trustworthiness of their studies.

Methods of Data Collection

Aigen (2008) notes that it is often difficult to establish distinctions between data collection sources and data collection procedures or methods. Some methods are strongly associated with a particular type of data, such as interviews, which are associated with spoken language. However, observation may be associated with spoken language, actions, and music. Patton (2006, pp. 4–5) discusses three types of qualitative data: interviews, observations, and documents. Music therapy researchers may include types of data in addition to documents, so documents and artifacts are included in one section in this chapter. Thus, the next section of this chapter is organized by interviews, observation, and collection of documents and artifacts. Each subsection includes examples from interpretivist research in music therapy. The concerns and issues presented to this point are relevant for each of these methods.

Interviews

The research interview is one of the foundational methods from the social sciences and is used across a wide variety of disciplines. Researchers typically conduct in-depth interviews consisting of open-ended questions and probes, in order to gain access to people's experiences, perceptions, opinions, feelings, and knowledge (Patton, 2006, p. 4). Researchers in the social sciences have developed a spectrum of approaches to the research interview, from a structured sequence of three interviews (Seidman, 1998) to interviews guided by a loose sequence of themes (Kvale, 1998). This suggests that one of the key factors to consider is the degree of structure in the interview, even within semi-structured

interviews. Despite different levels of structure, it is possible to make the claim that the interview is a place of knowledge (or data) *construction*; this is especially apt when researchers work from a relatively unstructured interview guide rather than a series of set questions.

The type of data collected in interviews is fairly clear, as interviews are predominantly verbal interactions between two or more people. Therefore most researchers who use interviews are collecting verbal data from participants. In most cases, this is spoken language. The level of engagement with the data during interviews varies, depending on the purpose. The level of structure also varies. Some researchers base their work in a clearly planned method and use a set series of questions. Others may start off with little plan and no clear line of questioning, in an attempt to be deliberately naïve about the topic (Kvale, 1998, p. 33). There is no *right* method of interviewing but instead a spectrum of options that are applicable for different research purposes. In this way, interpretivist interviews are like conversations, which can develop naturally (unstructured interviews) or have a predetermined idea of structure (semi-structured or structured interviews; Kvale, 1998, p. 12). In terms of the level of engagement, most interviews represent something related to an experimental practice within interpretivist research, because the researcher has to set them up; in this way, they are artificial.

Most interviews are described as semi-structured. The purpose of any research interview is different from the purpose of a conversation. In a conversation, people usually switch between leading and following, as the topic becomes the focus of the conversation. In a research interview, by contrast, the interviewer usually leads—there is an imbalance of power (Kvale, 1998, p. 20). This means that the researcher must plan the interview guide so that it makes good logical sense. The research questions are usually not good interview questions because they are typically formal, general, and too large for any individual participant to answer. Instead, the interview questions are derived from the research questions. They are informal and more conversational. They are sequenced (i.e., semi-structured) in a way to help both the researcher and the participant to access and develop knowledge on the topic at hand—the lived world of the research participant. For example, Bullard (2011) interviewed members of an inpatient music therapy group, using the following questions in her group interviews:

- Can you tell me about your experience with music in your life, and how you use it day to day?
- What made you agree to be part of this study?
- What were your expectations going in to the group?
- What was the group like for you?
- What kinds of things did you learn from being part of this group?
- How did you relate to the people in the group?
- What was the most valuable experience you got out of the group?

- Did anything surprise you in the group?
- What was the most challenging thing for you to do in the group?
- Is there anything you would change about the group or the sessions?
- What about the experiences in the group—how would you compare the first day to the second day?
- What part of the group had the biggest impact on you?
- Did you feel safe opening up here?
- Did you express feelings through your playing, and how was that different from doing it verbally?
- What was the most helpful thing in the group? (p. 115)

Interviews may be conducted with individuals or with groups. The two types of interviews may be quite different. In individual interviews, the participant and researcher are the only people present, and the dynamics of that relationship are mostly affected by these two roles. Other things can always affect these dynamics, such as power relationships that may be present, agendas, and existing histories, but in a group interview, the interpersonal dynamics are magnified, and one must take group dynamics into account. On a very basic level, people may go to some lengths to *preserve front* around others (Rubin & Rubin, 1995, p. 28). People are often unwilling to state things about themselves that put them in a negative light. Practically, the presence of other people means that participants are likely to ask questions of one another, making data collection even more unpredictable. Music therapy researchers are therefore well advised to consider whether they wish to conduct individual or group interviews.

The purpose of an *individual semi-structured interview*, in most cases, is to understand the lived world of the research participant. The lived world is a constructed world, one in which the person being interviewed creates meaning and understands reality in his or her own way. This is the reason that interview questions are typically open-ended, designed to *get* people talking.

Researchers conducting *group interviews* assemble groups of people to collect data on particular experiences that people in the group may have had. Typically, researchers encourage participants to share their feelings, insights, and opinions in a nonthreatening and permissive environment. The term *focus group* is often used interchangeably with group interview, but much of the research base involving focus groups is rooted in marketing research. The usefulness of focus groups is not limited to marketing and other entrepreneurial purposes, though. For example, Freire (1970) used focus groups as part of his work to develop an educational model for oppressed groups in Brazil. Group interviews can be viewed as a method (possibly a group of methods) that can function across multiple fields of inquiry. Topics for group interviews range in breadth from quite narrow to rather broad (Rubin & Rubin, 1995, p. 27). The researcher must carefully plan group interviews; depending

on the purpose of the group, they may or may not encourage members to reach consensus on a topic. In a music therapy example, Hoskyns (2013) conducted group interviews (focus groups) with supervisors and students in a master's degree in music therapy program in order to explore the challenge of integrating research and practice during various stages of professional life.

In many forms of research (not only interpretivist), it is common to *pilot test* one's methods before beginning formal data collection. In individual semi-structured interviews, this might mean developing a draft of the interview guide and using it to interview initial participants, then using those experiences to adjust questions and/or any accompanying procedures.

When planning individual or group interviews, the primary consideration is the purpose of the research, including the research question(s). What do you want to know? What question(s) are you trying to answer? How can you structure your interview so that it will help you to answer them?

Music therapy researchers have used several approaches to structuring interviews, including (a) structuring them chronologically or using (b) artifacts, (c) storytelling, or (d) experiences.

Chronological. One approach is to structure the interview chronologically. This approach may fit well when the researcher may want interviewees to think about a process that happened sequentially. Day, Baker, and Darlington (2009) interviewed women with a history of childhood abuse who had participated in a songwriting program. In this study, the researchers structured the interviews around the different phases of the program, starting with the songwriting group, moving through the phases of performing and recording, and finishing with a discussion of current uses of the song. The researchers noted that this structure helped participants to develop separate perspectives on past and present reflections. Zanders (2012) interviewed adolescents who had been in foster care to learn about their personal and musical biographies. He asked his participants about their lives and musical involvement prior to entering foster care, during foster care, and currently. He closed the interview with an open-ended question, asking if there was anything else musical or biographical that the adolescents wanted to talk about.

Using Artifacts. A second approach is to use an artifact of some kind to prompt the research participant. Fidelibus (2004) and Cooper (2010) both studied the experience of Nordoff-Robbins music therapists who were improvising with clients. In both these cases, the researchers asked participants to select video recordings of significant sessions and to view these with the researcher. Cooper asked them to identify meaningful musical moments during the viewing, stopped the video at these moments, and asked questions that focused on the participants' awareness of self and client, and on how they were using music at those moments. Fidelibus asked participants to identify moments when they shifted into an experience of *flow* during music therapy improvisations. In a slightly different approach, Gonzalez (2011) studied therapists' lived experiences in their musical cultures. She asked participants to bring in a piece of music, art, or other artifact that represented their music culture and interviewed them in the presence of this item. The interviews that followed were structured chronologically, asking participants to focus on different phases of their life in order.

Storytelling. A third approach to structuring interpretivist interviews is to ask participants to tell a story. While not prominent in music therapy research, the work of some practitioners of Guided Imagery and Music (GIM) may resemble this approach. In this approach to interviewing, the interview takes the form of a storytelling session, with the participant in the role of storyteller and the researcher in the role of listener. Culturally, this places the participant in a powerful position, similar to that of an elder in a community. It emphasizes the participant's expertise on a subject and the relative ignorance of the researcher, suggesting its potential usefulness in obtaining user perspectives. Tuastad and Stige (2015) conducted a narrative inquiry study with members of a rock band who had all been incarcerated. Their focus was on an incident in which one of the band members was attacked and seriously injured. It is easy to imagine other creative uses of storytelling. For example, a researcher could engage participants in an improvisational experience and ask them to develop a story based on it. Another example might include asking participants to tell the story of their favorite music: their history with it, its meaning, and so forth.

Experiences. A fourth approach is to organize the interview around specific experiences. Sorel (2010) studied the relationship between a client and his mother, both of whom participated in music therapy. In her study, she conducted individual interviews with music therapists who had worked with the client and also interviewed the client's mother. Sorel drew on other sources of data, including session notes and index sheets, treatments summaries, reports from parent conferences, researcher logs and memos, and music transcriptions. Abrams (2009) studied transpersonal experiences of therapists during the Bonny Method of Guided Imagery and Music (BMGIM). Abrams interviewed BMGIM Fellows and asked them to describe experiences they considered to be transpersonal and those they did not consider to be transpersonal. Using contrasting experiences to structure interviews will be discussed in a later section.

Some music therapy researchers have also conducted group interviews focused on experiences. Murphy (2007) conducted group interviews with graduate music therapy students who had taken courses that incorporated experiential learning. Her questions focused in particular on

(a) the nature of experiential learning; (b) the influence of experiential learning on understanding of music therapy; (c) the influence of experiential learning on clinical work; and (d) the influence of experiential learning on self-knowledge. Grocke (2009) interviewed people with severe and enduring mental illnesses, focusing on several issues: (a) their experience as part of the project, (b) which features were valued, (c) potential improvements, and (d) whether participants would recommend it to others.

In these group interview studies, it is interesting to note that since the groups followed lengthy engagement in a particular kind of experience, the research participants (music therapy students or music therapy clients) were given a chance to reflect on these experiences and to give voice to their thoughts. These are useful examples of giving voice to user perspectives, a topic addressed later in this chapter. It is interesting to note that group interviews were not the only data collection method in these examples and that they were often embedded in a larger process of education or therapy. In both educational and therapeutic contexts, these reflective, multidimensional practices can augment benefits of the therapy itself or improve future educational practices.

The role of the researcher in group interviews deserves some attention. For example, if the person conducting the interview is the same person who led the music therapy groups (McFerran, Roberts, & O'Grady, 2010), how does that affect the group? Some participants, especially being asked about benefits of the music therapy experience, may feel the need to please the researcher/therapist (or for that matter, to displease him or her!). By contrast, if the person conducting the interview is not the same person, this influence is minimized. However, the identity of the researcher can always influence the research process and outcomes, as each researcher brings his or her own identity to the research process. This concern about the influence of the researcher on the process or the results indicates the postpositivist leanings of some group interviews: the idea that a personal factor can influence the results, and that this would be problematic.

Preparing the Interview Guide. Music therapy researchers typically develop an *interview guide* before conducting interviews. These interview guides serve to structure the interview in order to obtain the best possible information from the interviewees. Typically, these guides begin with general questions about the topic, and interviewers follow up with probes or clarifying questions. One approach that appears to be useful when trying to understand the dimensions of an experience is to ask participants to describe contrasting experiences. Comeau (2004) studied music therapists' experiences of being effective and ineffective. He asked participants to reflect on specific experiences they had had of being effective and ineffective. Kim (2008) studied music therapists' experiences of feeling understood and misunderstood in cross-cultural supervision.

Researchers may need to redirect or guide participants

throughout the interview in various ways. Kim (2008) worked from prepared questions in her interviews, but found it important to use amplification and clarification to help participants maintain their focus on the experiences. Murphy (2007) and Grocke (2009) both used prompts and follow-up questions to encourage participants to stay focused on their experiences and to deepen their thought processes.

In some cases, researchers may ask participants to prepare for an interview. Some researchers use prompts such as video recordings or other artifacts. These may require some preparation on the part of the interviewee ahead of time. The value of this preparation is that participants have time to think about specific experiences and to gather thoughts on them. Participants may also have questions of their own for the researcher, and these questions can be instructive for further development of the interview guide.

Sometimes researchers combine interviews (individual, group, or both) with multiple methods of data collection. Snow et al. (2008) studied the lived experience of individuals with developmental disabilities who were involved in a 3-year ethnodrama performance project. At the beginning of the study, the researchers held individual interviews. This phase was followed by months of group work in music, art, and dance movement. The individual interviews played a primary role in developing materials for the arts-based work that followed them, which was led by creative arts therapists. Here, the interviews resemble a step in the assessment process of music therapy. This study, complex and requiring a great deal of commitment, is noteworthy for its lengthy immersion with the research participants. Near the end of the study, the researchers held focus groups with the individuals in the project, exploring topics that came from individual interviews, in particular that the participants did not view themselves as having disabilities.

Warner (2005) conducted individual and group interviews in a study of music therapy with adults with severe and profound disabilities. Interviews were conducted with caregivers (music therapists and residential home staff) in the form of group meetings, in which the caregivers were instrumentally involved in planning each step of the research study. These interviews were recorded and transcribed. In the next step, Warner listened to the recorded meetings with the staff and asked them to read the transcripts. Here, one group of research participants (the staff) was given the opportunity to provide additional data and also shape the further steps in the research. Additional steps of this complex research study are discussed in the section of this chapter labeled Observation.

Interview studies, by focusing on verbal input from interviewees, give voice to user perspectives, especially those of people who use the services of music therapist—typically people often referred to as patients, clients, or consumers. An important consideration when considering the impact of interviews on users (clients or other participants) is the cognitive, physical, and emotional capacities of the persons

to be interviewed. In an interview with someone with an intellectual disability, questions should be formulated in a way that participants can understand. In some cases, one can expect these participants to provide answers that are shorter and consist of more basic language. However, people with intellectual disabilities are just as varied in terms of sociability or *people skills* as the rest of us. Researchers interested in interviewing people on the autistic spectrum should take into consideration these people's challenges with understanding and communicating their own interior world to other people. This is not to suggest that interview studies with these individuals are not worth pursuing but rather that the researcher must take more things into consideration than with many other people. By taking user perspectives and individual needs into account, researchers acknowledge their accountability for the well-being of their interviewees. This is perhaps even more prominent when working with people with emotional or behavioral problems. Researchers should consider the potential impacts of sensitive topics in an interview and that some people may respond unpredictably to any topic.

Observation

The second major method of interpretivist data collection is observation. Observation involves collecting data on observable behavior, broadly defined: actions, interactions, musical behavior, and so forth. The researcher observes what people (clients, therapists, other participants) are doing. This is not to suggest that observation is associated with behavioral research. In interpretivist research, the purpose of the observation is usually description rather than measurement. Observations result in written descriptions of people's actions, behaviors, interactions, conversations, organizational processes, and other observable human behavior (Patton, 2006, p. 4). Observation can be described in several ways: by time frame, by type, and by data sources.

Time Frame. The first way of describing observation is by the time frame in which observation takes place. In music therapy research, observation occurs either during a course of therapy or other process or retrospectively. Observation during a course of therapy may occur live or from video recordings. Many music therapists write session notes after music therapy sessions. These notes and other forms of clinical documentation are akin to field notes in ethnography, suggesting an affinity between certain ethnography and music therapy practices. Both share the potential for prolonged engagement with groups of people. In an example of an interpretivist case study, O'Grady (2011) described a project with incarcerated women. In this naturalist study, O'Grady and a small group of collaborators worked with the women for 10 weeks to develop and perform a musical. Her observations produced 24 pages of session notes, which contained information on attendance, observations, significant events, and the researcher's reactions to these events. This clinical documentation is interesting in that it represents observations of occurrences both external and internal to the researcher.

Retrospective observation may involve viewing video recordings or referring to other forms of documentation. While video recordings could be considered a type of artifact, for the purposes of this chapter, video recordings serve primarily as a means of observation, rather than a document or artifact serving as a data source.

Type of Observation. Observations may also be described by type, the two types being clinical observation and participant observation. These types are defined by the role of the researcher. In *clinical observation,* the researcher remains in the role of observer, with relatively clear role boundaries: She or he is the researcher (and may be the clinician) and also observes the participants (who may be clients). Clinical observation occurs throughout all stages of music therapy. For example, during assessment, music therapists report things that they observe their client doing in various contexts. During treatment, music therapists frequently write down their observations for the purpose of documentation. During evaluation, observation often serves as evidence of therapeutic progress. During any of these phases, they may of course also observe themselves and their interactions with clients. This prevalence of observation underscores its potential value for music therapy researchers, because of its familiarity to most practitioners.

Wheeler (1999) and Sokira (2007) both used video to examine their own experiences working with clients. Wheeler (1999) studied video recordings of her music therapy sessions with children with severe handicapping conditions, focusing on her experiences of pleasure working with them. Sokira (2007) also studied video recordings of her music therapy sessions, but focused on how she interpreted communicative behaviors on the part of girls with Rett syndrome. These self-inquiries use video archive creatively to understand aspects of the client–therapist relationship and the therapeutic process. While they do not incorporate user perspectives as Warner (2001) did, they do offer an insider perspective in the therapeutic relationship.

In Nordoff-Robbins Music Therapy, nearly all sessions are recorded on video and later viewed for clinical and research purposes. To name a few examples, Kim (2008) studied the intentionality of people with autism when engaged in improvisational music therapy. Kim asked Nordoff-Robbins music therapists to identify past clients with the diagnosis of autism who had shown natural interest in the process of improvisation. Kim then viewed archival video of these clients, taken from the beginning, middle, and end of music therapy. In a similar study, Sorel (2010) explored the mother–son relationship in Nordoff-Robbins Music Therapy, drawing on video archives of a course of music therapy, in addition to other sources, which are discussed elsewhere in this chapter.

The second main type of observation is *participant observation,* which some music therapists have adapted from ethnography. Participant observation typically requires prolonged presence in a culture. This is usually called *hanging out* or *deep hanging* out (Procter, 2013). When hanging out in a culture, the researcher has time to acclimate to the setting, and the people in the setting have time to acclimate to the researcher. In music therapy research, one can imagine that the people with whom music therapists often work (e.g., individuals with various disabilities) may require significant periods of time to acclimate to unfamiliar people. In addition to hanging out, ethnographic researchers often *join in,* thus becoming less of a peripheral observer and more of a member of the community. Stige and Aarø (2012, p. 244) describe the useful practice of alternating between hanging out and joining in; this alternating helps researchers understand the culture by viewing and experiencing it in many roles: observer, participant, outsider, and something like insider. Both hanging out and joining in offer opportunities for researchers to obtain direct quotes from the people from whom they are learning, to observe how people function together in groups or individually and how they function in different contexts. In terms of the level of engagement with the data, hanging out and joining in are typically (but not always) naturalistic, focusing on the way people in a culture or group act, how they function, etc. When joining in, the researcher may engage more directly with the phenomena of interest, which can potentially shift the level of engagement.

Aigen (2003) practiced *hanging out* in his study of popular music styles in Nordoff-Robbins Music Therapy. Aigen was a member of a band, along with adolescents with various disabling conditions. His observations were supplemented by clinical documentation notes from the music therapy sessions.

Warner (2005) collected and analyzed audio and video recordings of music therapy sessions with adults with severe and profound disabilities. In addition to serving as a form of raw data, these videos were also shown to the research participants on the videos (the adults with severe and profound disabilities). While the participants watched the videos, Warner observed the participants observing themselves. This step was a careful and thoughtful way to incorporate user perspectives of people who are frequently viewed as difficult to incorporate.

In an example from South Africa, Pavlicevic (2010) describes a Community Music Therapy project that lasted several months, involving working with a choir of 35 adolescents in an impoverished area to prepare for a community concert. Here, the researcher was a type of participant observer, although in a leadership role as a music therapist. While it is difficult to describe concisely how to *do* participant observation, Pavlicevic shares a vignette that may be instructive. She took video data many times during this project. During a rehearsal break, she spotted a group of seven children in *collaborative musicing*—impromptu, unrehearsed, spontaneous music-making. Pavlicevic used this data she had collected as a participant observer to develop an understanding of what happens when a group of people make music together in music therapy. To obtain this information, Pavlicevic had to be in prolonged engagement with this group of people, because moments like this are unpredictable and because (as stated above) they require trust between the researcher/observer and the participants.

Holck (2007) used observation in an ethnographically informed study. Like Pavlicevic, she used video recording and analyzed short excerpts. Holck looked for indicators of communication and social interaction in music therapy with clients with severe communication limitations. This type of research may serve to confirm or reject interpretations of client actions as being social attempts to take part in the interaction, even though these actions may seem vague, arbitrary, or ambivalent. In Holck's ethnographically informed approach to observational analysis: Common sense is held to be complex and sophisticated, instead of naïve and misguided.

Sampling Issues. Observational methods differ in their sampling strategies. When a researcher is observing any actions, she or he can only sample so much information at a time. How does the researcher decide what is important and what can be left out? This important question can possibly be answered through reflective practice, but it is hard to imagine ever fully answering this question. Instead, reflective practice requires researchers to communicate their decisions about sampling. In addition to this question, researchers observing directly must make sampling decisions in the moment. By contrast, researchers working from written notes or video material can review materials multiple times, allowing them to develop sampling strategies according to the data with which they are working.

When using video, researchers can potentially amass a large amount of data, such as hours of video. Sometimes, nothing much happens in the video, but sometimes a great deal happens. Either of these presents the researcher with a challenge: how to *sample* video data and do justice to the research phenomenon. Holck's (2007) work is based on the developing tradition of microanalysis in music therapy research (Wosch & Wigram, 2007). She describes two options for handling data sampling in microanalysis. One option is the *problem-based analysis approach*, in which the data selection is deliberate, focused on a particular problem. Another option, *open analysis approach*, reviews sequences of 5–10 minutes' duration to see clearly what is happening between client and therapist. The latter approach is closer to ethnography (Holck, 2007). It should be noted that fieldwork (the umbrella term for most methods in ethnographic research) offers similar challenges: Researchers have to decide on what to focus—and, by extension, on what not to focus.

Observation and Other Methods. In interpretivist research, observation often provides one of several perspectives. It is frequently combined with other data collection methods and

sources of information about the phenomenon at hand. In terms of the level of engagement with the data, observation can occur on all three levels: experimental, naturalistic, and retrospective. Observational methods differ in the degree to which they incorporate user perspectives. It appears that studies that incorporate participant observation are better able to incorporate user perspectives than those in which the researcher is only an observer.

Observation can often provide information that interviews or other data collection methods might miss. For example, Holck (2007) points out that interviews exclude people who cannot answer questions on a subject. There are many reasons why this may be the case; in music therapy, many clients are nonverbal or cognitively impaired to the degree that they are unable to speak on a topic. In many cases, even if participants can use language effectively, their knowledge on the topic may be implicit rather than explicit. Observation gives information about unacknowledged patterns of action; interviews require participants to express their thoughts on the subject verbally. For example, O'Grady (2011) incorporated interviews after the performance to supplement her observational data, and Snow et al. (2008) used individual interviews, performances, and focus groups. This is one way to respect and incorporate perspectives of people participating in the research study. The *insider perspective* that participants can provide augments the *outsider perspective* of the researcher, who is usually an outsider to the community of focus. The studies by Warner (2001), O'Grady (2011), and Snow et al. (2008) are examples of interpretivist studies that creatively incorporate user perspectives.

Documents and Artifacts

The third and final type of data collection is the collection of documents and artifacts. For the purposes of this chapter, a *document* consists of written material from organizational, clinical, or program records: memoranda, publications, and public and private texts (Patton, 2006, p. 4). In most cases, this text existed prior to the research. Examples in music therapy include session notes that were created in the past or song lyrics that were written by clients. An ***artifact*** is an object that is not (or predominantly not) text, such as written music (Aasgaard, 2002), audio recordings (Stige & Aarø, 2012), art or photographs (Patton, 2006), or music videos. While research with this type of data is not that common at this time in music therapy research, music therapy commonly produces both texts and artifacts. Music therapists may collect written or spoken data as documents, and individuals or groups in music therapy often write songs and perform them in various contexts. Client music—whether improvised, composed, or re-created—is often recorded. These diverse materials are potentially very interesting and rich sources of data for interested music therapy researchers.

The level of engagement with documents varies. In some cases, researchers engage with documents and artifacts on a retrospective level (Ahonen-Eerikäinen, 1999); in others (Warner, 2005), on a naturalistic level; and in still others, on an experimental level (Keith, 2007). User perspectives may also be well represented in documents and artifacts (Keith, 2007; Warner, 2005). In terms of sampling documents and artifacts, it is helpful to consider existing practices from ethnographic research (see Stige & Aarø, 2012, pp. 242–246) and to keep in mind that documents and artifacts can be useful supplements to other forms of data and should be selected purposively. In an example of engaging with data on an experimental level, Ledger (2010) asked music therapists to write narratives about their experiences in service development.

In clinical practice, music therapists typically document their work in written forms, producing potentially large volumes of clinical documentation such as session notes of various kinds and video transcriptions. Depending on methodology, researchers may engage retrospectively, naturalistically, or experimentally with documents and artifacts. In most cases, documents such as session notes would be considered observational data. However, when researchers engage with such data retrospectively, it seems reasonable to consider them as documents. Handled ethically, documents from past music therapy work can serve as valuable data sources for research.

In a retrospective study that drew primarily on documentation from music therapy sessions in the past, Ahonen-Eerikäinen (1999) examined written reports by 54 music therapists. She used these session reports to describe the forms of music therapy and the working styles that music therapists used. Interviews with therapists followed this initial step in data collection, to supplement and provide a framework for understanding the written documents.

In her study of a parent–child relationship in Nordoff-Robbins Music Therapy, Sorel (2010) analyzed various types of written documents from a course of music therapy. These included session notes (reflective notes completed after sessions), index sheets (detailed, minute-by-minute descriptions of music therapy sessions), treatment summaries, and parent conference meeting reports. This retrospective study was conducted after the clients had stopped music therapy, but Sorel also employed naturalistic strategies of engagement with other data.

Tetens and Probst (2009) analyzed written protocols of 21 music activity sessions of a child with autism spectrum disorder. In this naturalistic case study, the researchers focused on social communication between the client and the music therapist.

Warner (2005) collected various types of written documents in a cooperative inquiry study of a group home. These included postsession questionnaires, communication reports from speech/language pathologists, and other documents from the home staff. The contrasts with Tetens and Probst (2009) and Sorel (2010) are interesting. Warner's study included written documents with information about many people involved in the study, including clients and other participants, such as home staff. Tetens and Probst and Sorel included data only on the client(s). Warner's participatory action research study also involved collecting documents on current happenings (music therapy sessions and other interactions), rather than events that occurred in the past.

Other written documents also emerge from music therapy. Songwriting is a common type of compositional experience that music therapists use to engage clients, and songwriting can potentially result in written lyrics and other materials. Music therapy researchers may not need to plan specific data collection procedures in these cases, because they typically engage with the data retrospectively. Song lyrics by clients or patients have been the subject of several qualitative studies.

O'Callaghan (1996) studied the lyrics of 64 songs created by patients in palliative care, exploring the intended meaning of the lyrics. The song lyrics were created in a clinical context and later analyzed. The researcher described her paradigm of song creation, which was flexible enough to accommodate patients on many functioning levels. The inclusion of the song paradigm suggests that this study is a form of naturalistic inquiry, because patients were engaged in songwriting as a part of music therapy.

McFerran, Baker, Patton, and Sawyer (2006) conducted a retrospective analysis of lyrics created by teenagers with anorexia. The researchers studied the lyrics as text and did not analyze the music of the songs. Aasgaard (2002), in addition to directly observing children with cancer, also analyzed the song creations of these children. In a similar study, Roberts and McFerran (2013) studied the lyrics of songs written by grieving children in a music therapy program. In this study, the participants created music and lyrics for songs as a part of a multiweek individual music therapy program. These studies are examples of engagement with the data on a retrospective level, despite the fact that the data were created in a natural setting, because the researchers first engaged the participants to create the data and then collected the data retrospectively.

In an interesting retrospective study involving both documents and musical artifacts, Turry (2010) engaged with improvised songs that a client had created in a course of music therapy. He selected particular songs and engaged with them in multiple ways, including listening to recordings, singing and playing along with recordings, reading and playing from transcriptions, and improvising to the songs.

While it is unclear whether the musical and other arts-related materials were treated as artifacts, the project that Snow et al. (2008) describe appears to include these elements. In this study, it is difficult to discern how the researchers collected these data. One can think of these, however, in a way similar to that for other types of data, such as video of interactions between people or observations of the same. Researchers must make some similar decisions about sampling, in addition to later (and sometimes concurrent) decisions about analysis.

Some music therapy researchers engage with documents or artifacts on an experimental level. Bruscia et al. (2005) used a collaborative heuristic method to study imagery in a specific music listening program in GIM. The GIM sessions served to produce written transcriptions of participants' imagery.

While music therapists frequently create music with clients and also frequently analyze the resulting music for clinical purposes, relatively few researchers have collected musical data for research. This may be because improvised music does not easily fit the forms that most formal music analysis requires, such as clearly delineated phrases, harmony, and so forth. Nordoff and Robbins (1977) created several rating scales as a way of using music to analyze the therapeutic relationship and various factors of client music. Some music therapy researchers have used traditional music analysis techniques, requiring transcription of music. With the emergence of technology that transcribes music, this has become much easier. Lee (1992, 1996) has collected musical data (client improvisations) and used traditional music analysis to understand them.

Other researchers have developed diverse methods of collecting and analyzing improvised music without transcribing it. Langenberg, Frommer, and Tress (1993) recorded client improvisations and asked a musician to analyze the music without transcribing it. The most thorough process developed at this time for analyzing improvised music as heard, however, is the Improvisation Assessment Profiles (IAP), developed by Bruscia (1987). Researchers using the IAP typically ask clients to play or sing a series of improvisation for purposes of assessment. The level of engagement with the data is thus often experimental. In many cases, musical data serves as one of several types of data. Langenberg, Frommer, and Tress (1993, 1995) recorded improvisations (artifacts) from music therapy sessions and subjected them to various forms of analysis. The individual client in the course of therapy was involved in selecting the improvisation to be analyzed and was also asked to provide a written description of the improvisation (a document). In addition, external observers were also asked to write descriptions of the improvised music (documents). Both the music and the resulting documents were analyzed.

Gardstrom (2004) improvised music with participants and recorded these. Following the improvisations, she and the participants immediately listened to the recording and discussed it in an interview, in a process inspired by Lee (2000). Thus, the sessions produced two types of data: music and language. After the session, Gardstrom wrote field notes about the sessions, which formed a third source of data. In a similar study, Keith (2007) collected artifacts of two types: written descriptions or responses to improvised music and recordings of the improvised music itself. In this study, the participants (and sometimes the researcher) improvised music, which was recorded. Immediately after playing, both the researcher and the participants wrote responses to the music that had just been improvised. Next, they listened to a recording of the music and discussed it; this discussion was also recorded and later transcribed. Thus, the sessions produced three types of data: music, speech, and written text. After the research session, the recorded music was a fourth source of data. The studies by both Gardstrom and Keith are examples of engagement with data on an experimental level that produce multiple types of data. Gardstrom, in particular, is noteworthy for her strong inclusion of user perspectives, notably users who were music therapy clients.

Data Storage

Researchers who conduct interpretivist research must think carefully about the confidentiality of raw research data. In this regard, interpretivist research is no different from objectivist research, except that in objectivist research, data is often in the form of numbers and other decontextualized information; thus, it is difficult to connect raw data with individual participants. By contrast, data from interpretivist research are often in the form of written documents, video recordings, and other forms that make it relatively easy to identify participants. The rapidly changing nature of technology makes it impossible to describe specific procedures for safeguarding data, but, in general, music therapy researchers must follow ethical and legal guidelines set in place by the institutions in which they conduct research and by the music therapy associations of which they may be members. The American Music Therapy Association Code of Ethics refers once to the security of research data: "8.4 The MT will store data in a secure location accessible to the researcher. The researcher will determine a set period of time after completion of the study by which all research data must be shredded or erased" (American Music Therapy Association, 2014, n.p.).

Conclusion

In summary, music therapy researchers who conduct interpretivist research must consider multiple issues when planning their method of data collection. Once researchers decide on a focus, the first issue is the purpose of the study. All other decisions flow primarily from the purpose. Depending on the purpose and focus of the study, researchers may choose any number of data collection methods; prominent among these are the interview, observation, and collection of documents and artifacts. Further issues include the type of data to be collected by the method, the level of engagement with the data, and sampling. Given the claim that music therapy is a helping profession, researchers should also consider the role of user perspectives in research.

Finally, one cannot overestimate the importance of reflexive practice throughout the research process. Without reflexivity, research consumers have no reason to trust the research. By contrast, clearly communicated interpretivist practices have the potential to build trustworthiness.

References

Aasgaard, T. (2002). *Song creations of children with cancer—Process and meaning* (Unpublished doctoral dissertation). Aalborg University, Aalborg, Denmark.

Abrams, B. (2009). Definitions of transpersonal BMGIM experiences. *Nordic Journal of Music Therapy, 11,* 103–126. doi:10.1080/08098130209478054

Ahonen-Eerikäinen, H. (1999). Different forms of music therapy and working styles of music therapists—A qualitative study. *Nordic Journal of Music Therapy, 8,* 156–167. doi:10.1080/08098139909477969

Aigen, K. (2003). *Playin' in the band: A qualitative study of popular music styles as clinical improvisation.* Gilsum, NH: Barcelona.

Aigen, K. (2008). An analysis of qualitative music therapy research reports, 1987–2006: Doctoral studies. *Arts in Psychotherapy, 35,* 307–319. doi:10.1016/j.aip.2008.05.001

American Music Therapy Association. (2014). *Code of ethics.* Retrieved from http://www.musictherapy.org/about/ethics/

Brescia, T. (2005). A qualitative study of intuition as experienced and used by music therapists. *Qualitative Inquiries in Music Therapy, 2,* 62–112.

Bruscia, K. E. (1987). *Improvisational methods of music therapy.* Springfield, IL: Charles C Thomas.

Bruscia, K. E. (1991). Embracing life with AIDS: Psychotherapy through Guided Imagery and Music (GIM). In K. E. Bruscia (Ed.), *Case studies in music therapy* (pp. 58–602). Gilsum, NH: Barcelona.

Bruscia, K. E. (1998). *Defining music therapy* (2nd ed.). Gilsum, NH: Barcelona.

Bruscia, K. E. (2005). Designing qualitative research. In B. L. Wheeler (Ed.), *Music therapy research* (2nd ed.; pp. 129–137). Gilsum, NH: Barcelona.

Bruscia, K. E., Abbott, E., Cadesky, N., Condron, D., Hunt, A. M., Miller, D., & Thomae, L. (2005). A collaborative heuristic analysis of *Imagery–M:* A classical music program used in the Bonny Method of Guided Imagery and Music (BMGIM). *Qualitative Inquiries in Music Therapy, 2,* 1–35.

Bullard, E. (2011). Music therapy as an intervention for inpatient treatment of suicidal ideation. *Qualitative Inquiries in Music Therapy, 6,* 75–121.

Comeau, P. (2004). A phenomenological investigation of being effective as a music therapist. *Qualitative Inquiries in Music Therapy, 1,* 19–36.

Cooper, M. (2010). Clinical-musical responses of Nordoff-Robbins music therapists: The process of clinical improvisation. *Qualitative Inquiries in Music Therapy, 5,* 86–115.

Corbin, J., & Strauss, A. (2015). *Basics of qualitative research: Techniques and procedures for developing grounded theory* (3rd ed.). Thousand Oaks, CA: Sage.

Day, T., Baker, F., & Darlington, Y. (2009). Experiences of song writing in a group progamme for mothers who had experienced childhood abuse. *Nordic Journal of Music Therapy, 18,* 133–149. doi:10.1080/08098130903062405.

Eyre, L. (2007). Changes in images, life events, and music in Analytical Music Therapy: A reconstruction of Mary Priestley's case study of "Curtis." *Qualitative Inquiries in Music Therapy, 3,* 1–30.

Fidelibus, J. F. (2004). *Mindfulness in music therapy clinical improvisation: When the music flows* (Doctoral dissertation). New York University, New York, NY. Retrieved from http://steinhardt.nyu.edu/scmsAdmin/media/users/jts390/Dissertations/Fidelibus_Joseph_2004.pdf

Freire, P. (1970). *Pedagogy of the oppressed.* New York, NY: Continuum.

Gardstrom, S. (2004). An investigation of meaning in clinical music improvisation with troubled adolescents. *Qualitative Inquiries in Music Therapy, 1,* 77–160.

Gonzalez, P. (2011). The impact of music therapists' music cultures on the development of their professional identities. *Qualitative Inquiries in Music Therapy, 6,* 1–33.

Grocke, D. (2009). The effect of group music therapy on quality of life for participants living with a severe and enduring mental illness. *Journal of Music Therapy, 46,* 90–104. doi:10.1093/jmt/46.2.90

Hibben, J. (1999). *Inside music therapy: Client perspectives.* Gilsum, NH: Barcelona.

Holck, U. (2007). An ethnographic descriptive approach to video microanalysis. In T. Wosch & T. Wigram (Eds.), *Microanalysis in music therapy* (pp. 29–40). Philadelphia, PA: Jessica Kingsley.

Hoskyns, S. (2013). *Enabling the curious practitioner: Perceptions on the integration of research and practice in the education of music therapy students at master's level* (Unpublished doctoral dissertation). New Zealand School of Music, Wellington, New Zealand. Retrieved from http://mro.massey.ac.nz/handle/10179/4982

Keith, D. R. (2007). Understanding music improvisations: A comparison of methods of meaning-making. *Qualitative Inquiries in Music Therapy, 3,* 62–102.

Kim, S. (2008). The supervisee's experience of cross-cultural music therapy supervision. *Qualitative Inquiries in Music Therapy, 4,* 1–44.

Kvale, S. (1998). *InterViews: An introduction to qualitative research interviewing.* Thousand Oaks, CA: Sage.

Langenberg, M., Frommer, J., & Tress, W. (1993). A qualitative research approach to Analytical Music Therapy. *Music Therapy, 12,* 59–84. doi:10.1093/mt/12.1.59

Langenberg, M., Frommer, J., & Tress, W. (1995). From isolation to bonding: A music therapy case study of a patient with chronic migraines. *Arts in Psychotherapy, 22,* 87–101. doi:10.1016/0197-4556(95)00005-P

Ledger, A. J. (2010). *Am I a founder or am I a fraud? Music therapists' experiences of developing services in healthcare organizations* (Unpublished doctoral dissertation). University of Limerick, Irish World Academy of Music and Dance, Limerick, Ireland. Retrieved from http://ulir.ul.ie/handle/10344/1131

Lee, C. (1992). *The analysis of therapeutic improvisatory music with people living with the virus HIV and AIDS* (Unpublished doctoral dissertation). City University of London, London, UK.

Lee, C. (1996). *Music at the edge: Music therapy experiences of a musician with AIDS*. London, UK: Routledge.

Lee, C. (2000). A method of analyzing improvisations in music therapy. *Journal of Music Therapy, 37*, 147–167. doi:10.1093/jmt/37.2.147

McFerran, K., Baker, F., Patton, G. C., & Sawyer S. M. (2006). A retrospective lyrical analysis of songs written by adolescents with anorexia nervosa. *European Eating Disorders Review, 14*, 397–403. doi:10.1002/erv.746

McFerran, K. M., Roberts, M., & O'Grady, L. (2010). Music therapy with bereaved teenagers: A mixed methods perspective. *Death Studies, 34*, 541–565. doi:10.1080/07481181003765428

Miles, M. M., & Huberman, A. M. (1994). *Qualitative data analysis: An expanded sourcebook*. Thousand Oaks, CA: Sage.

Morse, J. M. (2004). Sampling in qualitative research. In M. S. Lewis, A. Bryman, & T. F. Lia (Eds.), *Sage encyclopedia of social science research methods* (Vol. 3; pp. 993–995). Thousand Oaks, CA: Sage.

Murphy, K. (2007). Experiential learning in music therapy: Faculty and student perspectives. *Qualitative Inquiries in Music Therapy, 3*, 31–61.

O'Callaghan, C. C. (1996). Lyrical themes in songs written by palliative care patients. *Journal of Music Therapy, 33*, 74–92. doi:10.1093.jmt/33.2.74.

O'Grady, L. (2011). The therapeutic potentials of creating and performing music with women in prison: A qualitative case study. *Qualitative Inquiries in Music Therapy, 6*, 122–152.

Patton, M. Q. (2006). *Qualitative research and evaluation methods*. Thousand Oaks, CA: Sage.

Pavlicevic, M. (2010). Because it's cool: Community Music Therapy in Heideveld, South Africa. In B. Stige, G. Ansdell, C. Elevant, & M. Pavlicevic (Eds.), *Where music helps: Community Music Therapy in action and reflection* (pp. 99–112). Burlington, VT: Ashgate.

Procter, S. (2013). *Music therapy: What is it for whom? An ethnography of music therapy in a community mental health resource centre* (Doctoral dissertation, Exeter University). Retrieved from https://ore.exeter.ac.uk/repository/handle/10871/11101

Roberts, M., & McFerran, K. (2013). A mixed methods analysis of songs written by bereaved preadolescents in individual music therapy. *Journal of Music Therapy, 50*,

25–52. doi:10.1093/jmt/50.1.25

Rubin, H. J., & Rubin, I. S. (1995). *Qualitative interviewing: The art of hearing data*. Thousand Oaks, CA: Sage.

Seidman, I. (1998). *Interviewing as qualitative research: A guide for researchers in education and the social sciences* (2nd ed.). New York, NY: Teachers College Press.

Snow, S., Snow, S., & D'Amico, M. (2008). Interdisciplinary research through community music therapy and performance ethnography [Recherche interdisciplinaire: musicothérapie communautaire et ethnographie de la performance]. *Canadian Journal of Music Therapy, 14*, 30–46.

Solli, H. P., Rolvsjord, R., & Borg, M. (2013). Toward understanding music therapy as a recovery-oriented practice within mental health care: A meta-synthesis of service users' experiences. *Journal of Music Therapy, 50*, 244–273. doi:10.1093/jmt/50.4.244

Sokira, J. (2007). Interpreting the communicative behaviors of clients with Rett Syndrome in music therapy: A self-inquiry. *Qualitative Inquiries in Music Therapy, 3*, 103–131.

Sorel, S. (2010). Presenting Carly and Elliott: Exploring roles and relationships in a mother–son dyad in Nordoff-Robbins Music Therapy. *Qualitative Inquiries in Music Therapy, 5*, 173–238.

Stige, B., & Aarø, L. E. (2012). *Invitation to Community Music Therapy*. New York, NY: Routledge.

Tetens, J., & Probst, P. (2009). *Sozialkommunikatives Förderprogramm für Kinder und Jugendliche mit Autismus: Systematische Fallstudie an einem 12-jährigen Jungen unter besonderer Berücksichtigung musiktherapeutischer Prozesse* [Music therapy program to enhance social communication in autistic children and adolescents: Systematic case study of a 12-year-old boy]. *Musiktherapeutische Umschau, 30*(1), 31–41.

Tuastad, L., & Stige, B. (2015). The revenge of Me and the THE BAND'its: A narrative inquiry of identity constructions in a rock band of ex-inmates. *Nordic Journal of Music Therapy, 24*, 252–275. doi:10.1080/08098131.2014.967713.

Turry, A. (2010). Integrating musical and psychotherapeutic thinking: Research on the relationship between words and music in clinically improvised songs. *Qualitative Inquiries in Music Therapy, 5*, 116–172.

Warner, C. (2005). *Music therapy with adults with learning difficulties and "severe challenging behaviour." An action research inquiry into the benefits of group music therapy within a community home* (Doctoral dissertation, University of the West of England). Retrieved from http://europepmc.org/abstract/ETH/418450/reload=0;jsessionid=UmKJmgVFDAwTA4jKnNtW.4

Watt, D. (2007). On becoming a qualitative researcher: The value of reflexivity. *The Qualitative Report, 12*. 82–101.

Wheeler, B. L. (1999). Experiencing pleasure in working with severely disabled children. *Journal of Music Therapy, 36*, 56–80. doi:10.1093/jmt/36.1.56

Wosch, T., & Wigram, T. (2007). *Microanalysis in music therapy: Methods, techniques, and applications for clinicians, researchers, educators, and students.* London, UK: Jessica Kingsley.

Zanders, M. (2012). The musical and personal biographies of adolescents with foster care experience. *Qualitative Inquiries in Music Therapy, 7,* 71–109.

Chapter 14

TYPES OF OBJECTIVIST RESEARCH

Kenneth E. Bruscia

Types of objectivist research are usually called ***designs***. These designs are methodological procedures or ways of doing research that are commonly used across the natural and social sciences. The designs vary according to:

- whether the study involves one or more individuals or groups,
- whether the participants are compared to themselves or another group;
- whether the participants are already members of an existing group rather than specially selected for the study;
- whether the participants will receive treatment of some kind, and if so how many;
- whether observations are made before, after, or during treatment; and
- whether the design can provide strong evidence of cause-effect relationships.

The designs presented here are classified and sequenced in the traditional way, and though the intent is to sequence them according to the strength of the evidence they provide, this is not always the case. In fact, all of the variables cited above determine the strength of the evidence, and it is difficult to consider all of them simultaneously in creating an evidence hierarchy.

Single Subject and Small N Research

Single subject and small n research involves the analysis and comparison of the effects of one or more treatments on an individual or group of individuals, accomplished through the repeated measurement of the baseline (dependent variable) before and after one or more treatment (independent variable) for each individual. These designs differ from the others in that in-depth and rich data are collected for single or small samples, rather than limited data on larger samples, thus facilitating the discovery of cause-effect relationships.

Objectivist Case Study

An *objectivist case study* is an in-depth, empirical study of an individual or group using a quasi-experimental design (as explained below). The aim is to determine the effects of intervention (the independent variable) on a target behavior (the dependent variable). An objectivist case study has several defining features: It allows for "the exploration of complexity through the use of multiple data sources" (Ridder & Fachner, 2016, p. 291), such as behavioral and physiological measures, and observation; it is conducted in a real-life setting; it reduces the data through quantification and thereby allows for the analysis and triangulation of different types of data; and it involves thick description of the findings.

Case studies can be used to identify best practices, explain the effects of treatment, and develop clinical manuals and protocols. (Ridder & Fachner, 2016). Unfortunately, diverse terminology has been used in the literature to label case studies, so it is very difficult to define specific types; nevertheless, many case studies can be found in the music therapy literature. Examples include: Ridder (2003); Fachner, Gold, Ala-Ruona, Punkanen, and Erkkilä (2010); and Hackett, Morison, and Pullen (2013).

Withdrawal and Reversal Designs

Withdrawal and reversal designs involve the analysis and comparison of the effects of one or more treatments on an individual or group of individuals, accomplished through the repeated measurement of the baseline before and after treatment for each individual. Other defining features are: the use of each participant as his or her own control; the use of purposive sampling without matching participants as in experimental groups; the use of individual rather than mean scores; and the capability of making generalizations when the necessary information is provided on participants, settings, and procedures (Jones & Brown, 2016).

A distinction should be made between applied behavior analysis and single subject research. *Applied behavior analysis* refers only to treatment using behavioral techniques (e.g., contingent reinforcement, behavior shaping and extinction), whereas *single subject research* may involve a variety of clinical orientations (e.g., psychodynamic, cognitive).

When describing the various design options, "A" has been conventionally used for the baseline measure (independent variable), and "B" (and subsequent letters) for the intervention (or dependent variable); however, this convention has not been used by all researchers. In this chapter, A and B are used as conventionally used. The most common withdrawal design options are: AB, ABA, ABAB, ABAC, and ABACA.

The *AB* design is the simplest, and affords the least amount of experimental control. It involves only one baseline measure and one treatment. An example is the study by Hanser, Butterfield-Whitcomb, Kawata, and Collins (2011) that looked at the effects of music-facilitated stress reduction on individuals with dementia.

The *ABA* design provides more experimental control in that a measure is taken both before and after treatment to determine whether the treatment was effective. For example, Carruth (1997) used this design to study the effect of singing specially composed songs on familiar name recognition in older adults with memory problems. Carnahan, Musti-Rao, and Bailey (2009) examined the effects of reading different materials on the engagement of individual children with autism.

The *ABACA* design is similar in the return of the baseline measure after treatment, but here the effects of two different treatments are evaluated instead of one.

The *ABAB* design repeats the same treatment with no baseline measures taken after the final intervention. Pasiali (2004) used this design to examine the effect of a specially composed song on the reduction of problem behaviors in children with autism.

A similar design is *ABAC*, which is used when two interventions are of interest, with no baseline measures taken after the final intervention. Kern, Wolery, and Aldridge (2007) used this design to test the effects of different versions of a song on improving the morning routines of individual children with autism.

Multiple Baseline Designs

Multiple baseline designs are used to study the effects of (a) either one or more treatments (independent variable) on (b) either one or more persons, in (c) either one or more setting (Napoles, 2016). To do this, the researcher takes separate baselines for each person, intervention, or setting, and when a consistent response is observed, the intervention is introduced. Once there is a clear change in the target behavior, the process continues with the other individual, intervention, or setting, one at a time. This allows the researcher to compare the cases who have received treatment with subsequent cases that have not yet received the treatment and thereby determine whether the treatment induces the desired change.

Jellison, Brooks, and Huck (1984) compared the effects of three music teaching conditions (circle instruction, group participation, and music contingency) on the frequency of positive social interactions in elementary students with and without disabilities. They provided 12 sessions to four classrooms and found that the music contingency group was most effective, and that the sixth grade students in a homogenous group showed the greatest degree of change. Another example of multiple baseline designs is the study by Kern and Aldridge (2006), who compared the interactions of four boys with autism in four different play settings.

Changing Criterion Designs

Changing criterion designs are used to study the effects of intervention on incremental changes in a behavior leading to a long-term goal (Napoles, 2016). This design is especially useful when the target behavior is more likely to be achieved in steps or with time, rather than immediately or all at once. It does not involve withdrawing or temporarily suspending the intervention, and it does not involve more than one individual, intervention or setting. Rather it demonstrates how a behavior changes in the desired direction based on repeated observations after repeated interventions.

Hsueh (2001) used a changing criterion design with a girl with Down syndrome, to test the effectiveness of contingent music rewards in improving number identification, and increasing length of stay at her mother's side while shopping.

Multiple Treatment Designs

Multiple treatment designs involve the analysis and comparison of the effects of two or more interventions on a single response (Napoles, 2016). The observations take place during the different treatments so that changes in the response can be compared across treatments. A baseline may or may not be used before the treatments begin. Thus, when comparing the effects of two treatments on the desired response, the designs would be BCBC or ABCBC.

Gadberry (2010) used this design to compare augmentative and alternative communication systems in increasing intentional communicative acts. Finnigan (2008) compared playing with toys with and without music on social responsiveness.

Descriptive Research

Descriptive research is the study of the characteristics of a population or phenomenon when the researcher does not manipulate any of the variables. The aims are to describe: the incidence of selected variable(s), the degree to which they vary in relation to one another in some predictable way, and the extent to which they change as a function of time or age.

Survey Research

Survey research is the study of selected characteristics of a particular population or changes in a population, using a predetermined set of questions presented in questionnaires or interviews. The aim is to use data of a representative sample to describe the population from which the sample was drawn, or to determine the extent of change in the population at two or more points in time.

Curtis (2016) provides a wealth of examples of surveys on three main topics in music therapy: clinical practice, the profession and its members, and education and training.

Correlation and Regression

Correlation is a type of statistical analysis rather than a research method. In bivariate or simple correlation, it is the analysis of how closely two variables co-vary in relation to one another when neither variable is manipulated. The aim is to evaluate how strong the relationship is between the variables. A positive correlation shows that as one variable increases so does the other; whereas a negative correlation shows that as one variable increases, the other decreases.

Correlational studies are an important type of music therapy research. They can provide information on many relationships. For example, correlational studies may deal with how the traits of music therapists relate to one another (e.g., self-confidence and longevity in the field), how client characteristics relate to one another (e.g., depression and spontaneous tempo), how client characteristics relate to the outcome of therapy (e.g., depression and positive imagery), how therapist characteristics relate to client outcomes (e.g., directiveness and positive imagery), and many other such comparisons. For examples in the music therapy literature, see Ghetti (2016).

Another important use of correlation is to determine the reliability and validity of any measurement. For example, to evaluate reliability, the researcher can examine how scores on one version of a test correlate with another version of the same test, or how scores on one part of the test correlate with scores on another part. For example, does one version of a rhythmic imitation task correlate with another version that uses different but matched items? Or, does half of the scores on the rhythmic imitation task correlate with the other half?

To test validity, the researcher can examine how scores on an *invalidated* test correlate with scores on a *validated* test measuring the target variable. For example, how do scores on a rhythmic imitation task which has been designed to test short-term memory but has not been validated, relate to scores on a digital recall test that has been validated as a test of short-term memory? Is rhythmic imitation a valid measure of short-term memory?

Regression is similar to correlation but goes further. Correlation reveals the strength and direction of the relationship between two variables; regression yields an equation that allows the actual prediction of scores on one variable to scores on another. In regression analysis, the independent variable is called the predictor variable (X), and the dependent variable is called the criterion variable (Y). A simple regression examines one predictor variable and one criterion variable. For example, how well can IQ predict rhythmic short term memory?

A multiple regression examines how different predictor variables contribute partially or fully to variations in the criterion variable. An example of multiple regression would be a study on which traits on a personality test are the best predictors of music aptitude. For more information on the different types of regression, see Ghetti (2016).

Views about correlation and regression have evolved in recent years. Both types of statistical analyses have been traditionally categorized as descriptive research in that they are usually used to analyze nonexperimental data. Ghetti

(2016) argues that correlation and regression can also be used to analyze data from experimental or quasi-experimental studies, and when properly done, can provide some evidence of cause-effect relationships.

Economic Analysis

Economic analysis is an untapped but vital area of music therapy research. It involves the calculation and comparison of the finances required to provide music therapy services (Else, 2016). Specific aims may be to determine the financial risks, costs, and outcome involved in:

- implementing one or more therapy programs or interventions
- achieving one or more clinical outcomes through music therapy;
- providing effective music therapy services to individuals with a certain diagnostic condition;
- evaluating how music therapy services affects patient costs
- comparing the cost-effectiveness of music therapy services with another type of service;
- evaluating financial risks against potential outcomes of music therapy. (Else, 2016)

Like correlation and regression, economic analysis may involve both nonexperimental and experimental data. Thus, technically speaking, it may go beyond the boundaries of purely descriptive research to be categorized as experimental.

Delphi Technique

The *Delphi technique* is the use of repeatedly refined questionnaires to gather data on a particular topic from experts. The purpose is to identify points of consensus and disagreement (Cassity, 2016). Several models can be used.

In the first, the *questionnaire model*, the study begins by sending an open-ended questionnaire to the participants, and then using their responses to refine the content of items on a second questionnaire. The format of the second questionnaire is also re-designed to require the participants to rate their responses to each item. The researcher then analyzes the ratings on the second questionnaire by computing the mean and standard deviation for the combined ratings on each item. The results are then returned to the participants so that they re-consider and modify their previous ratings as necessary. The researcher then analyzes areas of agreement and disagreement in the final data set.

The second model, the *literature model*, begins with a search all relevant writings and studies on the topic, which are then used as the basis for developing the first questionnaire. Participants are asked to complete the questionnaire and to add comments or information to the items. Based on their responses, a rating-scale questionnaire is then returned to the participants, and the researcher once again calculates the mean and standard deviation for each item, and returns the third questionnaire to the participants to adjust their ratings. The researcher then analyzes areas of agreement and disagreement.

In the *mixed model*, the above procedural steps are combined in various ways, and in the *E-Delphi model*, the Internet is used as a primary source of data.

Examples in music therapy research include studies by Edwards (2000) and Cassity (2007). Edwards compared music therapists with other pediatric professionals to establish research priorities for pediatric music therapy. Cassity used the Delphi technique to predict the likelihood that theoretical changes will take place in psychiatric music therapy.

Longitudinal Designs

Longitudinal designs are those that study how time, age, or interventions affect the variables of interest. This is done by collecting data from the same sample, multiple times after different periods of time. Longitudinal designs are not the same as cross-sectional designs where samples are compared from different sets of participants who are at different stages or ages.

Baker and Ledger (2016) emphasize the need for more longitudinal research in music therapy. Studies of the effects of music therapy over time and the "trajectory of improvement or stabilization are needed to illustrate the more permanent or long-term effects of music therapy on various well-being measures" (p. 358).

Longitudinal studies can be divided into four types. In the *prospective* type, the same group is studied over a period of time in the future. For example, Ledger and Baker (2007) used a prospective longitudinal design to study whether agitation decreased in people with Alzheimer's disease during a 12-month course of music therapy. They took measurements five times during the year as treatment progressed, and thereby developed a better understanding of how and why agitation changed over time, and what predictive and risk factors were involved. Dingle, Brander, Ballantyne, and Baker (2013) studied the benefits of weekly participation in a choir, at the beginning of the choir, and then 6 and 12 months afterwards. Argstatter, Grapp, Plinkert, and Bolay (2012) evaluated outcomes of a music therapy intervention for people with chronic tinnitus before, immediately after, and six months after participating in the therapy program. Klaphajone et al. (2014) studied changes in the physical and emotional functioning of children with physical disabilities, before, after 9 months, and after 18 months of participation in music therapy.

In the *retrospective* type, the same group is studied by recalling a period of time in the past. For example, Bergh (2010) interviewed adults about their experiences as children in a multi-cultural music project several years after the project.

In the *repeated cross-section* type, different samples are used to determine the likelihood of change over time, but the same sample is not tested more than once. In the *revolving* types, new participants are added to the primary sample after the study is in progress. Examples of these types were not found in the music therapy literature.

Pre-Experimental Designs

Pre-experimental designs are those in which only one group of participants receive a treatment, and measures are taken to determine the effects of treatment on the same group. There are two main types, the posttest only design and the one-group pretest-posttest design.

Posttest Only Design

Also called a **one-shot case study,** the **posttest only design** involves taking measures on the dependent variable after treatment only (Jones, 2016). It is important for the researcher to study the group before treatment and then use these observations to design the treatment and speculate on what changes might result.

One-Group Pretest-Posttest Design

In this design, as implied in its name, a single group is observed on the dependent variable before and after treatment. This design has been used to test the effects of music therapy on one group, using pretests and posttests on physiological variables (Nakayama, Kikuta, & Takeda, 2009), mood (Gallagher, Lagman, Walsh, Davis, & LeGrand, 2006), pain (Krout, 2001), speech prosody (Staum, 1987), symptoms after transplant surgery (Madson & Silverman, 2010), intergenerational interactions, attitudes, and well-being (Belgrave, 2011), affective qualities (Madson & Silverman, 2010), and mental health symptoms (Schwantes & McKinney, 2010).

Quasi Experimental Designs

A design that compares the effects of treatment on an existing group with another existing group that has not received the treatment. The groups have to be closely matched.

Static Group Design

In a **static group design,** an existing group receives treatment, and then measures are taken of its effects on that group. The same measures are then taken of another existing group(s) who has received no treatment or a different treatment. Then these post-test measures of both groups are compared to see if there are any differences. The groups are static because they already exist as intact groups; thus, participants in each group have not been selected randomly (de L'Etoile, 2016).

Here are a few examples in music therapy where effects of treatment and no treatment were compared. McMahon (1979) compared two intact first grade classes. One class received music therapy (singing specially designed songs and engaging in auditory discrimination tasks), and the other class received no music therapy. Both classes were tested on reading achievement before and after the experimental group completed training. The experimental group performed five of the eight reading tasks better than the comparison group.

Silverman, Christenson, Golden, and Chaput-McGovern (2012) compared patient satisfaction in two groups of university students in the waiting room of a student health clinic. One group experienced live music and the other did not; the group experiencing music had higher satisfaction than the no music group.

Pretest-Postest Static Group Comparison Design

Already existing groups are observed on the dependent variable both prior to and after equivalent treatment periods. The experimental group receives the treatment being tested, and the control group receives usual or traditional care or a different treatment. Because the groups already exist, and have not been randomly sampled, the two groups may not be sufficiently matched or equivalent.

Hilliard (2006) provided an example of this design in comparing two treatments. He compared the effects of ecological versus didactic approaches to music therapy on compassion fatigue in two groups of hospice care-workers. No differences were found.

The *strong* version of this design, also called the *cluster* or *group random assignment* design, uses two intact groups that are randomly assigned to the treatment and no-treatment groups. Specifically, half of each intact group is randomly assigned to the treatment condition, and the other half to the no-treatment condition (de L'Etoile, 2016). Vanderark, Newman, and Bell (1983) compared the self-concept and attitudes of residents in two nursing homes. Half of the groups in each nursing home received a music program, and the other halves did not. Then the treatment halves from both nursing homes were compared to the no-treatment halves from both homes. Significant improvements were found for the experimental (or music) treatment.

Experimental Designs

Two or more groups are created specifically for purposes of experimentation. Ideally, participants of each group are randomly selected from a clearly defined population. Pretests may or may not be administered. The groups then receive the same or different treatments, and post-tests are administered. Experiments are designed to determine if-then or cause-effect relationships.

Parallel Groups Designs

In a parallel group experimental design, two or more groups are compared before and after experimental versus control conditions. The purpose is to determine whether there are differences between the groups in the amount of change they demonstrated after their respective conditions. More specifically, this design is used to determine whether "changes in the dependent variable are attributable to the independent variable that participants in experimental condition received" (Silverman, 2016, p. 381). Here are some types of parallel group designs.

Non-randomized parallel group designs are those wherein participants in the groups are not selected randomly. For example, Kwon, Gang, and Oh (2013) selected their groups from patients who were already in different hospital wards to minimize treatment contamination. In their study, patients who did and did not receive music therapy were compared, and found that those in the treatment group had improved more in brain waves, cognitive functioning, and behaviors.

Randomized parallel group designs are those wherein participants in the groups are randomly sampled. An example is the study by Jacobsen, McKinney, and Holck (2014) who compared child-parent interactions before and after a music therapy program, as compared to no program. Eighteen dyads were randomly assigned to each group. Nonverbal communication and mutual attunement improved more in the music therapy group.

Posttest parallel group designs are those in which group participants are selected randomly, and each group is tested after but not before treatment. This design allows the research to compare an entire treatment program with different components of the program. An example is the study by Silverman (2014) who compared four randomized groups that received different music therapy conditions to determine if any induced more trust in the therapist. The study showed that live music therapy fosters more trust than a recorded version.

Pretest, posttest parallel groups designs include pre-testing of participants in all groups, then they are tested again after receiving experimental and control conditions. This allows the researcher to determine whether there were differences *between* the groups in pretest scores and in post-test scores, while also identifying differences *within* each group between pre-test and posttests. Robb et al. (2014) used this design to study the effects of therapeutic music videos on the resilience of young adults and adolescents undergoing stem cell transplant.

The Solomon four-group design uses two experimental groups that receive pre- and post-tests, and two control groups that receive only the posttest. Johnson and Darrow (1997) used this design to compare the attitudinal effects of a video showing how students with special needs can be integrated in a band on four student groups.

Cross-Over Designs

In a *cross-over design,* each participant in a group receives more than one treatment and/or no treatment, over two or more time periods; and the effects of treatment are measured at the end of each period. This design is to be used when treatment effects are not likely to be long-lasting (DeLoach, Murphy, & Wheeler, 2016). The following studies are a few examples of the design.

Bruer, Sptiznagal, and Cloninger (2007) gave adults with cognitive impairments two alternating treatments. The experimental condition was music therapy, and the control condition was a movie. Each adult received both conditions three times, and measures were taken after receiving each condition. The music therapy condition led to significant improvements in cognitive functioning on the morning after treatment.

Gerdner (2000) used the cross-over design to compare the effects of listening to classical versus preferred music on the agitation behaviors of people with Alzheimer's disease. Participants were randomly assigned to two groups. Each group provided baseline data for one month before the experimental conditions were given. Using the baseline data, the participants were then re-assigned so that the groups were matched in age, gender, and cognitive functioning. Each group then received both listening conditions in the opposite order, with a two-week wash-out period following each condition. No listening conditions were given during the wash-out period to avoid carryover or cumulative effects of each listening condition. Agitation was significantly reduced during and after the classical music condition.

Cohen-Mansfield and Werner (1997) compared the verbally disrupted behavior of nursing home residents after four treatment conditions (music listening, videotapes of family interaction, one-to-one interaction, and no intervention). Each condition was followed by a one-week washout period. The target behaviors decreased from most to least by one-to-one interaction, videotaped families, music, and no intervention.

Factorial Designs

Factorial designs involve comparison of two or more groups on the effects of two or more independent variables on a single dependent variable. Levels in each independent variable are compared with levels in the other independent variable(s) to identify *factors* that they have in common. These factors and how they interact among the independent variables are then statistically tested to determine their individual effects on the dependent variable. The two types of factorial designs used in music therapy are the full factorial design and the split-plot design.

The *full factorial design* compares each level of factor to all levels of the other(s). The *split-plot factorial design* compares the effects of experimental and control conditions on individual participants in each group at different points in time (McKinney, 2016).

Here are selected examples of the full factorial design. Anshel and Kipper (1988) explored the effects of two music conditions (singing, listening) and two control conditions (reading poetry and file viewing) on trust and cooperation in adults receiving continuing education. Participants were randomly assigned to one of two groups, with one group receiving the music conditions and the other receiving the control conditions.

McKinney and Tims (1995) examined the role of two factors on the quality of imagery created by participants. One factor was imaging ability (high and low), and the other factor was music (classical music versus silence during the imagery experience). Thus the design was a 2 x 2 analysis, first comparing the *main* effects (the difference between high versus low imaging ability participants on the dependent variable, and the difference between music versus silence), and then the *interaction effects* (whether the two main effects were significant different). The results showed that music versus silence was a bigger factor in the quality of imagery for the high imagers but not the low imagers. Music made more of a difference for the high rather than low imagers.

Band, Quilter, and Miller (2001–2002) compared two types of relaxation inductions (structured versus unstructured) crossed with three music conditions (classical, impressionistic, and no music), randomly assigning these conditions to six classes of undergraduate students. This 2 x 3 factorial design allows the evaluation of main effects (between the two inductions, and between the three music conditions) while also evaluating which main effect(s) were greater. The results showed that the music increased the quality of imaging, and the structured induction affected the type of images generated.

The following are selected examples of the split-plot design. Jacobsen, McKinney, and Holck (2014) studied families in which parents had emotionally neglected a child by comparing the effects of music therapy versus no music therapy on parent-child interactions and parenting competencies. Pre- and post-tests were given to each participant. This 2 x 2 split-plot was used to test differences in main effects between the music therapy and control conditions, the difference in main effects between parent-child interactions and parenting competency, and the difference between these two main effects.

McKinney, Antoni, Tims, Kumar, and McCabe (1997) studied the mood and level of cortisol in the blood of healthy participants randomly assigned to a music-imaging condition and wait-list control. Mood and cortisol were measured three times during the treatment period for each individual, thus yielding a 2 x 3 split plot design, that is two levels of Factor 1 (music-imaging versus wait-list), and three levels of Factor 2 (measurements taken at three points in time).

References

Anshel, A., & Kipper, D. A. (1988). The influence of group singing on trust and cooperation. *Journal of Music Therapy, 145–155.* doi:10.1093/jmt/25.3.145

Argstatter, H., Grapp, M., Plinkert, P. K., & Bolay, H. V. (2012). Heidelberg Neuro-Music Therapy for chronic tonal tinnitus – Treatment outline and psychometric evaluation. *International Tinnitus Journal, 17*(1), 31–41.

Baker, F., & Ledger, A. (2016). Longitudinal designs. In B. L. Wheeler & K. M. Murphy (Eds.), *Music therapy research* (3rd ed.; pp. 358–364). Dallas, TX: Barcelona.

Band, J. P., Quilter, S. M., & Miller, G. M. (2001–2002). The influence of selected music and inductions on mental imagery: Implications for practitioners of Guided Imagery and Music. *Journal of the Association for Music and Imagery, 8,* 13–33.

Belgrave, M. (2011). The effect of a music therapy intergenerational program on children and older adults' intergenerational interactions, cross-age attitudes, and older adults' psychosocial well- being. *Journal of Music Therapy, 48,* 486–508. doi:10.1093/jmt/48.4.486

Bergh, A. (2010). *I'd like to teach the world to sing: Music and conflict transformation.* University of Exeter, Exeter, UK. Retrieved from https://ore.exeter.ac.uk/repository/bitstream/handle/10036/97884/BerghA.pdf?sequence=2

Bruer, R. A., Spitznagal, E., & Cloninger, C. R. (2007). The temporal limits of cognitive change from music therapy in elderly persons with dementia or dementia-like cognitive impairment: A randomized controlled trial. *Journal of Music Therapy, 44*(4), 308–328. doi:10.1093/jmt/44.4.308

Carnahan, C., Musti-Rao, S. & Bailey, J. (2009). Promoting active engagement in small group learning experiences for students with autism and significant learning needs. *Education and Treatment of Children, 32,* 37–61. doi:10.1353/etc.0.0047

Carruth, E. K. (1997). The effects of singing and the spaced retrieval technique on improving face-name recognition in nursing home residents with memory loss. *Journal of Music Therapy, 34,* 165–186. doi:10.1093/jmt/34.3.165

Cassity, M. (2016). The Delphi technique. In B. L. Wheeler & K. M. Murphy (Eds.), *Music therapy research* (3rd ed.; pp. 350–357). Dallas, TX: Barcelona.

Cassity, M. D., (2007). Psychiatric music therapy in 2016: A Delphi poll of the future. *Music Therapy Perspectives, 25*(2), 86–93. doi:10.1093/mtp/25.2.86

Cohen-Mansfield, J. & Werner, P. (1997). Management of verbally disruptive behaviors in nursing home residents. *Journal of Gerontology, 52A*(6), M369-M377.

Curtis, S. (2016). Survey research. In B. L. Wheeler & K. M. Murphy (Eds.), *Music therapy research* (3rd ed.; pp. 322–330). Dallas, TX: Barcelona.

De l'Etoile, S. (2016). Pre-experimental designs: Static group comparison. In B. L. Wheeler & K. M. Murphy (Eds.), *Music therapy research* (3rd ed; pp. 372–380). Dallas, TX: Barcelona.

DeLoach, D., Murphy, K. M., & Wheeler, B. L. (2016). Cross-over designs. In B. L. Wheeler & K. M. Murphy (Eds.), *Music therapy research* (3rd ed.; pp. 389-395). Dallas, TX: Barcelona.

Dingle, G., Brander, C., Ballantyne, J., & Baker, F. A. (2013). "To Be Heard" – the social and mental health benefits of choir singing for disadvantaged adults. *Psychology of Music, 41*(4), 405–421. doi:10.1177/0305735611430081

Edwards, J. M. (2000). *Developing a platform for research to inform music therapy practice with hospitalised children* (Unpublished doctoral dissertation). University of Queensland, Brisbane, Australia.

Else, B. (2016). Economic analysis. In B. L. Wheeler & K. M. Murphy (Eds.), *Music therapy research* (3rd ed.: pp. 339–349). Dallas, TX: Barcelona.

Fachner, J., Gold, C., Ala-Ruona, E., Punkanen, M., & Erkkilä, J. (2010). Depression and music therapy treatment—clinical validity and reliability of EEG alpha asymmetry and frontal midline theta: three case studies. In S. M. Demorest, S. J. Morrison, & P. S. Campbell (Eds.), *Proceedings of the 11th International Conference on Music Perception and Cognition (CD-ROM)* (pp. 11–18). Seattle: University of Washington, School of Music.

Finnigan, E. (2008). *Increasing social responsiveness in a child with autism: A comparison of music and non–music interventions* (Master's thesis). Retrieved from ProQuest Digital Dissertations & Theses. (UMI No. MR82089)

Gadberry, A. (2010). *Communicative acts in music therapy interventions with and without aided augmentative and alternative communication systems* (Doctoral dissertation). Retrieved from ProQuest Digital Dissertations & Theses. (UMI No. 3458215)

Gallagher, L. M., Lagman, R., Walsh, D., Davis, M. P., & LeGrand, S. B. (2006). The clinical effects of music therapy in palliative medicine. *Supportive Care in Cancer, 14,* 850–866. doi:10.1007/s00520-005- 0013-6

Gerdner, L. A. (2000). Effects of individualized versus classical "relaxation" music on the frequency of agitation in elderly persons with Alzheimer's disease and related disorders. *International Psychogeriatrics, 12*(1), 49–65.

Ghetti, C. M. (2016). Correlation and regression in nonexperimental and experimental research. In B. L. Wheeler & K. M. Murphy (Eds.), *Music therapy research* (3rd ed.; pp. 331–338). Dallas, TX: Barcelona.

Hackett, S., Morison, C.- J., & Pullen, C. (2013). A retrospective practice based evaluation of music therapy: A single-case study of a four-year-old girl with Rett syndrome—Rebecca's story. *Arts in Psychotherapy, 40*(5), 473–477. doi:10.1016/j.aip.2013.09.005

Hanser, S., Butterfield-Whitcomb, J., Kawata, M., & Collins, B. E. (2011). Home-based music strategies with individuals who have dementia and their family caregivers. *Journal of Music Therapy, 48*(1), 2–27. doi:10.1093/jmt/48.1.2

Hilliard, R. E. (2006). The effect of music therapy sessions on compassion fatigue and team: Building of professional hospice caregivers. *Arts in Psychotherapy, 33,* 395–401. doi:10.1016/j.aip.2006.06.002

Hsueh, M. Y. (2001). *The effects of music on behavioral and cognitive skills in an individual with Down syndrome* (Doctoral dissertation). Retrieved from ProQuest Digital Dissertations & Theses. (UMI No. 1407358) http://www.biostathandbook.com/twowayanova.html

Jacobsen, S. L., McKinney, C. H., & Holck, U. (2014). Effects of a dyadic music therapy intervention on parent–child interaction, parent stress, and parent–child relationship in families with emotionally neglected children: A randomized controlled trial. *Journal of Music Therapy, 51,* 310–332. doi:10.1093/jmt/thu028

Jacobsen, S. L., McKinney, C. H., & Holck, U. (2014). Effects of dyadic music therapy intervention on parent-child interaction, parent stress, and parent-child relationship in families with emotionally neglected children: A randomized controlled trial. *Journal of Music Therapy, 51,* 310–332. doi:10.1093/jmt/thu028

Jellison, J. A., Brooks, B. H., & Huck, B. M. (1984). Structuring small groups and music reinforcement to facilitate positive interactions and acceptance of severely handicapped students in the regular music classroom. *Journal of Research in Music Education, 32,* 243– 264. doi:10.2307/3344923

Johnson, C. M., & Darrow, A. A. (1997). The effect of positive models of inclusion on band students' attitudinal statements regarding the integration of students with disabilities. *Journal of Research in Music Education, 45,* 173–184. doi:10.2307/3345578

Jones, J. (2016). Pre-experimental designs: One-sample designs. In B. L. Wheeler & K. M. Murphy (Eds.), *Music therapy research* (3rd ed.; pp. 365–370). Dallas, TX: Barcelona.

Jones, J., & Brown, L. (2016). AB, ABA, ABAB, and other withdrawal designs. In B. L. Wheeler & K. M. Murphy (Eds.), *Music therapy research* (3rd ed.; pp. 303–313). Dallas, TX: Barcelona.

Kern, P., & Aldridge, D. (2006). Using embedded music therapy interventions to support outdoor play of young children with autism in an inclusive community–based child care program. *Journal of Music Therapy, 43,* 270–294. doi:10.1093/jmt/43.4.270

Kern, P., Wolery, M., & Aldridge, D. (2007). Use of songs to promote independence in morning greeting routines for young children with autism. *Journal of Autism and Developmental Disorders, 37,* 1264–1271. doi:10.1007/s10803-006-0272-1

Klaphajone, J., Thaikruea, L., Boontrakulpoontawee, M., Vivatwongwana, P., Kanongnuch, S., & Tantong, A. (2013). Assessment of music therapy for rehabilitation among physically disabled people in Chiang Mai Province: A pilot study. *Music and Medicine, 5,* 23–30. doi:10.1177/1943862112470462

Krout, R. E. (2001). The effects of single-session music therapy interventions on the observed and self- reported levels of pain control, physical comfort, and relaxation of hospice patients. *American Journal of Hospice and Palliative Medicine, 18,* 383–390. doi:10.1177/104990910101800607

Ledger, A., & Baker, F. (2007). An investigation of long-term effects of group music therapy on agitation levels of people with Alzheimer's disease. *Aging & Mental Health, 11*(3), 330–338. doi:10.1080/13607860600963406

Madson, A. T., & Silverman, M. J. (2010). The effect of music therapy on relaxation, anxiety, pain perception, and nausea in adult solid organ transplant patients. *Journal of Music Therapy, 47,* 220–232. doi:10.1093/jmt/47.3.220

McKinney, C., Antoni, M., Kumar, M., Tims, F., & McCabe, P. (1997). Effects of Guided Imagery and Music (GIM) therapy on mood and cortisol in healthy adults. *Health Psychology: Official Journal of The Division of Health Psychology, American Psychological Association, 16*(4), 390–400.

McKinney, C. H., & Tims, F. C. (1995). Differential effects of selected classical music on the imagery of high versus low imagers: Two studies. *Journal of Music Therapy, 32,* 22–45. doi:10.1093/jmt/32.1.22

McKinney, K. (2016). Factorial designs. In B. L. Wheeler & K. M. Murphy (Eds.), *Music therapy research* (3rd ed.; pp. 396–405). Dallas, TX: Barcelona.

McMahon, O. (1979). The relationship of music discrimination training to reading and associated auditory skills. *Bulletin of the Council for Research in Music Education, 59,* 68–72.

Nakayama, H., Kikuta, F., & Takeda, H. (2009). A pilot study on effectiveness of music therapy in hospice in Japan. *Journal of Music Therapy, 46,* 160–172. doi:10.1093/jmt/46.2.160

Napoles, J. (2016). Multiple baseline, changing criterion, and multiple treatment designs. In B. L. Wheeler & K. M. Murphy (Eds.), *Music therapy research* (3rd ed.; pp. 314–321). Dallas, TX: Barcelona.

Pasiali, V. (2004). The use of prescriptive therapeutic songs in a home-based environment to promote social skills acquisition by children with autism: Three case studies. *Music Therapy Perspectives, 22,* 11–20. doi:10.1093/mtp/22.1.11

Ridder, H. M. O. (2003). *Singing dialogue. Music therapy with persons in advanced stages of dementia. A case study research design* (Unpublished doctoral dissertation). Aalborg University, Aalborg, Denmark.

Ridder, H. M., & Fachner, J. (2016). Single subject and small n research: Objectivist case study research. In B. L. Wheeler & K. M. Murphy (Eds.), *Music therapy research* (3rd ed.; pp. 291–302). Dallas, TX: Barcelona.

Robb, S. L., Burns, D. S., Stegenga, K. A., Haut, P. R.,

Monahan, P. O., Meza, J., . . . Haase, J. E. (2014). Randomized clinical trial of therapeutic music video intervention for resilience outcomes in adolescents/young adults undergoing hematopoietic stem cell transplant: A report from the Children's Oncology Group. *Cancer, 120,* 909–917. doi:10.1002/cncr.28355

Schwantes, M., & McKinney, C. (2010). Music therapy with Mexican migrant farmworkers: A pilot study. *Music Therapy Perspectives, 28,* 22–28. doi:10.1093/mtp/28.1.22

Silverman, M. (2016). Parallel group designs. In B. L. Wheeler & K. M. Murphy (Eds.), *Music therapy research* (3rd ed.; pp. 381–388). Dallas, TX: Barcelona.

Silverman, M. J. (2014). Effects of a live educational music therapy intervention on acute psychiatric inpatients' perceived social support and trust in the therapist: A four-group randomized effectiveness study. *Journal of Music Therapy, 51,* 228–249. doi:10.1093/jmt/thu011

Silverman, M. J., Christenson, G. A., Golden, D., & Chaput-McGovern, J. (2012). Effects of live music on satisfaction of students waiting for treatment in a university health clinic. *Music Therapy Perspectives, 30*(1), 43–48. doi:10.1093/mtp/30.1.43

Staum, M. J. (1987). Music notation to improve the speech prosody of hearing impaired children. *Journal of Music Therapy, 24,* 146–159. doi:10.1093/jmt/24.3.146

Vanderark, S., Newman, I., & Bell, S. (1983). The effects of music participation on quality of life of the elderly. *Music Therapy, 3*(1), 71–81. doi:10.1093/mt/3.1.71

Chapter 15
TYPES OF INTERPRETIVIST RESEARCH

Kenneth E. Bruscia

Types of interpretivist research are very difficult to define and classify for several reasons. First, each approach is flexible and emergent in design, and is not limited to a narrowly defined focus or to a particular sequence of procedures for processing the data. Approaches are often redirected or modified in the process of processing the data. Thus, as outlined by Zanders (2016), one approach may easily evolve and shift into another approach, and the research study then becomes difficult to classify as one or the other. As a result, pure examples of any approach are much less common than mixed approaches.

The second reason is that, because each discipline selects and tailors each approach to meet its own research interests, the focus and methods of data processing vary significantly from one discipline to another. Thus, the way that one discipline defines and uses a particular approach may not be relevant to another discipline. For example, the way sociology defines and uses ethnography may not be relevant to music therapy, other human sciences, or the arts. As a result, it is difficult to find a uniform definition of most interpretivist approaches that carries across disciplines.

This poses many definitional problems in an interdisciplinary field such as music therapy, where research can be approached from diverse perspectives, such as musicology, psychology, sociology, anthropology, medicine, and so forth. Consequently, interpretivist research in music therapy is often defined according to the biases of other disciplines. And of greater concern, it is easy for music therapy researchers to mislabel their own studies, not only because definitions from other disciplines may be irrelevant, but also because there is widespread confusion over the aims and boundaries of each approach.

The definitions and classification system presented below were constructed and organized by the author based on the following notions. First, the definitions and classifications must be relevant to music therapy research interests and needs. Thus, the definitions of some approaches may be different from definitions borrowed from other disciplines. Second, each definition has been constructed to embrace the many different ways that each approach has been implemented in music therapy research, regardless of the definitions used to label them. In other words, the definitions here are synthetic descriptions by the present author, not always exact quotes from other disciplines. Lastly, the definitions were constructed so that clear and relevant distinctions can be made between approaches that have been used in music therapy research. As a result, since most definitions were constructed by the author, sometimes

different from those provided by chapters in the main book, not all definitions and classifications have been referenced.

The classification is based primarily on the focus or purpose of the research, and therein the type of data that is of greatest interest. Six types have been identified: approaches focusing on a natural setting, experience (phenomenology), meanings, language, cases, and theory. These types were identified based on different aspects of the music therapy process itself.

> Client and therapist interact … (Natural Setting Approaches)
> Using various media … (Meaning-focused and Language Focused Approaches)
> To engage the client … (Case Approaches)
> In therapeutic experiences … (Phenomenological Approaches)
> That can be understood in various ways … (Theoretical Approaches)

The above approaches have been presented in this chapter in a different sequence, in order to facilitate a better understanding of each approach.

Natural Setting Approaches

Natural setting approaches are concerned with what people do, think or feel, and how they interact in real-world settings, along with the many contingencies, dimensions, and consequences implicated therein. The natural or real-world setting may be a group of people (e.g., existing groups, communities, cultures), a particular geographical area, a shared trait (gender, diagnosis), or a shared event, situation, or context. Once defined, the setting provides a meaningful boundary for the study. Data collection may focus on in-vivo behaviors, actions, interactions, experiences, values, beliefs, events, as well as aspects of society, culture, environment, and life circumstances that affect people in the defined setting. Below are the main types.

Ethnography

Ethnography is the in-vivo study of a segment of society or part of social life through fieldwork involving participation, observation, interview, examination of artifacts, and so forth. The ultimate aim is to study "human interaction and meaning-making in context" Stige and Ledger (2016, p. 417). Ethnography, then, is more than a study of what happens in a particular context, it is also concerned with the meaning of what happens, and the process by which people make or create those meaning. To study *in context* means to give attention to the conditions and circumstances of the field setting as well as how these contexts influence and are influenced by its members. The aim is to discover regularities in interaction and meaning-making in the setting and its members as an integral whole.

Examples of ethnographic research in music therapy are beginning to appear. Stige (2010) studied the various ways that individuals with intellectual disabilities participated in a community festival. Ledger (2010) did extensive fieldwork in a hospital to see how music therapists interacted with other staff to establish a music therapy program. Procter (2013) examined what clients in a community center think, feel, and value about the music therapy services they received.

Naturalistic Inquiry

Naturalistic inquiry is the study of how people act, interact, experience, and make meaning within a specifically defined real-world *situation*. Note that the kinds of data collected are the same as ethnography, however, the field setting is more delimited, at least in this definition.

Because naturalistic inquiry originated in the social sciences, it was broadly defined as the study of the "social world." This implies relatively large field settings and quite diverse activities among its members. By necessity, however, the setting for naturalistic inquiry in music therapy has been much more delimited; so far it has been specifically focused on what happens in a particular situation, namely a music therapy setting. Thus, whereas ethnography may be more broadly focused on how people live in a social space, naturalistic inquiry, at least in music therapy, may be more specifically focused on how people create and find meaning in a particular situation, namely the music therapy setting.

Aigen (2005) proposes that what distinguishes naturalistic inquiry from other types of research in music therapy is its focus on actual music therapy sessions. "According to naturalistic precepts, to generate research findings that are applicable to actual music therapy sessions, it is essential to study music therapy sessions as they exist in their natural state, that is, without artificial constraints placed [on] them because of research protocols" (p. 363).

Examples in the music therapy literature confirm this focus on actual sessions. Aigen (1997) studied the music therapy sessions of a group of adolescents over the period of a year. Arnason (1998) studied how professional music therapists interact in an improvisational music therapy group. The study included various types of data, including a musical analysis of the improvisations themselves. Turry (2010) described the process of music therapy in his work with a female adult with cancer, using song improvisations. This study also included various types of data, including music and lyric analyses. These studies stand in contrast to the examples given for ethnographic research. Specifically, Stige (2010) and Ledger (2010) situate music therapy in a community center, a community festival, and a hospital, all of which are larger field settings than a therapy session or process. For more examples, see Arnason (2016).

As originated, naturalistic inquiry is steeped in the philosophy of constructivism (Lincoln & Guba, 1985). In constructivism, realities are multiple instead of singular, and research findings are based on the constructs of the researcher. In fact, the very purpose of naturalistic inquiry is to gather the data needed for the researcher to create trustworthy constructions that give greater insight into the setting and its members. In contrast, ethnography is viewed as a method rather than an entire paradigm requiring a particular epistemology such as constructivism. As a result, ethnography can be implemented within different epistemologies, whereas naturalistic inquiry, by definition, is implemented from a constructivist perspective. Essentially this means that ethnographers may seek to describe the field as it *really is* (objectivist) or as various members in the setting describe it (interpretivist), whereas naturalistic inquiry is more likely to describe it as the researcher *construes* the field and its members.

Action Research

Action research aims at finding the most effective way for the researcher to work with others to accomplish a common goal in a real-life situation. It is an in-vivo study of the researcher's actions and interactions with participants, while engaged in a purposeful endeavor (e.g., education, therapy, social work). Through ongoing experimentation and feedback, the researcher learns how to be effective in helping others to accomplish mutual goals. Often the ultimate goal is positive social change.

A sub-type of action research is *participatory action research.* Here consumers or beneficiaries design and implement a study to discover ways to address their own problems as a group (e.g., oppression, marginalization). Qualified members serve as facilitators, but the entire group sets agendas, methods, and dissemination. Once again experimentation and feedback are central.

Note that both variants of action research involve the researcher and participants in trying out different ways of interacting among themselves and acting upon their environment. In contrast, neither ethnography and naturalistic inquiry involves the researcher in providing treatment to the participants or manipulating the field setting in any way (even though the researcher may observe participants receiving treatment from others). Thus, it could be said that these active forms of naturalistic research have an experimental component, not found in ethnography or naturalistic inquiry.

For more details, see Stige and McFerran (2016).

Comparisons

- *Ethnography:* I study how segments of society live in a particular setting, shape their lives, and make them meaningful, when studied and reported from various perspectives
- *Naturalistic inquiry:* I study how people act, interact, experience, and make meaning within a defined real-world situation, and construct trustworthy descriptions of them.
- *Action research:* I try out and study different ways of working effectively with others to accomplish our goals.
- *Participatory action research:* We try out and study ways we can improve our lives.

Phenomenology

Phenomenology can be defined as the study of any *lived* phenomenon: (a) as it presents itself, or (b) as it is experienced by the researcher and/or research participants. A lived phenomenon is anything that human beings commonly experience. For a more detailed discussion, see Jackson (2016).

As originally conceived, phenomenology is an attempt to study a phenomenon *as it unfolds in its own* way. Early phenomenologists argued that imposing any methodological or conceptual framework over the phenomenon to be studied creates blinders that prevent the researcher from observing how the phenomenon reveals itself fully and in its own way. Similarly, when the researcher brings his or her own pre-understandings about the phenomenon to the inquiry, the phenomenon itself is further obscured. These phenomenologists were suggesting that the commonly accepted objective approach of formulating the research question and method before studying a phenomenon was actually tainted with subjectivity. Instead, they were recommending that researchers allow the phenomenon to present itself without interference or preconceptions, and thereby return the focus to studying the phenomenon itself, unfettered by pre-designed methods or researcher pre-understandings. Ironically, these early phenomenologists considered their approach more objective than the standard objectivist approach, which they considered to be quite subjective.

As phenomenological research developed, it was argued that this setting aside of methodological and conceptual preconceptions was not humanly possible. These phenomenologists believed that the phenomenon being studied and the researcher studying it are inseparable; consequently, an object of study can only be understood in terms of the particular subject relating to it. Consequently, the purpose of phenomenology modulated from how *it* (the phenomenon) unfolds, to how humans experience the phenomenon unfolding. The aim changed accordingly, from defining the essence of the *phenomenon* to identifying the essence of the human *experience* of it. Phenomenology therein went from studying *objects* to studying *subjects* in relation to the objects.

Unsurprisingly, this led to an expansion in how experience itself was conceptualized. It was no longer limited to an inner, unobservable process, instead it expanded to also include the behaviors and other observable reactions that one has during the inner process, and eventually, the meanings one attaches to all of these components. This more comprehensive encounter of the phenomenon was termed one's *lived experience* of the phenomenon. Altogether then, phenomenology evolved from studying the essence of a mere object (phenomenon) to studying the essence of one's inner experience of the object (lived phenomenon) to studying the integral relationship between the object and the myriad ways that humans relate to and derive meaning from it (lived experience of the phenomenon).

All of these philosophical turns led to numerous adaptations and very subtle variations of phenomenology, some of which are still very difficult to distinguish. For purposes of clarity, this category of research has been separated into two streams: phenomenological inquiry (the study of others) and first person research (the study of self). Both streams overlap with one another as well as other methods of research; nevertheless, the examples below have been selected to illustrate the myriad ways that phenomenology can be implemented.

Types of Phenomenological Inquiry

In this classification system, **phenomenological inquiry** includes both the study of a phenomenon as well as how humans experience and give meaning to it. This may involve a disciplined analysis of the phenomenon by the researcher, and/or the collection of data on how others experience it. The following examples illustrate how phenomenology has been varied, expanded, and modified since its inception. See Jackson (2016) for details.

Transcendental phenomenology is a researcher's philosophical reflection on the essential structure of a phenomenon. As such, it is a study of the phenomenon itself by an individual rather than a study of oneself, others, or anyone else's experience of it. Three main steps are involved. The first is setting aside one's natural attitudes toward and pre-understandings of the phenomenon to be studied. This process is often referred to as the researcher's **epoché** or **bracketing** of the phenomenon. The aim is to enable the researcher to study the phenomenon openly and naively, and thereby *reduce* the data to only what belongs to the phenomenon itself, free from any pre-conceptions of it. The second step is imagining as many different ways that the phenomenon can be modified or changed, and thereby determining which aspects of the phenomenon are essential and nonessential to its identity. This is often called distilling the "essence" of the phenomenon. The third step is constructing a new understanding of the phenomenon based on insights gained from the previous two steps. An example of this type of inquiry is the study of adult experiences of metal music during adolescence (Hines & McFerran, 2014).

Reductive phenomenology puts special emphasis on the researcher setting aside previous understandings and thereby reducing the phenomenon to what it is without researcher bias. In this type, however, the researcher does not merely reflect on the phenomenon, but rather gathers descriptions from others on their experience of the phenomenon. The aim is to use these descriptions to reveal what is *given* in the phenomenon—its essence. Though commonalities in how the participants describe their experiences of the phenomenon are used to illuminate the essence of the *phenomenon*, the ultimate goal is not to describe the essence of their *experiences.* An example is Wheeler's (2002) study of how students experience practicum training in music therapy.

Scientific phenomenology, also called *descriptive phenomenology,* was developed by Giorgi (2012). In this approach, the researcher begins with a different process of reducing the phenomenon than the epoché and bracketing processes described above. In this type of reduction, the researcher resists from assuming that the phenomenon itself actually exists in the real world, but instead regards the phenomenon merely as an appearance to human consciousness. We cannot study what it actually, we can only apprehend how it appears to us. Thus, we cannot understand the phenomenon itself, only how it enters and progresses through our consciousness. Once this reduction is accomplished, data are gathered on how others experience the phenomenon, and a very different way of analyzing the data is used. Taking each participant's description, the researcher gets a sense of the whole, segments the data into meaningful units, and then unlike other types of phenomenological inquiry, translates the words of the participant into terms that are most relevant to the researcher's discipline (e.g., psychology, music therapy), and to the topic or focus of the phenomenon (e.g., improvisation, song-writing). Thus, the relevance of the data to the purpose of the research is explicated. *Imaginal variation* is then used to identify the essential structure of the experience for each participant. This involves imagining how the phenomenon might be varied, and how each variation would affect what is and what is not essential to the phenomenon itself. The final step is providing a synthetic description of the essences identified across participants in the language appropriate to the discipline and the topic. An example is Murphy's (2007) study of experiential teaching and learning in graduate music therapy studies.

Essential phenomenology emphasizes "the discovery of structures that are implicit in a given phenomenon that allow it to be recognized as such. What is it about an experience that makes it what it is?" (Jackson, 2016, p. 444) This type does not involve imaginal variation. Instead, it involves analyzing and comparing the experiences of different individuals (the second step of scientific phenomenology),

and identifying those aspects of the experience that are the same across individuals. Notice that, unlike reductive phenomenology, commonalities in the experiences of the phenomenon are regarded as the essence of the phenomenon. An example of this type is Muller's (2008) study of the music therapist's experience of *being present* to clients.

Existential phenomenology is the threefold study of: the phenomenon, one's lived experience of it, and the way one's experience of it engages one's entire state of being. Here the phenomenon does not exist independently as *given*, rather it only exists interdependently on the way it is encountered fully in the experiencer's own world. Thus the meaning of a phenomenon can only be understood as a *lived* experience of one's *being-in-the-world* with the phenomenon, which is an experience that involves all aspects of being-in-the-world. An example is Blom's (2011) study of transpersonal-spiritual experiences in Guided Imagery and Music (GIM) and meanings derived from them.

Empirical phenomenology is like existential phenomenology in its focus on how the significance and meaning of a phenomenon reveals itself through one's lived experience of being in the world. Descriptions are gathered from persons who have experienced the phenomenon, and the data are faithfully analyzed and synthesized by the researcher. Like scientific phenomenology, empirical phenomenology stays close to the data, and follows specific procedures in processing and reporting the data. An example is the study by Hudgins (2013) who studied the shared meanings given by clients upon experiencing the termination of a music therapy group.

Hermeneutic phenomenology is the study of what meanings can be given to a phenomenon and one's experiences of it. Hermeneutic analysis is described later in this chapter. An example is Keith's (2007) study of the relative value of different methods of giving meaning to an improvisation.

Comparisons of Phenomenological Inquiry

- *Transcendental phenomenology:* I reflect upon the essence of a phenomenon by bracketing my own pre-suppositions, imagining variations in the phenomenon, and explicating its essence.
- *Reductive phenomenology:* I bracket my own pre-suppositions, study how a phenomenon reveals itself to others, and identify what is given in the phenomenon based on their descriptions.
- *Scientific phenomenology:* I assume that the phenomenon does not exist, gather naïve descriptions from others, use my professional knowledge and language to identify the essential structure of their experiences, and provide a synthetic description of the phenomenon.
- *Essential phenomenology:* I study how others describe their experiences of the phenomenon to identify the essence of their experiences.

- *Existential phenomenology:* I study the lived experience of a phenomenon by others as an integral part of their way of being-in-the-world, and use disciplined reflection to ascribe meaning to them.
- *Empirical phenomenology:* I study the lived experience of a phenomenon by others as an integral part of their way of being in the world, and provide thematic and situated descriptions of the synthesized data.
- *Hermeneutic phenomenology:* I study how others ascribe meaning to their experiences of the phenomenon.

First-Person Research

First-person research is "any method in which researchers or participants gather data from themselves, using processes such as introspection, retrospection, self-perception, self-observation, self-reflection, self-inquiry, and so forth" (Bruscia, 2005, p. 379). It is the study of one's own encounters with a particular phenomenon or experience. The aim is to gain insight about different aspects of one's own world and how this insight might inform oneself and others about their respective worlds. For more details, see Hunt (2016).

First-person research has numerous variations, in fact, too many to fully describe here. Thus, only selected variations will be presented. The most economical way of describing these variations is again by the use of pronouns. The main types are:

- I study us: Researcher studies self and participants.
- I study me: Researcher studies self.
- They study them: Participants study themselves.
- We study us: Researchers study themselves.

Researcher Studies Self and Participants. *Heuristic inquiry* is a combination of phenomenological inquiry and first-person research. As designed by Moustakas (1990), the researcher studies his or her own experiences, as well as the experiences of others. In addition, other sources of data may also be used (e.g., literary references) Thus, instead of bracketing out one's own pre-conceptions of the phenomenon, the researcher uses them to achieve a richer and more informed description of how the phenomenon is experienced. An example is the study by Summers (1999) who interviewed members of a geriatric choir she led, and examined her own experiences and therapeutic methods in order to better understand how the choir built a sense of community. Another example is Bruscia's (1999) approach to analyzing a music program used in GIM by experiencing it at different levels of consciousness.

Researcher Studies Self. *Reflexive phenomenology* is the detailed study of one's own personal experiences of a phenomenon. In music therapy, this has been undertaken by clients as well as therapists. For example, Hadley (1998) studied her experiences as a client in improvisational music therapy; Hintz (1995) and Pellitteri (1998) studied their

experiences as clients in GIM. Forinash and Gonzalez (1989) studied their experiences as music therapists working with different clients who were dying. Wheeler (1999) studied her own experiences of pleasure in providing music therapy to children with severe disabilities.

Clinical introspection is the detailed analysis of one's own work clinical as a therapist. Here the focus goes beyond one's personal experiences as a therapist to include the various rationales, techniques, and outcomes of one's actual work with clients. Examples include: Meadows' study (1995) on his work with client with profound disabilities; studies by Bruscia (1995, 1998a, 1998b), who analyzed his work with AIDS clients in GIM; a study by Short (2005-2006), who analyzed various clinical materials from her GIM work to evaluate her cultural awareness, sensitivity, and competence; and O'Callaghan's (2005) reflexive analysis of her clinical journals to clarify her own ways of working with people with cancer.

Embodied phenomenology is the study of how one experiences a phenomenon in one's body. The main question is how humans experience and understand the world through their physical being. Bonny (1993) was the first to explore this type of inquiry by developing a way of understanding music by moving to it. Viega (2009-2010) then used Bonny's approach to analyze a music program used in GIM by moving to it multiple times, and studying his own movements and experiences.

Autoethnography is "a combination of studying the ethnography of one's own group and writing an autobiography within an ethnographic context" (Bruscia, 2005, p. 384). It is the study of oneself as a member of a particular setting in order to understand that setting. An example is Bruscia's study (1996) of his participation in a group of peers during a symposium on qualitative research. The result was a metaphoric story that described the participants, their relationships, and their contribution to the group effort. Another example is Woodward's (2015) study of her own experiences working as member of team providing music therapy to children traumatized by war.

Researcher autobiography is "the use of the researcher's own life narratives as a primary source of data" (Bruscia, 2005, p. 386). An example is the use of his own autobiography (Bruscia, 1982) as the basis for developing a theory on the various dimensions of one's relationship to music. Hibben (1999) gathered self-stories by therapists, clients, and significant others on their experiences in music therapy.

Co-Researchers Study Themselves. *Cooperative* or *collaborative research* erases traditional boundaries between researcher and participants by giving both equal voice and status in the research process. Thus, rather than involving one researcher and several participants, all participants are co-researchers studying themselves through both individual and group formats. An example is a collaborative heuristic analysis of a music program used in GIM (Bruscia et al., 2005). The purpose was to gain a deeper and richer understanding of the musical and imaginal potentials of the music. This was accomplished by each co-researcher serving as guide and traveler to the same program.

Another example combines collaborative and heuristic approaches with thematic analysis and grounded theory. O'Callaghan, Petering, Thomas, and Crappsley (2009) did a reflexive review of their own clinical records and memories of their music therapy work with persons at the end of life. Varied sources of data were analyzed to better understand the nature of incomplete legacies.

Comparisons. Comparisons of the subtypes of first-person research are:

- *Heuristic inquiry:* I study my experiences in relation to yours and other data to gain a comprehensive understanding of the phenomenon.
- *Reflexive phenomenology:* I study my own personal experiences of a phenomenon in order to better understand the phenomenon.
- *Clinical introspection:* I study my own clinical work to better understand how to work with clients.
- *Embodied phenomenology:* I study my own body experiences of a phenomenon to better understand the phenomenon.
- *Autoethnography:* I study me as a member of my own community to better understand that community.
- *Researcher autobiography:* I study my own life narrative to better understand a phenomenon.
- *Collaborative research:* We are both researcher and participant with equal status in studying a phenomenon through our own experiences of it.

Meaning-Focused Research

In relation to music therapy, *meaning-focused research* can be defined as the study of how materials, actions, and experiences can be interpreted for their potential meanings and thereby better understood. Of particular interest in music therapy is what do the various clinical data mean? How can various types of clinical data be interpreted in order to gain insights into the client, the therapist, and the therapeutic process? A primary focus is the different interpretations of the various verbal and nonverbal materials that result from the actions and experiences of client and therapist during a session. This may include an audio or video recording of a session or the music made by the client and therapist, a musical score or graph of the music, a drawing or sculpture, a journal entry, a poem or story, or a transcript of imagery or verbal dialogue. Examples of this approach appear below.

Hermeneutics

In relation to music therapy, *hermeneutics* can be defined as the study of what a text, artwork, piece of music, artifact, or any material form of data means, either when interpreted as it was intended and understood by its originators, or when

perceived by the researcher and/or other consultants. A central concept in this approach is the *hermeneutic circle.* The circle is conceived as a way of reconciling the various interpretations given to the data, by going back and forth between them to identify commonalities and differences.

From an *objectivist* perspective, hermeneutics can be the *recovery* of meaning as it was originally conceived and in its historical perspective. Here the hermeneutic circle goes back and forth between the subjectivity of the researcher and the objectivity of the materials being studied, until these ways of understanding can be reconciled. Notice that here the integrity of the findings depends upon reconciling subjectivity and objectivity. It should be noted that, by its very nature, hermeneutic research does not prove whether an interpretation is real or true, rather it can only reveal how reality is constructed by our interpretations (see Ruud, 2005, and Loewy & Paulander, 2016).

From an *interpretivist* perspective, hermeneutics involves the *generation and reconciliation* of multiple interpretations by one or more individuals. Here the hermeneutic circle goes back and forth between the various interpretations until they can be reconciled. The integrity of the findings depends upon comparing one subjective perspective with another, until intersubjective agreement can be found in the interpretations.

Interpretivist hermeneutic is also referred to as *alethic hermeneutics*, which means the interpretation of something unseen, hidden, or masked. Something implied in the material must be inferred or uncovered by the interpreter. (See Ruud, 2005; and Loewy & Paulander, 2016). The three main variants are:

- *Existential hermeneutics:* As proposed by Martin Heidegger, it is the examination of how our situatedness in the world, our own *being-in-the world,* gives us pre-understandings of a phenomenon that influence our understanding of it. The hermeneutic circle here is between our pre-understanding and a newly found understanding that is independent of those pre-understandings.
- *Poetic hermeneutics:* As proposed by Paul Ricouer, the examination of how a phenomenon can be revealed by comparing language and other modes of expression such as music. Here the hermeneutic circle compares the structure, rhetoric, metaphors and narratives of language with corresponding elements of the other modality. For example, what meaning is hidden in silence: does a silence in a conversation mean the same as a silence in music?
- *The hermeneutics of suspicion:* As proposed by Sigmund Freud, the uncovering of something shameful or unacceptable, such as the interpretation of unconscious drives and conflicts.

One of the earliest examples of hermeneutic music therapy research is the work of Mechtild Langenberg, who developed a system of comparing the interpretations of the client, therapist, and independent observers in her practice of Analytical Music Therapy (Langenberg, Frömmer, & Tress, 1993). Loewy (1995) followed with a panel comparison of a music therapy assessment with an emotionally disturbed boy. McKnight (1998) compared musical and nonmusical data from a client with Alzheimer's disease, taken from music therapy sessions. Luce (2008) compared different types of data on student experiences in undergraduate music therapy study. Olofsson and Fossum (2009) compared different perspectives on how music therapy can be used in nursing. Summer (2011) compared six client descriptions of their experiences in a music-centered form of GIM. Lindblad (2012) compared the verbal dialogues that took place in three different music therapy sessions. Lindström (2013) compared how three music therapists described and interpreted the music experiences of their patients with brain damage. Lindvang (2013) used two different systems to describe and interpret self-experiential learning in music therapy training contexts.

Hermeneutic analysis can be used in numerous ways and settings, and for this reason, it can be incorporated into most of the other approaches to interpretivist music therapy research. It can be easily incorporated into natural setting research, phenomenology, language research, and theoretical research.

Critical Inquiry

Critical Inquiry is (a) the study of how the *received* or *given* views about the social world need to be re-evaluated and modified in terms of their inherent biases and distortions; and (b) the identification of actions and strategies needed to counteract these views in ways that improve the lives of individuals. It refers to both the process and product of theorizing.

There are three main characteristics of critical inquiry (Schwandt, 2007). First, it is a reappraisal of what is *taken-for-granted* in the social world, and its undesired consequences. Second it relies upon the method of immanent critique. Instead of comparing beliefs, values, and practices to a set of external standards, this method looks at their internal consistency. The critical theorist works "from within categories of existing thought in order to radicalize those categories, reveal their internal contradictions and shortcomings, and demonstrate their unrecognized possibilities" (Schwandt, 2007, p. 55). Finally, it integrates theory with practice, and thoughts with actions. Thus, it requires both criticism and action planning.

Critical discourse analysis is a type of critical inquiry concerned with how the language used in various contexts needs to be reappraised for biases and distortions in the social world that lead to oppression. Discourse analysis is further discussed under Language-Focused Research.

Most critical inquiry in music therapy has been concerned with feminism. Rolvsjord and Hadley (2016) identify three different streams in the field: feminist theory, feminist

therapy, and feminist research. Feminist *theory* is concerned with how discourse in music therapy reflects the misogyny and assumptions about male superiority and centrality, as well as how it can inform future discourse. Examples can be found in the edited book by Hadley (2006)

Feminist *therapy* is the use of feminist values in conceptualizing clinical work and education and training in music therapy. Such values include the value of female perspectives, egalitarianism, mutuality, empowerment, and so forth. In addition to examples in Hadley, other studies include the work of Curtis (1997/2000, 2006, 2015) and Kim (2013).

Feminist *research* is not a specific methodology, but a perspective that can inform methodological decision-making. In addition to selected chapters in Hadley (2006), examples include Hahna (2011); Veltre and Hadley (2012); Hense, McFerran, and Gorry (2014; and Hense, (2015).

Arts-Based Research (ABR)

As evolving in music therapy, **arts-based research** may involve the analysis, interpretation, and/or communication of research findings using artistic values, processes, and materials. Put another way, it is any method wherein the researcher uses an art form, art experience, or art work as a means of producing or presenting data and insights about a phenomenon. The art speaks on behalf of the phenomenon being understood. For more details, see Viega and Forinash (2016).

The first example of ABR came in 1991 with Austin's (1997) creation of a musical play to describe meetings of Alcoholics Anonymous, where clients described themselves at various stages of recovery. Rykov (2008) used various arts media to describe her experiences of leading a music therapy support group for cancer patients. Vaillancourt (2009, 2011) studied mentorship by engaging graduated music therapists in various art projects. Schenstead (2012) studied her journal entries after improvising on the flute, and reported her findings in a performance piece. Viega (2013) studied the lived experiences of adolescents who had adverse childhoods by studying the Hip Hop songs they wrote. In addition, numerous unpublished studies have also been conducted.

Morphological Research

Morphological research is the comprehensive study of the myriad relationships found among different aspects (e.g., objects, experiences, concepts) of a particular phenomenon (e.g., therapy session, improvisation), based on the reflexive interpretations of independent observers. Emphasis is given to understanding the *Gestalt* of a phenomenon, which includes the whole, the parts in relation to the whole, and the parts in relationship to one another. In this process, the entire therapeutic process can be understood in terms of multiple variables instead of a single variable. Weymann and Tüpker (2016) explain:

In music therapy, the entire therapeutic process (music, conversations, emotions, behavior, etc.) can be thought of as a *gestalt formation* and be related to other relevant gestalt formations in the patient (biography, organization of daily life, symptoms, etc.). This is primarily a psychological perspective, since it is related to formations of the psyche, but it includes musicological perspectives also. To think about music as a psychological object means above all to investigate it from an experiential aspect, that is, to understand it as a *gestalt of effects*. Therefore morphological research methods may be useful in understanding the entire therapeutic process rather than looking at a single variable. (p. 505)

Improvisation has been a focal interest of morphological research. This focus is based on the notion that the structure of a client's improvisation with the therapist is directly related to the structure of the client's psyche, as well as the client's life and therapeutic needs. Because of this, improvisation has great value in complementing the limits of language-based description and interpretation of the music therapy process (Weymann & Tüpker, 2016).

Typical morphological research has examined the relationships between a client's improvisations and other aspects of the session, as they are observed in individuals with schizophrenia (Kunkel, 2008), borderline personality disorder (Plitt, 2012), psychosomatic pain (Kalle-Krapf, 2012), and anorexia nervosa and bulimia (Reichert, 2012). Another area of interest is the comprehensive description of the music therapy treatment process of individual cases and groups (Weymann & Tüpker, 2016).

Comparisons

- *Hermeneutics:* I study the meaning of a phenomenon by reconciling various interpretations of it, as I understand them.
- *Critical inquiry:* I study and propose how the received views about our world need to be re-evaluated and modified in terms of their inherent biases and potentials for oppression.
- *Arts-based research:* I use artistic values, processes, and works to produce, analyze, and communicate research findings.
- *Morphological research:* I use Gestalt concepts of part-whole to discover relationships among various sets and types of data.

Language-Focused Research

Language-focused research is concerned with how people use words to express themselves, communicate with and influence others, find meaning in life, and induce changes in their worlds. Below are the different variations.

Discourse Analysis

Discourse analysis is the study of how discourse (i.e., text, narratives, and spoken language) is used to find and communicate meaning, to construct identities and ideologies, to influence others, and to better understand and potentially change social issues related to oppression. For example, Ansdell (1996) compared what music therapists do with what they say and what they know. In another study, Ansdell (1999) critiqued how music therapists use language to describe music and music therapy. Pavlicevic (1999, 2005) examined how music therapists talk about their clinical work and find meaning in it using the discourses of other disciplines. O'Callaghan and McDermott (2007) used discourse analysis to understand how social reality is created by the various dialogues about music therapy patients with cancer. Rolvsjord (2010) analyzed the writings of several authors to establish a foundation for resource-oriented music therapy. McCaffrey (2013) examined how two music therapists experience and describe themselves in clinical improvisation (instead of verbal dialogue) implying that music is a type of discourse in itself. For more information, see Talbot (2016).

A particular type of discourse analysis is a form of critical inquiry.

Content Analysis

Content analysis is the analysis and classification of topics, issues, or themes contained in any form of discourse (e.g., text, transcript, narrative, conversation). The analysis may focus on the manifest (obvious) or latent (underlying) content of the discourse. For more details, see Ghetti and Keith (2016).

Several music therapists have used qualitative content analysis. Wolfe, O'Connell, and Epps (1998) analyzed the verbal interventions of a music therapist during group sessions. Sutton (2002) compared how free improvisation and verbal conversation were similar in the devices they provide for enabling conversation, with special focus on silences in the therapy room. Tetens and Probst (2009) analyzed written protocols of music therapy sessions to compare the frequency of different improvisational techniques. Mössler and Fuchs (2014) analyzed music therapy session logs to examine a client's capacities for relationship in music-related activities. Hose (2011) compared the perceptions of music teachers on the extent to which they considered their work as education or therapy. Chong (2010) studied survey results to identify the different benefits that university students gained from singing. Roberts and McFerran (2013) analyzed the content of song lyrics written by bereaved preadolescents. In addition, a number of other studies have employed content analysis in conjunction with other research methods.

Narrative Inquiry

Narrative inquiry is the study of how individuals and groups use stories to describe and explain themselves, their lives, and the contexts in which they live. A narrative is not any text or discussion, rather it is a story with characters, plot, and setting. There are many different kinds of narratives. These include: stories about one's life; stories about certain life events or recurrent themes; stories about social or identity issues that impact one's life (e.g., gender, race, class); stories about the various settings in which one lives; hypothetical stories; and stories told through art, music, dance, drama, and poetry (Hadley & Edwards, 2016).

In research, a narrative can have three functions. It can provide the focus or main source of data for the study (i.e., stories told or written by research participants); it can provide various methods for analyzing stories; and it can be used as a reporting device.

Narrative research in music therapy dates back to Hadley (1998), who narrated the lives of Mary Priestley and Clive Robbins based on interviews, and then related themes in their narratives to basic premises found in their respective music therapy approaches. Bonde (2000, 2004, 2005, 2007a, 2007b) demonstrated how narrative inquiry can be used to better understand client transcripts from their GIM sessions. The transcripts contain images created while listening to music, many of which tell rich and sometimes metaphoric stories of their lives. Hadley (2013) asked music therapists to narrate how their racial identity was implicated in their clinical work. Tuastad and Stige (2014) gathered and analyzed narratives from two groups of inmates who had formed a band. The aim was to understand the band's decision not to take revenge after a knife attack.

Narrative approaches to research easily overlap with other approaches. For example, when the stories focus on lived experiences of the participants, the study has a phenomenological dimension. When the researcher interprets the various meanings of a story, the study has a hermeneutic dimension. And when the story is told through any of the arts, the study has an arts-based dimension.

Comparisons

- *Discourse analysis:* I study how you use language to interact and to communicate meanings, identities, and ideologies within social, cultural, historical, and political contexts.
- *Content analysis:* I study your writings and texts to identify and classify recurring topics and themes.
- *Narrative inquiry:* I study how you use stories to describe and understand your world.

Theoretical Approaches

Theoretical approaches are those that derive theories from

various kinds of data. As such, they are methods of data analysis and interpretation, rather than research paradigms. The variants are described below.

Grounded Theory

Grounded theory is an iterative method of developing and evaluating a theory based on findings that emerge while the data are being analyzed and interpreted. The process is called iterative because while developing the theory, the researcher continually cycles between the data and the theory, to ensure that the theory is *grounded* in the data. The process involves segmenting the data into meaningful units, developing a descriptive label or code for each unit, identifying regularities and patterns among the units, relating and arranging the coded data until a theory emerges, and continually grounding the theory in the data (O'Callaghan, 2016). The data may be of various types (observational, transcripts, etc.).

As presented in O'Callaghan's table (2016), grounded theory has been used to study the music therapy experiences of cancer patients (Barry, O'Callaghan, Wheeler, & Grocke, 2010; Bonde, 2007b; McClean, Bunt, & Daykin, 2012), children with spinal or neurological injury (Edwards & Kennelly, 2004), bereaved adolescents (McFerran, 2010; McFerran, O'Grady, & Roberts, 2010), music therapy professionals or students (Amir & Bodner, 2013; Baker, 2013a, b, c; Gao et al, 2013), and oncology staff and bystanders (O'Callaghan & Magill, 2009).

Repertory-Grid (Rep-Grid) Technique

This approach to research grew out of personal construct psychology, a theory of personality developed by George Kelly (1955). Central to the theory and this research technique is the notion that people develop their own constructs to find meaning in their lives, and that these constructs cluster together in various configurations and systems that are unique to the individual. Thus, understanding an individual's way of making meaning in one's world involves studying one's unique constructs of a phenomenon, as well as how other related constructs are configured around it.

The *Rep-Grid Technique* is a computerized method for clarifying the constructs that an individual uses to understand and phenomenon, and for analyzing how these constructs fit together into a meaningful whole. Each construct is examined according to a unique continuum of opposite characteristics or qualities assigned to the construct by the individual. For example, one person might describe a phenomenon using the construct of *rigid* and its opposite as *free;* whereas another person who uses the *rigid* construct might define the opposite as *relaxed*. Thus, each construct is defined by a continuum of opposites that is unique to each individual. For more detailed information, see Abrams (2016).

Rep-Grid has piqued the interest of several music

therapists. Hoskyns (1988) used Rep-Grid to study how different recidivist offenders perceived and experienced group music therapy program. Aldridge (1996) compared the constructions of four individuals with regard to various aspects of clinical work and supervision in music therapy. Aldridge and Aldridge (1996) utilized RepGrid to compare one music therapist's perceptions of several melodic improvisations. This study was followed up by the use of Rep-Grid in a method of music therapy assessment the authors called Therapeutic Narrative Analysis (Aldridge & Aldridge, 2002; Aldridge, 2008), which was also used by Gilbertson (2006). J. Abrams (1999) used the Rep-Grid to compare how two music therapists perceived the same musical compositions. Meadows (2002) examined the perceptions of GIM therapists with regard to the gender qualities they attributed to their clients. Abrams (2002) compared the constructs that different GIM therapists used to describe their own transpersonal experiences. Lindvang (2013) used Rep-Grid to study the self-experiences of music therapy students. Finally, Summer (2011) compared client perceptions of the music used in GIM to help her better understand her own music-centered approach.

Consensual Qualitative Research

Consensual qualitative research is a group process of building agreement around a particular topic or issue, based on repeated dialogues among the participants and the data that emerges from these dialogues. Because it was developed very recently, only two studies have employed this approach in music therapy research. Kim (2010) used this approach to study the experience of female music therapists' during training in Nordoff-Robbins Music Therapy. Kim, Jeong, and Ko (2013) examined factors in the turnover and burnout of Korean music therapists. For more details, see Kim (2016).

Thematic Analysis

Thematic analysis (also called *interpretive content analysis*) is a way of analyzing the content of various kinds of qualitative data. It involves segmenting and coding the data according to whether the data illuminates a theme of interest to the researcher. For a detailed discussion, see Hoskyns (2016).

Krout, Baker, and Muhlberger (2010) used thematic analysis to study the experiences of music therapy students as they worked with other students to write songs through teleconferencing and face-to-face interactions. Hoskyns (2013) studied themes in how music therapy professionals and students thought about the integration of practice and research. Gadberry (2014) studied diary and interview data of a music therapist starting to practice in another country. Pool and Odell-Miller (2011) examined themes in how three music therapists described a client's aggressive behavior and how it related to creativity. Baker and Ballantyne (2013) used thematic analysis to study the group song writing

experiences of aging Australians. Tamplin, Baker, Grocke, and Berlowitz (2014) examined themes in the group music therapy experiences of individuals with paraplegia.

Comparisons

- *Grounded theory:* I develop a theory about a phenomenon as I gather and analyze data about it from others.
- *Rep-Grid technique:* I study your constructs about a phenomenon to see how they relate to one another in an integral way.
- *Consensual qualitative research:* We develop theoretical consensus around an issue of concern to us through continual dialogue.
- *Thematic analysis:* I analyze the themes embedded in various types of data.

Case Approaches

A *case approach* is any in-depth study of a single entity within discernable boundaries (Murphy, 2016). Here the focus shifts from specific types of data (actions, experiences, materials, etc.) to the very nature of the person or group involved in them, or the very nature of the phenomenon itself.

The aims of case study research may be to describe a phenomenon in its real-life context, to identify the need for future research, or to explain the how and why of a phenomenon (Murphy, 2016). Three types of case studies have been identified (Stake, 2005):

- An *intrinsic case study* deals with describing and/or explaining one particular case only in reference to itself, that is, not in relation to any other cases. No attempt is made to develop a theory or make generalizations.
- An *instrumental case study* aims at gaining insights about a phenomenon from one case that will contribute to theory or research on the phenomenon. Here an attempt is made to generalize the findings in some way.
- A *multiple* or *collective case study* is the analysis of several instrumental case studies selected for their relevance to a particular theme or issue. The aim is to enhance understanding of the theme or issue.

Examples of case study research in music therapy show that it is often combined with other research approaches, such as: first-person research Bruscia (1995), grounded theory (Pasiali, 2013), naturalistic inquiry (Sorel, 2010), action research (Smeijsters & Storm, 1996), narrative inquiry (Hadley, 2003), phenomenology (Amir, 1990; Forinash & Gonzalez, 1989), thematic analysis (Pool & Odell-Miller, 2011), and mixed designs combining objectivist and interpretivist approaches (Gilboa & Roginsky, 2010; Pool & Odell-Miller, 2011; and Ridder, Wigram, & Ottesen, 2009).

Comparisons

- *Intrinsic case study:* I gather and synthesize data about an individual to better understand the individual.
- *Instrumental case study:* I gather and synthesize data on one individual's encounter with a phenomenon, to better understand the phenomenon.
- *Multiple or collective case study:* I gather and synthesize data on several individuals in relation to a particular phenomenon, to better understand the phenomenon.

References

Abrams, B. (2002). Definitions of transpersonal BMGIM experience. *Nordic Journal of Music Therapy, 11*, 103–126. doi:10.1080/08098130209478054

Abrams, B. (2016). Personal Construct Psychology and the Repertory Grid Technique. In B. L. Wheeler & K. M. Murphy (Eds.), *Music therapy research* (3rd ed.; pp. 550–557). Dallas, TX: Barcelona.

Abrams, J. (1999*). An exploration of the RepGrid in revealing how music therapists experience music.* Unpublished manuscript, Temple University, Philadelphia, PA.

Aigen, K. (1997). *Here we are in music: One year with an adolescent Creative Music Therapy group.* Gilsum, NH: Barcelona.

Aigen, K. (2005). Naturalistic inquiry. In B. L. Wheeler (Ed.), *Music therapy research* (2nd ed.; pp. 352–364).

Aldridge, D. (1996). *Music therapy research and practice in medicine: From out of the silence.* Bristol, PA: Jessica Kingsley.

Aldridge, D. (2008). Therapeutic narrative analysis: Methodological proposal for the interpretation of musical traces. In P. Liamputtong & J. Rumbold (Eds.), *Knowing differently: Arts-based and collaborative research methods* (pp. 205–227). New York, NY: Nova Science.

Aldridge, D., & Aldridge, G. (1996). A personal construct methodology for validating subjectivity in qualitative research. *Arts in Psychotherapy, 23*, 225–236. doi:10.1016/0197-4556(96)00023-8

Aldridge, D., & Aldridge, G. (2002, December). Therapeutic narrative analysis: A methodological proposal for the interpretation of music therapy traces. *Music Therapy Today* (online). Retrieved from http://musictherapyworld.net

Amir, D. (1990). A song is born: Discovering meaning in improvised songs through a phenomenological analysis of two music therapy sessions with a traumatic spinal-cord injured adult. *Music Therapy, 9*, 62–81. doi:10.1093/mt/9.1.62

Amir, D., & Bodner, E. (2013). Music therapy students' reflections on their participation in a music therapy group. *Nordic Journal of Music Therapy, 22*, 243–273. doi:10.1093/jmt/36.2.144)

Ansdell, G. (1996). Talking about music therapy. A dilemma and a qualitative experiment. *British Journal of Music Therapy, 10*(1), 4–16.

Ansdell, G. (1999). Challenging premises. *British Journal of Music Therapy, 13*(2), 72–76.

Arnason, C. (1998). The experience of music therapists in an improvisational music therapy group (Doctoral dissertation, New York University, 1998). *Dissertation Abstracts International, 59*(09), 3386.

Arnason, C. (2016). Naturalistic inquiry. In B. L. Wheeler & K. M. Murphy (Eds.), *Music therapy research* (3rd ed.; pp. 421–428). Dallas, TX: Barcelona.

Austin, D. (1997, June). *Grace Street: A qualitative study of Alcoholics Anonymous.* Paper presented at the Annual Conference of the American Association of Music Therapy, Monticello, NY.

Baker, F., & Ballantyne, J. (2013) "You've got to accentuate the positive:" Group songwriting to promote a life of enjoyment, engagement, and meaning in aging Australians. *Nordic Journal of Music Therapy, 22*(1), 7–24. doi:10.1080/08098131.2012.678372

Baker, F. A. (2013a). The ongoing life of participant-composed songs within and beyond the clinical setting. *Musicae Scientiae, 17*, 40–56. doi:10.1177/1029864912471674

Baker, F. A. (2013b). Front and center stage: Participants performing songs created during music therapy. *Arts in Psychotherapy, 40*, 20–28. doi:10.1016/j.aip.2012.09.004

Baker, F. A. (2013c). The environmental conditions that support or constrain the therapeutic songwriting process. *Arts in Psychotherapy, 40*, 230–238. doi:10.1016/j.aip.2013.02.001

Barry, P., O'Callaghan, C., Grocke, D., & Wheeler, G. (2010). Music therapy CD creation for initial pediatric radiation therapy: A mixed methods analysis. *Journal of Music Therapy, 48*, 223–263. doi:10.1093/jmt/47.3.233

Blom, K. M. (2011). Transpersonal-spiritual BMGIM experiences and the process of surrender. *Nordic Journal of Music Therapy, 20*(2), 185–203. doi:10.1080/08098131.2010.487645

Bonde, L. O. (2000). Metaphor and narrative in Guided Imagery and Music. *Journal of the Association for Music and Imagery, 7*, 59–76.

Bonde, L. O. (2004). "To draw from bits and pieces a more supportable narrative:" An introduction to Paul Ricoeur's theory of metaphor and narrative and a discussion of its relevance for a hermeneutic understanding of music-assisted imagery in the Bonny Method of Guided Imagery and Music (BMGIM). *Canadian Journal of Music Therapy, 11*(1), 31–56.

Bonde, L. O. (2005). "Finding a new place…" Metaphor and narrative in one cancer survivor's BMGIM therapy. *Nordic Journal of Music Therapy, 14*(2), 137–153. doi:0.1080/08098130509478135

Bonde, L. O. (2007a). Music as metaphor and analogy. *Nordic Journal of Music Therapy, 16*(1), 60–81.

doi:10.1080/08098130709478173

Bonde, L. O. (2007b). Imagery, metaphor and perceived outcomes in six cancer survivors' BMGIM therapy. *Qualitative Inquiries in Music Therapy, 3,* 132–164.

Bonny, H. (1993). Body listening: A new way to review the GIM tapes. *Journal of the Association for Music and Imagery, 2,* 3–10.

Bruscia, K. (1982). *Music in the life of one man: Ontological foundations of music therapy.* Paper presented at the New York University Symposium on Music in the Life of Man. New York, NY.

Bruscia, K. (1995). Modes of consciousness in Guided Imagery and Music (GIM): A therapist's experience of the guiding process. In C. Kenny (Ed.), *Listening, playing, creating: Essays on the power of sound* (pp. 165–197). Albany, NY: State University of New York Press.

Bruscia, K. (1996). Daedalus and the labyrinth: A mythical research fantasy. In M. Langenberg, K. Aigen, & J. Frommer (Eds.), *Qualitative music therapy research: Beginning dialogues* (pp. 205–212). Gilsum, NH: Barcelona.

Bruscia, K. E. (1998a). Re-imaging client images: A technique for uncovering countertransference in Guided Imagery and Music (GIM). In K. E. Bruscia (Ed.), *The dynamics of music psychotherapy* (pp. 527–548). Gilsum, NH: Barcelona.

Bruscia, K. E. (1998b). Re-imaging client images: A technique for uncovering projective identification. In K. E. Bruscia (Ed.), *The dynamics of music psychotherapy* (pp. 549–560). Gilsum, NH: Barcelona.

Bruscia, K. (1999). A heuristic method of analyzing music programs in Guided Imagery and Music (GIM). In *Manual for BMGIM training* (pp. 9–17). Unpublished manuscript.

Bruscia, K. (2005). First-person research. In B. L. Wheeler (Ed.), *Music therapy research* (2nd ed.; pp. 378–391). Gilsum, NH: Barcelona.

Bruscia, K., Abbott, E., Cadesky, N., Condron, D., Hunt, A., Miller, D., & Thomae, L. (2005). A collaborative heuristic analysis of *Imagery—M*: A classical music program used in the Bonny Method of Guided Imagery and Music (BMGIM). *Qualitative Inquiries in Music Therapy, 2,* 1–35.

Chong, H. J. (2010). Do we all enjoy singing? A content analysis of non-vocalists' attitudes toward singing. *Arts in Psychotherapy, 37* (2), 120–124. doi:10.1016/j.aip.2010.01.001

Curtis, S. L. (1997/2000). Singing subversion, singing soul: Women's voices in feminist music therapy. (Doctoral dissertation, Concordia University, 1997). *Dissertation Abstracts International, 60*(12-A), 4240.

Curtis, S. L. (2006). Feminist music therapy: Transforming theory, transforming lives. In S. Hadley (Ed.), *Feminist perspectives in music therapy* (pp. 227–244). Gilsum, NH: Barcelona.

Curtis, S. L. (2015). Feminist music therapists in North

America: Their lives and their practices. *Voices: A World Forum For Music Therapy, 15*(2). doi:10.15845/voices.v15i2.812. Retrieved from https://voices.no/index.php/voices/article/view/812

Edwards, J., & Kennelly, J. (2004). Music therapy in paediatric rehabilitation: The application of modified grounded theA103A103+A106ory to identify categories of techniques used by a music therapist. *Nordic Journal of Music Therapy, 13,* 112–126. doi:10.1080/08098130409478108)

Forinash, M., & Gonzalez (1989). A phenomenological perspective on music therapy. *Music Therapy, 8,* 35–46. doi:10.1093/mt/8.1.35

Gadberry, A. L. (2014). Cross-cultural perspective: A thematic analysis of a music therapist's experience providing treatment in a foreign country. *Australian Journal of Music Therapy, 25,* 66–80.

Gao, T., O'Callaghan, C., Magill, L., Lin, S. S., Zhang, J. H., Zhang, J. W., …Shi, X. M. (2013). A music therapy educator's and undergraduate students' perceptions of their music project's relevance for Sichuan earthquake survivors. *Nordic Journal of Music Therapy, 22,* 107–130. doi:10.1080/08098131.2012.691106

Ghetti, C., & Keith, D. (2016). Qualitative content analysis. In B. L. Wheeler & K. M. Murphy (Eds.), *Music therapy research* (3rd ed.; pp. 521–526). Dallas, TX: Barcelona.

Gilbertson, S. (2006). Music therapy in early neurorehabilitation with people who have experienced traumatic brain injury. *Music Therapy Today* (Online), 7(3) 662–693.

Gilboa, A., & Roginsky, E. (2010). Examining the dyadic music therapy treatment (DUET): The case of a CP child and his mother. *Nordic Journal of Music Therapy, 19,* 103–132. doi:10.1080/08098131.2010.500742

Giorgi, A. (2012). The descriptive phenomenological psychological method. *Journal of Phenomenological Psychology, 43,* 3–12. doi:10.1163/156916212X632934

Hadley S. (Ed.). (2006). *Feminist perspectives in music therapy.* Gilsum, NH: Barcelona.

Hadley, S. (1998). *Exploring relationships between life and work in music therapy: The stories of Mary Priestley and Clive Robbins* (Unpublished doctoral dissertation). Philadelphia, PA: Temple University.

Hadley, S. (2003). Meaning making through narrative inquiry. *Nordic Journal of Music Therapy, 12,* 33–53. doi:10.1080/08098130309478071

Hadley, S. (2013). *Experiencing race as a music therapist: Personal narratives.* Gilsum, NH: Barcelona.

Hadley, S., & Edwards, J. (2016). Narrative inquiry. In B. L. Wheeler & K. M. Murphy (Eds.), *Music therapy research* (3rd ed.; pp. 527–537). Dallas, TX: Barcelona.

Hahna, N. (2011). Conversations from the classroom: Reflections on feminist music therapy pedagogy in teaching music therapy. *Dissertation Abstracts International: Section A. Humanities and Social Sciences,*

72(07), 0413.

Hense, C. (2015). Feminist-informed collaborative interviews with young people recovering from mental illness. In C. Hense, G. Mc.Gibbon, C. Philips, & S. Rudolf (Eds.), *Researching for social change*. Melbourne, Australia: Melbourne University Social Equity Institute.

Hense, C., McFerran, K., & Gorry, P. (2014). Constructing a grounded theory of young people's recovery of musical identity in mental illness. *Arts in Psychotherapy, 41,* 594–603. doi.org/10.1016/j.aip.2014.10.010

Hibben, J. (Ed.) (1999). *Inside music therapy: Client experiences*. Gilsum, NH: Barcelona.

Hines, M., & McFerran, K. S. (2014). Metal made me who I am: Seven adult men reflect on their engagement with metal music during adolescence. *International Journal of Community Music, 7*(2), 205–222. doi:10.1386/ijcm.7.2.205_1

Hintz, M (1995). *Empowerment through spiritual experiences in Guided Imagery and Music: A personal exploration* (Unpublished master's project). Temple University, Philadelphia, PA.

Hose, S. (2011). *Musikunterricht in Förderzentren—Ein empirischer Vergleich von Schulen mit den Förderschwerpunkten „geistige Entwicklung" und „körperliche und motorische Entwicklung"* [Music lessons in special needs schools—an empirical comparison of schools with emphases in intellectual development and physical and motoric development] (Unpublished master's thesis). University of the Arts, Berlin, Germany. Retrieved from http://fem-berlin.de/files/Masterarbeit_Hose.pdf

Hoskyns, S. (1988). Studying group music therapy with adult offenders: Research in progress. *Psychology of Music, 16,* 25–41. doi:10.1177/0305735688161003

Hoskyns, S. (2013). *Enabling the curious practitioner: Perceptions on the integration of research and practice in the education of music therapy students at Masters' level* (Unpublished doctoral dissertation). Massey and Victoria Universities, Wellington, New Zealand.

Hoskyns, S. (2016). Thematic analysis. In B. L. Wheeler & K. M. Murphy (Eds.), *Music therapy research* (3rd ed.; pp. 563–569). Dallas, TX: Barcelona.

Hudgins, L. (2013). Closing time: Clients' shared experiences of termination of a music therapy group in community mental health. *Qualitative Inquiries in Music Therapy, 8,* 51–78.

Hunt, A. (2016). First-person research. In B. L. Wheeler & K. M. Murphy (Eds.), *Music therapy research* (3rd ed.; pp. 453–467). Dallas, TX: Barcelona.

Jackson, N. (2016). Phenomenological inquiry. In B. L. Wheeler & K. M. Murphy (Eds.), *Music therapy research* (3rd ed.; pp. 441–452). Dallas, TX: Barcelona.

Kalle-Krapf (2012). *Anhaltende somatoforme Schmerzstörung: [Persistent somatoform pain disorder]* (2nd ed). Saarbrücken, Germany: Akademikerverlag.

Keith, D. (2007). Understanding music improvisations: A comparison of methods of meaning- making. *Qualitative Inquiries in Music Therapy, 3,* 62–102.

Kelly, G. A. (1955). *The psychology of personal constructs*. New York, NY: W. W. Norton.

Kim, D. M. (2010). Towards musical individuation: Korean female music therapists' experiences in the Nordoff-Robbins Music Therapy certification training. *Arts in Psychotherapy, 37,* 353–362. doi:10.1014/j.aip.2010.09.005

Kim, D. M. (2016). Consensual qualitative research. In B. L. Wheeler & K. M. Murphy (Eds.), *Music therapy research* (3rd ed.; pp. 558–562). Dallas, TX: Barcelona.

Kim, S-A. (2013). Re-discovering voice: Korean immigrant women in group music therapy. *Arts in Psychotherapy, 40,* 428–435. doi:10.1016/j.aip.2013.05.005

Kim, Y., Jeong, J., & Ko, M. (2013). A qualitative study of Korean music therapists' turnover experiences. *Arts in Psychotherapy, 40,* 449–457. doi:10.1016/j.aip.2013.09.006

Krout, R. E., Baker, F., & Muhlberger, R. (2010). Information sharing. *Music Therapy Perspectives, 28*(1), 79–85. doi:10.1093/mtp/28.1.79

Kunkel, S. (2008). *Jenseits von Jedem?* [Beyond everything?] online-edition: http://ediss.sub.uni-hamburg.de/volltexte/2009/3954/pdf/Dissertation_Kunkel

Langenberg, M., Frömmer, J., & Tress, W. (1993). A qualitative research approach to Analytical Music Therapy. *Music Therapy, 12,* 59–84. doi:10.1093/mt/12.1.59

Ledger, A. J. (2010). *Am I a founder or am I a fraud? Music therapists' experiences of developing services in healthcare organizations* (Unpublished doctoral dissertation). University of Limerick, Limerick, Ireland. Retrieved from http://ulir.ul.ie/handle/10344/1131

Lincoln, Y., & Guba, E. (1985). *Naturalistic inquiry*. Thousand Oaks CA: Sage.

Lindblad, K. (2012). *The verbal dialogue in music therapy: A hermeneutic analysis of three music therapy sessions* (Unpublished doctoral dissertation). Stockholm, Sweden: Royal College of Music.

Lindstöm, Å. (2013). *Music experiences after acquired brain injury: A qualitative interview study of music therapy practice* (Unpublished master's thesis). Royal College of Music, Stockholm, Sweden.

Lindvang, L. (2013). Resonant learning: A qualitative inquiry into music therapy students' self-experiential learning processes. *Qualitative Inquiries in Music Therapy, 8,* 1–30.

Loewy, J. V. (1995). A hermeneutic panel study of music therapy assessment with an emotionally disturbed boy (Doctoral dissertation, New York University, 1994). *Dissertation Abstracts International, 55*(09), 2631.

Loewy, J., & Paulander, S. (2016). Hermeneutic Inquiry. In B. L. Wheeler & K. M. Murphy (Eds.), *Music therapy research* (3rd ed.; pp. 468–476). Dallas, TX: Barcelona.

Luce, W. (2008). Epistemological development and collaborative learning: A hermeneutic analysis of music therapy students' experience. *Journal of Music Therapy* 45(1), 21–51. doi:10.1093/jmt/45.1.21

McCaffrey, T. (2013). Music therapists' experience of self in clinical improvisation in music therapy: A phenomenological investigation. *Arts in Psychotherapy, 40*(3), 306–311. doi:10.1016/j.aip.2013.05.018

McClean, S., Bunt, B., & Daykin, N. (2012). The healing and spiritual properties of music therapy at a cancer care center. *Journal of Alternative & Complimentary Medicine, 18,* 402–407. doi:10.1080/08098130809478204

McFerran, K. (2010). Tipping the scales: A substantive theory on the value of group music therapy for supporting grieving teenagers. *Qualitative Inquiries in Music Therapy, 5,* 1–42.

McFerran, K., O'Grady, L., & Roberts, M. (2010). Music therapy with bereaved teenagers: A mixed methods perspective. *Death Studies, 34,* 541–565. doi:10.1080/07481181003765428

McKnight, S. (1998). *Music therapy and an elder with probable Alzheimer's disease—Looking For meaning in responses: A hermeneutic analysis* (Unpublished master's thesis). Lesley University, Cambridge MA.

Meadows, A. (1995). *How do I understand a child's experience in music therapy?* (Unpublished master's project). Temple University, Philadelphia, PA.

Meadows, A. (2002). Gender implications in therapists' constructs of their clients. *Nordic Journal of Music Therapy, 11,* 127–141. doi:10.1080/08098130209478055

Mössler, K., & Fuchs, K. (2014). Musical progress towards therapeutic change: A qualitative study on how to develop a focus in music therapy. *Nordic Journal of Music Therapy.* doi:10.1080/08098131.2014.966748

Moustakas, C. (1990). *Heuristic research: Design, methodology, and applications.* Newbury Park, CA: Sage.

Muller, B. (2008). A phenomenological investigation of the music therapist's experience of being present to clients. *Qualitative Inquiries in Music Therapy, 4,* 69–112

Murphy, K. (2007). Experiential learning in music therapy: Faculty and student perspectives. *Qualitative Inquiries in Music Therapy, 3,* 31–61.

Murphy, K. (2016). Interpretivist case study research. In B. L. Wheeler & K. M. Murphy (Eds.), *Music therapy research* (3rd ed.; pp. 570–577). Dallas, TX: Barcelona.

O'Callaghan, C. (2005). Qualitative data-mining through reflexive journal analysis: Implications for music therapy practice development. *Journal of Social Work Research and Evaluation, 6*(2), 217–229.

O'Callaghan, C. (2016). Grounded theory. In B. L. Wheeler & K. M. Murphy (Eds.), *Music therapy research* (3rd ed.; pp. 538—549). Dallas, TX: Barcelona.

O'Callaghan, C., & Magill, L. (2009). Effect of music therapy on oncologic staff bystanders: A substantive grounded theory. *Palliative & Supportive Care, 7,* 219–228.

doi:10.1017/S1478951509000285

O'Callaghan, C., & McDermott, F. (2007). Discourse analysis reframes oncologic music therapy research findings. *Arts in Psychotherapy, 34*(5), 398–408. doi:10.1016/j.aip.2007.08.005

O'Callaghan, C., Petering, H., Thomas, A., & Crappsley, R. (2009). Dealing with palliative care patients' incomplete music therapy legacies: Reflexive group supervision research. *Journal of Palliative Care, 25*(3), 197–205.

Olofsson, A., & Fossum, B. (2009). Perspectives on music therapy in adult cancer care: A hermeneutic study. *Oncology Nursing Forum, 36*(4), E223-31. doi:10.1188/09.ONF.E223-E231.

Pasiali, V. (2013). A clinical case study of family-based music therapy. *Journal of Creativity in Mental Health, 8,* 249–264.

Pavlicevic, M. (1999). With listeners in mind: Creating meaning in music therapy dialogues. *Arts in Psychotherapy, 26*(2), 85–94. doi:10.1016/S0197-4556(98)00065-3

Pavlicevic, M. (2005). *Music therapy in context: Music, meaning and relationship.* London, UK: Jessica Kingsley.

Pellitteri, J. (1998). A self-analysis of transference in Guided Imagery and Music (GIM). In K. E. Bruscia (Ed.),*The dynamics of music psychotherapy* (pp. 481–490). Gilsum, NH: Barcelona.

Plitt, H. (2012). *Intersubjektivität erleben: Musiktherapie als Chance für Borderline-Patienten [Experience intersubjectivity {Music therapy as a chance for patients with borderline personality disorder].* Marburg, Germany: Tectum

Pool, J., & Odell-Miller, H. (2011). Aggression in music therapy and its role in creativity with reference to personality disorder. *Arts in Psychotherapy, 38*(3), 169–177. doi:10.1016/j.aip.2011.04.003

Procter, S. (2013). *Music therapy: What is it for whom? An ethnography of music therapy in a community mental health resource centre* (Unpublished doctoral dissertation). University of Exeter, Exeter, UK. Retrieved from https://ore.exeter.ac.uk/repository/handle/10871/11101

Reichert, B. (2012). *Ess-Störungen und musiktherapeutische Diagnostik [Eating diseases and music therapeutical diagnosis].* Wiesbaden, Germany: Reichert

Ridder, H. M., Wigram, T., & Ottesen, A. M. (2009). A pilot study on the effects of music therapy on frontotemporal dementia—Developing a research protocol. *Nordic Journal of Music Therapy, 18,* 103–132. doi:10.1080/08098130903062371

Roberts, M., & McFerran, K. (2013). A mixed methods analysis of songs written by bereaved preadolescents in individual music therapy. *Journal of Music Therapy, 50*(1), 25–52. doi:10.1093/jmt/50.1.25

Rolvsjord, R. (2010). *Resource-oriented music therapy in mental health care.* Gilsum, NH: Barcelona.

Rolvsjord, R., & Hadley, S. (2016). Critical inquiries:

Feminist perspectives and transformative research. In B. L. Wheeler & K. M. Murphy (Eds.), *Music therapy research* (3rd ed.; pp.477–490). Dallas, TX: Barcelona.

Ruud, E. (2005). Philosophy and theory of science. In B. L. Wheeler (Ed.), *Music therapy research* (2nd ed.; pp. 33–44). Gilsum, NH: Barcelona.

Rykov, M. H. (2008). Experiencing music therapy cancer support. *Journal of Health Psychology, 13*(2), 190–200. doi:10.1177/1359105307086708

Schenstead, A. R. (2012). The timelessness of arts-based research: Looking back upon a heuristic self-study and the arts-based reflexivity data analysis method. *Voices: A World Forum for Music Therapy, 12*(1). doi:10.15845/voices.v12i1.589. Retrieved from https://normt.uib.no/index.php/voices/article/view/589/514

Schwandt, T. (Ed.) (2007). Critical theory. *The Sage dictionary of qualitative inquiry* (3rd ed.; p. 55). Thousand Oaks, CA: Sage.

Short, A. (2005–2006). Cultural dimensions of music and imagery: Archetype and ethnicity in GIM practice. *Journal of the Association for Music and Imagery, 10*, 75–90.

Smeijsters, H., & Storm, H. (1996). Becoming friends with your mother: Techniques of qualitative research illustrated with examples from the short-term treatment of a girl with enuresis. *Music Therapy, 14*, 61–83. doi:10.1093/mt/14.1.61

Sorel, S. (2010). Presenting Carly and Elliott: Exploring roles and relationships in a mother-son dyad in Nordoff-Robbins Music Therapy. *Qualitative Inquires in Music Therapy, 5*, 173–238

Stake, R. (2005). Case study. In N. K. Denzin & Y. S. Lincoln (Eds.) *The Sage handbook of qualitative research* (3rd ed.; pp. 443–466). Thousand Oaks, CA: Sage.

Stige, B. (2010). Musical participation, social space, and everyday ritual. In B. Stige, G. Ansdell, C. Elefant, & M. Pavlicevic. *Where music helps: Community Music Therapy in action and reflection* (pp. 125–150). Farnham, UK: Ashgate.

Stige, B., & Ledger, A. (2016). Ethnographic research. In B. L. Wheeler & K. M. Murphy (Eds.), *Music therapy research* (3rd ed.; pp.404–420). Dallas, TX: Barcelona.

Stige, B., & McFerran, K. (2016). Action research. In B. L. Wheeler & K. M. Murphy (Eds.), *Music therapy research* (3rd ed.; pp.429–420). Dallas, TX: Barcelona.

Summer, L. (2011). Client perspectives on the music in the Guided Imagery and Music (GIM). *Qualitative Inquiries in Music Therapy, 6*, 34–74.

Summers, S. G. (1999). *A tapestry of voices: Community building with a geriatric choir reflected in a music therapy model of practise* (Order No. MQ57917). Available from ProQuest Dissertations & Theses A&I. (304574136).

Sutton, J. (2002). The pause that follows . . . silence, improvised music, and music therapy. *Nordic Journal of Music Therapy, 11*(1), 27–38.

doi:10.1080/08098130209478040

Talbot, B. (2016). Discourse analysis. In B. L. Wheeler & K. M. Murphy (Eds.), *Music therapy research* (3rd ed.; pp.510–520). Dallas, TX: Barcelona.

Tamplin, J., Baker, F. A., Grocke, D., & Berlowitz, D. J. (2014). Thematic analysis of the experience of group music therapy for people with chronic quadriplegia. *Topics in Spinal Cord Injury Rehabilitation, 20*(3), 236–247. doi:10.1310/sci2003-236

Tetens, J., & Probst, P. (2009). Sozialkommunikatives Förderprogramm für Kinder und Jugendliche mit Autismus: Systematische Fallstudie an einem 12-jährigem Jungen unter besonderer Berücksichtigung musiktherapeutischer Prozesse. [A social communication enhancement program for children and adolescents with autism: A systematic case study of the music therapy process of a 12-year-old boy]. *Musiktherapeutische Umschau, 30*(1), 31–41.

Tuastad, L., & Stige, B. (2014). The revenge of me and THE BAND'its: A narrative inquiry of identity constructions in a rock band of ex-inmates. *Nordic Journal of Music Therapy, 24*(3), 252–275. doi:10.1080/08098131.2014.967713

Turry, A. (2010). Integrating musical and psychotherapeutic thinking: Research on the relationship between words and music in clinically improvised songs. *Qualitative Inquiries in Music Therapy, 5*, 116–172.

Vaillancourt, G. (2009). *Mentoring apprentice music therapists for peace and social justice through community music therapy: An arts-based study* (Unpublished doctoral dissertation). Antioch University, Yellow Springs, OH. Retrieved from http://rave.ohiolink.edu/etdc/view?acc_num=antioch1255546013

Vaillancourt, G. (2011). Creating an apprenticeship music therapy model through arts-based research. *Voices: A World Forum for Music Therapy, 11*(1). doi:http://dx.doi.org/10.15845/voices.v11i1.341. Retrieved from https://normt.uib.no/index.php/voices/article/view/341/446

Veltre, V. J., & Hadley, S. (2012). It's bigger than Hip-Hop. A Hip-Hop feminist approach to music therapy with adolescent females. In S. Hadley & G. Yancy (Eds.), *Therapeutic uses of rap and hip-hop* (pp. 79–98). New York, NY: Routledge.

Viega, M., & Forinash, M. (2016). Arts-based research. In B. L. Wheeler & K. M. Murphy (Eds.), *Music therapy research* (3rd ed.; pp. 491–504). Dallas, TX: Barcelona.

Viega, M. (2009–2010). Body listening as a method of understanding a music program used in the Bonny Method of Guided Imagery and Music (BMGIM). *Journal of the Association for Music and Imagery, 12*, 21–45.

Viega, M. (2013). *"Loving me and my butterfly wings:" A study of hip–hop songs created by adolescents in music therapy* (Unpublished doctoral dissertation). Temple University,

177

Philadelphia, PA.

Weymann, E., & Tüpker, R. (2016). Morphological research. In B. L. Wheeler & K. M. Murphy (Eds.), *Music therapy research* (3rd ed.; pp.505–509). Dallas, TX: Barcelona.

Wheeler, B. (1999). Experiencing pleasure in working with severely disabled children. *Journal of Music Therapy, 36,* 56–80. doi:10.1093/jmt/36.1.56

Wheeler, B. L. (2002). Experiences and concerns of students during music therapy practica. *Journal of Music Therapy, 39,* 274–304. doi:10.1093/jmt/39.4.274

Wolfe, D., O'Connell, A. and Epps, K. (1998). A content analysis of therapist verbalizations during group music therapy: Implications for the training of music therapists. *Music Therapy Perspectives, 16*(1), 13–20. doi:10.1093/mtp/16.1.13

Woodward, A. (2015). *Tapestry of tears: An autoethnography of leadership, personal transformation, and music therapy in humanitarian aid in Bosnia Herzegovina* (Unpublished doctoral dissertation). Yellow Springs, OH: Antioch University. Retrieved from http://rave.ohiolink.edu/etdc/view?acc_num=antioch1425584421

Zanders, M. (2016). Mixing interpretivist methods. In B. L. Wheeler & K. M. Murphy (Eds.), *Music therapy research* (3rd ed.; pp.614–621). Dallas, TX: Barcelona.

Chapter 16

OTHER TYPES OF RESEARCH

Kenneth E. Bruscia

This chapter presents types of research that may be objectivist or interpretivist in perspective, but for one reason or another, cannot be easily classified as either. Specifically, microanalysis is a method of collecting data rather than a complete research method in itself, and the data gathered may be processed in either an objectivist or interpretivist fashion. Music-focused research is a primary concern of research in music therapy, but is not necessarily a method or paradigm in itself. Mixed methods research involves collecting a combination of quantitative and/or qualitative data, while considering the different objectivist and interpretivist epistemologies implicated in doing so. Systematic review, meta-analysis, and interpretivist synthesis are methods of integrating previous findings of only objectivist studies, only interpretive studies, or a combination of both. Historical research is different from all other research in that new data are not generated or collected; instead already existing sources data are carefully analyzed. In addition, historical research can be implemented within either an objectivist or interpretivist approach. And finally, philosophical inquiry is different from all other research in that it scrutinizes ideas and ways of thinking rather than gathering and analyzing traditional forms of data. It also does not favor one epistemology over another, but rather continually challenges their assumptions, meanings, and implications.

Microanalysis

Microanalysis is the study of very small segments of a sequential process, called microprocesses. For example, in music therapy, a session, series of sessions, or segments thereof are reduced to a representative set of short samples that illuminates the phenomenon under study. The basic premise is that when properly sampled, very small segments of a process can reveal themes and other important details about the entire process. Wosch and Wigram (2007) define *microprocesses* as follows.

> Microprocesses are processes and changes/progressions within one session of music therapy. The amount of time can be one minute (moment) or five minutes (therapy event) of one session, one clinical improvisation (episode), or one complete session. To analyse process over time, several microanalyses can be undertaken to look at several events. (p. 22)

The aims may be to describe or explain: the process of therapy, the practice of therapy in a naturalistic setting, client assessment, and hypothesis generation. Three sources of microanalytic data gathered in music therapy are video recordings, audio recordings, and texts. These types of data can be processed using various observational techniques and computer software.

Microanalysis may be implemented in an objectivist and/or interpretivist approach. For details on each approach see Wosch and Erkkilä (2016) and Trondalen and Wosch (2016). An objectivist approach is steeped in a positivistic or post-positivistic epistemology, and relies on quantitative data to find cause-effect relationships. Interpretivist approaches are steeped in various non-positivist epistemologies, and rely on qualitative data to explicate and better understand a phenomenon.

Objectivist microanalysis has been particular useful in music therapy research, as evidenced by the relatively large number of studies employing the method. Wosch and Wigram (2007) have edited a collection of writings on various approaches to microanalysis, and Wosch and Erkkilä (2016) have provided a comprehensive list of microanalytic studies within an objectivist perspective.

Examples of interpretivist microanalysis have focused on clients with psychiatric disorders (De Backer & Wigram, 2007; Ortlieb et al., 2007); developmental disorders (Holck, 2007); and clients with social, mental, and behavioral disorders (Trondalen, 2007).

Music-Focused Research

Music-focused research is central to the study of music therapy as well as many other music-related fields such as musicology, psychology of music, music education, and so forth. Thus, much of the research in these related fields contribute greatly to the research interests and needs of music therapy (see Fachner, 2016). On the other hand, because music therapy is also a health-related discipline, it also has research interests and needs of its own, different from other health and music-related disciplines. This is why music-focused research is considered a separate and unique area within music therapy research.

Music-focused research is not a method or paradigm in itself, rather it is a special area of research for music therapy. It can be conducted from both objectivist and interpretivist perspectives, with each perspective posing different questions and employing different methods of research.

Objectivist Music-Focused Research

Objectivist music-focused research seeks to operationalize and measure the stimulus properties of music as well as the myriad human responses to music. More specifically, it focuses on how the various properties, types, and applications of music influence and are influenced by various aspects of an individual, group, or community. And in music therapy, music-focused research is concerned with how music influences and is influenced those with health needs. Here is a small sample of the kinds of music questions that might be asked in music therapy research (Bruscia, 2005b):

- How well do children with intellectual disabilities score on a test of rhythmic ability? Are the scores reliable and valid? Are they related to or predictive of scores on another music or psychological test?
- What factors (e.g., memory) are implicated in their performance on this test?
- Do their scores change with age or time?
- Do these children perform the same as individuals with no intellectual disabilities?
- What other variables (e.g., culture) affect how the test scores of these two groups compare?
- Does rhythmic training improve the duration of attention in these children?
- Is rhythmic training as effective as melodic training in improving short-term memory?
- How often do therapists use rhythmic training versus melodic training when working with this population?

Interpretivist Music-Focused Research

Bonde (2016) describes interpretivist music-focused research as a process of description, analysis, and interpretation of music, as distinguished from operationalization and statistical analysis of the properties of music in objectivist research.

Description is the use of musical and/or nonmusical terminology to describe music as seen in a score or transcription, or as heard from a recording—as the music unfolds from moment to moment. The description may also include short music notations of significant events or qualities of the music.

Analysis goes beyond description by finding regularities, patterns, and relationships. Bonde (2016) provides a more detailed explanation:

> Analysis seeks to identify and classify observable and describable events and their relationship across the timespan: What is figure and ground? What is the role of a specific part in the whole? This is done through the study of similarities and differences: identification of musical patterns (in all elements and parameters), repetitions, and

variations; types of interaction between parts or performers; the presentation and development of motives, themes, and roles. (p. 248).

Interpretation is concerned with what the music means, either in and of itself, or in reference to something or someone other than the music. For instance, in music therapy, interpretation is used to link the client's music to the client's life. For example, what does a client's improvisation reveal about the client's feelings or thoughts, or the client's therapeutic needs and resources, or even more broadly, the client's personality or living circumstances? Here are some examples of questions that might be posed in interpretivist music-focused research (Bruscia, 2005b, pp. 87–89).

- What happens in a music therapy session? How do clients and therapists interact, musically, verbally and nonverbally?
- What do clients and therapists experience about each other and their shared music experiences?
- How do client and therapists use language to communicate and influence each other?
- What does the client's music mean? What does the therapist's music mean?
- How can we describe and understand a client's growth process in music therapy?
- What can we learn from this client that will inform our work with other clients?

Mixed Methods Research

Magee (2016) describes **mixed methods research** as the process of "collecting both objectivist and interpretivist data and integrating the different methods in ways in which one approach informs and influences the other" (p. 608). In addition to combining objectivist and interpretivist approaches, mixed methods may also involve combining different interpretivist approaches.

Burns and Masko (2016) explain how the various approaches or *strands* of mixed method research relate to one another in a study:

> Strands can be independent or interactive, have priority or be equivalent, occur sequentially or concurrently, and be mixed at several points throughout the analysis and interpretation phases of the study. Rigorous use of mixed methods designs addresses decisions at these various points throughout study design, implementation, and interpretation. What is most critical within a mixed methods research study or program is that both strands meet the same rigor as they would if used in isolation. (p. 600).

Four types of mixed methods research will be described

here, each with its own configuration for combining the strands. They are:

- *Explanatory sequential designs:* "In this design, quantitative data are collected first, followed by qualitative data … The qualitative data are used to clarify, contextualize, or address questions that arise from the quantitative results" (Burns & Masko, 2016, p. 601). Thus, quantitative data has priority over the qualitative data. An example is the study by Chwalek and McKinney (2015), which examines the thoughts of music therapists around the use of dialectical behavior therapy in a mental health setting.
- *Convergent parallel designs:* This design involves collecting quantitative and qualitative simultaneously, analyzing each strand separately, and merging the two data sets for final interpretation. Each strand is independent and equal in priority" (Burns & Masko, 2016, p. 602). No examples of this design were found in the music therapy literature.
- *Exploratory sequential designs:* In this design qualitative data are gathered and processed first, using interpretivist approaches. The findings are then used to design objectivist methods for gathering and processing quantitative data. The findings are then integrated. The primary aim is to determine if the qualitative findings can be generalized or applied to different groups or settings (Magee, 2016). An example is Masko's (2013) study on how hospice chaplains viewed the role of music therapists within a hospice team providing patients with spiritual care.
- *Mixed interpretive designs:* In this type of mixed methods research, different aspects of interpretivist approaches are combined within one study. For example, the characteristic focus of one approach (language) may shift to the characteristic focus of another approach (action); or the sources of data (actions, interactions) may extend beyond those used in one approach to those in another (language); or the method data analysis and interpretation in one approach may be used with types of data gathered in another approach (Zanders, 2016). An example is the study by Amir and Yair (2008), who examined the meanings of three piano improvisations using components of phenomenology, hermeneutics, and morphology.

Systematic Review, Meta-Analysis, and Synthesis

Objectivist Systematic Review and Meta-Analysis

A *systematic review* is a synthesis of the best available objective evidence on a particular research question, implemented with the aim of minimizing researcher bias (Bradt, 2016). The evidence may consist of clinical research findings that meet stringent criteria on how the research study was conducted. Typically, this includes randomized controlled trials (RCTs) and controlled clinical trials (CCTs).

A meta-analysis is the second step in a systematic review, implemented only when warranted by the quality of the research findings included in the review. It involves calculating the *effect size* yielded in each study, and the combined effect size for all the studies included. The effect size is how large or small of an effect the experimental versus control conditions had on the participants in the study. More simply, how much effect did the independent variable have on the dependent variable?

Unfortunately, several studies in the literature are labelled as systematic reviews, when, in fact, they are not (Bradt, 2016). When looking for systematic reviews, it is important to exclude those reviews that base their conclusions on writings that do not meet the required research criteria, such as clinical reports, theories, and case studies, and to exclude reviews that do not summarize the findings of the studies. Also to be excluded are content analyses of published studies, which by definition use different procedures than those used in systematic review. Finally, it is important to note whether a meta-analysis has or has not been included, and whether there is sufficient rationale for making this decision.

Systematic reviews and meta-analyses are crucially important to summarizing the research findings in a health-related discipline, and especially in music therapy, where the research studies are scattered among so many disciplines and publication venues. They are crucially important because it is becoming increasingly difficult to find and digest the staggering amount of research findings now available through the many electronic databases, and the steady increase in the number of research studies being conducted.

Fortunately, music therapy researchers have recognized the significance and need for these kinds of data reviews. Bradt (2016) provides tables summarizing a number of systematic reviews and meta-analyses that have already been conducted in music therapy.

Interpretivist Synthesis

Interpretivist synthesis is a set of methodologies aimed at integrating "the findings from a number of interpretivist research studies into a *meta* perspective based on an analysis and/or interpretation of these collected studies" (Meadows & Wimpenny, 2016a, p. 636). The findings of a synthesis may be used to develop theory, identify gaps in knowledge, complement existing research and meta-analyses, and avoid duplication in research efforts (Major & Savin-Baden, 2010).

Interpretivist synthesis could be a great value in music therapy, especially in this stage of research history when interpretivist research is growing so quickly. Unfortunately, however, this approach has not been fully explored.

Meadows and Wimpenny (2016a) identify three main variants of this approach that might provide models for future music therapy research:

- *Meta-ethnography* is the synthesis of ethnographic research. It involves identifying overarching concepts across studies, exploring inconsistencies in their findings, and constructing a view of the whole in relation to the parts.
- *Meta-study is* a method of synthesis that involves developing a new understanding of a phenomenon based on the tripartite analysis of findings, methods, and theory.
- *Meta-aggregation* is a method of interpretivist synthesis that is most similar to objectivist meta-analysis. The first step is to identify similarities and differences in the findings of studies; the second is to assess and summarize the practical value of the findings; and the third is to make recommendations for practice. In this way, meta-aggregation integrates research, theory, and practice on a particular topic rather than constructing new insights or interpretations.
- *Realist synthesis* is the study of the various ways that a particular intervention has been used in a particular setting. "The main goal of realist synthesis is not to prove whether the intervention works, but to explain *how, why, for whom, in what circumstances*, and *to what extent* it works" (Meadows & Wimpenny, 2016a, p.637). Realist synthesis serves to provide policy-makers and researchers a guide for areas and methods of needed research.

Mixed Methods Synthesis

Mixed methods synthesis is the combination of "findings from qualitative, quantitative, and mixed methods studies in ways that integrate these findings to inform policy makers, practitioners, and fellow researchers regarding recent developments on a particular topic" (Meadows & Wimpenny, 2016b, p. 646). Procedural approaches vary according to: (a) whether the sets of quantitative and qualitative findings from all the studies are segregated or integrated, that is, whether the differences between the two sets are minimized or maximized, and whether the findings are treated separately or in relation to one another; and (b) whether the findings from one set of data are used to inform the synthesis of the other set. Thus, there are three basic types: segregated, integrated, and contingent. An example of mixed method synthesis is the study by McFerran, Garrido, and Saarikallio (2013), who examined 33 studies from different fields, to critique and integrate existing findings on how the mental health of youth can be enhanced by their use of music in everyday life.

Historical Research

As researchers have begun to recognize the relevance of interpretivist epistemologies, all areas and types of research have had to be reconsidered. Historical research in music therapy is one area where the interpretivist approach has not been as fully acknowledged and explored as the objectivist approach. Nevertheless, there is growing awareness that historical research is concerned not only with historical realities and truths, but also individual and collective constructions of history that make no such assumptions regarding the nature of reality or truth. Music therapy has a rich history of objectivist history, but is only now beginning to turn its attention to interpretivist history.

Objectivist History

Historical research is the process of "gaining knowledge about the past by systematically studying the evidence of the past" (Solomon & Davis, 2016, p. 654). In relation to music therapy, it is "the systematic study of the past practices, materials, and institutions involved in therapeutic applications of music" (Solomon & Heller, 1982). The aim may be to better understand the historical significance of people, places, events and ideas; to identify continuities and developmental processes, to provide explanations of the present, and to construct something new based on the past.

Objectivist historical research is based on the premise that "there is a *real* past, with retrievable *facts*, that can be *objectively* described as it actually happened" (Hadley, 2016). Thus, an important concern is to ensure that the researcher has the objectivity and necessary evidence to discover truths about past realities.

Sources of evidence for historical research may include photographs, drawings, official records, letters, interviews, and objects or artifacts of the past (e.g., musical scores, instruments, recordings). Each piece of evidence must be evaluated in terms of its credibility and accuracy. This is done through external and internal criticism, respectively. "External criticism authenticates evidence—that is, it helps us determine whether the evidence is what we think it is, what it appears to be, or what someone claims it to be;" whereas internal criticism "seeks to determine the truthfulness of the information provided by the evidence" (Solomon & Davis, 2016, p. 657).

Types of historical research include: biography, oral history (a first-hand account of the memories people have about the past), and historiography (an historical narrative developed through critical examination of the evidence).

Interpretivist History

Interpretivist historical research is a study of the past as reconstructed by the researcher. Unlike objectivist history, this type of history does not assume that the past exists as reality, and that it can be understood by recovering facts in an objective way. Instead the past is reconstructed based on any combination of the following premises (Hadley, 2016).

1. Historical research is interpretive rather than objective. It is not possible to gain objective truths from the study of the past for reasons cited below.
2. Language shapes and is shaped by realities of the past. It is "the structure in which historical acts engage signs/symbols that are sculpting, as it were, reality" Hadley (2016, p. 665). Thus, the past cannot be studied independent of language. That is, because language is what makes reality intelligible, and because it varies from one linguistic community to another, history can only be understood from the linguistic perspective of its users.
3. Our understanding of the past is shaped not only by language, but also by all other coded systems of meaning that remain static within a culture, and which are not open to multiple interpretations.
4. Because discourse relies upon intersubjectivity, the situatedness of each subject must be considered. In historical research, both the discourse and researcher must be clearly situated.
5. Static systems of language and meaning imply and produce power relationships. Thus, history can favor dominant discourses about race, gender, sexual orientation, etc., rather than emancipate marginalized groups.
6. Many taken-for-granted notions must be deconstructed, so that what is hidden in discourse can be uncovered. Such deconstructions can illuminate and transform our understanding of the past.

Philosophical Inquiry

Philosophical inquiry is the reasoned search for answers to "fundamental questions such as what exists, how we come to know what is and what is not, how we go about determining what is right and wrong, and what has value and beauty" (Bruscia, 2005, p. 141). This reasoned search involves rigorous questioning, criticism, argumentation, and speculation, rather than the gathering of data through observation and experimentation. The main topics of philosophical inquiry include:

- the nature of existence and reality (ontology and metaphysics),
- the nature of knowledge and ways of knowing (epistemology),
- the foundations and principles moral judgment (ethics),
- the foundation and significance of human values (axiology),
- the nature of art, beauty, and aesthetic experience (aesthetics), and

- the interrelationships of all the above to various areas of knowledge.

As defined above, philosophy is an academic discipline in itself. "It is the discipline of disciplines" in that it lays the foundation for all forms of knowledge (Bruscia, 2005, p. 541). In relation to music therapy, philosophical inquiry is the critical examination of the assumptions, principles, and concepts embedded in music therapy practice, theory, and research. The aim is to make explicit what is implicit in music therapy knowledge while also identifying the implications of this knowledge.

Aigen (2005) gives examples of philosophical inquiry in music therapy as a way of describing characteristic procedures used by philosophers. Bruscia's (2014) efforts to define and delimit music therapy as a discipline are an example of *clarifying terms*. Ruud's (1980) investigation of how music therapy can be conceived in relation to various treatment theories (e.g., psychoanalytic) is an example of *exposing and evaluating assumptions*. Kenny's (1985) efforts to connect music therapy to various systems of thought provide an example of *developing theory*. Finally, Aigen's (1991) dissertation evaluating the dominant research paradigm in music therapy provides an example of *using argumentation*.

References

Aigen, K. (1991). The roots of music therapy: Towards an indigenous research paradigm. Doctoral dissertation, New York University. *Dissertation Abstracts International, 52*(6), 1933A.

Aigen, K. (2005). Philosophical inquiry. In B. L. Wheeler (Ed.), *Music therapy research* (2nd ed.; pp. 526–539). Gilsum, NH: Barcelona.

Amir, D., & Yair, M. (2008). When the piano talks: Finding meaning in piano improvisations created by three children at risk who live in residential care. *Qualitative Inquiries in Music Therapy, 4*, 113–166.

Bonde, L. (2016). Analysis and interpretation of musical data in interpretivist research. In B. L. Wheeler & K. M. Murphy (Eds.), *Music therapy research* (3rd ed.; pp. 245–262). Dallas TX: Barcelona.

Bradt, J. (2016). Systematic review and meta-analysis. In B. L. Wheeler & K. M. Murphy (Eds.). *Music therapy research* (3rd ed.; pp. 622–633). Dallas TX: Barcelona.

Bruscia, K. (2005a). Developing theory. In B. L. Wheeler (Ed.), *Music therapy research* (2nd ed.; pp. 540–561). Gilsum, NH: Barcelona.

Bruscia, K. E. (2005b). Research topics and questions in music therapy. In B. L. Wheeler (Ed.), *Music therapy research* (2nd ed.; pp. 81–94). Gilsum, NH: Barcelona.

Bruscia, K. E. (2014). *Defining music therapy* (3rd ed.). Dallas TX: Barcelona.

Burns, D., & Masko, M. (2016). Combining interpretivist with objective methods in explanatory sequential designs. In B. L. Wheeler & K. M. Murphy (Eds.). *Music therapy research* (3rd ed.; pp. 509–607). Dallas TX: Barcelona.

Chwalek, C. M., & McKinney, C. H. (2015). The use of dialectical behavior therapy (DBT) in music therapy: A sequential explanatory study. *Journal of Music Therapy, 52,* 282–318. doi: 10.1093/jmt/thv002

DeBacker, J., & Wigram, T. (2007). Analysis of notated music examples selected from improvisations of psychotic patients. In T. Wosch & T. Wigram (Eds.) *Microanalysis in music therapy: Methods, techniques and applications for clinicians, researchers, educators, and students* (pp. 120–133). London, UK: Jessica Kingsley.

Fachner, J. (2016). Measurement of music and musical responses. In B. L. Wheeler & K. M. Murphy (Eds.), *Music therapy research* (3rd ed.; pp. 153–168). Dallas TX: Barcelona.

Hadley, S. (2016). Interpretivist historical research. In B. L. Wheeler & K. M. Murphy (Eds.), *Music therapy research* (3rd ed.; pp. 664–671). Dallas TX: Barcelona.

Holck, U. (2007). An ethnographic descriptive approach to video microanalysis. In T. Wosch & T. Wigram (Eds.). *Microanalysis in music therapy: Methods, techniques and applications for clinicians, researchers, educators, and students* (pp. 29–40). London, UK: Jessica Kingsley.

Kenny C. (1985). Music: A whole systems approach. *Music Therapy, 5,* 3–11. doi:10.1093/mt/5.1.3

Magee W. (2016). Combining objectivist with interpretive methods in exploratory sequential designs. In B. L. Wheeler & K. M. Murphy (Eds.), *Music therapy research* (3rd ed.; pp. 608–613). Dallas TX: Barcelona.

Major, C., & Savin-Baden, M. (2010) *An introduction to qualitative research synthesis: Managing the information explosion in social science research.* Routledge, UK: London.

Masko, M. K. (2013). *Music therapy and spiritual care in end-of-life: Ethical and training issues identified by chaplains and music therapists* (Unpublished doctoral dissertation). University of Iowa, Iowa City, IA. Retrieved from http://ir.uiowa.edu/etd/5021

McFerran, K., Garrido, S., & Saarikallio, S. (2013). A critical interpretive synthesis of the literature linking music and adolescent mental health. *Youth & Society,* 20(10), 1–18. doi:10.1177/0044118X13501343

Meadows, A., & Wimpenny, K. (2016a). Synthesis of interpretivist research. In B. L. Wheeler & K. M. Murphy (Eds.), *Music therapy research* (3rd ed.; pp. 635–645). Dallas TX: Barcelona.

Meadows, A., & Wimpenny, K. (2016b). Synthesis of mixed methods research. In B. L. Wheeler & K. M. Murphy (Eds.), *Music therapy research* (3rd ed.; pp. 646–653). Dallas TX: Barcelona.

Ortlieb, K., Sembdner, M., Wosch, T., & Frommer, J. (2007). Text analysis method for microprocesses (TAMP) of single music therapy sessions. In T. Wosch & T. Wigram (Eds.), *Micro-analysis in music therapy: Methods, techniques and applications for clinicians, researchers, educators and students* (pp. 285–297). London, UK: Jessica Kingsley.

Ruud, E. (1980). *Music therapy and its relationship to current treatment theories.* St. Louis, MO: MMB Music.

Solomon, A. L., & Heller, G. N. (1982). Historical research in music therapy: An important avenue for studying the profession. *Journal of Music Therapy, 19,* 161–178. doi:10.1093/jmt/19.3.161

Solomon, A., & Davis, W. (2016). Objectivist historical research. In B. L. Wheeler & K. M. Murphy (Eds.), *Music therapy research* (3rd ed.; pp. 654–663). Dallas TX: Barcelona.

Trondalen, G. (2007). A phenomenologically inspired approach to microanalysis of improvisation in music therapy. In T. Wosch & T. Wigram (Eds.), *Microanalysis in music therapy: Methods, techniques and applications for clinicians, researchers, educators, and students* (pp. 198–210). London, UK: Jessica Kingsley.

Trondalen, G., & Wosch, T. (2016). Microanalysis in interpretivist research. In B. L. Wheeler & K. M. Murphy (Eds.), *Music therapy research* (3rd ed.; pp. 589–598). Dallas TX: Barcelona.

Wosch, T., & Erkkilä, J. (2016). Microanalysis in objectivist research. In B. L. Wheeler & K. M. Murphy (Eds.), *Music therapy research* (3rd ed.; pp. 578–588). Dallas TX: Barcelona.

Wosch, T., & Wigram, T. (Eds.) (2007). *Microanalysis in music therapy: Methods, techniques and applications for clinicians, researchers, and students.* London, UK: Jessica Kingsley.

Zanders, M. (2016). Mixing interpretivist research. In B. L. Wheeler & K. M. Murphy (Eds.), *Music therapy research* (3rd ed.; pp. 614–621). Dallas TX: Barcelona.

Chapter 17

EVALUATING OBJECTIVIST RESEARCH[1]

Cathy H. McKinney

Objectivist researchers employ a variety of criteria and methods to monitor and evaluate the integrity of the research study. This chapter will explore some of these, with particular attention to their relation to music therapy research. Among the criteria that will be discussed are theoretical grounding and the validity of research and statistical hypotheses; reliability and validity in data collection procedures; the integrity of data analysis, including the limitations of statistical significance testing; and drawing evidence-based conclusions. Finally, this chapter considers three ultimate criteria for evaluating the integrity of objectivist research—replicability, conflicts of interest and biases, and clinical importance.

Criteria for Evaluation

Theoretical Grounding and Hypothesis Validity

In effective objectivist research design, theory generates research hypotheses that lead to congruent statistical hypotheses that, in turn, reveal the results of the study. Reversing the process, inference from the results leads to decisions about the statistical hypotheses (such as how to assess the magnitude of effect), which indicate whether the research hypotheses are verified. In this way, the theory is corroborated or falsified (Wampold, Davis, & Good, 2003). This is labeled *theoretical grounding.* Thaut (2000) emphasized the importance of grounding music therapy studies in theory, asserting that "studies need to be preceded by an epistemological structure of valid scientific theory that will help us understand how the data contribute to an understanding of music in therapy" (pp. 7–8). He noted that data not rooted in underlying theory are subject to misinterpretation and may create a disjunct and confusing *data puzzle* rather than contribute to an understanding of the phenomena in question. Thus, evaluation of objectivist research begins with the theory and research hypotheses being tested by the research study.

Wampold et al. (2003) employed the phrase *hypothesis validity* to refer "to the extent to which research results reflect theoretically derived predictions about the relations between or among constructs" (p. 390). The greater the hypothesis validity, the more a research study will contribute to the advancement of theory. Conversely, studies with low hypothesis validity may actually result in ambiguity about the relations among constructs and hinder the development of underlying theory (Wampold et al.). Their chapter provides a comprehensive discussion of potential threats to hypothesis validity. These threats include inconsequential or ambiguous research hypotheses, incongruence between research and statistical hypotheses, and diffuse statistical hypotheses and tests.

Reliability and Validity in Data Collection

The integrity of data collection procedures in objectivist research contributes substantially to the quality of the body of the research and the applicability of the results. Girden and Kabacoff (2011) identified three issues central to the evaluation of the integrity of data collection in objectivist research: (a) controlled observation, (b) reliability, and (c) validity. Problems in any of these three areas can compromise the study, rendering the results useless, misleading, or even harmful.

"*Controlled observation* refers to the precision of conditions under which data are collected" (Girden & Kabacoff, 2011, p. 3; italics added). Every effort is made to minimize sources of extraneous variance so that the observed variance in the dependent variables results from the independent variables and not from *noise* arising from individual differences among human beings, the experimental environment, or too diverse a sample.

One of the primary techniques for equally distributing the extraneous variance resulting from individual differences in human participants is randomized assignment of experimental condition to each participant (Bradt, 2012). In addition to equal distribution of variance, true randomization eliminates selection bias, the differential assignment of participants with respect to anticipated response to the intervention (Bradt, 2012). Detailed reporting of randomization procedures in outcome studies is essential to the accurate evaluation of the results, since inadequate reporting may result in bias in estimating treatment effectiveness (Schulz, Altman, & Moher, 2010). Because achieving true equivalence among experimental conditions is based on mathematical probability and, therefore, is particularly challenging with small samples (Bradt, 2012), the researcher may choose block or stratified randomization. Regardless of the type of randomization employed, researchers with small sample sizes need to confirm and report the outcome of the randomization by statistically testing for differences among groups in potentially confounding variables.

In objectivist research, controls also are applied to the experimental procedure itself. Potential controls include administering identical instructions under identical conditions to all groups or individuals and sequencing the procedure the same way for each administration. Although some considerations are true for many studies involving human participants, such as room temperature, lighting, type of seating or other furniture arrangement, and type and extent of interaction with the researcher, there are additional considerations for music therapy studies. For example, in music therapy studies employing recorded music, controls may include specification of the range of decibel levels or the peak decibel level of any music played; the specific pieces played; the specific recording, including the performers and the format; and the equipment used to play the music, including any use of headphones. In studies of active music therapy, the specific instruments available, their arrangement in the room, and the participants' access to them may need to be specified and fully described in the research report.

In order to observe under sufficiently controlled conditions, it may be necessary to apply controls to the participant sample. Controls may be applied through selection or exclusion criteria or through measurement of potential confounding variables relevant to the dependent variables of interest. For example, in a study of a specific music therapy procedure for adults undergoing treatment for cancer, some potential sources of extraneous variance might include the age range and gender of the participants; type, location, and stage of the cancer; time since diagnosis; type of treatment; whether adjuvant treatment is ongoing or completed; and level of social support. If the number of participants in the study is large, these factors may be controlled through collecting the relevant data and using statistical procedures to ensure equality among subgroups prior to any intervention. If the number of participants is small, as in most music therapy studies, it may be impossible to examine subgroups. In this case, it is necessary to narrow the selection criteria, recognizing that doing so will limit the generalizability of the findings to others with the same characteristics as the participants in the study.

A second criterion by which the integrity of objectivist data collection may be evaluated is the *reliability* of the measures employed in the study. Reliability refers to the consistency with which an instrument or method of measurement will reveal the same result for the same participant under the same conditions. Therefore, reliability of the observations collected is a function of both the precision of the instruments or observational methods used and their appropriate use. The more precise the instrument or method, the more likely it is to yield the same result. For example, a calibrated metronome will provide more reliable data concerning the tempo of a client's playing or her or his walking speed than the music therapist's unaided ear or eye. In another example, a reliable measure for a stable variable will achieve similar results when administered twice to the same person at a one-week interval, thereby demonstrating *test–retest reliability.* Two observers rating a subjective dimension of a client's improvisation are more likely to assess the target reliably and demonstrate *interrater reliability*, when indicators and definitions of the phenomenon have been agreed upon prior

to the observations. The reliability of the measures employed is reported in the form of correlation coefficients. Girden and Kabacoff (2011) recommended a coefficient of at least $r = 0.65$ to establish the reliability of a measure.

Validity, which applies to both the measures used in a study and the study's design, is the extent to which a study or a measurement procedure allows the researcher to draw useful and truthful conclusions about the hypotheses. There are several types of validity. **Content validity** is the accuracy and thoroughness with which test items within an instrument measure the variable in question. **Construct validity** is whether the test accurately measures the phenomenon it purports to measure. Even when the test items or testing procedure measures the underlying construct, one also must consider that instruments are devised and validated based on constructs considered to be meaningful at the time. However, the validity of the construct itself is heavily affected by societal beliefs and professional opinions, among other factors. For example, writing in the *New Orleans Medical and Surgical Journal* in 1851, physician Samuel Cartwright described a mental disorder among slaves, drapetomania, which caused slaves to run away from their masters. While observation of the population of slaves could certainly confirm the presence of this so-called "disorder" with reliability, the false validity of the construct itself was firmly rooted in perceptions based on the belief system prevailing in the American South at the time.

Internal validity and external validity both apply to the design of an experimental study. **Internal validity** concerns the degree of assurance with which causal relationships between the independent variable and dependent variable(s) can be made and is diminished by failure or inability to control adequately for confounding variables or bias. **External validity** is how accurately the results of the study can be applied to situations and people beyond the study itself. For further information on the types and nature of validity, the reader is referred to the clear and concise table offered by Haynes (2003).

Leavitt (2001) urged researchers to search thoroughly for an existing instrument before constructing a new one, since "good measures are refined and standardized over time, while less satisfactory ones are winnowed out" (p. 62). A second advantage is that use of the same measure facilitates comparisons among studies (Gold, Voracek, & Wigram, 2004). However, as Haynes (2003) noted, a test that was valid when developed some years ago may no longer be valid today because the understanding of the construct that it was designed to measure may have evolved. "The validity of an assessment instrument can diminish over time, and past validity indices should not be presumed to be generalizable to contemporaneous applications of the instrument" (Haynes, 2003, p. 250).

One major challenge to quantitative researchers is to devise meaningful **operational definitions** of highly abstract constructs. For example, defining what constitutes *improvement* in the client as a result of a therapeutic intervention is a highly subjective task, and the range of possible correct definitions is broad, even for a given diagnosis or disorder. Nevertheless, without clear operational definitions, systematic, replicable observation is impossible; conversely, definitions may be so narrowly defined as to be meaningless for practical purposes or even absurd. For example, in 1950, Freeman and Watts (as cited in Whitaker, 2002), the pioneers of the contemporaneously acclaimed psychosurgical lobotomy, wrote a book describing 623 individuals with mental illness on whom they had operated, reporting that 80% had been helped by their new therapy, consistent with the glowing outcome studies reported in the medical literature. A closer examination of their definition of *helped*, however, reveals a disturbing picture. They reported that about 25% of patients never recovered beyond "surgically induced childhood" and therefore required lifelong hospitalization, and about 25% of those discharged could be "considered as adjusting at the level of a domestic invalid or household pet" (Freeman & Watts, 1950, as cited in Whitaker, 2002, p. 124). The loss of creativity, imagination, feelings, and spiritual yearnings were seen as positive outcomes (Whitaker, 2002).

This need to balance operational definitions with practical meaningfulness also applies to the selection of measurement procedures in objectivist studies. Any instrument, no matter how reliable and well validated, measures only an aspect of the broader construct. Kazdin (1995) noted that this fact underscores the need for employing multiple assessment procedures related to the construct and claimed that the use of a single measure for a primary dependent variable may be viewed as a limitation in the interpretation of the results. The use of multiple measures more broadly represents the construct and may increase the relevance to the clinical world.

Integrity of Data Analysis

Beyond the issues of sample selection and data collection, several criteria are essential to the evaluation of the integrity of data analysis in objectivist research. These include use of appropriate statistical tests given the levels of measurement, confirmation of underlying assumptions for statistical tests, and recognition of the limitations of statistical significance testing.

As was noted in Chapter 18, Introduction to Statistical Concepts, parametric statistical tests require that the data be of an interval or ratio scale. Ordinal or nominal data are appropriately analyzed using nonparametric statistics. For example, while a parametric test may be used to determine if there is a significant difference between groups in the ratio scale variables of age or years of formal music training, a nonparametric test would be used to ascertain differences between groups in nominal scale variables, such as the number of string players versus wind players in each.

A second requirement of all parametric statistics is that certain **assumptions** regarding the data must be met. These vary according to the test statistic and experimental design. All uses of analysis of variance require that observations be random samples independently drawn from normally distributed populations and that the variances of the sets of scores from the groups represent estimates of the same population variance (Kirk, 1994). The researcher is advised to take care to minimize any bias in recruitment and allocation procedures and statistically to confirm that the data meet the assumptions that underlie the test statistic. Ideally, in objectivist studies involving analysis of variance, these confirmations include appropriate statistical tests demonstrating that the groups are equivalent prior to any intervention. Kline (2013) called the common failure of researchers to report evidence that their data meet the assumptions of the statistical tests a *"reporting crisis"* (p. 13). Moreover, a detailed description of attrition is needed to ascertain whether the results may be skewed by withdrawal from the study. The ***Consolidated Standards for Reporting Trials (CONSORT) Guidelines,*** developed by an international group of medical editors and researchers to improve the quality of reports of clinical outcome studies, provide recommendations for a flowchart that tracks each individual through all phases of a study (Schulz et al., 2010).

One well-documented but seldom-acknowledged challenge to the integrity of quantitative research lies in the limitations of statistical significance testing and the failure of researchers to recognize those limitations (Cohen, 1994, 2003; Gold, 2004). Probability values from statistical tests do not answer researchers' questions (Kline, 2013). What researchers seek to know is the "probability that the null hypothesis is true given that we have obtained a set of data" (Kirk, 1996, p. 747). Instead, the procedure tells us the "probability of obtaining these or more extreme data if the null hypothesis is true" (Kirk, 1996, p. 747). Unfortunately, finding a low probability value for the latter does not indicate that the probability of the former is also low.

Through generally adopted research conventions, objectivist researchers assume that if the *p* value associated with a given test statistic is low, then the null hypothesis is probably false (Cohen, 1994, 2003). Cohen (1994) demonstrated the deductive fallacy that is at the core of the researcher's thinking. He presented the following syllogism that is reflected in most of the objectivist music therapy literature:

If the H_0 [null hypothesis] is true, then this result (statistical significance) would probably not occur.
This result has occurred.
Then H_0 is probably not true and therefore formally invalid. (p. 998)

He elucidated the error inherent in this reasoning by substituting an example from Pollard and Richardson (cited in Cohen, 1994):

If a person is an American, then he is probably not a

member of Congress. (True, right?)
This person is a member of Congress.
Therefore, he is probably not an American. (p. 998)

Falk and Greenbaum (1995) termed this form of deduction the "illusion of probabilistic proof by contradiction" (p. 76).

Further complicating our unquestioning adoption of this illogic in research practice are two widespread erroneous beliefs: (a) that a low p value indicates the probability that replication will result in a similarly significant result (Cohen, 1994; Kirk, 1996; Thompson, 1996), and (b) that a low p value signifies that the effect is important or large (Cohen, 2003; Thompson, 1996). About the former, Falk (1998) has acknowledged the compelling nature of the faulty assumption of replicability, suggesting that it is based on "a sound intuitive need to answer the natural and most pressing questions: 'Could this be a coincidence?' and 'Will the finding recur in similar circumstances?'" (p. 315). However, Rosenthal (1993) showed that in three replications of a study, given the typical level of power for medium *effect sizes* ($d = .50$) employed by many researchers, only one study in eight would have significant results in all three replications.

Concerning the assumption of association between statistical significance and the importance of an effect, Thompson (1996) noted that the importance of findings can be determined not by statistics, but only by subjective judgment. Contrary to the objectivist roots out of which quantitative methods arose, he maintained that "empirical science is inescapably a subjective business" (p. 28). As to the relation between p values and effect size, the p value simply says that the effect probably exists and indicates nothing about the size of the effect (Cohen, 2003).

Ultimately, the focus on p values and the rejection of the null hypothesis leads the researcher away from the goal of research, which is discovering whether the findings support the hypothesis and have practical applicability (Cohen, 1994). In a review of 266 published studies in psychology, Hoekstra, Finch, Kiers, and Johnson (2006) concluded that the emphasis on p values encourages misinterpretation of the findings through *accept/reject*, dichotomous thinking. Kirk (1996) noted that two researchers focused on p values could obtain the same treatment effects yet draw diametrically opposed conclusions. For example, a researcher whose study yields a p value of .06 would be likely to choose not to reject the null hypothesis, while another researcher who has a few more participants would find $p = .05$ and reject the null hypothesis. These contradictory actions could result from identical treatment effects. In the small sample sizes often employed in music therapy studies, this hypothetical scenario is quite likely. Gold (2004) has demonstrated how the small sample size of a music therapy study may yield no statistically significant difference despite a medium effect size of the intervention and, thus, a clinically significant result.

Kirk (1996) declared that testing the significance of the null hypothesis is a trivial exercise. He and others (e.g., Körlin & Wrangsjö, 2002) have noted that the null hypothesis is always false if the sample is sufficiently large or the variance is sufficiently low. More importantly, he has asserted that the preoccupation with p values coupled with failure to consider practical significance has often led to ignoring the real questions of whether or not the data support the research hypotheses and are useful. He went so far as to lament that "our science has paid a high price for its ritualistic adherence to null hypothesis significance testing" (Kirk, 1996, p. 756). Kirk was not alone in his dismay over the misuse of p values. In the 1990s, discussion in the psychology community included the possibility of a ban on the use of significance testing (Kline, 2013). The sixth edition of the APA *Publication Manual* added language guidelines calling for the inclusion of the size and direction of the effect in studies that employ inferential statistical tests (APA, 2010).

Meanwhile, many research methodologists have recommended the use of **confidence intervals** to replace the use of the p value (Cohen, 1994; Kirk, 1996; Schmidt, 2003). Confidence intervals have three advantages over significance testing:

1. Rather than indicate an absolute decision to reject or not, confidence intervals indicate the range of values within which the real difference is likely to occur.
2. Confidence intervals reveal relationships among the results of different studies of the same measure that are not revealed by significance testing (Schmidt, 2003). As noted above, significance testing sometimes would lead one to believe that the results of two studies are contradictory when in fact they are not.
3. "Unlike the significance test, the confidence interval does hold the error rate to the desired level" (Schmidt, 2003, p. 447), thereby reducing Type II errors.

The APA *Publication Manual* recommends the reporting of confidence intervals whenever point estimates, such as means, differences between means, or effect sizes, are included (APA, 2010).

Despite the fact that statisticians have implored researchers since 1925 to employ measures of practical significance in addition to significance tests in analyses of variance, reports of such measures are not routinely made (Kirk, 1996). More recently and more closely related to the music therapy literature, music psychologist Tunks (1978) and Bonny Method of Guided Imagery and Music therapists/researchers Körlin and Wrangsjö (2002) have advocated that researchers test not only statistical significance but also strength of association or effect size. As a harbinger of increasing awareness of this issue among music therapists, Gold (2004) clearly articulated this issue for the music therapy community. Prentice and Miller (2003) noted that effect sizes confer many benefits.

1. They indicate the degree to which a phenomenon is

present in a population on a continuous scale, with zero always indicating that the phenomenon is absent.

2. They come with conventions for what values constitute a small, medium, and large effect.

3. They provide some indication of the practical significance of an effect.

4. They can be used to compare quantitatively the results of two or more studies.

5. They can be used in power analyses to guide decisions about how many subjects are needed in a study. (p. 128)

Kelly and Preacher (2012) recommended that effect sizes should be reported regardless of the p value, and Kline (2013) further advocated that confidence intervals be reported for the effect size. The CONSORT guidelines require both effect size and a measure of precision, such as confidence intervals, for each outcome variable (Schulz et al., 2010). Similarly, the Australian Physiotherapy Evidence Database (PEDro) criteria include both measures of treatment effect and variability (Centre for Evidence-Based Physiotherapy, 1999). An informal survey by this author of the studies that employed inferential statistics and were published in the *Journal of Music Therapy* between 2010 and 2014 revealed that confidence intervals were reported in a total of five articles (11%), three of which were published in 2012. Values for eta squared or partial eta squared, measures of strength of association, or Cohen's *d*, a measure of effect size, were reported in 33% of studies. Only two studies reported both confidence intervals and a measure of strength of association. While the percentage of studies reporting strength of association is more than double that found through a similar informal survey 10 years earlier (McKinney, 2005, p. 240), these data show that music therapy research does not yet commonly include measures of precision or the magnitude of effect of the intervention. Researchers are encouraged to consult Gold (2004) for his review of several of the most commonly used measures of effect size and Kirk's (1996) list of 40 different measures of effect magnitude with guidelines for interpreting several of the most used measures.

Evidence-Based Conclusions

The final threat to the integrity of an objectivist research study lies in the conclusions drawn by the researcher. Heller and O'Connor (2002) noted that "often the conclusions reported in published research articles are not appropriate to the evidence provided" (p. 1093). A common error is the overgeneralization of the results of the study. To be externally valid, the findings of a particular study may be generalized only within the limits of the design of the study, including both the population studied and the statistical results. As described above, a small sample size may require that the population parameters be narrowly defined in order to control for extraneous variance in the variables of interest. However, in so doing, the researcher limits generalization of

the findings to the same narrowly defined population. For example, the music therapy researcher who tests a music therapy intervention in preschool children hospitalized to treat cancer cannot assume that the results of the study will apply to school-age children hospitalized for cancer or to preschoolers hospitalized for disorders other than cancer.[2]

Findings of an externally valid study may be generalized only within the limits of the statistical results of the study. If inferential statistics were not used, the researcher cannot generalize the results beyond the present sample. The researcher may discuss the present data and their possible implications, but may draw no conclusions about anyone except those included in the study. Similarly, when a statistical test is not significant, no difference may be predicted in the population (Heller & O'Connor, 2002). For example, in a study of the effects of different types of music on relaxation, if post hoc tests find that there is no statistically significant difference among types, the researcher who proceeds to discuss that one type is more effective than the others has generalized the results beyond the evidence and made an invalid statistical conclusion.

Bias may result in the over- or underestimation of the effect of the intervention studied, leading to false conclusions. While bias can arise during the interpretation of the data, bias also may be introduced by failure to adhere to best-practice procedures for objectivist studies. Boutron et al. (2005) developed criteria to be used in evaluating reports of nonpharmacological intervention studies. The *Cochrane Handbook* (Higgins & Green, 2011) has articulated similar criteria for the evaluation of risk of bias for studies being considered for inclusion in Cochrane reviews. These include the following areas related to study design and implementation: (a) randomization procedures, (b) concealed allocation to intervention groups prior to and during enrollment, (c) masking study personnel and those involved in assessing dependent variables from knowledge of participants' group assignments, and (d) analyzing data based on the intention-to-treat principle, which includes data from all randomized participants, regardless of compliance with the study protocol. Music therapy researchers are advised to be mindful of these criteria as they design, implement, and report their studies.

Ultimate Criteria

While criteria developed by international bodies, such as CONSORT and PEDro, may be useful in planning and evaluating research studies, three additional factors contribute to the ultimate evaluation of the integrity of quantitative research in music therapy. The first is the replicability of the study, since replication is the only way to increase certainty in the results; the second is real or potential conflicts of interest and research biases of the researcher; and the third is the clinical importance of the findings.

Replicability

In the final analysis, the only way to determine whether an observed effect is due to chance sampling error is through *replication* of the study (Falk, 1998; Kline, 2013). Falk noted that the essential role of replication in scientific advancement is one point of agreement among statisticians and research methodologists and that successful replication lends credence to the trustworthiness of the evidence. Roediger (2012) went so far as to recommend that researchers replicate their own work prior to publication. Yet, the common practice of viewing statistical significance as the final word in research (Falk, 1998) and bias against publication of replications (Francis, 2012) may discourage replication attempts.

The music therapy literature contains few replications. Moreover, many articles contain insufficient information to allow replication. Careful documentation of the circumstances of each aspect of the data collection process is necessary for another researcher to re-create the conditions of the experiment in order to replicate the study. This has not always been done in music therapy research. For example, an examination of the numerous studies that have investigated physiological effects of music will show that, while some researchers specified the musical selections used, many neglected to document even the piece of music used, instead employing descriptive terms such as *agreeably exciting, beautiful music,* or *anxiolytic music.* A researcher attempting to understand the body of literature or preparing to replicate the study needs to know not only the specific piece, but also the particular recording used. A comparative journey through the first 16 bars of 10 different recordings of Pachelbel's *Canon in D* will illustrate clearly that specific recordings may vary in many dimensions that may affect the research outcome, including tempo, instrumentation, motion, style, and other aspects.

Since inferential statistics are based on probability, a single replication of an effect cannot achieve certainty. To achieve certainty would require that one reach infinite probability. Since infinity cannot be reached, certainty cannot be achieved, but only approached (Falk, 1998). Nevertheless, successful replication can increase confidence in theories of music therapy, the underlying mechanisms, and the evidence for efficacy of music therapy interventions.

Conflicts of Interest

Many choices are exercised in the decision-making process leading to objectivist research, including what to research, how to approach the problem, what interpretations to make of the data, which results to publish, and how to disseminate the findings. These decisions are influenced by a number of factors, both intrinsic and extrinsic to the research. These factors may converge to create conflicting pressures on the researcher, leading to *conflicts of interest* that may influence the outcome of an individual research study and ultimately the body of published research (Bradley, 1995).

One potential source of conflict of interest is the funding source of a research study, especially when the funding agent has a commercial interest in the subject of the research. Such a conflict may introduce a direct or indirect effect upon the findings (Bradley, 1995). For example, in research studies of new drugs, only 13% of studies funded by sources without obvious bias favored the new drug over traditional therapies versus 43% of studies funded by the drug company (Davidson, as cited in Leavitt, 2001). While this source of conflict has been less often present in music therapy research because of the historical lack of corporate funding, recent increased interest shown by commercial sources in funding research may present dilemmas for the music therapist–researcher. Whether or not the funding agent makes any overt statements of desirable outcome, the therapist–researcher may experience real or perceived pressure to obtain findings that will please the funding source and thus increase the likelihood of future financial support. Research in which the funding source has an obvious financial interest must be carefully considered.

A second way that corporate funding sources and clinical agencies sometimes introduce bias into the published literature is through control of the dissemination of research results. Because of their financial interest in the outcome of research studies, some corporations suppress the publication of unsatisfactory results through clauses in the grant contract that require approval of any results prior to submission for publication (Bradley, 1995; Leavitt, 2001). This trend has been recognized as a violation of academic freedom, and some university systems have adopted policies precluding the universities from entering into any agreement, including accepting a grant that restricts the rights of faculty or students to publish (personal communication, D. Cole, July 31, 2015). Entering into a contractual agreement with any party that restricts the right to publish may place the music therapist/researcher in an uncomfortable ethical dilemma.

Clinical Importance

In music therapy, the connection between research and clinical practice has at times been tenuous. Music therapy clinicians (and other professionals in clinical practice) sometimes claim that the research studies are unrelated to their work with clients, that they fail to contribute to their clinical decisions, and that they are jargon-laden and hard to comprehend. The result of this uneasy relationship between research and practice may be that ineffective methods continue to be used and effective methods are slow to be adopted (Reynolds, 2000).

One process first developed in medicine and later applied to psychotherapy in an effort to strengthen the research–practice relationship is evidence-based practice (Abrams, 2010; Reynolds, 2000; Sackett, Richardson, Rosenberg, & Haynes, 1998). *Evidence-based practice* encourages the clinician to combine the best of personal experience and external evidence, including professional guidelines and research studies, in making clinical decisions about individual clients (Sackett et al., 1998). Evaluation of external evidence consists of both establishing the validity of the results and deciding whether the results are clinically important. Establishing the validity of a single study is accomplished through examination of many aspects of the research already considered in this chapter, including randomization, accounting for attrition, and controlling for extraneous sources of variance.

In evidence-based practice, the concept of statistical significance may be replaced by the concept of clinical importance. *Clinical importance* is determined by calculations of the number needed to treat (NNT) and the number needed to harm (NNH). NNT and NNH convert the results of studies of a treatment procedure into quantitative indicators of "how many patients would have to be treated with the treatment method in order to bring about one good outcome or one harmful outcome" (Reynolds, 2000, pp. 260–261). In addition, the size of the treatment effect on clinically important outcome measures is a major factor in determining whether a given treatment is worth the cost and effort of treatment. The results of a quantitative meta-analysis of more than one high-quality randomized controlled trial are seen as the optimal source of evidence (Guyatt, Sinclair, Cook, & Glasziou, 1999). Combining the evaluation of research evidence, the clinical importance of the treatment, and the size of the treatment effect with the personal experience, expertise, and judgment of the clinician and the personal preferences and values of the client allows the clinician to determine whether or not the treatment may be appropriate for an individual client. While some fields rely solely on results from studies from an objectivist epistemology, several music therapists have advocated broader inclusion criteria when determining what constitutes *evidence* in the profession (Abrams, 2010; Bradt, 2012, Wigram & Gold, 2012).

The Cochrane Library disseminates systematic reviews of clinical outcome research in healthcare prepared according to exacting standards set by the international Cochrane Collaboration, an independent, not-for-profit organization dedicated to promoting informed decisions about healthcare (Cochrane Collaboration, 2015). Each review is based on randomized, quasi-randomized, and clinical controlled trials and includes a meta-analysis, if sufficient high-quality studies are available. As of January 2016, reviews of music therapy literature have been completed in nine areas: dementia, schizophrenia and schizophrenia-like illnesses, pain relief, autism spectrum disorders, acquired brain injury, end-of-life, cancer, depression, and anxiety in individuals on mechanical ventilation (Cochrane Collaboration, 2015). With the exception of the reviews of cancer and mechanical ventilation studies, which included studies of both music therapy and listening to recorded music, each review found at most 10 reports that met the inclusion criteria. While six reviews found that music therapy may have beneficial effects, two found insufficient high-quality evidence to support positive outcomes of music therapy. Music therapists conducting and reporting studies of treatment outcomes will find the Cochrane criteria to be a helpful resource.

Some music therapists have decried the demand for quantitative evidence of clinical efficacy of music therapy, citing concerns for the applicability of evidence-based practice methods to music therapy (Edwards, 2004) and for the potential that misapplication will impair clinical services (Aldridge, 2003). Others have stressed the importance of evidence-based data in securing funding for services (Wigram, Pedersen, & Bonde, 2002), justifying positions (Edwards, 2002), and meeting the demands of the healthcare industry (Bradt, 2012). Researchers have begun to report the evidence base for music therapy with specific populations using the more stringent inclusion criteria of evidence-based methods (Gold et al., 2004; Standley, 2012). Despite the concerns voiced by music therapists, it appears that the criteria of evidence-based methods will continue to influence the evaluation of objectivist research in music therapy for some time to come.

Conclusion

Objectivist researchers have a number of criteria and methods at their disposal for monitoring and evaluating the integrity of both their research and the research literature. In music therapy, researchers have attended to some of these, such as controlled observations and the reliability of measures. However, they have given less attention to others, such as the reporting of effect sizes and confidence intervals, and some methods, such as replication and systematically minimizing risk of bias, are rarely observed in the music therapy literature. If music therapy is to advance in its clarity and understanding of the efficacy of and indications for its various clinical methods, researchers will need to embrace every means available for building a body of knowledge that meets the highest standards of integrity.

References

Abrams, B. (2010). Evidence-based music therapy practice: An integral understanding. *Journal of Music Therapy, 47,* 351–379. doi:10.1093/jmt/47.4.351

Aldridge, D. (2003, November). Staying close to practice: Which evidence, for whom, by whom. *Music Therapy Today, 4*(4). Retrieved from http://www.wfmt.info/Musictherapyworld/modules/mmmagazine/issues/20031103132043/20031103132433/DA_Nov03.pdf

Boutron, I., Moher, D., Tugwell, P., Giraudeau, B., Poiraudeau, S., Nizard, R., & Ravaud, P. (2005). A checklist to evaluate a report of nonpharmacological trials (CLEAR NPT) was developed using consensus.

Journal of Clinical Epidemiology, 58, 1233–1240. doi:10.1016/j.jclinepi.2005.05.004

Bradley, S. G. (1995). Conflict of interest. In F. L. Macrina (Ed.), *Scientific integrity: An introductory text with cases* (pp. 161–187). Washington, DC: ASM Press.

Bradt, J. (2012). Randomized controlled trials in music therapy: Guidelines for design and implementation. *Journal of Music Therapy, 49,* 120–149. doi:10.1093/jmt/49.2.120

Cartwright, S. (1851). Diseases and peculiarities of the Negro race. Retrieved from http://www.pbs.org/wgbh/aia/part4/4h3106t.html

Centre for Evidence-Based Physiotherapy. (1999). *PEDro scale.* Retrieved from http://www.pedro.org.au/english/downloads/pedro-scale/

Cochrane Collaboration. (2015). *Cochrane reviews.* Retrieved from http://www.cochranelibrary.com/

Cohen, J. (1994). The earth is round ($p < .05$). *American Psychologist, 49,* 997–1003. doi:10.1037/0003-066X.49.12.997

Cohen, J. (2003). Things I have learned (so far). In A. E. Kazdin (Ed.), *Methodological issues and strategies in clinical research* (3rd ed., pp. 407–424). Washington, DC: American Psychological Association.

Edwards, J. (2002). Using the evidence-based medicine framework to support music therapy posts in health care settings. *British Journal of Music Therapy, 16,* 29–34.

Edwards, J. (2004, August). Can music therapy in medical contexts ever be evidence-based? *Music Therapy Today, 5*(4). Retrieved from http://musictherapyworld.net

Falk, R. (1998). Replication—A step in the right direction: Commentary on Sohn. *Theory & Psychology, 8,* 313–321. doi:10.1177/0959354398083002

Falk, R., & Greenbaum, C. W. (1995). Significance tests die-hard: The amazing persistence of a probabilistic misconception. *Theory & Psychology, 5,* 75–98. doi:10.1177/0959354395051004

Francis, G. (2012). Publication bias and the failure of replication in experimental psychology. *Psychonomic Bulletin and Review, 19,* 975–991. doi:10.3758/S13423-012-0322-y

Girden, E. R., & Kabacoff, R. I. (2011). *Evaluating research articles: From start to finish* (3rd ed.). Thousand Oaks, CA: Sage.

Gold, C. (2004). The use of effect sizes in music therapy research. *Music Therapy Perspectives, 22,* 91–95. doi:10.1093/mtp/22.2.91

Gold, C., Voracek, M., & Wigram, T. (2004). Effects of music therapy for children and adolescents with psychopathology: A meta-analysis. *Journal of Child Psychology and Psychiatry, 45,* 1054–1063. doi:10.1111/j.1469-7610.2004.t01-1-00298.x

Guyatt, G. H., Sinclair, J., Cook, D. J., & Glasziou, P. (1999). Users' guides to the medical literature XVI: How to use a treatment recommendation. *Journal of the American Medical Association, 281,* 1836–1843. doi:10.1001/jama.281.19.1836

Haynes, S. N. (2003). Clinical applications of analogue behavioral observation: Dimensions of psychometric evaluation. In A. E. Kazdin (Ed.), *Methodological issues and strategies in clinical research* (3rd ed., pp. 235–264). Washington, DC: American Psychological Association.

Heller, J. J., & O'Connor, E. J. P. (2002). Maintaining quality in research and reporting. In *The new handbook of research on music teaching and learning* (pp. 1089–1107). New York, NY: Oxford University Press.

Higgins, J. P. T., & Green, S. (Eds.). (2011). *Cochrane handbook for systematic reviews of interventions.* Retrieved from http://handbook.cochrane.org/

Hoekstra, R., Finch, S., Kiers, H. A. L., & Johnson, A. (2016). Probability as certainty: Dichotomous thinking and the misuse of p values. *Psychonomic Bulletin and Review, 13,* 1033–1037. doi:10.3758/BF03213921

Kazdin, A. E. (1995). Preparing and evaluating research reports. *Psychological Assessment, 7,* 228–237. doi:10.1037/1040-3590.7.3.228

Kelly, K., & Preacher, K. J. (2012). On effect size. *Psychological Methods, 17,* 137–152.

Kirk, R. E. (1994). *Experimental design: Procedures for the behavioral sciences* (3rd ed.). Pacific Grove, CA: Brooks/Cole.

Kirk, R. E. (1996). Practical significance: A concept whose time has come. *Educational and Psychological Measurement, 56,* 746–759. doi:10.1177/0013164496056005002

Kline, R. B. (2013). *Beyond significance testing: Statistics reform in the behavioral sciences* (2nd ed.). Washington, DC: American Psychological Association.

Körlin, D., & Wrangsjö, B. (2002). Treatment effects of GIM therapy. *Nordic Journal of Music Therapy, 11,* 3–15. doi:10.1080/08098130209478038

Leavitt, F. (2001). *Evaluating scientific research: Separating fact from fiction.* Upper Saddle River, NJ: Prentice-Hall.

McKinney, C. (2005). Evaluating quantitative music therapy research. In B. L. Wheeler (Ed.), *Music therapy research* (2nd ed.; pp. 236–245). Gilsum, NH: Barcelona.

Prentice, D. A., & Miller, D. T. (2003). When small effects are impressive. In A. E. Kazdin (Ed.), *Methodological issues and strategies in clinical research* (3rd ed., pp. 127–137). Washington, DC: American Psychological Association.

Reynolds, S. (2000). Evidence-based practice and psychotherapy research. *Journal of Mental Health, 8,* 257–266. doi:10.1080/jmh.9.3.257.266

Roediger, H. L. (2012). Psychological woes and a partial cure: The value of replication. *APS Observer, 25*(2).

Rosenthal, R. (1993). Cumulating evidence. In G. Keren & C. Lewis (Eds.), *A handbook for data analysis in the behavioral sciences: Methodological issues* (pp. 519–559). Hillsdale, NJ: Erlbaum.

Sackett, D. L., Richardson, W. S., Rosenberg, W., & Haynes,

R. B. (1998). *Evidence-based medicine: How to practice and teach EBM.* New York, NY: Churchill Livingstone.

Schmidt, F. L. (2003). Statistical significance testing and cumulative knowledge in psychology: Implications for training of researchers. In A. E. Kazdin (Ed.), *Methodological issues and strategies in clinical research* (3rd ed., pp. 437–464). Washington, DC: American Psychological Association.

Schulz, K. F., Altman, D. G., & Moher, D., for the CONSORT Group. (2010). CONSORT 2010 Statement: Updated guidelines for reporting parallel group randomised trials. *Annals of Internal Medicine, 152,* 726–732. doi:10.7326/0003-4819-152-11-201006010-00232

Standley, J. M. (2012). A discussion of evidence-based music therapy to facilitate feeding skills of premature infants: The power of contingent music. *Arts in Psychotherapy, 39,* 379–382. doi:10.1016/j.aip.2012.06.009

Thaut, M. H. (2000). *A scientific model of music in therapy and medicine.* San Antonio, TX: IMR Press.

Thompson, B. (1996). AERA editorial policies regarding statistical significance testing: Three suggested reforms. *Educational Researcher, 25*(2), 26–30.

Tunks, T. (1978). The use of omega squared in interpreting statistical significance. *Council for Research in Music Education Bulletin, 57,* 28–34.

Wampold, B. E., Davis, B., & Good, R. H. (2003). Hypothesis validity of clinical research. In A. E. Kazdin (Ed.), *Methodological issues and strategies in clinical research* (3rd ed., pp. 389–406). Washington, DC: American Psychological Association.

Whitaker, R. (2002). *Mad in America: Bad science, bad medicine, and the enduring mistreatment of the mentally ill.* Cambridge, MA: Perseus Books.

Wigram, T., & Gold, C. (2012). The religion of evidence-based practice: Helpful or harmful to health and well-being? In R. A. R. MacDonald, G. Kreutz, & L. Mitchell (Eds.), *Music, health, and well-being* (pp. 164–182). New York, NY: Oxford University Press.

Wigram, T., Pedersen, I. N., & Bonde, L. O. (2002). *A comprehensive guide to music therapy: Theory, clinical practice, research and training.* London, UK: Jessica Kingsley.

1. Portions of this chapter are based on the chapter by the same author in the previous edition of this book.
2. It should be noted, though, that it is appropriate and often necessary for a clinician to apply the most closely related research available. (As Sackett, Richardson, Rosenberg, and Haynes [1997] noted, applying research results to an individual patient from a similar population by a clinician is a basic tenet of evidence-based practice.) However, it would be inappropriate for the researcher to extend the conclusions to a population beyond that sampled for the study.

Chapter 18

EVALUATING INTERPRETIVIST RESEARCH[1]

Brian Abrams

Evaluating research is a vital part of optimizing its benefit and impact. Evaluating interpretivist research, however, can be a particularly complex matter. The term *interpretivist research*, for the purposes of this chapter, will be treated synonymously with the term *qualitative research*, as it appears in the literature. ***Interpretivist research*** refers a diversity of methods, rooted in a wide range of perspectives, values, and purposes (Bruscia, 1998). The purpose of the present chapter is to elaborate upon major categories of interpretivist research evaluation found in the literature, relevant to the field of music therapy.

In general, interpretivist research is evaluated according to the rigor and integrity with which it is designed, conducted, and documented, as well as the richness, meaningfulness, relevance, and sophistication of the new knowledge it produces, including how that knowledge enlarges constructions of the world and helps to create individual meanings therein (Bruscia, 1998). Yet, evaluation based upon these general principles defies adherence to any fixed set of standards. Appraisal of interpretivist research cannot be meaningfully accomplished *monologically*, independently of contextual variation. Rather, interpretivist research must be evaluated *dialogically*, in a dynamic, interactive process of conversation and collaboration, incorporating the many interrelationships between the research, the environment and sociocultural circumstances, and the interests and lives of various stakeholders involved in the research and the evaluation process. The specific nature of the evaluation process in interpretivist research depends upon who does the evaluation (such as members of the editorial staff of a professional journal, scholars or academic instructors, research experts of various kinds, peers, readers, members of the public, research participants, or the researchers themselves), and the evaluator's orientation within one or more specific cultures embodying certain perspectives (or worldviews) and sets of values concerning research. Moreover, according to Sandelowski and Barroso (2002), evaluation of interpretivist research requires exercising one's informed sensibilities concerning the merits of a work, which Eisner (1991) refers to as *connoisseurship*.

Lincoln (1995) cautions that evaluation of interpretivist research is beyond "firm and fixed criteria" (p. 2), just as Reicher (2000) warns against what is known as *methodolatry*. Likewise, Bruscia (1998) states: "There are as many qualitative [interpretivist] standards as there are nonpositivistic epistemologies. This is certainly not a problem to be avoided or resolved—it is a fundamental condition of research" (p. 178). While certain criteria utilized in evaluating

interpretivist research have been considered epistemologically analogous or parallel to those utilized in evaluating objectivist research (Cobb & Hagemaster, 1987; Lincoln & Guba, 1985; Smeijsters, 1996a, 1996b; Stiles, 1993), their radically differing, underlying epistemologies call for very different ways of understanding evaluation. Thus, as Bruscia has stated: "One simply cannot impose standards for quantitative [objectivist] research onto qualitative [interpretivist] research, no matter how intellectually tempting or convenient that would be" (p. 177). From an interpretivist framework, *axiology* (the study of values, ethics, and aesthetics) holds relevance equal to or greater than epistemology (the study of knowledge) in evaluating research (Creswell, 1998; Hiles, 2008), a point of consideration that often emerges in the context of mixed methods research (Tashakkori & Teddlie, 2010).

Interpretivist research evaluation is based upon nonpositivist tenets such as *truthfulness*, or honesty and trustworthiness, as opposed to *truth*, or independently verifiable fact (Wilber, 1997), as well as multifaceted meanings and realities composed of multiple, co-constructed, intersubjective realities, versus positivistic notions of objective, bias-free accuracy concerning an immutable, singular reality. Interpretivist research varies in form (Popay, Rogers, & Williams, 1998; Tierney, 1995), with goals that target maximizing depth, comprehensiveness, richness, and diversity. Evaluation of interpretivist research poses the additional challenge of differentiating appraisal of the research as actually performed from that of the representation of the research in a written report.

Certain general guidelines for evaluating interpretivist research within specific, established methodological traditions, such as phenomenology, hermeneutics, heuristics, grounded theory, historical inquiry, and ethnography, have been developed. Moreover, certain scholarly journals, such as *Action Research International, Educational Action Research, The Journal of Occupational and Organizational Psychology*, and *Qualitative Research in Psychology*, have established evaluation criteria for publication. Sandelowski and Barroso (2002) have provided a comprehensive framework for reading and evaluating qualitative research studies across the general literature. (Although Sandelowski and Barroso prefer the term *appraisal* to evaluation, as the latter does not necessarily imply an estimation of value, these terms will be utilized interchangeably here.)

Sets of guidelines for evaluating interpretivist research have also been developed specifically from within the music therapy field. A notable set was formulated by Stige,

Malterud, and Midtgarden (2009), who developed a comprehensive framework consisting of the *agenda items* Engaging, Processing, Interpretation, Critique, Usefulness, Relevance, and Ethics—together forming the acronym *EPICURE*—each associated with specific themes for dialogue and discussion comprising the evaluation process. EPICURE has become a standard evaluative resource in the field. Certain sets of guidelines have also been developed expressly for appraising the integrity of research submitted to scholarly music therapy journals (Stige, 2002b) or monographs (Bruscia, 2003). One of the most detailed is Aigen's (2012) guidelines for publishing qualitative research in the *Nordic Journal of Music Therapy*. Notably, the *Journal of Music Therapy* (American Music Therapy Association, 2015) has adopted Sandelowski and Barroso's (2002) guidelines for its instructions to prospective authors. However, none of these guidelines— whether developed within or outside of the music therapy field—specifically includes considerations about the unique intersections of music, health, and therapy that distinguish music therapy as a discipline and profession. Thus, presumably, this remains the responsibility of the evaluator(s).

Categories of Interpretivist Research Evaluation

Five interpretivist music therapy research evaluation categories are identified here, each representing its own foundation for appraisal: *Contextualization, Substantiation, Integration, Utilization,* and *Responsibility*. Literature both within and outside music therapy will be cited to support the bases for each category and will highlight the guidelines set forth by Aigen (2012), Sandelowski and Barroso (2002), and Stige et al. (2009), and as pertinent to a given component of a category, because of the prominent role they have played in contributing to the evaluation of interpretivist music therapy research. In certain cases, terminology denoting these categories appears explicitly in the literature; in other cases, the present author has selected terminology to represent implicit ideas and constructs. Elaboration upon each of these categories will include a consolidated matrix summarizing how that category may manifest across each phase of the research process: Formulating the Research Focus and Questions (Formulation), Defining and Selecting Participants (Participation), Collecting Data (Information), Preparing and Analyzing Data (Analysis), Interpreting Data (Interpretation), and Presenting the Research Process and Findings (Presentation). Tables 1–5 represent a summary of the significance of each evaluation category (by subcategory, where applicable) across each phase of research.

To illustrate how these categories might be applied in actual practice, examples are given of how each may apply in the evaluation of a fictitious study investigating musical and lyrical themes in a group songwriting experience with persons recovering from substance dependence. For purposes of brevity, these illustrations will feature one or

several stages of research only. The intent is not to establish a master set of standards or procedures but, rather, to present a synthesis of existing guidelines. Moreover, the reader should understand each category as a general construct only, not to be utilized as a substitute for the many case-specific considerations involved in the dialogical evaluation process.

Contextualization

Contextualization means inquiring into, situating, and disclosing the contexts of the researcher, the research participants, the phenomenon being studied, and the research study itself. According to Bruscia (1995b), "To contextualize is to identify the many different frameworks, orientations, systems, environments, and conditions in which a research study is taking place" (p. 404).

Contextualizing the researcher is essential in interpretivist research, as the researcher is the primary instrument of research (Aigen, 1995, 1996a; Stiles, 1993). Everything produced through a research study is the result of the researcher's interpretations, on some level (Stige, 2002a). Moreover, as Aigen (1995) states, "What you do as a qualitative [interpretivist] researcher directly reflects who you are" (p. 296). Thus, the research study cannot be disembedded from the living context of the researcher, as research constructions "do not exist outside of the persons who create and hold them; they are not part of some 'objective' world that exists apart from their constructors" (Guba & Lincoln, 1989, p. 143). The interpretivist researcher's personal, professional, and cultural identities are inextricable from the research (Aigen, 1995; Ansdell, 2002; Bruscia, 1995a).

In order to achieve researcher contextualization, the researcher must take ownership of, and responsibility for, her or his perspectives, assumptions, motives, values, and interests that inform the process of doing the research (Bruscia, 1996, 1998; Elliot, Fischer, & Rennie, 1999). This extends to anything conscious or unconscious about the researcher's personal identity (Bruscia, 1995a, 1996, 1998), the researcher's relationship to research participants (Cobb & Hagemaster, 1987), and the researcher's philosophical, theoretical, paradigmatic, and conceptual presuppositions (Edwards, 2002; Stige, 2002a; Stiles, 1993). It also extends to the researcher's own honest perceptions of both the virtues and the constraints of the method, and of both desirable and undesirable aspects of findings (Bruscia, 1996). In addition, it includes a researcher's consideration of how her or his social, cultural, political, historical, and linguistic realities, inform her or his expectations, values, and ways of making meaning (Stige, 2002a). The researcher's honest and conscientious self-inquiry, together with forthright and transparent disclosure about relationships to the research, comprise what is known as *reflexivity* (Rennie, 1995), or "self-awareness and agency within that self-awareness" (Rennie, 2004, p. 183). This reflexive dimension of contextualization has been called *monitoring of self* (Peshkin, 1988) and being *rigorously subjective*

	Contextualizing the Researcher	Contextualizing the Participants	Contextualizing the Phenomenon	Contextualizing the Research Study Itself
Formulation	The researcher's own relationship to the research focus and questions, in terms of experiences of the research phenomena (in both personal and professional contexts) and her or his own motives for conducting the study	The lived history of the participants, and their relationships to the research	The social history of the research phenomenon, how that history informs the research questions posed	The role and value of the focus and questions within existing music therapy research literature, as well as any historical, sociocultural, and ideological implications of the study with respect to the research community, such as motives for the research or attitudes on the research topic within the surrounding culture
Participation	Assumptions and value judgments about the persons sharing the demo-graphic and other characteristics of the participants, as informed by her or his personal or cultural background, along with any motives for involving these particular participants	Participants' clarity of voice (e.g., their roles, perspectives)	Participants' life experiences pertaining to the research phenomenon	Identities and roles of research participants, as featured in related literature
Information	Thoroughness of recording, documenting, and disclosing personal thoughts, feelings, reactions, and concerns of the researcher in relation to data collection	Understanding participant data as sociocultural capital, appropriated within a situated transaction, wherein certain stakeholders benefit in different ways (or to different extents)	How the data (whether arts-based or otherwise) represent phenomena that manifest and play roles in music therapy work, in society, and in the world	Forms of data on the phenomenon being studied as featured in related literature
Analysis	Relationships between researcher's identity and the researcher's process of deriving constructions of findings from data	Relationships between Participant identities and process of deriving constructions of findings from data	Circumstances and conditions surrounding the phenomena guiding derivation of constructions of findings from data	Circumstances and conditions informing the manner in which the constructions of findings are derived from data
Interpretation	Relationships between the researcher's life and the ways in which she or he derives meanings from findings, including significant personal and/or professional (client-based) experiences	Role of the participants' identities in the derivation of meanings from findings	Role of the nature of the phenomenon in informing meanings derived from findings	Relationships between the circumstances surrounding the research study and ways in which meanings are derived from the findings
Presentation	Documentation of the researcher's identity, as pertinent to the study, including the reflexive process and any resulting revelations and insights	Documentation of the participants' identities, as pertinent to the study	Documentation of the phenomenon's situated role, relative to individuals, communities, and society/culture	Documentation of the study's situated role, relative to individuals, communities, and society/culture

Table 1. Contextualization

(Jackson, 1990). Morrow (2005) emphasizes the interpretivist position that the researcher is a co-constructor of meaning in interpretivist research and has used the terms *subjectivity* and *social validity* in referring to researcher contextualization. Constructs that refer to contextualizing the researcher in interpretivist research include *epoché* in phenomenology; *stance of the researcher* in naturalistic inquiry; *self-hermeneutic* in hermeneutic research; and *movement between personal and public* in heuristic research (Aigen, 1995, 1996b).

It follows from the foregoing that researcher self-inquiry in interpretivist music therapy research must often include inquiring into the researcher's unique relationship to the musical experiences, processes, and products at the heart of the research. The researcher may consider these relationships in terms of individual and cultural dimensions, past personal and professional experiences, associations relating to the music or a particular instrument, and specific reactions and preferences. While complete researcher contextualization may not be possible, the researcher may nonetheless strive as closely for this ideal as awareness permits (Stiles, 1993) and to the extent that these relationships are relevant (Bruscia, 1996). As Rennie (1995) asserts on the imperfect nature of researcher contextualization, "A half-loaf is better than none" (p. 49).

For Sandelowski and Barroso (2002), researcher contextualization is a matter of *validity*, appraised according to how effectively the researcher conveys awareness of her or his influence upon the study and participants. For Stige et al. (2009), it is a matter both of *engagement*, in terms of how well the researcher situates herself or himself demographically and historically, and of *critique*, in terms of how rigorously the researcher engages in critical self-awareness around motives, biases, and so forth. For Aigen (2012), it is a matter of reflexivity, or self-situatedness, in which the researcher acknowledges roles, motives, and interests, including how any of these have an impact upon the study. Aigen is careful to point out that reflexivity and self-situatedness are not about removing bias to achieve context-free objectivity—rather, these are about self-awareness and transparency concerning the influences of the researcher's lifeworld.

Contextualizing the participants (or sample) entails working to observe, study, and understand participants according to their own personal identities, life experiences, and cultural backgrounds. Given that, in interpretivist research, participants are typically selected purposively to provide the most information-rich data possible (Morrow, 2005), it is important for the researcher to engage the contexts underlying participant selection. Contextualizing the participants further entails an understanding of the participants' relationships to the researcher within the shared, lived world in which the study takes place (Bruscia, 1998). On this topic, Fine (1992) cites the importance of "positioning researchers as self-conscious, critical, and participatory analysts, engaged with but still distinct from our informants" (p. 220). Elliot et al. (1999) refer to this aspect of contextualization as *situating the sample*. From a sociocultural perspective, and in accordance

with the resource-oriented music therapy literature (e.g., Rolvsjord, 2010), this may include a consideration of how the contributions of research participants, such as data, may be understood as a form of human capital, appropriated within a situated transaction, wherein certain stakeholders benefit in different ways (or to different extents). Part of contextualizing the participants is *clarity of voice* (Bruscia, 1998), or the degree to which the researcher explicitly acknowledges the specific identity, role, and lived experience of each individual involved in the study (researcher, participant, consultant, and so forth). Even when the role boundaries of researcher and participant are not absolutely distinct (such as in participatory action research), striving toward maximal clarity of voice helps to explicate sources of data and distribution of roles, thereby deepening the integrity of the research. In music therapy research, the participants' musical identities and relationships to music may be an important part of helping to ensure clarity of voice and other important dimensions of participant contextualization.

For Sandelowski and Barroso (2002), contextualizing participants is a matter of the *sample* and how well participants and other components that situate participants are described (such as the site where recruitment and/or data collection has taken place and artifacts that embody aspects of participant identity). For Stige et al. (2009), it is a matter of *engagement*, in terms of demonstrating the ways in which the researcher has interacted with participants during the course of the study (participant observation).

Contextualizing the research phenomenon entails understanding and disclosing the biographical, historical, cultural, and other factors pertaining to the phenomenon being studied. In research about the arts, this means explicating the contexts surrounding the art (Wilber, 1997). Specifically in interpretivist music therapy research, it means examining the ways in which the music being studied is created, expressed, and experienced by those involved in the study.

For Sandelowski and Barroso (2002), contextualizing the research phenomenon is a matter of the *mind-set toward the target phenomenon*, including consideration and disclosure of any perspectives, assumptions, conceptual/theoretical frameworks, and philosophies regarding the phenomenon that may guide or inform the research for the researcher. For Stige et al. (2009), it is a matter of *engagement*—specifically, the degree to which the work demonstrates continuous researcher interaction with, and relationship to, the phenomenon or situation being studied.

Contextualization of the research study itself is yet another basis for research evaluation. Stige (2002a) emphasizes the significance of contextualizing the research purpose, data, processes, interpretations, and outcomes in terms of their historical, sociocultural, political, and ideological bases. For Aldridge (2002), this type of contextualization is particularly important with respect to understanding the values of the community within which the study is conducted and how those values may or may not legitimize the study. Often, the related literature serves as the primary resource for this form of contextualization, as it embodies much of the history and value centers of a given community or culture of inquiry. In interpretivist research that is arts-informed or arts-based (as can be the case in interpretivist music therapy research), the artistic processes and forms must be considered a part of contextualizing the study by situating it with respect to its most relevant media.

For Sandelowski and Barroso (2002), contextualizing the research study itself is a matter of the *research problem*, including the articulation of an applied (i.e., clinical) or theoretical issue, thus establishing the significance of the fundamental purpose of the research. For them, it is also a matter of the literature review, in terms of what is believed, known, and not known about a problem. For Stige et al. (2009), it is a matter of *relevance*, in the sense of how the study is situated as something related to, yet needed within, an existing body of knowledge within the current community of music therapy and related disciplines (something typically demonstrated via the literature review). For Aigen (2012), it concerns *orienting the focus, research question, and research problem*, or the extent to which the purpose behind a research study is articulated, and the extent to which sources of various methods employed are identified.

As an example of evaluating contextualization, consider the fictitious study of musical and lyrical themes in group songwriting with persons recovering from substance dependence. Evaluating contextualization of the research formulation phase may entail an examination of how well the researcher's own relationship to, and experiences of, substance dependence (under both personal and professional circumstances) have been addressed—as well as how carefully the researcher's personal motives and cultural pretexts for conducting the study and for posing the research question have been considered, in light of who the researcher is (biographically, ethnically/racially, socioeconomically, etc.). Likewise, it may include an examination of how well the researcher has considered the group members' social histories of substance dependence and how they create, express, and experience writing songs, both as individuals and as part of a group. It may further include examination of how thoroughly the researcher has considered societal value systems imposed upon the matter of substance dependence, as well as upon those who have struggled with it. Finally, it could include an examination of how well the researcher has considered the role and value of the research focus and questions within the existing music therapy research literature, as well as any historical, sociocultural, and ideological implications of the study with respect to the research community, such as motives for research on chemical dependency and songwriting or attitudes on the research topic within the surrounding culture.

	Intersubjectivity	Groundedness
Formulation	Consulting with others concerning the value and implications of the research focus and questioning ways in which any feedback from others is utilized	Formulating the study in terms of constructions indigenous to circumstances surrounding the research
Participation	Consulting with others concerning the participant selection process, to honor the research purpose and general research integrity	Selection of participants representing the living circumstances (lifeworlds) of the topic(s) upon which the research is based
Information	Consulting with others concerning methods of data collection; consulting with participants on accuracy of data as recorded	Practicing prolonged engagement, persistent observation, triangulation, and fidelity to the natural unfolding of data as they are collected
Analysis	Consulting with others concerning methods of data processing; consulting with participants on meaningfulness of constructions derived from data	Consulting literature for relationships to research findings; practicing iterative processes when processing data; alignment between the nature of data analysis and the nature of the phenomena being studied
Interpretation	Consultation with others on the situatedness of interpreted findings in accordance with circumstances and environmental factors surrounding the research study	Traceability of interpreted findings back to the data in their original, lived circumstances
Presentation	Documentation with a style, form, and tone that resonate with lived, individual and sociocultural circumstances surrounding those involved in the research study; dialogical disposition with others in the process of presentation	Transparent disclosure of how findings are anchored in, and derived from, original data (including examples of data analysis, or *analytic frameworks*)

Table 2. Substantiation

Substantiation

Substantiation means to affirm as legitimate and authentic, based upon sufficient weight and strength of concordance with persons, phenomena, and available information. Trustworthiness in interpretivist research depends upon establishing and demonstrating an adequate substantive basis. Without it, a researcher's work can be construed as little more than their own ideas alone, colored by their own biases, and not anchored in any shared realities. Epistemologically, substantiation establishes solid foundations in forms of inquiry that acknowledge multiple constructions of reality. Substantiation, as will be described here, consists primarily of two major facets found in the literature on evaluating interpretivist research: *Intersubjectivity* and *Groundedness*.

Intersubjectivity is the degree of fidelity with which the researcher incorporates the perspectives of others throughout the various stages of the research. This includes those directly involved in the research (participants, research collaborators, etc.), as well as those not directly involved (external consultants, the literature, etc.). Terms that have been applied to intersubjectively substantiated interpretivist research include *confirmability* (Lincoln & Guba, 1985) and *neutrality* (Bruscia, 1995b). Approaches to supporting intersubjectivity may include collaboration with research participants, to which some have referred as *member-checking* (Aigen, 1995; Elliot et al., 1999), a procedure by which participants compare their own experiences and meanings with the ways in which the researcher represents and conveys research data and findings. (It is worthy of note that postanalysis member-checking—or consulting with participants after new constructions have been created—may or may not be considered appropriate, depending upon the researcher's perspectives, the role of the participants in constructing findings, and other circumstances.) Intersubjectivity may also be promoted via consultation with knowledgeable authorities or experts regarding research processes and practices, to which certain terms have been applied, such as *auditing* and *peer debriefing* (Aigen, 1995; Elliot et al., 1999; Hill, Knox, Thompson, Williams, Hess, & Ladany, 2005; Hill, Thompson, & Williams, 1997; Morrow & Smith, 2000; Stiles, 1993). Smeijsters (1996a) asserts that this form of consultation helps to reduce negative ramifications of the researcher's preconceptions about the research. Rossman and Rallis (2003) refer to a "community of practice," made up of knowledgeable colleagues for engaging in "critical and sustained discussion" (p. 69). Of course, consulting the literature is yet another means of intersubjectivity, as it expands the researcher's understanding of multiple ways of viewing the research (Morrow, 2005).

Both forms of intersubjective consultation (participants and peers) are more than one-way appraisals, typically involving a dynamic process of dialogue, support, guidance, feedback, scrutiny, uncovering, and arrival at new insights. It should be noted that intersubjectivity is not merely about the degree to which a researcher's work reflects what others think it should be (Aigen, 1995). The researcher is expected to be well oriented to the research process (Cobb & Hagemaster, 1987); thus, participants, peers, and any others who contribute to the intersubjectivity of the work are not merely imparting privileged understandings of the study's value that supplant those of the researcher, but also contributing meaningful perspectives on experiences, methods, and constructed findings, in the context of the purpose and scope of the research.

For Sandelowski and Barroso (2002), intersubjectivity is a matter of *validity*, calling for various forms of intersubjective consultation that should be a part of the research protocol and should be demonstrated in the report. For Stige et al. (2009), it is something that must be considered throughout implementation of the research in a general way, without reliance upon *technical fixes* (specific procedures of intersubjective consultation) alone. For Aigen (2012), it must be demonstrated in ways that are consistent with the nature of the research, regardless of the specific approach taken.

Groundedness refers to how well the researcher aligns certain aspects of research processes, data, and findings with the experiences of research participants and manifestations of research phenomena, under their original circumstances (Ansdell, 2002; Glaser & Strauss, 1967; Lincoln & Guba, 1990; Smeijsters, 1996a). This is based upon the interpretivist research ideal of *accommodating* the multiple realities of research participants and phenomena, as opposed to *assimilating* them into preconceived theories, methods, and research agendas (Bruscia, 1996, 1998; Stiles, 1993). Along these lines, it is important to address potentials for forced, contrived, or inauthentic constructions that fail to honor the natural realities of the research (Stige, 2002b). Groundedness is achieved through engaging and interacting with research data (Stige, 2002b) in systematic, purposive ways (Stiles, 1993) that maintain fidelity to the nature of the research phenomena it manifests in the lived world, as reported by participants and as experienced by the researcher (Bruscia, 1996, 1998), in terms of both form and process.

While collecting data, groundedness can be achieved through *prolonged engagement*, or the observation and study of research participants and phenomena across contexts and time (Lincoln & Guba, 1985); *persistent observation*, or the researcher's intensive involvement with research participants and phenomena (Lincoln & Guba, 1985), also known as *immersion* (Morrow, 2005); *triangulation*, or the consultation of multiple data sources (Aigen, 1995; Bruscia, 1995b; Elliot et al., 1999; Lincoln & Guba, 1985; Morrow & Smith, 2000; Rennie, 1995; Stiles, 1993); and *stepwise replication* (Guba, 1981), in which different researchers apply identical methods to gather data, involving different samples. While analyzing data, groundedness can be achieved through *iterative cycling*, or the alternation between data collection and data analysis in the process of formulating new constructions, meanings, theories, and so forth (Stiles, 1993), sometimes in pursuit of *saturation*, when additional data collection no longer yields any significantly new constructions (Glaser & Strauss, 1967). Groundedness is also informed by both adequate volume and diversity of evidence (Erickson, 1986; Morrow, 2005). When presenting the research, a number of mechanisms can help support groundedness. For example, the researcher may provide the reader with *analytic frameworks* (Morrow, 2005), or specific instances of how data are transformed into findings through analysis (e.g., as is practiced in phenomenology). Likewise, the researcher may take steps to provide a *thick description*, or convey data and findings with sufficient depth and detail to illustrate their unique, individual qualities (Lincoln & Guba, 1985; Morrow, 2005), and in ways faithful to the lived circumstances under which these qualities manifest (Geertz, 1993).

For Sandelowski and Barroso (2002), groundedness is a matter of numerous parts of the research process and documentation. It concerns the research *sample*, to the extent that sample size and configuration support claims of data saturation (as employed within grounded theory), or of intensiveness, comprehensiveness, or holism of findings; *data management*, to the extent that there is a clear plan for analytically linking components such as interviews, observations, documents, and/or artifact data sets; *data collection and sources*, to the extent that it is demonstrated how sources of data are the basis of the findings; *findings*, to the extent that it is demonstrated how interpretations of data are

plausible and/or sufficiently substantiated by data, and in how the data are analyzed and interpreted, including how variations are addressed; *discussion*, to the extent that findings can be linked to findings in other studies, or to other relevant literatures; and *validity*, to the extent that the distinctive limitations of the study are summarized in a transparent, trustworthy way that honestly delimits the scope of the study. For Stige et al. (2009), it is a matter of *engagement* as continuous interaction with persons and data and of *interpretation* as depth of detail in conveying derived meanings. For Aigen (2012), it is a matter of establishing a basis for constructed findings and interpretations in raw data (which renders the study not only more trustworthy, but also more readable and engaging).

As an example of evaluating substantiation, consider the fictitious study of musical and lyrical themes in group songwriting with persons recovering from substance dependence. Evaluating the formulation phase of the research may include the question of how the researcher has consulted others for feedback on the value of and justifiable grounds for the purpose of the inquiry (for intersubjectivity). Evaluating the information phase of the research may include the question of how the researcher has peer-debriefed, or consulted others with a working orientation to substance dependency and/or songwriting on the process of *gathering* song data (for intersubjectivity), and of the extent to which the researcher's engagement in the data collection has been

	Intersubjectivity	Groundedness
Formulation	Consulting with others concerning the value and implications of the research focus and questions; ways in which any feedback from others is utilized	Formulating the study in terms of constructions indigenous to circumstances surrounding the research
Participation	Consulting with others concerning the participant selection process, to honor the research purpose and general research integrity	Selection of participants representing the living circumstances (lifeworlds) of the topic(s) upon which the research is based
Information	Consulting with others concerning methods of data collection; consulting with participants on accuracy of data as recorded	Practicing prolonged engagement, persistent observation, triangulation, and fidelity to the natural unfolding of data as they are collected
Analysis	Consulting with others concerning methods of data processing; consulting with participants on meaningfulness of constructions derived from data	Consulting literature for relationships to research findings; practicing iterative processes when processing data; alignment between the nature of data analysis and the nature of the phenomena being studied
Interpretation	Consultation with others on the situatedness of interpreted findings in accordance with circumstances and environmental factors surrounding the research study	Traceability of interpreted findings back to the data in their original, lived circumstances
Presentation	Documentation with a style, form, and tone that resonate with lived, individual and sociocultural circumstances surrounding those involved in the research study; dialogical disposition with others in the process of presentation	Transparent disclosure of how findings are anchored in, and derived from, original data (including examples of data analysis, or *analytic frameworks*)

Table 3. Integration

sufficiently thorough and prolonged (for groundedness). In addition, it may include the question of how well the researcher has conducted member-checking in order to ascertain how participants feel about the representation of the data (for intersubjectivity), as well as the question of how well the researcher has triangulated with other persons or sources of data (for groundedness). Finally, evaluating the analysis phase of the research may involve questions such as how well the researcher has implemented additional member-checking after processing the data into new constructions (for intersubjectivity), as well as how well the researcher has implemented iterative cycling in the construction of musical and lyrical themes from the data, while in the midst of the group process itself and while seeking evidence of category saturation (for groundedness).

Integration

Integration means the procedural and structural coherence, as well as the artistic virtue of the research process, findings, and report. This is an essential dimension by which interpretivist research must be evaluated, as the purpose of enlarging meaningful constructions of knowledge transcends the matter of functionality alone. Just as architecture serves as space in which to conduct human affairs—domestic, professional, communal, or otherwise—its structural integrity and balance are inextricable from its very humanity. Several key aspects of integration are congruence, comprehensibility, and aesthetic depth.

Congruence is the degree to which the various components of a given study—its purpose, method, findings, and report, along with the researcher's own understandings, values, and paradigmatic orientation—all align as a cohesive, harmonious whole. A study that is congruent demonstrates resonance with, and is perpetually guided by, the researcher's sense of her or his own intentions, values, and ideals (Bruscia, 1998; Stiles, 1993)—all of which must manifest clearly and steadfastly throughout the research process, findings, and report. This sort of internal consistency helps to prevent duplicity, diffusion, and obfuscation of intent or purpose and averts use of incompatible paradigms or theoretical frameworks. Congruent studies also cogently demonstrate methodological appropriateness, accommodating the study purpose (Aigen, 1995; Bruscia, 1996; Cobb & Hagemaster, 1987; Elliot et al., 1999) with a deliberate, noncontrived approach consistent with the specific aims of the research (Bruscia, 1996; Stige, 2002b).

For Sandelowski and Barroso (2002), congruence is a matter of numerous parts of the research process and documentation. It concerns the research *problem*, to the extent that there is a discernible problem that led to the study and that is related to the research purpose and/or the literature review; *literature review*, to the extent that it is related to the research problem and shows a discernible logic that points toward the research purpose; *mind-set toward the target*

phenomenon, to the extent that the theoretical frame fits (and is not forced onto) the target phenomenon; *method*, to the extent that it fits the research purpose; *sampling strategy and technique*, to the extent that it fits the purpose and method, including the site where sampling occurs; *sample*, to the extent that the sample size and configuration fit the purpose and sampling strategy and that sites of recruitment fit the evolving needs of the study; *data collection techniques and sources*, to the extent that they fit the purpose and mind-sets of the study, that specific data collection techniques are tailored to the reported study, that the sequence and timing of data collection strategies fit the purpose and mind-sets of the study, and that alterations in techniques fit the evolving needs of the study; *data management*, to the extent that techniques fit the purposes and data and that specific data management techniques are tailored to the reported study; *findings*, to the extent that they address the research purpose and that data analysis fits the nature of the data; *discussion*, to the extent that discussion of findings is based upon the study findings described in the report; *validity*, to the extent that techniques for validation fit the purpose, method, sample, data, and findings and are tailored to the reported study; and *form*, to the extent that (a) the overall literary style of the study fits its purpose, method, and findings, (b) elements of the research report are placed where readers are likely to find them, (c) there is a coherent logic to the presentation of findings, (d) there are visual displays, quotes, cases, and numbers that clarify, summarize, substantiate, or otherwise illuminate the findings, (d) themes or concepts are presented in a comparative and parallel fashion, and (e) titles of paper and section headers reflect the content in the paper and sections. For Stige et al. (2009), it is a matter of *processing*, in terms of organization and expression. (Questions concerning these aspects include: How clear is the research focus? How effectively is the empirical material systematized, analyzed, and presented? How clear are the researcher's position and perspective? How effectively is the empirical material processed and presented, through both text and any other expressive media?) For Aigen (2012), it is a matter of the alignment between focus and method, of consistent application of method, of compatibility among any multiple methods, and of consistency among the form of findings, research focus, and research method.

Comprehensibility is the extent to which the research report is accessible and understandable both to those directly involved in the research and to others with interests in the research and its findings (Glaser & Strauss, 1967). Comprehensibility also concerns how well the report is understood by audiences both within and outside of the central discipline featured in the research. A researcher may promote comprehensibility by ensuring that the study purpose is clear (Cobb & Hagemaster, 1987) and that the theoretical frameworks are explicit (Glaser & Strauss, 1967). Likewise, the researcher may accomplish this by adequately articulating sampling procedures and sample characteristics

(Cobb & Hagemaster, 1987) and presenting data in an organized and accessible manner (Cobb & Hagemaster, 1987; Stige, 2002b). Essentially, the report must carefully and deliberately accommodate the reader. As Aigen (1996b) states: "Instead of establishing the necessary connections to readers in an oblique or unconscious way, we recognize the importance of directly and overtly accessing our readers' body of assumptions and common experiences in order to make the full meaning of the research document available to them" (p. 12).

For Sandelowski and Barroso (2002), comprehensibility is a matter of numerous parts of the research process and documentation. It concerns the research *problem*, to the extent that it is accurately depicted; *purposes and questions*, to the extent that these are discernible; *mind-set toward the phenomenon*, to the extent that a frame of reference is explicit and accurately rendered; *method*, to the extent that it is explicit and accurately rendered; *sampling strategy and techniques*, to the extent that these are described and accurately rendered; *sample*, to the extent that features of the sample critical to the understanding of findings are described; *data collection techniques and sources*, to the extent that the time period for data collection is explicitly stated; *data management*, to the extent that techniques are described and are accurately rendered; *findings*, to the extent that a set of results

distinguishable from the data and other components of the study is discernible and to the extent that concepts or ideas are well-developed, precise, and meaningfully linked; and *form*, to the extent that there is a coherent logic to the presentation of findings and other components. For Stige et al. (2009), it is a matter of *processing*, in terms of organization and expression of the work (questions concerning these aspects include the same ones posed under *comprehensibility*, above). For Aigen (2012), it is a matter of *method*, in terms of how it is described (including articulation of the rationale for applying it), how well its variations are sufficiently distinguished, how well selection criteria are specified, how well data-gathering procedures are described, and how well data analysis is described (and, preferably, illustrated or demonstrated); it is also a matter of *findings*, to the extent that distinct types of categories are differentiated.

Aesthetic depth is the artistic virtue of the research process and report. Interpretivist research involves an artistic (as opposed to scientific) way of knowing (Bruscia, 1998; Eisner, 1985). Aesthetic depth is composed of emotional, intuitive, and value-centered dimensions (Aigen, 1996b), particularly when art (i.e., the music in music therapy) is a prominent part of the inquiry. Findings themselves can be communicated utilizing numerous artistic means, such as novels, poems, pottery, drama, and dance (Eisner, 1985; Norris, 1997;

	Usefulness	Durability
Formulation	Value of the research to researcher (personally and professionally), participants (in terms of raised awareness, personal development, social empowerment, etc.), and society as a whole (via contributions to practical knowledge of one or more disciplines that serve that society)	Stability of meaning of the findings and value of those findings, across multiple iterations of research method and/or multiple contexts
Participation	Value of the research to potential participants and inclusiveness of participants with potential interests in the research; evident, shared contexts between participants in the study and those involved in past or future related studies	Applicability of the experiences of research participants to other contexts beyond the study
Information	Relevance of data to the welfare of the various stakeholders in the research and/or to society in general; data collected via multiple iterations (stepwise replication)	Evident relationships between data collection method in the research study and in other, related studies; applicability of data beyond their indigenous context(s)
Analysis	Relevance of constructed findings to the well-being of the study's stakeholders; evident relationships between manner of constructing findings in the research study and in other related studies	Applicability of constructed findings to contexts beyond the research study
Interpretation	Pertinence of interpreted findings to the interests of stakeholders and/or to the enrichment of society	Compatibility of interpreted findings with those of other related studies; interpretations endure in the face of challenge and scrutiny
Presentation	Applied value of findings and conclusions, as presented	Documentation of research in a manner establishing stability of findings, across replications and applications in diverse contexts

Table 4. Utilization

Richardson, 2000b). Yet, arts-oriented criteria can be applied to the written, interpretivist research report as well, such as coherence, attractiveness, and economy. A reader may consider findings and other aspects of a research report vivid, lifeless, coherent, confusing, novel, pedestrian, or as ringing true or false (Eisner, 1985) and is thereby rendering a judgment that is both personal and communal (Bochner, 2000; Richardson, 2000a) and, of course, aesthetic (Lynch & Edgerton, 1988).

Thus, the integrity of interpretivist research must, in some way, be evaluated according to the rigors of art. Interpretivist music therapy research presents the challenge of conveying dimensions of music experience in words (Stige, 2002b) that are neither reductionist nor contrived and in beautiful ways that do justice to the richness of the experiences (Ansdell, 2002). This can, at times, mean incorporating artistic, creative expression into the research report, in such a way that informs with elegance, grace, flow, poignancy, and economy of expression. The data preparation and analysis phase of research can play an important role in supporting both the orderedness (via sorting and organization) and economy (via culling and elimination) dimensions of aesthetic depth. Of course, the presentation phrase is perhaps the most prominent with respect to aesthetic depth. Aesthetically integrated research reports are compelling and convincing (Glaser & Strauss, 1967) and resonate with the reader (Elliot et al., 1999), through employment of richly detailed descriptions and meaningful presentation of topics, foci, findings, and theories (Aigen, 1995). In arts-based expressions of interpretivist research, aesthetic sensibilities should, as an axiological principle, be evident in all phases of the research (Viega, 2016; Viega & Forinash, 2016). Specific standards for judging the integrity of the arts-based research have been suggested (Barone & Eisner, 2012) (see Chapter 44 in this book for details).

Bruscia (1998) proposes several aspects by which aesthetic depth in interpretivist music therapy research can be evaluated. One is *creativity*, or the degree to which the researcher generates new possibilities for being on behalf of participants, audience, and self, as well as new possibilities for manifestations of the study phenomenon. Another is *structural beauty*, or the economy, clarity, cohesion, harmony, balance, and wholeness of the research. A third is *expressive beauty*, or the poignancy and imagination of the research report, including the effective use of creative media. As an extension of this third standard, Stige (2002b) suggests the need for nonconventional manuscript format guidelines for interpretivist research reports due to the highly individual, creative, and sometimes arts-based nature of these reports.

For Stige et al. (2009), aesthetic depth is a matter of *processing*, in terms of organization and expression of the work (questions concerning these aspects include the same ones posed under *comprehensibility* above).

As an example of evaluating integration, consider the fictitious study of musical and lyrical themes in group songwriting with persons recovering from substance dependence. Evaluating the presentation phase of the research may include the question of the internal consistency of the research report, which helps the reader to clearly apprehend the relationships among participants, their songs, and the emergent themes (for congruence); the clarity, organization, and accessibility of the writing suited for specific and/or multiple audiences, including, for example, members of recovery communities (for comprehensibility); and the creativity, structural beauty, and expressive beauty of the report, properly honoring the artistic work of the participants (for aesthetic depth).

Utilization

Utilization refers to the strength of research—both the study and its findings—as put into action and use. It centrally concerns the relevance, meaningfulness, and novelty of the knowledge generated through the process of inquiry. It also extends to the social impact of the inquiry and findings. Moreover, utilization can be evaluated according to how well the virtues of the inquiry and findings remain intact, as applied across multiple contexts and over time. Two major components of utilization are *usefulness* and *durability*.

Usefulness is the applied value of interpretivist research (Polkinghorne, 1983). Interpretivist research should generate outcomes of variation, breadth, and depth sufficient to enlarge the constructions and human potentials of the participants, the researcher, and others (Bruscia, 1998). Research findings should contribute to practical knowledge within a discipline (Cobb & Hagemaster, 1987; Polkinghorne, 1983; Stige, 2002a) and should be applicable to everyday contexts (Stiles, 1993). One specific way in which interpretivist research can be useful is in its promotion of theory development (Cobb & Hagemaster, 1987), particularly when it is applicable to everyday, lived situations (Glaser & Strauss, 1967). Interpretivist research can also be useful by raising awareness and empowering participants, researchers, members of disciplines, and society to engage in meaningful and constructive action (Guba & Lincoln, 1989; Stige, 2002a; Stiles, 1993).

For Sandelowski and Barroso (2002), usefulness is a matter of *findings*, to the extent that the results offer new information about, insight into, or formulation of the target phenomenon and that the findings are relevant for contemporary use; of *discussion*, to the extent that clinical, policy, theoretical, disciplinary, and/or other significance of the findings is thoughtfully considered; and of *form*, to the extent that the report fits the audience for whom it was intended. For Stige et al. (2009), it is a matter of *critique*, to the extent that the work is socially transformative; of *usefulness* (Stige et al.'s own category), to the extent that the work serves the human potential interests of various stakeholders, and of *relevance*, to the extent that the findings are applicable in any number of ways. Viega (2016) emphasizes this point concerning socially transformational value from the perspective of arts-based research. For Aigen (2012), it is a matter of the extent to which the raw data have been sufficiently analyzed and interpreted in order to produce interesting and valuable findings (versus remaining in an unfinished state).

Durability is the resilience and robustness of an interpretivist research study and its findings when put into use in various ways. This includes its *dependability*, or the consistency and stability of the general meaning of findings, throughout the stepwise replication (i.e., repeated application) of the research method (Lincoln & Guba, 1985), including shifting modes of data collection (Bruscia, 1995b). It also includes its *transferability* (Lincoln & Guba, 1985) or *permeability* (Stiles, 1993), in which the study and the general meaning of the findings stand up to reformulation in response to factual variations (Wertz, 1986) and contextual variations (Glaser & Strauss, 1967), beyond those indigenous to the participant life worlds or circumstances of the study. In addition, it includes the capacity of the findings to endure in the face of *negative cases*, or new instances of the study phenomenon that fail to conform with any of the existing category schemes, theories, or other conceptual frameworks in the findings (Guba & Lincoln, 1989; Lincoln & Guba, 1985). Related terms for this phenomenon include *disconfirming evidence* or *discrepant cases* (Erickson, 1986; Morrow, 2005). In addition to offering an opportunity for demonstrating the strength of findings by standing up to the challenge of divergent evidence, the negative case can enhance the durability of the findings by establishing secure boundaries around a conceptual framework concerning the findings (by better defining its limits).

For Sandelowski and Barroso (2002), durability is a matter of validity, to the extent that techniques for validation are correctly used (and that nonconforming cases and evidence are embraced rather than rejected).

As an example of evaluating utilization, consider the fictitious study of musical and lyrical themes in group songwriting with persons recovering from substance dependence. Evaluating the interpretation phase of the research may include the question of the extent to which the interpretations of findings are directly applicable to the empowerment of individuals involved in drug rehabilitation and other recovery-based services for chemical dependency and the extent to which they may inform future clinical work employing group songwriting and other means of promoting recovery via creative interpersonal processes (for usefulness). Evaluating this phase for utilization may also examine the compatibility of interpretations of the study's findings with those of a related study on music and substance dependence and how well the interpretations maintain their validity even in the face of negative cases—for example, an interpretation of "powerlessness" associated with a constructed category of "giving in to substance cravings" maintaining its meaningfulness in spite of an alternative interpretation by a different researcher, who attributes to giving in a sense of

"power" (for durability). Evaluating the presentation phase of the research may involve the question of how accessibly the report reads to those who stand to benefit the study's findings (for usefulness) and how the report's permeability allows for continued meaningfulness across different disciplinary contexts, such as professional music, healthcare, public health policy, and so forth (for durability).

Responsibility

Responsibility, as the term is being applied here, means ethical integrity in interpretivist research. It means working with participants in ways that are just, equitable, and both individually and culturally sensitive. This aspect has been assigned considerable evaluative weight as a core concern in the interpretivist research literature (Guba & Lincoln, 1989, 1994). Pertaining specifically to music therapy research, the American Music Therapy Association has established a set of basic guidelines for responsible research in its *Code of Ethics* (AMTA, 2014), whereas individual scholars such as Dileo (2000) have articulated various dimensions of this topic in greater depth.

According to Bruscia (1998), the interpretivist researcher must maintain a genuine concern for the welfare of all persons involved in the study, throughout all phases of research. This consists of honoring human rights by preventing harm to anyone's humanity, such as any form of manipulation, coercion, exploitation, abuse, gratuitous or malevolent critique, misuse of researcher privilege, and so forth. In interpretivist research, honoring the humanity and agency of participants is part of responsible inquiry. This means acknowledging that participants are not merely *knowns*, but are also *knowers*, and engage with the researcher in a sort of participatory consciousness (Heshusius, 1994), or connected knowing, in which *being with* participants replaces simply observing participants as objects (Belenky, Clinchy, Goldberger, & Tarule, 1986).

Ethical research also requires a concern for the well-being of other elements of the research, such as the phenomenon being studied and the study itself. Participants give of their time and energy and undergo some manner of risk by virtue of serving a participant—therefore, the design and implementation of the research must be optimized. As part of weighing the relative risks for human participants against the benefits of the research, the research protocol should be reviewed by an Institutional Review Board, or IRB (a requirement for any research conducted under the auspices of a U.S. institution receiving federal aid of any kind), including an evaluation of factors such as confidentiality, coercion, and informed consent. Because some interpretivist research involves emergent design (or a design that evolves during the implementation of the actual research), ongoing consultation with an IRB may be necessary. Approval by an IRB, along with other ethical precautions exercised by the researcher, should be documented in the written research report. Beyond formal, sanctioned approval of the planned protocol (such as by an IRB), the researcher must take responsibility for her or his own actions throughout the actual implementation of the research process (Bruscia, 1996, 1998), requiring ongoing self-inquiry and conscientiousness that combines contextualizing the researcher (as described previously in this chapter) and ethical care.

For Sandelowski and Barroso (2002), responsibility is a matter of (a) issues and practices relating to the recruitment, retention, and well-being of human participants in a study, including how participants were approached and enrolled for a study, informed consent procedures, risks and benefits to which participants were subjected, inducements and protections offered, and ways in which participants responded to participation in the study; (b) risks and benefits distinctive to the study (as opposed to textbook or rote descriptions of human subjects issues without consideration of their particular relevance to the reported study); (c) recruitment and consent techniques and how well they were tailored to fit the sensitivity of the subject matter and/or vulnerability of subjects; (d) data collection and management techniques and how well they were tailored to fit the sensitivity of the subject matter and/or vulnerability of subjects; and (e) representation of the participants, and how fairly this is accomplished in the research report. For Stige et al. (2009), it is a matter of *ethics*. (Questions concerning these aspects include: To what extent is the research process respectful to participants? How effectively does the researcher demonstrate awareness of consequences that the research poses? How does the researcher manage issues such as confidentiality and informed consent? What are the hierarchical relationships between participants and researcher? And, to what degree is diversity of interests and perspectives within the group of participants conveyed?)

As an example of evaluating responsibility, consider the fictitious study of musical and lyrical themes in group songwriting with persons recovering from substance dependence. Evaluating the participation phase of the research may include the question of how well the researcher conducted recruitment in a sensitive and equitable manner, by averting coercion and consenting participants (persons with substance dependence) via materials that articulate risks and benefits. Likewise, evaluating the analysis phase may include considerations of whether data were stored and handled securely and with confidentiality and whether the song data were analyzed in a manner honoring the human genesis of the songs in their lived, social context (as opposed to treating those data as dehumanized objects).

Conclusion

The various categories of interpretivist music therapy research evaluation identified here raise a number of questions and carry a number of implications. One question concerns whether evaluation of interpretivist music therapy research can be based upon general standards or whether it must always be based upon standards indigenous to music therapy. For example, given that music therapy is composed of the elements of music, health, and therapeutic relationship, one could argue that contextualization in interpretivist music therapy research must always include the researcher's self-awareness about her or his relationships to music, health, and persons. Likewise, given that music therapy is an intrinsically aesthetic phenomenon, one could argue that the aesthetic depth component of integrity must always apply to the evaluation of interpretivist music therapy research.

Another issue concerns the question of who exactly has the authority to evaluate interpretivist music therapy

Formulation	Study framed in a manner considering the well-being and humanity of research participants; study framed in a manner demonstrating care and concern for the phenomenon and study; process of framing the research self-monitored
Participation	Welfare and humanity of participants considered throughout selection and recruitment process; fairness and equitability of selection and recruitment; process of selection and recruitment self-monitored; formal, sanctioned approval of research protocol, such as by an IRB
Information	Welfare and humanity of participants protected throughout collection and handling of data; process of data collection process self-monitored
Analysis	Security of data management; acknowledgment of humanity embodied in data throughout analysis process; thoroughness and care in data analysis that reflects care and concern for the research phenomenon and study; process of data analysis self-monitored
Interpretation	Process of interpretation rooted in the humanity of the participants and the research phenomenon; process of interpretation self-monitored
Presentation	Welfare and humanity of participants protected in the documentation and reporting of the research and its findings, including matters of confidentiality and/or anonymity; thorough documentation and reporting of all ethical precautions exercised by the researcher; documentation and reporting of formal, sanctioned approval of research protocol, such as by an IRB

Table 5. Responsibility

research. According to Bruscia (1995a, 1996), it is the researcher who appraises the design and implementation of the research, makes revisions if needed, and is ultimately responsible for how consistently and coherently she or he has maintained and expressed her or his intentions and values through the research. For Aigen (1996a), this intrasubjective perspective "relieves us from the impossible task of becoming 'authenticity police' judging fellow researchers" (p. 169). In contrast to intrasubjective perspectives on accountability, culture-centered, or intersubjective, perspectives hold that evaluation of research must unfold within the collective set of values in a culture (Stige, 2002a, 2002b). Thus, evaluative authority may depend upon perspective and circumstances surrounding a given application of inquiry.

A final issue concerns the establishment of comprehensive standards for evaluation of interpretivist music therapy research. While such a set of meta-criteria might be helpful in some ways, the potential context insensitivity might fail to acknowledge the complexity and multifaceted nature of the research, hence impeding potentially meaningful discovery. As a result of considerations such as these, Bernstein (1976, 1983) argues for *nonfoundational* ways of evaluating research, or evaluation without any fixed sets of standards. On the other hand, to avoid the perils of utter relativism, this sort of approach should be accompanied by dynamic dialogues among stakeholders in the evaluation, so that each may contribute to some form of common, shared consensus. Moreover, it is worthy of note that evaluating interpretivist research (particularly when concerning the arts) may require certain unconventional modes of awareness on the part of the evaluator(s). Braud (1998), for example, suggests modes of awareness rooted in emotions, intuition, bodily wisdom, and other sensibilities. In conclusion, it is the author's hope that further exploration through dialogue and practical application will lead to more integrated, well-informed, and sophisticated understandings of interpretivist music therapy research evaluation.

References

Abrams, B. (2005). Evaluating qualitative music therapy research. In B. Wheeler (Ed.), *Music therapy research* (2nd ed.; pp. 246–258). Gilsum, NH: Barcelona.

Aigen, K. (1995). Principles of qualitative research. In B. L. Wheeler (Ed.), *Music therapy research: Quantitative and qualitative perspectives* (pp. 283–311). Gilsum, NH: Barcelona.

Aigen, K. (1996a). The researcher's cultural identity. In M. Langenberg, K. Aigen, & J. Frommer (Eds.), *Qualitative music therapy research: Beginning dialogues* (pp. 165–176). Gilsum, NH: Barcelona.

Aigen, K. (1996b). The role of values in qualitative research. In M. Langenberg, K. Aigen, & J. Frommer (Eds.), *Qualitative music therapy research: Beginning dialogues* (pp. 9–33). Gilsum, NH: Barcelona.

Aigen, K. (2012). Publishing qualitative research in the *Nordic Journal of Music Therapy:* Guidelines for authors, reviewers, and editors for evaluating manuscripts. *Nordic Journal of Music Therapy, 21*(2), 109–110. doi:10.1080/08098131.2012.685274 (supplementary material available at http://www.tandfonline.com/doi/suppl/10.1080/08098131.2012.685274/suppl_file/rnjm_a_685274_sup_25596220.pdf)

Aldridge, D. (2002, May 3). *The politics of qualitative research criteria: A local solution within an ecosystemic ecology.* Message posted to forum topic, General Criteria for the Evaluation of Qualitative Research Articles, Forum: *Nordic Journal of Music Therapy,* http://www.hisf.no/njmt/forumqualart_3.html

American Music Therapy Association. (2014). *Code of ethics.* Retrieved from http://www.musictherapy.org/about/ethics/

American Music Therapy Association. (2015). *Journal of Music Therapy: Instructions to Authors.* http://www.oxfordjournals.org/our_journals/jmt/for_authors/

Ansdell, G. (2002, May 27). *Goethe's response: On qualifying the qualifiers.* Message posted to forum topic, General Criteria for the Evaluation of Qualitative Research Articles, Forum: *Nordic Journal of Music Therapy,* https://njmt.b.uib.no/nordic-journal-of-music-therapy/forum-online-discussions-1998-2006/general-criteria-for-the-evaluation-of-qualitative-research-articles/

Barone, T., & Eisner, E. W. (2012). *Arts-based research.* Los Angeles, CA: Sage.

Belenky, M. F., Clinchy, B. M., Goldberger, N. R., & Tarule, J. M. (1986). *Women's ways of knowing: The development of self, voice, and mind.* New York, NY: Basic Books.

Bernstein, R. J. (1976). *The restructuring of social and political theory.* Philadelphia, PA: University of Pennsylvania Press.

Bernstein, R. J. (1983). *Beyond objectivism and relativism: Science, hermeneutics, and praxis.* Philadelphia, PA: University of Pennsylvania Press.

Bochner, A. P. (2000). Criteria against ourselves. *Qualitative Inquiry, 6,* 266–272. doi:10.1177/107780040000600209

Braud, W. (1998). An expanded view of validity. In W. Braud & R. Anderson (Eds.), *Transpersonal research methods for the social sciences: Honoring human experience* (pp. 213–237). Thousand Oaks, CA: Sage.

Bruscia, K. E. (1995a). The process of doing qualitative research: Part I: Introduction. In B. L. Wheeler (Ed.), *Music therapy research: Quantitative and qualitative perspectives* (pp. 389–399). Gilsum, NH: Barcelona.

Bruscia, K. E. (1995b). The process of doing qualitative research: Part II: Procedural steps. In B. L. Wheeler (Ed.), *Music therapy research: Quantitative and qualitative perspectives* (pp. 401–427). Gilsum, NH: Barcelona.

Bruscia, K. E. (1996). Authenticity issues in qualitative

research. In M. Langenberg, K. Aigen, & J. Frommer (Eds.), *Qualitative music therapy research: Beginning dialogues* (pp. 81–107). Gilsum, NH: Barcelona.

Bruscia, K. E. (1998). Standards of integrity for qualitative music therapy research. *Journal of Music Therapy, 35*, 176–200. doi:10.1093/jmt/35.3.176

Bruscia, K. E. (2003). Editorial review form. *Qualitative Inquiries in Music Therapy* [research monograph series]. Unpublished manuscript.

Cobb, A. K., & Hagemaster, J. N. (1987). Ten criteria for evaluating qualitative research proposals. *Journal of Nursing Education, 26*, 138–143.

Creswell, J. (1998). *Qualitative inquiry and research design: Choosing among five traditions.* Thousand Oaks, CA: Sage.

Dileo, C. (2000). *Ethical thinking in music therapy.* Cherry Hill, NJ: Jeffrey Books.

Edwards, J. (2002, June 4). *Another contribution to the forum.* Message posted to forum topic, General Criteria for the Evaluation of Qualitative Research Articles, Forum: *Nordic Journal of Music Therapy,* http://www.hisf.no/njmt/forumqualart_3.html

Eisner, E. (1985). Aesthetic modes of knowing. In E. Eisner (Ed.), *Learning and teaching the ways of knowing: Eighty-fourth yearbook of the National Society for the Study of Education, Part II* (pp. 23–36). Chicago, IL: National Society of the Study of Education.

Eisner, E. (1991). *The enlightened eye: Qualitative inquiry and the enhancement of educational practice.* New York, NY: Macmillan.

Elliot, R., Fischer, C. T., & Rennie, D. L. (1999). Evolving guidelines for publication of qualitative research studies in psychology and related fields. *British Journal of Clinical Psychology, 38*, 215–229. doi:10.1348/014466599162782

Erickson, F. (1986). Qualitative methods in research on teaching. In M. Wittrock (Ed.), *Handbook of research on teaching* (3rd ed.; pp. 119–161). New York, NY: Macmillan.

Fine, M. (1992). *Disruptive voices: The possibilities of feminist research.* Ann Arbor, MI: University of Michigan Press.

Geertz, C. (1993). *The interpretation of cultures.* London, UK: Fontana Press.

Glaser, B. G., & Strauss, A. L. (1967). *The discovery of grounded theory: Strategies for qualitative research.* New York, NY: Aldine De Gruyter.

Guba, E. G. (1981). Criteria for assessing the trustworthiness of naturalistic inquiries. *Educational Communication and Technology Journal, 29*, 75–92. doi:10.1007/BF02766777

Guba, E. G., & Lincoln, Y. S. (1989). *Fourth generation evaluation.* Newbury Park, CA: Sage.

Guba, E. G., & Lincoln, Y. S. (1994). Competing paradigms in qualitative research. In N. K. Denzin & Y. S. Lincoln (Eds.), *Handbook of qualitative research* (pp. 105–117). Thousand Oaks, CA: Sage.

Heshusius, L. (1994). Freeing ourselves from objectivity: Managing subjectivity or turning toward a participatory mode of consciousness? *Educational Researcher, 23*(3), 15–22. doi:10.3102/0013189X023003015

Hiles, D. R. (2008). Axiology. In L. M. Givens (Ed.), *Sage encyclopedia of qualitative research methods* (Vols. 1 & 2; pp. 52–56). Los Angeles, CA: Sage.

Hill, C. E., Knox, S., Thompson, B. J., Williams, E. N., Hess, S. A., & Ladany, N. (2005). Consensual qualitative research: An update. *Journal of Counseling Psychology, 52*, 196–205. doi:10.1037/0022-0167.52.2.196

Hill, C. E., Thompson, B. J., & Williams, E. N. (1997). A guide to conducting consensual qualitative research. *The Counseling Psychologist, 25*, 517–572. doi:10.1177/0011000097254001

Jackson, P. W. (1990). Looking for trouble: On the place of the ordinary in educational studies. In E. W. Eisner & A. Peshkin (Eds.), *Qualitative inquiry in education: The continuing debate.* New York, NY: Teachers College Press.

Lincoln, Y. S. (1995, April). *Emerging criteria for quality in qualitative and interpretive research.* Keynote address presented at the annual meeting of the American Educational Research Association, San Francisco, CA.

Lincoln, Y. S., & Guba, E. G. (1985). *Naturalistic inquiry.* Beverly Hills, CA: Sage.

Lincoln, Y. S., & Guba, E. G. (1990). Judging the quality of case study reports. *Qualitative Studies in Education, 3*, 53–59. doi:10.1080/0951839900030105

Lynch, M., & Edgerton, S. Y. (1988). Aesthetics and digital image processing: Representational craft in contemporary astronomy. In G. Fyfe & J. Law (Eds.), *Picturing power: Visual depiction and social relations* (pp. 184–220). London, UK: Routledge.

Morrow, S. L. (2005). Quality and trustworthiness in qualitative research in counseling psychology. *Journal of Counseling Psychology, 52*(2), 250–260. doi:10.1037/0022-0167.52.2.250

Morrow, S. L., & Smith, M. L. (2000). Qualitative research for counseling psychology. In S. D. Brown & R. W. Lent (Eds.), *Handbook of counseling psychology* (3rd ed.; pp. 199–230). New York, NY: Wiley.

Norris, J. R. (1997). Meaning through form: Alternative modes of knowledge representation. In J. M. Morse (Ed.), *Completing a qualitative project: Details and dialogue* (pp. 87–115). Thousand Oaks, CA: Sage.

Peshkin, A. (1988). In search of subjectivity—One's own. *Educational Researcher, 17*(7), 17–21. doi:10.3102/0013189X017007017

Polkinghorne, D. (1983). *Methodology for the human sciences: Systems of inquiry.* Albany, NY: State University of New York Press.

Popay, J., Rogers, A., & Williams, G. (1998). Rationale and standards for the systematic review of qualitative literature in health services research. *Qualitative Health Research, 8*, 341–351. doi:10.1177/104973239800800305

Reicher, S. (2000). Against methodolatry: Some comments

on Elliott, Fischer, and Rennie. *British Journal of Clinical Psychology, 39*, 1–6. doi:10.1348/014466500163031

Rennie, D. L. (1995). Plausible constructionism as the rigor of qualitative research. *Methods: A Journal for Human Science, Annual Edition*, 42–58.

Rennie, D. L. (2004). Reflexivity and person-centered counseling. *Journal of Humanistic Psychology, 44*, 182–203. doi:10.1177/0022167804263066

Richardson, L. (2000a). Evaluating ethnography. *Qualitative Inquiry, 6*, 253–255. doi:10.1177/ 107780040000600207

Richardson, L. (2000b). Writing: A method of inquiry. In N. K. Denzin & Y. S. Lincoln (Eds.), *Handbook of qualitative research* (2nd ed.; pp. 923–948). Thousand Oaks, CA: Sage.

Rolvsjord, R. (2010). *Resource-Oriented Music Therapy in mental health care*. Gilsum, NH: Barcelona.

Rossman, G. B., & Rallis, S. F. (2003). *Learning in the field: An introduction to qualitative research*. Thousand Oaks, CA: Sage.

Sandelowski, M., & Barroso, J. (2002). Reading qualitative studies. *International Journal of Qualitative Methods, 1*(1), 1–47.

Smeijsters, H. (1996a). Qualitative research in music therapy: New contents, new concepts, or both? In M. Langenberg, K. Aigen, & J. Frommer (Eds.), *Qualitative music therapy research: Beginning dialogues* (pp. 179–188). Gilsum, NH: Barcelona.

Smeijsters, H. (1996b). Qualitative single-case research in practice: A necessary, reliable, and valid alternative for music therapy research. In M. Langenberg, K. Aigen, & J. Frommer (Eds.), *Qualitative music therapy research: Beginning dialogues* (pp. 35–53). Gilsum, NH: Barcelona.

Stige, B. (2002a). *Culture-Centered Music Therapy*. Gilsum, NH: Barcelona.

Stige, B. (2002b, April 26). Do we need general criteria for the evaluation of qualitative research articles, and if we do, how could such criteria be formulated? Message posted to forum topic, General Criteria for the Evaluation of Qualitative Research Articles, Forum: *Nordic Journal of Music Therapy*, http://www.hisf.no/njmt/forumqualart_3.html

Stige, B., Malterud, K., & Midtgarden, T. (2009). Toward an agenda for evaluation of qualitative research. *Qualitative Health Research, 19*(10), 1504–1516. doi:10.1177/1049732309348501

Stiles, W. B. (1993). Quality control in qualitative research. *Clinical Psychology Review, 13*, 593–618. doi:10.1016/0272-7358(93)90048-Q

Tashakkori, A., & Teddlie, C. (Eds.). (2010). *Sage handbook of mixed methods in social & behavioral research* (2nd Ed.). Thousand Oaks, CA: Sage.

Tierney, W. G. (1995). (Re)presentation and voice. *Qualitative Inquiry, 1*, 379–390. doi:10.1177/107780049500100401

Viega, M. (2016a). Science of art: Axiology as the central component in methodology and evaluation of arts-based research (ABR). *Music Therapy Perspectives, 34*(1), 4-13. doi:10.1093/mtp/miv035

Wertz, F. J. (1986). The question of the reliability of psychological research. *Journal of Phenomenological Psychology, 17*, 181–205. doi:10.1163/156916286X00204

Wheeler, B. L. (Ed.). (2005). *Music therapy research* (2nd ed.). Gilsum, NH: Barcelona.

Wilber, K. (1997). *The eye of spirit: An integral vision for a world gone slightly mad*. Boston, MA: Shambhala.

1. This chapter represents a reformulation of a chapter on this topic (Abrams, 2005) included in the prior edition of the present text (Wheeler, 2005).

Chapter 19

READING, WRITING, AND SUBMITTING OBJECTIVIST RESEARCH

Anthony Meadows

Writing for publication is a complex, organic process. Intimidating for some, energizing for others, it draws upon all your skills and resources: clinical, theoretical, methodological, statistical, and ethical. Some researchers call it a process of discovery; others, a series of puzzle pieces, where all the elements join together to create a whole. Writing always involves being in *the unknown* and often involves feeling inadequate, as the process itself challenges different parts of you in different ways. Some writers are beautiful language crafters but struggle to structure concepts to give an overall picture of their research, whereas others have a clear sense of the overall concepts but struggle to be disciplined writers. Each of us has our own particular kinds of strengths and challenges, and writing is always about working with these as you move through the writing process. Being a writer is somewhat like being a therapist. It's about using your own voice to communicate ideas to others, using a set of guidelines and procedures when doing so. It's also about working through blocks and barriers that prevent you from finishing a project and submitting it for publication.

Writing for publication changes you, and I think this is the least recognized part of being a writer. As an art, it is a discovery process in which there are times of *not knowing*, changing ideas, formulating new ideas, and responding to data in unexpected, even novel ways. As a science, writing is about following specific structures, sequences, and guidelines that provide a framework for communicating the art of writing. Objectivist writing is a specific way of doing this. It emphasizes a tight, formed, direct statement of ideas, using predetermined headings, where each heading has specific content: Abstract, Introduction and literature review, Method, Results, and Discussion (AIMRaD; Cargill & O'Connor, 2013).

Writing always involves reading, and the two tasks are inextricably linked. You can rarely be a good writer without being a good reader, and the more you write, the better you read. Reading, in service of writing, has different purposes, which will be outlined below. Reading is always an active, goal-directed process, in which you engage with articles (and chapters) in different ways that help inform your research and writing. For example, sometimes you read to develop your understanding of something, while at other times you read to critique or apply.

This chapter addresses each of these elements—reading and writing—and then concludes with an overview of journal submission guidelines. Before continuing, though, a word on objectivist writing: What is it, exactly, and how can it be defined?

Objectivist research is grounded in the quantitative tradition. In general, quantitative research explains phenomena by collecting numerical data that are analyzed using mathematical methods (i.e., statistics). Quantitative research in the social sciences (e.g., music therapy, psychology, education) grew out of the basic sciences (e.g., biology), in which the language used in reporting research is often described as *objective*. Let's look at an example of this style from the music therapy literature, which addresses the impact of rhythmic auditory stimulation on gait for patients with Parkinson's disease (McIntosh, Brown, Rice, & Thaut, 1997). This excerpt describes the baseline measurements of two groups (treatment and control) prior to the intervention:

> In the absence of RAS [rhythmic auditory stimulation], all patients with Parkinson's disease showed abnormal gait patterns characteristic of Parkinson's disease. For the ON group, this included decreased velocity (mean 42.0 (SD 12.2) m/min) and shortened stride length (mean 0.86 (SD 0.19) m). The OFF group showed even further decreased velocity (mean 33.7 (SD 15.1) m/min), reduced stride length (mean 0.74 (SD 0.21) m), and moderate stride asymmetry (mean 0.82 (SD 0.15)%) when symmetry was calculated as the time ratio between two successive steps using the longer step time as denominator. The accepted normal age-matched values reported are 73 m/min for velocity and 1.27 m for stride length. Average cadence (steps/min) for the ON group was 98 (SD 10) and 91 (SD 12) steps/min for the OFF group compared with the 113 steps/min typical of normal age-matched subjects. The stride data of the normal elderly group fell well within normal age ranges (velocity 74.4 (SD 6.4) m/min, cadence 111 (SD 7) steps/min, stride length 1.34 (SD 0.17) m, symmetry 0.97 (SD 2)%). (McIntosh et al., 1997, p. 23)

Notice the emphasis on factual, succinct statements that convey findings and events as they occur, without embellishment or subjective interpretation. This way of writing has, traditionally, reflected positivism, a belief that the world exists according to fixed rules of cause and effect. Thus, writing style reflects underlying beliefs, with objectivist writing using language that reflects the researcher's goal of portraying the world *as it actually exists*, without interpretation or embellishment.

Of course, in reality, ascribing objectivist writing to positivism is far too simplistic. First, very few music therapy researchers are absolute positivists, and second, objectivist writing is becoming more a style of writing and less intimately connected to a particular worldview. While positivists, postpositivists, absolute realists, and pragmatists may be more likely to write in this style, it may be more helpful to think of objectivist writing as a way of communicating, consistent with a set of beliefs held by the researcher, along with the expectations of the journal to which the researcher is submitting his or her research regarding how information is to be communicated. Objectivist writing, when undertaken expertly, has its own beauty of form and style, with content guidelines (e.g., AIMRaD) giving a framework through which to communicate concepts and findings. As a cross-discipline language, it allows music therapy researchers to speak to others (music therapists and professionals in related fields) using a shared form and style that helps to create connections and increase mutual understanding.

Reading Objectivist Research

There are a number of ways to read objectivist research, and while interrelated, they serve different purposes. You can read to: (a) understand, (b) apply, (c) critique, or (d) replicate. While reading and critiquing will be the central focus of this section, let's look at each purpose briefly.

When you read to *understand*, your focus in on apprehending, processing, and interpreting information contained in an article. The focus, as such, is comprehension. Reading questions center on elements such as: What is the purpose of the research? What methods were undertaken to gather data? What were the results? What do the results mean?

When you read to *apply*, your goal is to take the knowledge contained in the research and transfer it to a clinical situation. This can include replicating the intervention used in the primary research, adapting the intervention, using the outcomes measures to inform practice, and, in general, applying the knowledge gained through the study. Applying questions center on: How can I relate this research to my own clinical setting? How can I incorporate this research into my own research?

When you *critique*, you use an evaluative framework to appraise an article. In doing so, a critical framework is often applied, using concepts important to the reader (e.g., how relevant and appropriate is the underlying theoretical framework?) or an objective checklist such as CONSORT (Consolidated Standards of Reporting Trials; Mohler et al., 2012). Objectivist research places an emphasis on critiquing, often using reporting guidelines and evaluative procedures that emphasize methodological rigor, statistical analysis, reliability, predictability, and, not surprisingly, objectivity. Critique questions center on elements such as: How well was this research conducted? How methodologically sound was it? How can it be improved?

When you read to *replicate*, your goal is to apply elements of or, indeed, the whole study to another clinical context. This can include replicating the study in exactly the same clinical context (e.g., adults with TBI), with another population (adults with dementia), or some hybrid of the two (e.g., children with TBI). The goal in doing so is to ascertain whether the same outcomes can be seen in the same/different clinical context. Replication questions center on: What can I replicate and where can it be replicated? Do the findings of the primary study apply to another clinical context?

Reading is always about *developing*—developing understanding, research ideas, clinical ideas, theory—and *improving*—improving interventions, research methods, and so forth. Reading is also a developmental process. When you read, you often begin by reading to understand, but as you develop a comprehensive understanding of a topic, you may combine this with critiquing and applying. By way of contrast, expert readers may begin reading through a critical lens, with a focus on replicating or developing. Thus, reading always involves an intention and is usually goal-directed.

Reading to Understand

Ideas for research are almost always generated through experience. For clinicians, this commonly comes from work with clients, the experiences of working with colleagues, and so forth. For researchers, it usually comes from the experiences of, and reflections upon, previous studies (their own and others), findings from other research, talking with clinicians, and so forth. Experiences lead to questions (or further questions), which are formulated into specific research question(s); thus, over time, an idea is shaped into a research project.

At some point in this process, you move from a focus on your own ideas to contextualizing these in the existing literature (sometimes called the published literature or *the literature*). You might think that there is a formal way of doing this, but this is not the case. It's very organic, akin to a process of discovery. In searching the literature, you are asking basic questions such as: What literature relates to my own ideas? How does this literature inform my study? How is my study different from the existing literature? How does this literature improve my own ideas?

In other words, these questions are about *understanding*. Reading to understand helps you to contextualize your own research within the larger frame of existing research, both within and outside the field of music therapy. The challenge of reading to understand is always about comprehensiveness and management. Reading ought to be comprehensive in the sense that you explore and read enough of the related literature to have a thorough understanding of the topic you've chosen. Managing this information involves keeping all the topical areas *in relation* to each other and your own topic. Thus, when you read to understand, you are building a knowledge base that informs your own understanding of the topic on which you are focused and thereby contextualizes your research. This is often a very complex thing to do, especially when approaching a topic for the first time.

With this in mind, there are three related elements in this process: factual, theoretical, and methodological. Factual reading is reading to gather information: What does the published literature reveal about the topic you have chosen? In this way, the AIMRaD framework is very helpful, as it provides information under specific topical headings:

Abstract
  1. An overview of the entire article.
Introduction
  1. The goal(s) of the research,
  2. How the research relates to existing literature,
  3. Why the research is useful, important, or interesting in relation to existing literature.
Method
  1. How the study was designed,
  2. How the data were collected,
  3. How the data were analyzed.
Results
  1. What the data revealed.
Discussion
  1. The extent to which the research question(s) were answered, and what these answers were,
  2. Specific problems encountered by the researcher,
  3. How the findings relate to previously published research,
  4. The extent to which the researcher finds the results important/valuable,
  5. Suggestions for further research (which may inform your own research).

The AIMRaD framework also provides information about the methodological components of each study. This includes the study design, how participants were recruited and assigned to groups, and the intervention (when a treatment study), along with information about the ways in which data were collected and analyzed. In other words, methodological information provides a framework through which to understand how each study was actually undertaken and with whom.

The final reading lens is theoretical. "A theory is a way of thinking about what we do and what we know" (Bruscia, 2005, p. 540). This can include propositions, constructs, formal theories, and less formal theoretical writings (Bruscia, 2005). Burns (2012) refines this further, within the context of research, suggesting that "theoretical frameworks … illuminate how variables and intervention content are related" (p. 15). While not always explicitly stated, theory always underpins research, as it provides links between client need(s), music therapy intervention(s), the nature of methodological design, and data collection and analysis. Theoretical frameworks are important in that research can

be linked theoretically, with each study building upon a theory or theories while also addressing effectiveness, process, and so forth.

Reading to Critique

The process of critical reading builds upon reading for understanding. It is a perspective aimed at evaluating the extent to which the author has met certain quality criteria (e.g., CONSORT). Not surprisingly, you can read critically for content, method, and/or theory. Critical reading is both objective and subjective. It is objective in that it is possible to evaluate the extent to which an article is comprehensive, sound, and sophisticated, yet subjective in that each reader may give a different value to the research, based upon his or her reading perspective. For example, a clinician reading a research article may find it difficult to relate the intervention to his or her own clinical practice, thereby reducing the meaningfulness of the research, whereas a researcher may find methodological flaws in the design that question the underlying meaningfulness of the data and associated analysis.

In addition to content, writing style is always evaluated. Two interrelated elements are compared when doing this. The first is the extent to which the author(s) have met the *style* requirements of the journal to which the author is submitting for review and publication. The guidelines from the *Publication Manual of the American Psychological Association*, 6th Edition (American Psychological Association, 2010), are used as the style guide for most music therapy journals (e.g., the *Journal of Music Therapy*, the *Nordic Journal of Music Therapy*, and *Music Therapy Perspectives*) and contain detailed information about citations (referencing), formatting, headings, and language.

The second element of writing style is more subjective, but no less important. *Accessibility* is the extent to which the author(s) write(s) in a way that is accessible, engaging, and clear. Put in another way, one might ask: "Is the article well written?" And, as you might imagine, this is open to interpretation. The challenge of objectivist writing is always one of accessibility, as the more an author writes in tight, formed, direct statements, the less connected the reader might feel, as this writing style can convey a feeling of abstraction to which readers may find it difficult to relate. In contrast, some researchers find that this way of writing reflects a purity of thought and communication that is clear and concise, without undue interpretation and embellishment.

Additional information and another perspective on evaluating objectivist research is found in Chapter 65, Evaluating Objectivist Research.

Writing Objectivist Research

In addition to giving the reader a structural framework to help in digesting research, the AIMRaD structure provides writers with specific content guidelines that shape the writing process. For example, the purpose of the literature review is always to discuss pertinent literature related to the research topic and to frame the research question(s). Further, each section informs the following: The introduction contextualizes the literature review; the literature reviews leads to the research questions; questions to method, and so forth.

Cargill and O'Connor (2013) provide a visual guide to this process, along with accompanying content guidelines. Their work has been adapted in Figure 1.

Building upon this model (Cargill & O'Connor, 2013):

1. The Abstract provides a succinct summary of entire study, usually in 6–8 sentences, that addresses the goal(s), method, results, and major findings.
2. The Introduction has three primary functions:
   a. Discussing the research area by referring to the relevant literature;
   b. Demonstrating an area where more information could or should be added to the literature; and,
   c. Outlining the current study in terms of research objective(s), hypotheses, and/or structure.
3. The Method provides a detailed description of exactly how the research was conducted.
4. Results will illuminate key findings and indicate where the complete data set is located.
5. The Discussion commonly has four main parts:
   a. A statement about the completed research with regard to the research question(s);
   b. Mention of any problems or limitations related to the study design, method, analysis, or assumptions;

c. A comparison with similar studies; and
d. A conclusion that outlines implications of the findings and recommends future research.

While these frameworks provide clear guidance regarding the structure of journal articles, chapters and theses/dissertations have somewhat different requirements. Those who are writing for those formats should consult resources that deal with them, including requirements or guidelines from a book editor or institution.

Let us begin now to look at each section in more detail, focusing on structure, content, and process. Structure provides a writing framework (AIMRaD), content speaks to essential elements of each section, and process reflects the *work* that the writer undertakes to maximize writing quality (e.g., minimizing passive voice, linking and building concepts). Robb et al. (2008) will be used as an example, published in the journal *Psycho-Oncology*, whereby text from the article will be highlighted and analyzed for content and sequencing. The title of the article is "Randomized Controlled Trial of the Active Music Engagement (AME) Intervention on Children with Cancer."

The Abstract

After the title, the abstract is the most often read part of an article. The abstract is itself a miniature version of the entire paper, perhaps 200 words long, allowing readers to quickly gain an overview of the entire work. In general, four elements are included: problem statement, methodology, main findings, and conclusion. These are linked together to show

- The introduction begins with a broad focus, and the starting point you select for your Introduction should attract the lively interest of your audience
- Background information from previous studies is woven together to logically connect the relevant problem with the approach taken in the work to be presented
- The introduction ends with a focus exactly parallel to the Results: Often this is a statement of the aim or purpose of the work, expressed in goals or hypotheses

- The method section, or its equivalent, establishes credibility for the Results by showing how they were obtained
- Typically, the Method includes a series of interrelated sections: Study design, participants, procedures, measurements, method(s) of data analysis

- The whole structure of the paper is guided by the Results: Everything in the article must related to, and be connected with, the data and analysis presented in the Results section
- The Discussion begins

- The Discussion begins with the same breadth of focus as the Results, but ends at the same breadth as the starting point of the Introduction. By the end, the article addresses the broader issues raised at the start of the article, recognizes weaknesses in Method, and shows how the work is important in the "bigger picture."

Figure 1. AIMRaD: Key Elements of a Research Article, with Key Features Highlighted (Cargill & O'Connor, 2013, p. 12, adapted by Meadows)

how research questions, method, results, and conclusions are related. In general, the past tense is used, and only those findings discussed within the body of the article are included in the Abstract. In line with style guidelines for *Psycho-Oncology*, Robb et al. (2008) crafted the following abstract:

Background: Coping theorists argue that environmental factors affect how children perceive and respond to stressful events such as cancer. However, few studies have investigated how particular interventions can change coping behaviors. The active music engagement (AME) intervention was designed to counter stressful qualities of the in-patient hospital environment by introducing three forms of environmental support.

Method: The purpose of this multisite randomized controlled trial was to determine the efficacy of the AME intervention on three coping-related behaviors (i.e., positive facial affect, active engagement, and initiation). Eighty-three participants, ages 4–7, were randomly assigned to one of three conditions: AME ($n = 27$), music listening (ML; $n = 28$), or audio storybooks (ASB; $n = 28$). Conditions were videotaped to facilitate behavioral data collection using time-sampling procedures.

Results: After adjusting for baseline differences, repeated measure analyses indicated that AME participants had a significantly higher frequency of coping-related behaviors compared with ML or ASB. Positive facial affect and active engagement were significantly higher during AME compared with ML and ASB ($p < 0.0001$). Initiation was significantly higher during AME than ASB ($p < 0.05$).

Conclusion: This study supports the use of the AME intervention to encourage coping-related behaviors in hospitalized children aged 4–7 receiving cancer treatment. (p. 699)

Notice how the Abstract reads as a *stand-alone* document that includes the most important information in a highly condensed form. Notice, too, the sequencing of ideas, and how each element leads to the next.

Introduction

The Introduction, including the literature review, is the first major section of a research article. As such, it sets the tone and focus of the article and draws the reader into the research.

Cargill and O'Connor (2013) identify five essential writing tasks undertaken when crafting these sections:

1. *Locate your project within an existing field of research.*

Articles generally begin with an introduction. This usually consists of one to three paragraphs that give a broad context for the research. For example, this can include general information about the population of study, statistical information about treatment trends (or lack thereof), and extant theories of interest, along with a statement regarding the importance of the research. Notice that Robb et al. (2008) have a single introductory paragraph that orients the reader to the most important elements of the research and prepares the reader for the literature review that follows.

2. *Use referencing to highlight and link existing research, refining the topic as you do so.*

Although approached with precision and minimal elaboration, the main body of the literature review provides the reader with selected, related research in a way that educates, links, and builds. The literature review educates the reader regarding the most relevant research, theories, and interventions related to the current study. It also links each of these elements into a sequence that naturally and convincingly leads to the research question(s). In doing so, it builds a case (an *argument*) for the research. Novice writers often find this the most difficult section to write, as it requires discipline, conceptual sophistication, and the ability to manage large amounts of information.

Notice how Robb et al. (2008) undertake these tasks. First, they establish the purpose of the research (*The purpose of this study …*), provide a context (*Young children represent …*), make a statement of need (*Young children can experience significant stress …*), describe the clinical (research) environment (*Three qualities of the hospital environment …*), introduce a theory that frames the challenges of the clinical environment (*According to coping theorists …*), link a music-based intervention (*Music-based interventions hold promise …*), and provide hypotheses that *test* the intervention.

3. *Indicate gaps or niche areas.*

As much as Task 2 highlights the extent and value of existing research, Task 3 serves to highlights gaps, weaknesses, and niche areas. Unless the purpose of the research is replication, this section serves a very important transition—from what is *known* to what is *not known*. For example, Robb et al. (2008) use a transitional paragraph:

Method Section	Comments
Study design In this section, the authors describe the design, which included the experimental condition (active music engagement, AME) and two control conditions (music listening, ML, and auditory story books, ASB). They explain that ASB was used as a nonmusical, auditory control condition and how both conditions included contact with a trained interventionist to control for any effects of attention.	*Study design* This section describes the manner in which the research was undertaken; in this case, a true experimental design was used. Treatment conditions are indicated, along with any control conditions. Independent and dependent variables may be specifically identified.
Conditions Experimental condition: AME The AME condition is described as offering "numerous opportunities to experience mastery, make choices, and interact with other people through a variety of develop- mentally appropriate music activities" (p. 701). Materials are described, as are each of the activities, which are subdivided into five categories, with each beginning with a greeting song. These are described in detail, including a statement: "Throughout the AME, music therapists (MT-BCs) followed specific procedures for offering choices and incorporating patient comments and actions into music-based activities. Following the greeting song, participants selected activities from a 'musical menu' that had pictorial representations of activities from categories (b)–(d) listed above" (p. 701) and descriptions of possibilities for choice.	*Conditions (treatment, control)* Each condition (intervention) is identified and described with sufficient detail so as to be clearly understandable and easily replicated. Notice the level of specificity that allows the reader to visualize the session and imagine what the participants would have experience. The guidelines of Robb, Burns, and Carpenter (2011) are helpful here.
Control condition: ML During the ML condition, the children were asked to listen to a compact disc (CD) of children's music, using similar musical characteristics to the AME condition. The children were able to sit quietly and listen to the music ambiently, confirming that the volume was "at the right level" for them. Control condition: ASB The MT-BC presented participants with two commercially published audio books with an accompanying illustrated book, and asked to choose one. Each audio storybook was 10–15 min long. Stories were played from an audiocassette, without headphones.	The two control conditions are also described in sufficient detail that the interventions are easily understandable, thereby aiding in replication.
Participants "Eighty-three pediatric oncology patients were recruited from six hospitals within the United States. Inclusion criteria were: (a) age 4–7 years inclusively, (b) inpatient admission as a pediatric oncology patient, and (c) English as the primary language. Exclusion criteria were: (a) a mental age less than a 4-year equivalent as based on physician judgment or (b) admission to an intensive care setting" (p. 702).	*Participants* Important information regarding the characteristics of participants is included, in this case, age, diagnosis, and primary language. Exclusion criteria are also included.
Procedures The children and their families were invited to participate by study personnel and, after being given introductory information about the study, provided with an explanation of informed consent procedures. Once the consent form was signed, participants were assigned to one of the three treatment conditions in sequential order, following random assignment guidelines. Ten MT-BCs received 8 hours of training for human subjects' protections, hospital-specified procedures for infection control, and study protocols specific to each condition. They then delivered both experimental and low-dose treatment conditions and remained present in participants' rooms for the duration of all conditions. The children's parents were also asked to remain in the room for the duration of the intervention. Each session was videotaped to collect behavioral data, over three phases: (a) a 5-min pre-intervention baseline (b) a 20-min intervention (one of the three conditions), and (c) a 5-min postintervention baseline.	*Procedures* This section focuses on how the research was actually undertaken, including any training, methods of data collection, and the step-by-step description of how the intervention took place. Notice the level of detail that makes it clear how the researchers interacted with the participants. Notice, too, that *materials* are included in this section. Materials are items used by the participants during the intervention: instruments, video camera, etc. In this example, the treatment conditions are separated from the procedure, thereby providing two sources of information regarding materials.
Once the session was completed, the video and consent form were sent to the principal investigator, and kept locked and secured. If parents wanted the videotapes returned after analysis, they could request this, and these were returned at the completion of the study.	Information is included on how data were collected and how data collection intersected with the intervention.
Measurements Behavioral coding A behavioral coding form was used, based upon one developed from a previous pilot study. This was developed from Skinner and Wellborn's Motivational Theory of Coping, to "indicate the presence or absence of three coping-related behaviors: facial affect, active engagement, and initiation" (p. 702). These were evaluated and coded by independent observers, who rated each 10-sec time period. Each of the observers completed training in behavioral coding, and any discrepancies were discussed until agreed upon until intra-observer and inter-observer reliability reached a minimum criterion of 0.85. Behavioral coding was completed in 2-min time intervals, with an additional coping period for the pre- and post-condition baseline periods. "Material for baseline coding	*Measurements* Data collection Each method of data collection is identified and described. Training procedures are explained, if undertaken.

intervals was taken at the midpoint of each 5-min baseline period. Six time intervals were coded for experimental and control conditions, resulting in 12 min of coded material for each participant. Material for experimental and control conditions was coded at equal time points across the 20-min experience to account for any behavioral changes that occurred over time" (p. 703). As a result, data were collected for eight different time periods: one baseline, six during the intervention, and one postsession.	
Computation of mean scores Mean frequency scores were calculated for each time interval, to examine the extent to which behaviors changed over time. Additionally a total mean score for each condition was calculated for each condition and for each of the three coping-related behaviors: positive facial affect, active engagement, and initiation.	*Method(s) of data analysis* An explanation of how data were analyzed is always included. In this example, the data analyses are clearly explained and linked to the independent and dependent variables.
Statistical analyses Several analyses were then undertaken. First, univariate analyses were conducted to obtain descriptive statistics for all variables and their underlying distributions. Subsequently, a repeated measures analysis was undertaken for each outcome, and a mixed linear model examined the effects of group (condition), time (observation interval), and group-time interaction. "Interactions between group (condition) and other confounding variables were tested. To describe this interaction, the means of the outcomes for each time interval and group level were computed and graphed. ANCOVA was performed to (a) compute adjusted means for each group (AME, ML, and ASB) and (b) provide *post hoc* comparisons across groups while controlling for overall alpha using the Tukey–Kramer method" (p. 703).	

Table 1. Summary of Method Section from Robb et al. (2008)

Without supportive interventions that encourage engagement, young children undergoing active treatment for cancer may experience high levels of stress that prevent them from learning and using effective coping strategies. … Given that coping responses are hypothesized to be responsive to changes in the immediate environment, there is a need for intervention studies that investigate how particular interventions within the hospital environment might affect coping-related behaviors. (p. 700)

These authors then link this to the particular intervention, addressing the specific gap and links between the underlying theory, gap in research, and purpose of study.

4. *State the purpose of the main activity.*

At the end of the introduction, the author(s) set up the reader's expectations about the remainder of the paper, usually in the form of researcher questions or hypotheses. Robb et al. (2008) accomplish this by stating three directional hypotheses that lead naturally into the method section.

5. *Highlight benefits to the research and map the article.*

If not already accomplished, stating the researcher questions/hypotheses may also lead to a statement of benefits, in which the prospective outcomes are re-contextualized within a theory or direct clinical benefit. This may also lead to *mapping* the remainder of the article, whereby the author(s) guide the reader through the remaining sections of the article by highlighting important elements therein.

Method

The Method section serves two important functions. First, it "establishes credibility for the results [by providing] enough information about how the work was done for readers to evaluate the results, i.e., to decide for themselves whether the results actually mean what the authors claim they mean" (Cargill & O'Connor, 2013, p. 37). Second, it ought to provide sufficient information for another competent researcher to repeat (replicate) the research. In general, criticism of this section centers on a lack of detail that allows readers to evaluate the claims of the author(s) and/or replicate the study. Although the forthcoming sections serve as a guide to content areas in each method section, readers are encouraged to consult Mohler et al. (2010) and Robb, Burns, and Carpenter (2011).

At a practical level, the Method section is concerned with the *who, what, when, where, why,* and *how* of the study. This is undertaken formally through a series of subsections designed to communicate information about the study design, participants (including selection process), intervention(s), procedure, data collection, and methods of data analysis.

Pyrczak and Bruce (2011) have developed a set of guidelines for the Method section, summarized below:

1. First, describe the participants:
   a. Describe participants in enough detail that the reader can visualize them,
   b. Decide whether to use the term *participants* or

subjects,

c. If reporting demographics for a large data set, consider using a table(s),

d. When the sample is small, consider describing each participant.

2. Describe the informed consent procedures, if any.

3. Consider describing steps taken to maintain data confidentiality.

4. Describe the method of sampling.

5. Describe the data collection measures after the participants:

a. Describe the traits a measure was designed to measure, and the possible range of score values;

b. Summarize information on reliability and validity and/or provide appropriate references;

c. Make unpublished measures available.

Table 1, Column 1, contains the Method section, in summary form, from Robb et al. (2008). Column 2 includes comments regarding purpose and content. Reduction in content has been undertaken in line with both copyright and chapter length expectations. Readers are encouraged to review the Method section of this article, alongside the Comments (Column 2, below) for an expanded understanding of this section.

Results

The Results section is the primary place to present the findings from the data analysis. These are usually organized around the research questions/hypotheses, and as such, are simple statements of the data, without interpretation or embellishment. In general, descriptive statistics are presented before inferential, and tables are used to supplement and summarize these descriptions.

The writing challenge in the Results section is often around what should be included, and how to integrate visual data (e.g., tables and graphs) with narrative summaries. Robb et al. (2008) eloquently handle these challenges. Table 2 includes a summary of the narrative of their Results section (Column 1), along with comments regarding content and flow (Column 2). They also include tables and graphs, which the reader is encouraged to review in the original article, both in relation to the narrative, and as a way of presenting results. Notice how the authors report their primary findings in the narrative, using tables to supplement and expand upon these.

Readers are also encouraged to review Cargill and O'Connor (2013), Chapter 5 ("Results: Turning Data Into Knowledge") for helpful guidance on the presentation of figures and tables.

Discussion and Conclusion

The Discussion section plays an important role in demonstrating to the reader that the contribution is new and significant. "The Discussion section does this by contextualizing the main research findings within accepted knowledge, with an emphasis on qualifying what is new and important by reference to any limitations and by [theorizing] about the greater implications of the new knowledge" (Cargill & O'Connor, 2013 p. 59).

Cargill and O'Connor (2013) provide a series of elements most commonly encountered in a Discussion section, sequenced as follows:

1. Reference the main purpose or hypothesis(es) of the study;

2. Restate or review the most important findings, generally in order of significance, including:

a. Whether they support the original hypothesis(es)/research questions

b. Whether they agree with the findings of other researchers;

3. Explain the findings, supported by references to relevant literature (where possible);

4. Discuss any limitations that restrict or limit the extent to which the findings can be generalized beyond the study;

5. Discuss the implications of the study for the broader field;

6. Make recommendations for future research.

The Conclusion is a summary paragraph (or two) that restates the purpose of the research, method, results, and major findings from the study. It includes recommendations for future research and commonly includes a restatement of any limitations that might compromise the researcher's ability to generalize the findings.

References

Found at the end of a document, the References section is a comprehensive catalog (list) of all sources used in the paper, and includes detailed information that readers can use to locate the original sources. Note that articles not directly cited in the research article are not included, even though they may be used during the formative stages of manuscript preparation.

Two main referencing styles are used by music therapists. The most common writing and citation style found in music therapy journals has been developed by the American Psychological Association (2010). Colloquially known as *APA style,* it reflects guidelines set forth in the *Publication Manual of the American Psychological Association* (6th ed.). MLA (Modern Language Association) style is commonly used in *Music and Medicine* and in medical journals such as *Cancer* and *Psycho-Oncology* (among a wide range of journals). The *MLA Style Manual and Guide to Scholarly Publishing* (3rd ed.; Modern Language Association, 2008) and the *MLA Handbook for Writers of Research Papers* (7th ed.; Modern Language

Results Section	Comments
Hypothesis 1. When compared with ML or ASB, the AME intervention will result in greater positive facial affect. "Group assignment (i.e., condition) had a significant ($p < 0.0001$) effect on positive facial affect, measured by the mean frequency for time intervals 1–6" (p. 703). Following this initial statement of the main result, the section continues by providing the reader with detailed information on the three treatment conditions and mean scores for the three behavioral measures (positive affect, active engagement, and initiation). This section concludes with a discussion of positive facial affect, concluding that the AME condition had the highest frequency of positive facial affect for each time interval.	Notice how the Results are arranged according to the hypotheses. Results are presented in succinct, unembellished statements that clearly address the research questions. When a significant finding is presented, subsequent data are introduced to expand, clarify, and/or shape these findings.
Hypothesis 2. When compared with ML and ASB, the AME intervention will result in greater active engagement. "Group assignment (i.e., condition) had a significant ($p < 0.0001$) effect on active engagement, measured by the mean frequency scores for time intervals 1–6" (p. 704). Following this initial statement of the main result, the section continues by providing the reader with detailed information on the three treatment conditions and mean scores for the three behavioral measures (positive affect, active engagement, and initiation), with an emphasis on active engagement. This section concludes with a discussion of the interaction between each of the treatment conditions and time, concluding that the AME condition had highest frequency of positive facial affect at each time interval. This section concludes with a discussion of active engagement, concluding that the AME condition had highest frequency of active engagement for each time interval.	Tables and figures are used amplify findings, and, in the case of the figure, as the main data source, supplemented by narrative description.
Hypothesis 3. When compared with ML or ASB, the AME intervention will result in greater initiation. "Group assignment (i.e., condition) had a significant ($p = 0.002$) effect on Initiation, measured by the mean frequency of gestural and verbal initiation scores for time intervals 1–6" (p. 705). Following this initial statement of the main result, this section contains detailed information on the three treatment conditions and mean scores for the three behavioral measures (positive affect, active engagement, and initiation), with an emphasis on active engagement. This section concludes with a discussion of the interaction between each of the treatment conditions and time, concluding that the AME condition had highest frequency of positive facial affect at each time interval. This section continues with a discussion of a figure labeled "Mean scores for initiation by time interval/group assignment." This figure illustrates variations in initiation scores over time, with markings to indicate the occurrence of statistically significant differences among the conditions" (p. 705). The music listening (ML) condition had the highest frequency of initiation at every time interval except interval 5, whereas ML and AME scores were equal. The section concludes by comparing the number of initiation behaviors at each time point, indicating the relative strength of each treatment condition as it relates to initiation.	

Table 2. Summary of Results Section from Robb et al. (2008)

Association, 2009) offer examples for the general formatting of MLA research papers, in-text citations, endnotes/ footnotes, and the Works Cited page.

Writers are strongly encouraged to consult with the submitting journal website for style guide information (e.g., http://www.oxfordjournals.org/our_journals/jmt/for_auth ors/) and with manuals/publications related to each style. Further, university libraries often have style guide summaries that can be very helpful during the writing process, particularly for novice researchers.

Submitting Objectivist Research

There are many different ways to prepare a manuscript for publication, but two interrelated elements may be helpful for novice researchers to consider. These center on the ways in which the writing process is guided by the journal to which you plan to submit and the practicalities of journal publication guidelines.

Consider Your Target Audience and Journal

Before you begin the writing process, think carefully about your target audience, particularly within the context of the submission journal. For example, is it a journal for music therapists, educators, or nurses? And think about the very nature of the data itself. What is interesting about the data? How should it be focused and communicated? Is there more than one article in your data set?

Dixon (2001) poses a series of questions that can be asked:

• In addition to the main readers of your paper, who else might read it?
• What are likely to be the backgrounds of these readers, and what information may they need to understand the article?
• Are the readers likely to be familiar with the situation or circumstances of the research, and, if not, what additional information might they need to be adequately informed?

- Why do readers need to read this article? And, from the author's point of view, what is to be learned from the research?
- What do you want readers to do as a result of reading the article?

You should consider these questions not only from a reader's perspective, but also from the perspective of a journal editor. An editor "wants everything a reader wants, and more" (Dixon, 2001, p. 418). An editor wants research that excites and extends the readership of the journal, advances knowledge, and sparks new ideas, all presented in a format consistent with the journal's mission and publication guidelines.

Submission and Publication Guidelines

Always consider the journal for which you are writing before you begin the writing process. Consider the journal's mission statement, the kinds of articles commonly accepted into the journal, and the intended audience. Writing for a music therapy journal, for example, can be quite different than writing for a nursing, medical, or education journal. Supplemental information may also be valuable: In what databases is the journal indexed? What is its impact factor? Is the journal peer-reviewed?

The *Nordic Journal of Music Therapy*, for example, has very clear submission guidelines, available through the Taylor and Francis portal: http://www.tandfonline.com/action/authorSubmission?journalCode=rnjm20&page=instructions#mp_style. These guidelines include a mission statement, description of journal content, ethical considerations, and detailed information regarding manuscript preparation. Practical information is also included, such as copyright transfer and how to approach the submission process using the online submission system. Similar portals, including submission and review information, can also be found for the *Journal of Music Therapy* and *Music Therapy Perspectives*, among a range of music therapy journals.

Reporting guidelines are often included in these instructions. For example, the *Journal of Music Therapy* includes specific reporting guidelines based upon the type of submission, with hyperlinks to articles associated with these reporting guidelines. The following are provided for authors submitting manuscripts to the *Journal of Music Therapy* (retrieved from: http://www.oxfordjournals.org/our_journals/jmt/for_authors/):

- For randomized controlled trial designs, please refer to the *Consolidated Standards of Reporting Trials (CONSORT)*;
- For nonrandomized designs, please refer to *Transparent Reporting of Evaluations with Nonrandomized Designs (TREND)*;
- For music-based intervention studies (using randomized and nonrandomized designs), please refer to *Reporting Guidelines for Music-Based Interventions* (Robb, Carpenter, & Burns, 2010);
- For systematic reviews and meta-analyses, please refer to *Preferred Reporting Items for Systematic Reviews and Meta-Analyses (PRISMA)*.

The Review Process

Once submitted to a journal, an article is commonly sent for blind review. This usually means that the author(s) and reviewers do not know who the others are, allowing for an unbiased review. In general, each article is reviewed by two or three reviewers, who provide feedback to the author(s), via the editor.

Once reviews are submitted to the editor, he or she makes a decision regarding the manuscript. In general, there are four decision options: (a) accept, (b) accept with minor revision, (c) request major revisions and resubmittal, and (d) reject. If Level b or c is decided, the author(s) has a set time period (commonly 60–90 days) to revise and resubmit the manuscript. Depending on the level or revisions required, the manuscript may be returned to the reviewers for another review or accepted by the editor after review of the revised manuscript.

Preparing and submitting a research manuscript is a carefully considered, tactical process, focused on meeting the mission and style requirements of the submitting journal, while being faithful to the data. Most manuscripts require revision, so anticipate that your manuscript will be returned for reworking and refinement. The process is designed to help you improve your manuscript (and therefore your writing), not act as an undue barrier to publication.

Conclusion

Reading, writing, and submitting objectivist research are three interrelated components of a process that helps us to grow professionally and personally, often with the goal of publishing. Professionally, such undertakings help our field to expand and be challenged by new data, new ideas, and new methodologies. Personally, these processes help us to deepen our understanding of the music therapy processes that we undertake, while also allowing us to benefit from the ability to communicate and write with greater clarity and authority. Such processes never end, and while you never arrive at being *a writer*, the challenges that you encounter along the way and the things that you learn through the process are enriching, enlightening, and often of great benefit to colleagues and clients.

References

American Psychological Association. (2010). *Publication manual of the American Psychological Association* (6th ed.). Washington, DC: Author.

Andersson, B., Beveridge, A., & Singh K. (2007). *Literature review: Academic tip sheet*. Unpublished document, Edith Cowan University. Retrieved from http://intranet.ecu.edu.au/student/my-studies/study-advice/academic-tip-sheets

Bruscia, K., Dileo, C., Shultis, C., & Dennery, K. (2009). Expectations of hospitalized cancer and cardiac patients regarding the medical and psychotherapeutic benefits of music therapy. *Arts in Psychotherapy, 36*(4), 239–244. doi:10.1016/j.aip.2009.05.002

Bruscia, K. E. (2005). Developing theory. In B. L. Wheeler (Ed.), *Music therapy research* (2nd ed.; pp. 540–551). Gilsum, NH: Barcelona.

Burns, D. (2012). Theoretical rationale for music selection in oncology intervention research: An integrative review. *Journal of Music Therapy, 49*(1), 7–22. doi:10.1093/jmt/49.1.7

Burrows, T. (2011). Writing research articles for publication. Unpublished manuscript, the Asian Institute of Technology Language Center, Khlong Luang, Thailand. Retrieved from https://www.academia.edu/2457060/Writing_Research_Articles_for_Publication

Cargill, M., & O'Connor, P. (2013). *Writing scientific research articles: Strategy and steps* (2nd ed.). West Sussex, UK: Wiley-Blackwell.

Dixon, N. (2001). Writing for publication: A guide for new authors. *International Journal for Quality in Health Care, 13*(5), 417–421. doi:10.1093/intqhc/13.5.417

McIntosh, G., Brown, S. Rice, R., & Thaut, M. (1997). Rhythmic auditory-motor facilitation of gait patterns in patients with Parkinson's disease. *Journal of Neurology, Neurosurgery, and Psychiatry, 62*, 22–26. doi:10.1136/jnnp.62.1.22

Modern Language Association. (2008). *MLA style manual and guide to scholarly publishing* (3rd ed.). New York, NY: Modern Language Association of America.

Modern Language Association. (2009). *Handbook for writers of research papers* (7th ed.). New York, NY: Modern Language Association of America.

Mohler, D., Hopewell, S., Schulz, K., Montori, V., Gotzsche, P., Devereaux, P., ...Altman, D. (2012). CONSORT 2010 exploration and elaboration: Updated guidelines for reporting parallel group randomization. *International Journal of Surgery, 10*(1), 28–55. doi:10.1016/j.ijsu.2011.10.001

Pyrczak, F., & Bruce, R. (2011). *Writing empirical research reports* (7th ed.). Glendale, CA: Pyrczak.

Robb, S. L., Carpenter, J. S., & Burns, D. S. (2010). Reporting guidelines for music-based interventions. *Journal of Health Psychology, 16*(2), 342–352. doi:10.1177/1359105310374781

Robb, S., Clair, A., Watanabe, M., Monahan, P., Azzouz, F., Stouffer, J., ...Hannan, A. (2008). Randomized controlled trial of the active music engagement (AME) intervention on children with cancer, *Psycho-Oncology, 17*(7), 699–708. doi:10.1002/pon.1301

Chapter 20

READING, WRITING, AND SUBMITTING INTERPRETIVIST RESEARCH

Susan C. Gardstrom

As is evident from its title, this chapter focuses on considerations pertaining to three undertakings commonly associated with the research process: reading others' accounts of research, writing our own research reports, and proposing these reports for publication consideration. More specifically, I have addressed each of these endeavors as they pertain to music therapy research based on principles of interpretivism.

Essentially, the information in this chapter is a compilation and distillation of information garnered from pre-existing treatises, with added material from my own research experiences as well as advice from research advisors and music therapy colleagues. Where relevant and possible, I have cited treatises from the growing corpus of music therapy research of an interpretivist nature. To that end, I have relied extensively and with expressed permission on the prolific works of researchers Kenneth Aigen (1997, 2002, 2003, 2005a, 2005b, 2008a, 2008b, 2012) and Kenneth Bruscia (1987, 1991, 1995a, 1995b, 1995c, 1996, 1998a, 1998b, 2005, 2014).

The chapter title itself reveals three issues that demand immediate and somewhat detailed commentary. First, as you have noted, the terms *objectivist* and *interpretivist* are used in this book to convey fundamental differences in social science researchers' perspectives on both what it is possible for us to know (ontology) and how we can know what we know (epistemology). The objectivists among us generally assume that it is possible to discern an objective and measurable truth and that this truth exists independent of us and our measurement tools and processes. In this case, we test predetermined hypotheses and often focus on cause-and-effect mechanisms. The interpretivist researchers among us, on the other hand, embrace the belief that it is impossible to uncover a single, static, and measurable truth about certain phenomena; rather, we believe that there are multiple constructed and co-constructed truths, or meanings. From this perspective, we can know something about meanings and meaning-making processes exclusively through interpretive analysis of the data, or "our own constructions of other people's constructions" (Geertz, 1973).

Naturally, each of these two paradigms, or approaches, suggests a particular research question, study design, type of data, method of data collection, analytical method, and report of findings. In research of an objectivist nature, we aim to answer preformed and fixed questions. We make decisions and act in accordance with and bound to pre-established, external, and largely unyielding criteria for *goodness*, such as reliability, validity, and generalizability. What we assert as having learned from such inquiry is evaluated by a larger community of scholars in light of these same *objective* criteria. In inquiry of an interpretivist nature, our questions may emerge and evolve over time, as our primary desire is to "enlarge our constructions of the world and to find and create individual meanings therein" (Bruscia, 1998b, p. 176). All of our decisions and actions thus hinge not upon external, collective understandings and agreements, but rather upon our individual, *subjective* understandings of and responsiveness to the phenomenon under investigation. Shared, or *intersubjective*, understandings and agreements may occur as the scholarly community evaluates our decisions, actions, and conclusions according to unique standards of methodological, interpersonal, personal, and aesthetic integrity (Bruscia, 1998b).

In certain literature, the terms *objectivist* and *quantitative* are used synonymously, as are the terms *interpretivist* and *qualitative*. Yet, some authors believe these to be erroneous substitutions, claiming that it is the *data* that are either quantitative (e.g., numerical scores) or qualitative (e.g., text), not the research approach. Each type of data actually can be treated, or analyzed, in a manner consistent with either objectivist or interpretivist epistemologies and practices: Numerical data can be subjected to interpretive analysis (perhaps to discern and report contextual factors or patterns); likewise, textual data can be treated with quantitative content analysis, in which the researcher turns words into numbers (perhaps to discern and report word frequencies). Although I agree with this criticism, herein, when I cite specific publications in which the term *qualitative research* is used to describe research that I would characterize instead as *interpretivist*, I have preserved the authors' original terminology.

A second matter has to do with the word *considerations*. We might yearn for a set of rules or sequential and fixed procedures describing how to go about the three activities that are the focus of this chapter. But this way of thinking is misaligned with the idiosyncratic nature of interpretivist inquiry. Bruscia (2005) reminds us that "qualitative research is an emergent process rather than a determined sequence of step-by-step procedures … the [qualitative] research process is not predictable or linear, rather, it unfolds in ways that are unique to the phenomenon under study" (p. 129). Therefore, this chapter offers general considerations or recommendations, each of which you as the reader must evaluate for *goodness of fit* with your unique intentions and needs.

A third issue is that it would be easy to perceive the topic of this chapter as the *before* (reading), *during* (writing), and *after* (submitting) of inquiry. But it is not that simple: The acts of reading, writing, and submitting reports, although distinct human activities, are more realistically interwoven as we actualize our research projects. We read others' works not only in preparation for writing, but also as we write. And as we write, we commonly do so with submittal in mind. Furthermore, the processes of submittal and peer review more often than not result in further reading and writing. Nonetheless, there are unique considerations related to each of these three activities. Therefore, I have addressed each separately and in turn, without disregarding points of intersection.

Reading Interpretivist Research

Locating Relevant Studies

We can locate music therapy studies of an interpretive nature in books, monographs, journals (both print and online), and theses and dissertation collections. The resources enumerated here are limited to those published in English.

Companion articles by Aigen (2008a, 2008b) in *Arts in Psychotherapy* detail his analyses of qualitative music therapy research found between 1987 and 2006. Aigen's comprehensive overview remains unique: No other authors appear to have undertaken this type of analysis. In this regard, these two articles are a recommended first read for anyone who seeks to learn of the whereabouts and status of peer-reviewed and edited qualitative music therapy publications. (Note: Mixed methods studies were excluded from Aigen's analyses but are included in an updated, unpublished bibliography; K. Aigen, personal communication, February 17, 2014.)

There are a few books describing interpretivist music therapy research projects. These include Aigen (1997, 2002); Langenberg, Aigen, and Frommer (1996); Smeijsters (1997); and Wheeler (1995, 2005), and case study collections edited by Bruscia (1991), Hadley (2003), and Meadows (2011). The only consolidated collection of interpretivist monographs at the time of this writing is Barcelona Publishers' *Qualitative Inquiries in Music Therapy: A Monograph Series*, which includes 10 peer-reviewed volumes, each containing from three to five separate monographs (www.barcelonapublishers.com).

Two useful periodicals are *Nordic Journal of Music Therapy* (https://njmt.b.uib.no/) and *Voices: A World Forum for Music Therapy* (https://voices.no/index.php/voices/), the latter of which has enjoyed international circulation since 2001. *Arts in Psychotherapy*, referenced above, publishes treatises relevant to art, dance/movement, drama, music, and poetry psychotherapists, as well as psychiatrists, psychologists, and creative arts therapists. The British, Australian, Canadian, and New Zealand music therapy associations also publish periodicals in which one can find interpretivist research reports. *Music Therapy*, published between 1981 and 1996 by the former American Association of Music Therapy, is yet another source. *Journal of Music Therapy* and *Music Therapy Perspectives*, published by the American Music Therapy Association, have published less interpretivist than objectivist research, perhaps owing to a commitment to traditional print journal content and length restrictions. With a recent move to online publication, perhaps more such reports will appear in these two publications.

As Aigen (2008a) presents, some qualitative music therapy research appears in the periodicals of other creative arts therapy and health-/mental health–care disciplines, such as art therapy, nursing, counseling, social work, and so forth. A quick electronic survey indicates that, since Aigen's reviews were published, qualitative music therapy studies that meet his inclusion criteria have continued to be published in these types of journals. (See Table 1 in Chapter 13, Principles of Interpretivist Research, for a tally of interpretivist research published in journals from 2010 to 2015.)

Finally, while perhaps more difficult to obtain than other published manuscripts, master's theses and doctoral dissertations are another potential source of information about interpretivist research. See Aigen (2008b) for details on the prevalence and nature of qualitative doctoral dissertations located between 1987 and 2006.

Now that we know where to find materials, we must determine which of these will be of value to read. This depends on our reasons for reading. If our intentions are clear, our selections will be helpful and our time well spent.

Why Read?

Some people read research out of sheer curiosity or the joy of learning. If this pertains to us, we need to determine our topic of interest and simply get to it! Other individuals read research in order to improve their performance as a practitioner, benefiting from another's *practice wisdom* (Scott, 1990). If this is our impetus, we will want to select studies that relate somehow to our clinical practice, that is, those with kindred clientele, settings, treatment issues, and so forth. Still other people read as researchers, reviewing the literature that is most closely related to their chosen phenomenon or topic of study. If we are students or would-be researchers, interested primarily in the mechanics of interpretivist research, we need to select studies with clear and detailed descriptions of procedures. Finally, we may read because we have been invited to evaluate another's research report; in this case, the report will be assigned to us, likely with accompanying criteria for evaluation, such as proposed by Stige and colleagues (2009). (Note: Although reading and evaluation are inextricably linked processes, the evaluation of interpretivist research requires a more thorough examination than is possible here and thus is addressed separately in Chapter 66.)

Once we have determined our purposes, we are ready to begin the actual business of reading.

Digging into the Reading

Fish (1980) asserts that we all tend to align with particular *interpretive communities* that influence the way we read (and, certainly, the way we write) research. Additionally, we demonstrate individual tendencies in the way we approach a text. As Sandelowski and Barroso (2002) describe, we may adopt an aesthetic stance as we read qualitative research, attending to our total engagement with the text (Does the author write in an appealing manner?), an efferent stance, attending to the degree of clinically pertinent information in the report (Are the author's interpretations relevant to the topic and to our interests and needs?), or any number of other possible positions.

Reading research of an interpretivist nature could be described as a *reflexive* process. As reflexive readers, we strive to be fully attentive to how aspects of our community and personhood are influencing our interpretation of what the author has written, just as aspects of the author's community and personhood (e.g., age, environment, cultural identities and memberships, life histories, feelings, assumptions, and biases about the research topic) ultimately influenced the documented interpretation of the investigative process. In essence, we may *rewrite* a report as we read and reflect critically on what the author presents to us: Would we have gone about studying this topic in the same manner? Would we have interpreted the data in the same way, or would we perhaps have come to different conclusions? Are the findings ultimately meaningful? If the author has done an authentic, thorough, and compelling job of setting forth knowledge claims, we will not merely comprehend meanings but also vicariously experience them (Aigen, 2005b), which deepens our understandings, motivates us to employ these understandings in our clinical practices, and strengthens our ability to do so.

Time and Time Again. As will become quickly apparent, interpretivist research reports tend to be lengthier than other reports, as they often include original and unabridged data: highly detailed text, visual renderings, musical renderings, and other artifacts/objects. Textual data may include transcriptions of interviews or casual conversations, field notes, diaries, clinical documents, poetry or song lyrics, and other forms of literature. Visual data may include video recordings, artistic renderings (e.g., sketches, choreographies, sculptures), photographs, and other graphic devices (e.g., theoretical models, diagrams). Musical data may include conventionally or unconventionally notated scores or audio recordings. While we will not encounter actual artifacts/objects as we read, pictorial representations of artifacts/objects (e.g., musical instruments) may be included in the reports.

In order for us to glean something of value from what are typically lengthy and robust reports, we will need uninterrupted time. And just as a researcher conducts multiple readings of and reflections on data in preparation of the report, we may need to allow time for multiple readings of the report in order to fully comprehend the knowledge claims of the author.

Location, Location, Location. Qualitative research traditions emerged in the *human disciplines* (e.g., anthropology, education, psychology, social work, communications) and evolved through a number of *moments,* each with unique epistemic principles (Denzin & Lincoln, 1994). The fifth moment, defined by Denzin and Lincoln as beginning around 1990, revolved around a "new sensibility" (p. 2) characterized by the recognition that all knowledge is privileged and situated; thus, no universal or general knowledge claims can be asserted. Personal narratives must be read as situated not only within the personal and professional contexts of the researcher and participants but also within broader sociopolitical and economic contexts (Bruscia, 2005), including historical circumstances. On this subject, Etherington (2004) writes:

> Knowledge can only be partial and built upon the culturally defined stocks of knowledge available to us at any given time in history; reality is socially and personally constructed. … I know that what I write today on these matters may be different from what I might have written yesterday or will write tomorrow. Mine too is a story of its time. (p. 27)

Although more recent stages, or moments, in the development of qualitative research have been described (Denzin & Lincoln, 2000; Lincoln & Denzin, 2008; Onwuegbuzie, Leech, & Collins, 2010), the new sensibility described here as characterizing the fifth period continues to be relevant to our reading of interpretivist research.

As we read interpretivist treatises in our discipline, not only do we need to locate their messages within the multiple contexts in which they were written, but also we need to locate ourselves in relationship to the various *characters* of the *story*. With each subsequent reading, we may inhabit a different character in our attempts to understand multiple perspectives. For instance, during the first reading, we may take on the role of a bystander or observer. With subsequent readings, we may find it helpful to locate ourselves *in the shoes* of the researcher or to assume the role of the informant(s) or that of another person or object in the report (e.g., the piano). Naturally, identification and empathy with story characters can be facilitated by a researcher's/author's use of certain narrative devices, such as first-person point of view (see below).

Taking Notes. As we read, we likely will find it helpful to write notes, or memos, about that which strikes us as important at the time of the reading. Memos could include questions and curiosities, emotional reactions, and thematic or summarizing statements. If we inhabit the critic or editor role, we may note the problems that we perceive in design, data collection, or interpretation. We also may find it helpful to sketch, write poetry, or engage in other artistic endeavors in order to chronicle our thoughtful and feelingful reactions to what we read.

Making Notes. What I mean by making notes is to actualize any music that is notated in the studies that we read. If these data are included, it means that the author believed them to be essential. Consider that visually scanning a score without actualizing/hearing the music would be somewhat like professing to comprehend the taste of a cake by scanning the ingredients of the recipe! Playing through a score can help us to inhabit the scene more fully and intentionally and thereby deepen our understanding of (and perhaps our empathy for) one or more of the characters in the narrative.

In summary, considerations related to the process of reading interpretivist reports include the following:

- Consider the purposes for reading; this will bring intention to the decision of what to read.
- Locate relevant and useful studies from among books and monographs, peer-reviewed journal articles, and theses and dissertations.
- Identify your overall tendencies as a reader: For instance, do you adopt an aesthetic stance or read for clinical application?
- Allow ample time to read and reread each study in order to accommodate detailed descriptions, as well as a potentially wide array of data.
- With each subsequent reading, attempt to contextualize the study and inhabit various characters or positions in order to gain multiple perspectives.
- Take notes while reading (using varied modalities as needed) in order to capture what is perceived to be the most interesting, important, or even troubling aspects of the study.
- Render all musical examples.

Writing Interpretivist Research

In this section, with the author's permission, I have borrowed heavily from Aigen (2003, 2005b). Although Aigen tailors the information in his 2003 publication to nonresearch scholarly writing, many of his ideas are absolutely applicable to this section of the chapter.

Writing about a research project based on principles of interpretivism is a herculean task. There are many reasons for this. First, there are likely infinite designs and methods, each of which suggests a unique means of description. A fundamental task, then, is to select the means congruent with the nature of our own projects. Furthermore, massive amounts of (often diverse) data typically have been

collected/constructed. (My use of this term reflects the stance that certain data are not really collected but rather are created or co-created.) This can be—nay, *is*—difficult to manage, yet must be managed somehow. Furthermore, we are using words to describe processes that are, at their core, ineffable; we are attempting to describe the essential products and processes of music therapy—the nuanced experiences of the participants/clients and researchers/therapists involved in the study. Writing of this sort demands reflective rigor. Haphazard or convenient choices about how to treat the data not only will lead us further away from a *true* re-presentation of experience, but also will undermine our scholarly credibility and influence. Add to this the fact that inquiry in which interpretation figures prominently is a nonlinear process. This extends to the writing of the report as well; we likely will go around and around in circles, either at the hands of a certain methodology (as in hermeneutics), or because we encounter the formidable challenges already mentioned, or both.

Quite simply stated, then, if we intend to produce a report that does justice to the topic and the study participants and that is comprehensible, engaging, and meaningful (Sandelowski & Barroso, 2002), we can expect to devote considerable effort and time to its construction. In all probability, we will write numerous drafts and agonize over each one.

In the midst of our labors, it may be helpful to consider that writing is in itself a method of inquiry, and one that helps us to deepen our understanding and more clearly formulate and communicate our ideas about the topic, as declared by Richardson (1994):

> Although we usually think of writing as a mode of "telling" about the social world, writing is not just a mopping-up activity at the end of a research project. Writing is also a way of "knowing"—a method of discovery and analysis. By writing in different ways, we discover new aspects of our topic and our relationship to it. (p. 516)

In spite of the idiosyncrasies associated with the processes of writing the report (i.e., how we approach and manage its construction) and the actual product (i.e., the structure and content of what we construct), all researchers/authors confront certain questions and make key decisions that impact upon the report. In what follows, I have identified some of these questions and have offered related considerations and recommendations. The first few of these questions may relate more to so-called *prewriting tasks and attitudes* but may, in fact, be posed at various junctures during the writing process.

Getting Ready

Just as there are many reasons for reading reports, there are multiple reasons for writing them. Before we commence writing, we would be wise to identify our reasons, as these will suggest our target audience (e.g., students, clinicians, administrators), which may, in turn, suggest a publication venue and, to a substantial extent, guide our decisions about how and what we write. We also need to obtain necessary materials and support and reflect on ethical considerations.

Why Write? Some of us write because it is compulsory, as when we pursue a graduate degree or assume an academic position in which such scholarly productivity is expected. Some of us write because published research can leverage funding for continued research or clinical services. And, believe it or not, some among us write simply because we enjoy the act of writing as an aesthetic and creative process!

If we are committed to the ideas that we construct, co-construct, and re-construct, we may send them into the mainstream (or maelstrom?) of scholarly discourse with the hopes of enriching professional understanding and, ultimately, contributing to improved services for our clientele (Aigen, 2003), which could be argued as the single most important reason for a music therapist to write.

Do I Have What I Need? Ideally, every researcher/author will find or fashion a dedicated and private space in which to write. This is important for a couple of reasons. First, it is common to rely heavily on multiple resources during the writing process, and it is easier to go to a stack of books and journals on a dedicated desk than to tote that stack to another location. A designated workspace is also important from an ethical standpoint, to protect the participants' privacy. It is critical from a productivity standpoint, to minimize interruptions. Furthermore, a dedicated space can be organized just the way the researcher/author prefers it, with the lighting, ventilation, acoustics, vista, seating, and so forth selected or arranged for maximum efficiency and comfort.

The interpretivist report starts to take shape from the very outset of the research endeavor—the moment of study conception—rather than after all data have been collected/constructed and the participants have left the scene. This is because much of what ends up in the report is taken directly from the raw data that are amassed along the way—reflexive journals, transcribed text and music, and field notes. Obviously, then, the researcher/author will need a well-organized and efficient system for collecting, storing, and retrieving these materials. Computers used in research should be password protected. A device for backing up files is an absolute necessity. And because the interpretivist research report is built predominantly upon words, access to a dictionary and thesaurus is critical. Audio and video playback equipment will be necessary if data are represented in these modalities. One final suggestion here: The researcher/author may want to keep at the ready a small, portable device (e.g., spiral notebook, recorder, tablet) with which to chronicle ideas that come into awareness at unusual or unexpected times when a computer is unavailable or impractical.

What Kind of Support Do I Require? No research should be conceptualized as a solitary endeavor (Aigen, 2003). Without a doubt, one of the most helpful steps that an author can take is to enlist the aid of a research advisor and peers throughout the research process, but particularly as the data are analyzed, interpreted, and reported. If we are unable to contract with an advisor, we might (as I have done in the preparation of this chapter) ask a handful of colleagues to read and reread report drafts and to evaluate critically the content (e.g., Is the text well organized and well sequenced, easily understood, relevant, complete, accurate?), mechanics (e.g., grammar, punctuation), writing style/tone (e.g., is the tone congruent with the message to be communicated?), and formatting (e.g., are the headings, subheadings, and references accurately prepared?). If we are fortunate, we might have access to a scholarly think tank or writing group, composed of both novel and experienced researchers and authors who can provide meaningful critique from multiple varied perspectives.

What About Ethics? Ethical considerations must undergird all facets and phases of the research project. No individual should conduct research outside the scope of her or his training and supervision. Punch (1994) makes a powerful claim that "the neophyte [fieldwork] researcher can unwittingly become an unguided projectile bringing turbulence to the field, fostering personal traumas (for researcher and researched), and even causing damage to the discipline" (p. 83).

The ethical code of the American Music Therapy Association (2014) demands that we gain the appropriate consent to engage human beings in our research. This permission typically happens through university or clinical agency review boards before we begin our engagement with study participants and well before we chronicle this engagement. It is critical to maintain records of having sought and obtained this permission, as certain publishers require evidence of review board approval at the manuscript review stage, and some go further to require specific language about approval in all submitted manuscripts.

Review board approval is meant to ensure that the welfare and rights of study participants will be safeguarded in our interactions with them during the course of the study. Equally important yet often overlooked is our obligation to extend protection to the way we report our participants' involvement. As we make decisions about what information to share and how to convey it, we must intentionally reflect on whether we are adhering to our professional code and continuing to operate within core ethical principles such as beneficence, justice, fidelity, veracity, care and compassion, and accountability (Dileo, 2000). One example is the decision of whether or not to use pseudonyms in the written report to conceal participants' identities. Ethical considerations apply to all study participants, naturally, but are magnified in importance when these individuals have certain vulnerabilities related to age, status, disability, illness, and so forth.

Beyond commonly held beliefs and standards, however, are ethical matters perceived as being connected uniquely to qualitative inquiry. As Langenberg and colleagues (1996) note, qualitative researchers "have an expansive view of what constitutes an ethical concern in research, framing issues as a matter of ethics where other researchers would consider a particular concern a matter of research methodology without ethical implications" (p. 259). These authors go on to write, "however, it is important to consider that an obligation to engage in a thorough pursuit of truth—considered either as a singular or a multifaceted phenomenon—is an essential ethical principle of all kinds of research and is, arguably, a criterion of research success" (p. 259). From this viewpoint, a *thorough pursuit of truth* necessarily involves standards of trustworthiness and authenticity (Guba & Lincoln, 1989; Lincoln & Guba, 1985). Authenticity can be viewed as a process of awareness, honesty, and ownership that permeates the entire research process, including how we communicate our findings (Bruscia, 1996). A researcher/author who acts authentically in the preparation of the report will consequently disclose all information believed to be "essential for the reader to know in order to engage (with) the data and findings" (Bruscia, 1996, p. 106), just as the researcher/author has done, even when that information includes unexpected, disappointing, contradictory, or unflattering discoveries. In a synthesis of my doctoral dissertation, I wrote, "I anticipated that the experience of improvising with adolescents would be a pleasurable and personally meaningful one, which—as it turned out—was not always the case" (Gardstrom, 2004, p. 82). That I felt bored and found little meaning in certain improvisational interchanges with study informants was at once unpredicted and discouraging, and a discovery that, when revealed, might have left the reader with an unbecoming impression of me as a clinician; yet this finding was of import and needed to be exposed. Additionally related to communicating a context for the research project, Aigen (1996) writes, "in terms of ethics, it is essential for researchers to disclose any information that bears on their having a vested interest in obtaining certain research results, such as is the case when clinician-researchers study their own work" (p. 13).

An additional concern pertains to the particular manner in which we describe the participants and their actions; of course, this is the very *stuff* of this type of report and has to do largely with the narrative tone that we employ. (Writing tone is addressed in more detail below.) As researchers/authors, we would do well to ensure that the linguistic and rhetorical features of our writing align not only with our philosophy about music therapy, but also with our ethical principles. For illustrative purposes, let us contrast the subtle but consequential difference in spirit of the two narrative excerpts below, each of which describes the identical client and incident:

> She made eye contact and appeared to be listening, but would not answer. It took the researcher three tries to get the resident to respond to the verbal cue; she finally smiled and responded by beating a simple rhythmic pattern on the drum.

> She made eye contact and appeared to be listening, but did not answer immediately. With a third request from the researcher, the resident smiled and responded by beating a simple rhythmic pattern on the drum.

In the first example, the words and phrases *would not, to get the resident to respond*, and *finally* might first suggest to the reader that the client was resistant or even lazy. A deeper analysis might reveal a therapeutic approach based on authoritative privilege and coercion. I am not suggesting that an approach such as this can or should be *fixed* merely by changing how one writes—although over time and with the right conditions this may be the case, as our writing is thought to influence our thinking (Aigen, 2005a; Richardson, 1994); the point here is that we must guard against and be on the lookout for pronouncements that mistakenly and inadvertently communicate a lack of awareness of or concern for the participants' rights—in this particular case, autonomy and dignity.

Digging into the Writing

This section focuses on several considerations related to the actual creation of the report.

What About Structure? Some kind of structure will be necessary to organize the complicated and diverse material that results from interpretivist inquiry. Decisions about macro-structure may be guided by publisher's guidelines. For instance, the "Submission Guidelines for Contributors" in *Qualitative Inquiries in Music Therapy* (QIMT) state that authors should include sections titled Introduction, Review of Literature, Problem Statement, Method, Results, and Discussion, depending on the nature of the study. Thus, there are many examples of this traditional quantitative report structure and sequence in the QIMT volumes, such as Gardstrom's (2004) report about meaning in clinical improvisation, Abbott's (2005) report about clients' imagery experiences, and Albornoz' (2013) report about crying in music therapy.

To be sure, the study design itself will inform choices about the presentation of the findings. In this sense, it may be useful to look to other studies for ideas. In 2008, Aigen commented that, because the first qualitative music therapy research reports appeared in the late 1980s—much later than in our kindred disciplines—there were fewer discipline-specific epistemological and methodological models from which to select as we contemplated, conducted, and chronicled our own studies. As of 2006, only 92 articles and book chapters meeting Aigen's analysis criteria had been published. The good news is that, according to Aigen's updated, unpublished bibliography, this number has climbed to 192 as of mid-2012, which means that more publications appeared between 2007 and mid-2012 than in the 20 previous years (K. Aigen, personal communication, February 17, 2014). Barcelona Publishers has continued to publish *QIMT*, resulting in additional qualitative monographs addressing varied research topics through an impressive array of designs and methods. In Volume 3 alone, for instance, we find examples of historical reconstruction (Eyre, 2007), case study (Murphy, 2007), hermeneutics (Keith, 2007), self-inquiry (Sokira, 2007), and phenomenology and grounded theory (Bonde, 2007). These reports, while following the recommended macro-structure, include unique and diverse subheadings and a wide range of data, including audio improvisation excerpts, improvisation analyses, portions of transcribed interviews, numerical and textual tables, and figures of theoretical models.

If a fitting prototype is not available within the music therapy literature base, it may be necessary to look to other disciplines or to create such a structure. Additionally, it is suggested that the researcher remain open to the possibility of a functional structure emerging from and evolving throughout the writing process.

What About Narrative Methods? While it is beyond the scope of this chapter to provide a detailed description of narrative devices commonly used in interpretivist reports, point of view warrants mention, as it can have a strong impact on how one's reporting is received and comprehended. A publication's point of view reflects the perspective through which a story is told and thus the relationships between the researcher/author and the other characters and events in that story. First-person singular point of view (*I*) partners nicely with interpretivist practices because it most directly and intimately conveys the personal knowledge, thoughts, feelings, opinions, and interpretations of the author (see Elwafi, 2011). Music therapists also have used first-person narrative to infer client experiences (Aigen, 1997; Hibben, 1999), or what Aigen (2005b) refers to as *first-person/-participant's voice*. A greater sense of objectivity and distance is communicated by third-person point of view (*he, she, it, they*). Multiple points of view may be employed, as in an article by Jackson and Gardstrom (2012), where the reader encounters first-person singular (*I* found in verbatim participant narrative), first-person plural (*we*, as it refers to the researchers), and third-person singular and plural (*she* and *they*, as the researchers refer to the participants).

What About Self-Revelation? One important reflexive practice involves conscientious self-inquiry, its purpose being to discern and monitor how aspects of our personhood, or what we might think of as personal subjectivities or countertransferences, impact upon and are impacted by the research process (Abrams, 2005; Aigen, 2005b; Bruscia, 1995c, 1998a, 2005; Stige, 2002). There are different levels and applications of this self-exploration or *soul-searching* (Bruscia, 1995c). For instance, we may introspect about our own relationship to, role in, and reactions to the study (intrasubjectivity) or about our own relationships with other individuals involved in the study (intersubjectivity), such as participants, co-researchers, and consultants. Common practices of conscientious self-inquiry include personal journaling, dialoguing with co-researchers and study participants, and consulting with advisors. The use of "regular, ongoing, self-conscious documentation" (Huberman & Miles, 1994, p. 439) of coding schemes, conceptual arguments, and episodes of analysis are further proposed. Music-centered self-inquiry might draw upon Bruscia's (2014) music therapy methods to include music-assisted imagery, improvisation, re-creation of a client's improvised or composed music, and song composition as a form of music journaling.

We alone ultimately choose what to do with awarenesses gained through conscientious self-exploration. The extent to which uncovered countertransferences are integrated into the process of inquiry varies greatly, depending on our epistemology, focus, and purpose. That is, we may decide to acknowledge yet dismiss their relevance and significance, acknowledge yet bracket or suspend them in order to mitigate their unwanted interference, or acknowledge and incorporate them into all aspects and phases of the inquiry.

Shaw (2010) writes, "one aspect of reflexivity which induces anxiety in some researchers is what level of reflexive account, if any, should be included in written reports and journal articles" (p. 241). Each researcher/author must find a way to strike a balance between self-revelation (expounding on one's own discoveries about self) and a focus on participant process and experience. In other words, we must avoid "navel gazing" (Finlay, 2002, p. 215). For, as Doyle (2013) reminds us, "lengthy disclosures that fail to demonstrate the applicable links to the research project have missed the point" (p. 253). On this point, I again recommend enlisting the critical reviews of a research advisor and peer group.

What About Clinical Examples? Aigen recommends that we make "effective but judicious use of clinical examples" (p. 13) as we write the research report. The purpose of such examples is to help the reader comprehend certain constructs and enable them to apply these to their own clinical practice and clientele. The decision of which kinds and how much supportive media (Aigen, 2003) we decide to use should be based upon our understanding of who will be reading the report and what they will require in order to make sense of it. A nice example of the judicious yet helpful use of clinical material is found in "Client Perspectives on the Music in

Guided Imagery and Music (GIM)" by Summer (2011). In this article, six client perspectives are recounted and, while one of the clients created multiple mandala drawings after he imaged, Summer presents just one of his drawings, having carefully selected this one because it best supports the narrative description and conveys the essence of that client's experience.

What About the Aesthetics of Writing? Aigen (2003) purports that the aesthetics of our writing are absolutely relevant to the task of disseminating information. In building a case for "making a good story" (p. 15), he cites the importance of conveying the realities of human life and experience, inspiring others, and drawing the reader into vicarious engagement. He writes, "Aesthetic factors are not frills added on to human experience, and their presence facilitates the acquisition of many kinds of knowledge" (p. 15). When text is not only clear and thorough, but also elegantly constructed, the reader is better able to identify with the researchers' and study participants' perspectives, which may promote intersubjective agreement about the findings.

What About Writing Style? Many conventions and styles exist for scholarly writing. As for a style guide, the most commonly used in the social and behavioral sciences is the *Publication Manual of the American Psychological Association* (6th ed., 2010). This manual includes information about compositional structure and format, ethics, writing bias, plagiarism, reference citations, and a host of other useful topics. It is an essential resource for all researchers/authors in the field of music therapy. Other oft-used style guides include the *Chicago Manual of Style* (University of Chicago Press, 2010) and the *MLA [Modern Language Association] Style Manual and Guide to Scholarly Publishing* (3rd ed., 2008). Student researchers/authors, in particular, might benefit from the *MLA [Modern Language Association] Handbook for Writers of Research Papers* (7th ed., 2009), which caters to high school and undergraduate students and provides guidelines for publishing in an online environment. Whatever style is required, I recommend becoming familiar with and adopting it from the very beginning of the project if possible, as this is more efficient than making necessary alterations later in the scribing process.

What About Reporting Guidelines? Guidelines for comprehensive and explicit qualitative reporting began surfacing in the 1970s, with the initial intent being to promote trustworthiness. Guidelines have continued to evolve, contributing also to the legitimization of qualitative research, expansion of approaches and methods, and enabling of more relevant peer reviews. We may follow such guidelines, both with these aims in mind and because certain publications mandate or recommend adherence by submitted manuscripts. For instance, the *Journal of Music Therapy (JMT)* recommends that researchers/authors consult an article referenced above, "Reading Qualitative Studies"

(Sandelowski & Barroso, 2002). *JMT* also refers researchers/authors to an article by Stige, Malterud, and Midtgarden (2009): "EPICURE: Toward an Agenda for Evaluation of Qualitative Research."

Another option is **COREQ (Consolidated Criteria for Reporting Qualitative Research;** Tong, Sainsbury, & Craig, 2007), a 32-item checklist that was designed to improve reporting, specifically in health- and mental health–care research. COREQ applies most neatly to inquiry involving in-depth and semi-structured interviews and focus groups. Questions target aspects of reporting within three domains: (a) research team and reflexivity (e.g., What did the participants know about the researcher, e.g., personal goals, reasons for doing the research?); (b) study design (e.g., Were transcripts returned to participants for comment and/or correction?); and (c) data analysis and reporting (e.g., Did participants provide feedback on the findings?).

For researchers conducting meta-syntheses of qualitative research, one set of relevant guidelines is **ENTREQ: Enhancing Transparency in Reporting the Synthesis of Qualitative Research** (Tong, Flemming, McInnes, Oliver, & Craig, 2012). For further information on criteria and processes informing the construction and appraisal of interpretivist research, see Chapter 66.

In summary, recommendations for the process of writing the interpretivist report include the following:

- Consider the purposes for writing; this will make more purposive your decisions about how and what to write and may reveal the targeted audience;
- Organize your workspace and materials for optimal privacy and efficiency;
- Adhere to all relevant ethical codes; obtain informed consent according to review board regulations;
- Pay attention to the way participants' demographics and experiences are reported; check for and revise or eliminate any language that misrepresents them or undermines their human rights;
- Make good use of support from others, such as research advisors, colleagues, peer reviewers, and scholarly writing groups;
- Determine a structure for the report; use other studies as models, create an original structure, or embrace one that emerges from the writing process;
- Consider the narrative features of your report and use point of view in a manner that makes sense for your project and is congruent with the message you intend to convey;
- Strive for a balance between self-disclosure and maintaining focus on the subject at hand;
- Use clinical examples carefully, and always as a way to enhance the readers' comprehension and ability to generalize others' experiences to their own;
- Seek to improve the aesthetic qualities of the text toward full engagement and understanding of the

reader, thereby enhancing the probability of intersubjective agreements;

- Adhere to a consistent writing style (APA used in most cases);
- Consider using published reporting guidelines in report construction.

Submitting Interpretivist Research

Here, once again, I have turned to Aigen's (2003) work, as well as to his online treatise (2012), "Publishing Qualitative Research in the *Nordic Journal of Music Therapy*: Guidelines for Authors, Reviewers, and Editors for Evaluating Manuscripts" and its supplemental material (http://www.tandfonline.com/doi/suppl/10.1080/08098131.2012.685274/suppl_file/rnjm_a_685274_sup_25596220.pdf).

Navigating the Submission Process

Once we have completed a manuscript that we believe will make a novel and noteworthy contribution to the literature base, we may submit it for publication consideration. As with reading and writing processes, each of us will approach and navigate the submission process in a manner that is unique to our personal and professional aims and situations. Nonetheless, we will all face and make some of the same decisions along the way, even if the sequence and import of these decisions vary. Some considerations in this section are viable for the submission of all types of research; others relate specifically to interpretivist inquiry.

Location, Location, Location. Again, I write of location! One of our first steps is to decide where to locate our work. What *type* of publication befits our creation? Does it have the makings of a self-contained book? Or should it be a chapter within a book or monograph? Or is it best suited for a periodical, such as a scholarly journal that is published four times per year? It is not feasible to enumerate all of the many factors that might sway our decision about the type of publication to pursue; a few include purpose, length, and *goodness of fit*.

For a variety of reasons, we may elect to publish our own research, in which case we are not beholden to an external editor or editorial board, and we are solely responsible for the content of the publication. In that self-publication is inherently entirely self-monitored, it is especially useful to present the manuscript to an advisor or peers during its construction in an attempt to ensure authenticity, trustworthiness, and other attributes believed to be necessary constituents of *good* qualitative investigation and reporting (Aigen, 2008b; Bruscia, 1998b). Aigen (2003) reminds us that some qualitative methods involve verification of findings and conclusions with study participants or external auditors, a process that, when made transparent, may engender the readers' confidence in our knowledge claims.

We may be invited to contribute to an edited book or monograph, in which case we likely will have constructed our report with this particular venue and the editor's expectations and established rubric in mind. This type of submission may or may not be subject to critical evaluation, at the discretion of the editor.

We may also write with the intention of submitting our report to a journal in music therapy or another discipline. The decision regarding which journal to pursue must be made with care. Quite obviously, some journals are viewed as more reputable than others—an important consideration if we intend for our publication to advance our professional standing or employment status. Often, a journal's reputation has to do with its *impact factor*, a yearly calculation of the average number of citations to recent articles published in the journal that is thought to indicate relative importance in a particular field of inquiry. A related measure of merit is a journal's *acceptance rate*, which is the percentage of all submittals accepted for publication. Journals with a lower acceptance rate than others obviously are more selective and thus may be perceived as a more desirable option for publication. Free journals may be viewed as less discriminating and meritorious than paid subscription journals, even if this does not bear out.

Another critical consideration is our intended audience. Who would benefit most from reading about our research? If our report is meant to inform clinicians, for example, it would make more sense to submit it to a clinical journal than to a journal that specializes in theoretical or historical research. At this juncture, it is imperative to read the mission statement of each journal being considered in order to discern the goodness of fit. A related concern is whether or not the selected journal is in the business of publishing interpretivist research. This is important for two reasons. First, such a journal likely will employ reviewers who have experience with interpretivist practices, which means that they will *speak the language* necessary to provide a meaningful and relevant evaluation. Secondly, journals of this sort may be more prone to allow supportive media and materials (e.g., graphics, sound files) more characteristic of this research. An electronic, or online, journal specializing in qualitative inquiry may be an especially good choice if supportive material is disallowed in a print journal or if the length of the report exceeds typical print journal limits. The literature suggests that the benefits of online journal publication include not only speedier publication processes and higher acceptance rates for submissions, but also wider accessibility (Angell & Smith, 1998).

We must also consider whether the publication is a noncompetitive, nonjuried journal or a competitive, juried journal. Usually, the latter is valued more highly in academic circles. A juried publication may involve editorial review and/or peer review. Further, review may be open or anonymous (also called *blind, blinded,* or *masked*). Blinded review means that the researcher/author does not know the identities of the reviewers. In an attempt to reduce bias, reviews may be *double-blinded*, meaning that neither the researcher/author nor the reviewers are aware of the others' identities. This is considered by many to be the most rigorous and objective form of review, yielding the most reputable publication.

Specific Journal Requirements. Once we have targeted a journal, we first need to read the submission guidelines with careful attention to ethics, deadlines, and required styles/formats. Macro-structures for the written report may be suggested or mandated, as with *Qualitative Inquiries in Music Therapy*. Publication guidelines may include questions to facilitate the researcher's/author's self-appraisal prior to submittal: Is the purpose stated clearly? Is the method described and is it appropriate, correctly and consistently applied, and its variations accounted for? Are the selection criteria and data analysis thoroughly described? Has the researcher/author explicated various relationships to the topic and study participants? Are findings clearly reported and substantiated by the raw data? (Aigen, 2012). Again, pay attention to reporting guidelines that are mandated or recommended for submitting authors.

Review and Revision. The journal review process serves many functions. Initially, it provides a mechanism for the culling of irrelevant or inferior reports. It is also a means by which researchers/authors have the opportunity for their scholarship to be objectively and constructively reviewed by external experts in the field. It can be a way to strengthen the overall quality of the journal contents, which can boost both the researcher's/author's and journal's reputation. If we bear in mind that a review is intended to (and, in most cases, actually functions to) help us to become better researchers and communicators in order to benefit readers and, commensurately, to more effectively serve our music therapy clients, this may not seem so daunting a process.

The timetable for review will vary according to factors such as the review protocol of the specific journal (e.g., whether the journal provides for online submission and review, the number of reviewers assigned to each manuscript), the editorial workload (whether assistant or co-editors are employed), the number of submittals in any given review period, and so forth. The nature of the process itself will also vary; sometimes reviewers' verbatim comments are shared with the researcher/author and sometimes these comments are paraphrased and summarized by editorial staff before being disseminated. If revision is recommended, the researcher/author likely will be asked not only to incorporate the reviewers' specific feedback in the revised manuscript (e.g., making changes to sentence structure, adding or deleting content), but also to address each reviewer's comments one by one in terms of whether or not suggestions have been accepted, as well as a rationale for these decisions. To be certain, sometimes it is difficult to find a balance between accepting critique and incorporating recommended

changes and holding fast to one's beliefs about what should appear in a report; fundamental differences of opinion can make for a lengthy and conflictual review. Nonetheless, in all cases, communication between the researcher/author and the editor(s) and reviewers should be respectful.

In summary, recommendations for the process of submitting interpretivist research include the following:

- Consider the type of publication best aligned with your research project: book, monograph, non–peer-reviewed journal, peer-reviewed journal, online, or print.
- When self-publishing, electing to subject one's research to external review may help to ensure standards of integrity.
- When targeting journals for submittal, investigate statistics such as impact factor, acceptance rate, readership, and access; read the mission statement to determine *goodness of fit*.
- Look for journals that specialize in or accept research based on interpretivist practices.
- Consider that different levels of editorial and peer review may have an influence on others' perceptions of the merit of your journal publications.
- Read and carefully follow all submission guidelines, including those pertaining to ethics, deadlines, and styles/formats.
- Engage in the review and revision process with a positive attitude and the intent of improving your manuscript for the benefit of the readership; maintain direct yet respectful communication with the editor and reviewers.

Conclusion

Whether characterized as objectivist, interpretivist, or some amalgam of both, and whether our questions and methods are predetermined and static or emergent and evolving, again, *good* research is always a systematic process of investigation, characterized by some measure of intentionality. This intentionality must permeate also the processes of reading, writing, and submitting research reports for publication. Why would we engage in these various scholarly tasks in any other way? Many of the considerations offered in this chapter emanate from the fundamental concept of intentionality, which lends rigor and credibility to our scholarship.

In this chapter, I have put forth my own and others' thoughts about the processes of reading, writing, and submitting music therapy research of an interpretivist nature. Each one of these three complex scholarly activities certainly deserves more detailed attention than space permits here. Nonetheless, I hope that the practical recommendations—introduced in each section and appearing in bulleted form at the end—will be of use to those of you who intend to explore, or who already are immersed in, the dynamic and exciting world of interpretivist inquiry.

References

Abbott, E. (2005). Client experiences with the music in the Bonny Method of Guided Imagery and Music (BMGIM). *Qualitative Inquiries in Music Therapy, 2*, 36–61.

Abrams, B. (2005). Evaluating qualitative music therapy research. In B. L. Wheeler (Ed.), *Music therapy research* (2nd ed.; pp. 246–258). Gilsum, NH: Barcelona.

Aigen, K. (1997). *Here we are in music: One year with an adolescent Creative Music Therapy group.* Nordoff-Robbins Music Therapy Monograph Series #2. St. Louis, MO: MMB.

Aigen, K. (2002). *Playin' in the band: A qualitative study of popular music styles as clinical improvisation.* Gilsum, NH: Barcelona.

Aigen, K. (2003). *A guide to writing & presenting in music therapy.* Gilsum, NH: Barcelona.

Aigen, K. (2005a). Naturalistic inquiry. In B. L. Wheeler (Ed.), *Music therapy research* (2nd ed.; 352–364). Gilsum, NH: Barcelona.

Aigen, K. (2005b). Writing the qualitative research report. In B. L. Wheeler (Ed.), *Music therapy research* (2nd ed.; pp. 210–225). Gilsum, NH: Barcelona.

Aigen, K. (2008a). An analysis of qualitative music therapy research reports 1987–2006: Articles and book chapters. *Arts in Psychotherapy, 35*(4), 251–261. doi:10.1016/j.aip.2008.05.001

Aigen, K. (2008b). An analysis of qualitative music therapy research reports 1987–2006: Doctoral studies. *Arts in Psychotherapy, 35*(5), 307–319. doi:10.1016/j.aip.2008.06.001

Aigen, K. (2012). Publishing qualitative research in the *Nordic Journal of Music Therapy*: Guidelines for authors, reviewers, and editors for evaluating manuscripts. Retrieved from http://www.tandfonline.com/doi/suppl/10.1080/08098131.2012.685274/suppl_file/rnjm_a_685274_sup_25596220.pdf

Albornoz, Y. (2013). Crying in music therapy: An exploratory study. *Qualitative Inquiries in Music Therapy, 8*, 31–50.

American Music Therapy Association. (2014). *Code of ethics.* Silver Spring, MD: American Music Therapy Association. Retrieved from http://www.musictherapy.org/about/ethics/

American Psychological Association. (2010). *Publication manual of the American Psychological Association* (6th ed.). Washington, DC: Author.

Angell, B., & Smith, G. (1998). Print versus electronic: Editors' insights on the costs and benefits of online journals. *The Journal of Technology Studies, 24*(1).

Bonde, L. O. (2007). Imagery, metaphor and perceived outcome in six cancer survivors' BMGIM therapy. *Qualitative Inquiries in Music Therapy, 3*, 132–164.

Bruscia, K. (1987). *Improvisational models of music therapy.* Springfield, IL: Charles C Thomas.

Bruscia, K. (Ed.). (1991). *Case studies in music therapy.* Phoenixville, PA: Barcelona.

Bruscia, K. (1995a). The boundaries of music therapy research. In B. L. Wheeler (Ed.), *Music therapy research: Quantitative and qualitative perspectives* (pp. 17–27). Gilsum, NH: Barcelona.

Bruscia, K. (1995b). The process of doing qualitative research: Part II: Procedural steps. In B. L. Wheeler (Ed.), *Music therapy research: Quantitative and qualitative perspectives* (pp. 401–427). Gilsum, NH: Barcelona.

Bruscia, K. (1995c). The process of doing qualitative research: Part III: The human side. In B. L. Wheeler (Ed.), *Music therapy research: Quantitative and qualitative perspectives* (pp. 429–443). Gilsum, NH: Barcelona.

Bruscia, K. (1996). Authenticity issues in qualitative research. In M. Langenberg, K. Aigen, & J. Frommer (Eds.), *Qualitative music therapy research: Beginning dialogues* (pp. 81–107). Gilsum, NH: Barcelona.

Bruscia, K. (1998a). Understanding countertransference. In K. E. Bruscia (Ed.), *Dynamics of music psychotherapy* (pp. 51–70). Gilsum, NH: Barcelona.

Bruscia, K. (1998b). Standards of integrity for qualitative music therapy research. *Journal of Music Therapy, 35*, 176–200. doi:10.1093/jmt/35.3.176

Bruscia, K. (2005). Designing qualitative research. In B. L. Wheeler (Ed.), *Music therapy research* (2nd ed.; pp. 129–137). Gilsum, NH: Barcelona.

Bruscia, K. (2014). *Defining music therapy* (3rd ed.). University Park, IL: Barcelona.

Denzin, N., & Lincoln, Y. (1994). Introduction: Entering the field of qualitative research. In N. Denzin & Y. Lincoln (Eds.), *Handbook of qualitative research* (pp. 1–17). Thousand Oaks, CA: Sage.

Denzin, N. K., & Lincoln, Y. S. (2000). The discipline and practice of qualitative research. In N. K. Denzin & Y. S. Lincoln (Eds.), *Handbook of qualitative research* (2nd ed., pp. 1–28). Thousand Oaks, CA: Sage.

Dileo, C. (2000). *Ethical thinking in music therapy.* Cherry Hill, NJ: Jeffrey Books.

Doyle, S. (2013). Reflexivity and the capacity to think. *Qualitative Health Research, 23*(2), 248–255. doi:10.1177/1049732312467854

Elwafi, P. R. (2011). The impact of music therapists' religious beliefs on clinical identity. *Qualitative Inquiries in Music Therapy, 6*, 155–191.

Etherington, K. (2004). *Becoming a reflexive researcher: Using our selves in research.* London, UK: Jessica Kingsley.

Eyre, L. (2007). Changes in images, life events and music in Analytical Music Therapy: A reconstruction of Mary Priestley's case study of "Curtis." *Qualitative Inquiries in Music Therapy, 3*, 1–30.

Finlay, L. (2002). Negotiating the swamp: The opportunity and challenge of reflexivity in research practice. *Qualitative Research, 2*(2), 209–230. doi:10.1177/146879410200200205

Fish, S. (1980). *Is there a text in this class? The authority of interpretive communities.* Cambridge, MA: Harvard University Press.

Gardstrom, S. (2004). An investigation of meaning in clinical music improvisation with troubled adolescents. *Qualitative Inquiries in Music Therapy, 1,* 77–160.

Guba, E., & Lincoln, Y. (1989). *Fourth generation evaluation.* Newbury Park, CA: Sage.

Hadley, S. (2003). (Ed.). *Psychodynamic music therapy: Case studies.* Gilsum, NH: Barcelona.

Hibben, J. (1999). (Ed.). *Inside music therapy: Client experiences.* Gilsum, NH: Barcelona.

Huberman, A., & Miles, M. (1994). Data management and analysis methods. In N. Denzin & Y. Lincoln (Eds.), *Handbook of qualitative research* (pp. 428–444). Thousand Oaks, CA: Sage.

Jackson, N., & Gardstrom, S. (2012). Undergraduate music therapy students' experiences as clients in short-term group music therapy. *Music Therapy Perspectives, 30*(1), 65–82. doi:10.1093/mtp/30.1.65

Langenberg, M., Aigen, K., & Frommer, J. (Eds.). (1996). *Qualitative music therapy research: Beginning dialogues.* Gilsum, NH: Barcelona.

Keith, D. (2007). Understanding music improvisations: A comparison of methods of meaning-making. *Qualitative Inquiries in Music Therapy, 3,* 62–102.

Lincoln, Y. S., & Denzin, N. K. (2008). Epilogue: The eighth and ninth moments—Qualitative research in/and the fractured future. In N. K. Denzin & Y. S. Lincoln (Eds.), *The landscape of qualitative research* (pp. 539–554). Thousand Oaks, CA: Sage.

Lincoln, Y., & Guba, E. (1985). *Naturalistic inquiry.* Newbury Park, CA: Sage.

Meadows, A. (2011). (Ed.). *Developments in music therapy practice: Case study perspectives.* Gilsum, NH: Barcelona.

Modern Language Association. (2008). *MLA style manual and guide to scholarly publishing* (3rd ed.). New York, NY: Modern Language Association of America.

Modern Language Association. (2009). *Handbook for writers of research papers* (7th ed.). New York, NY: Modern Language Association of America.

Murphy, K. (2007). Experiential learning in music therapy: Faculty and student perspectives. *Qualitative Inquiries in Music Therapy, 3,* 31–61.

Onwuegbuzie, A. J., Leech, N. L., & Collins, K. M. T. (2010). Innovative data collection strategies in qualitative research. *The Qualitative Report, 15*(3), 696–726.

Sandelowski, M., & Barroso, J. (2002). Reading qualitative studies. *International Journal of Qualitative Methods, 1,* Article 5. Retrieved from http://www.ualberta.ca/~ijqm/

Scott, D. (1990). Practice wisdom: The neglected source of practice research. *Social Work, 35*(6), 564–568.

Shaw, R. (2010). Embedding reflexivity within experiential qualitative psychology. *Qualitative Research in Psychology,*

7, 233–243. doi:10.1080/14780880802699092

Smeijsters, H. (1997). *Multiple perspectives: A guide to qualitative research in music therapy.* Gilsum, NH: Barcelona.

Sokira, J. (2007). Interpreting the communicative behaviors of clients with Rett syndrome in music therapy: A self-inquiry. *Qualitative Inquiries in Music Therapy, 3,* 103–131.

Stige, B. (2002). *Culture-Centered Music Therapy.* Gilsum, NH: Barcelona.

Stige, B., Malterud, K., & Midtgarden, T. (2009). Toward an agenda for evaluation of qualitative research. *Qualitative Health Research, 19*(10), 1504–1516. doi:10.1177/1049732309348501

Summer, L. (2011). Client perspectives on the music in Guided Imagery and Music (GIM). *Qualitative Inquiries in Music Therapy, 6,* 34–74.

Tong, A., Flemming, K., McInnes, E., Oliver, S., & Craig, J. (2012). Enhancing transparency in reporting the synthesis of qualitative research: ENTREQ. *BMC Medical Research Methodology, 12*(1), 181. doi:10.1186/1471-2288-12-181

Tong, A., Sainsbury, P., & Craig, J. (2007). Consolidated criteria for reporting qualitative research (COREQ): A 32-item checklist for interviews and focus groups. *International Journal for Quality in Health Care, 19*(6), 349–357. doi:10.1093/intqhc/mzm042

University of Chicago Press. (2010). *The Chicago manual of style* (16th ed.). Chicago, IL: University of Chicago Press.

Wheeler, B. L. (Ed.). (1995). *Music therapy research: Quantitative and qualitative perspectives.* Gilsum, NH: Barcelona.

Wheeler, B. L. (Ed.). (2005). *Music therapy research* (2nd ed.). Gilsum, NH: Barcelona.

GLOSSARY

The terms included in this glossary are intended to help the reader understand aspects of the research process as covered in this book. The first step in compiling it was reviewing a computer-generated list of terms that were included in the chapters and determining which terms should be included. In later steps, the list was refined through adding and deleting terms. More detail is included for some chapters than for others. The definitions in the glossary come from various sources and may be original, paraphrases, or quotes. They are primarily from the book chapters, although some were combined from several chapters or taken from a dictionary or other sources outside of the book. When a definition comes from a chapter, the author of that chapter is listed following the term; if this is not done, the definition came from a different source or a variety of sources. Many terms are discussed in more than one chapter, but only the author(s) of the chapter from which definition as given (although not necessarily verbatim) is taken from is listed here. For citation purposes, please consult the chapter written by the author cited. A list of terms related to economic analysis is found in the Glossary of Terms at the end of Chapter 29, Economic Analysis.

AB design: a type of withdrawal design in single subject and small *n* research; involves the establishment of baseline (A) and the introduction of an experimental condition (B) (Jones & Brown)

ABA design: a type of withdrawal design in single subject and small *n* research; establishes some experimental control, in that if behavior returns to the same level as baseline without the treatment, there is some support that the introduction of the experimental condition is a possible reason for a change in behavior; a type of withdrawal design; see also *withdrawal design* (Jones & Brown)

ABAB design: a type of withdrawal design in single subject and small *n* research; establishes experimental control by reintroducing the identical experimental condition (B) a second time; see also *withdrawal design* (Jones & Brown)

abduction: making inferences from data and constructing a theory that is grounded in these inferences; to construct a data-based theory; to move from specific observations to overarching concepts

action research: term that covers a range of collaborative research approaches dealing with needs for change in lay and professional practice; related forms of inquiry include *participatory research, participatory action research,* *collaborative research, cooperative inquiry, community-based research,* and *emancipatory research* (Stige & McFerran)

aesthetics: the branch of philosophy dealing with judgments of beauty and art and the nature of people's experiences of them

alpha (a) level: see *probability level*

alternate forms reliability: method of determining reliability that provides an estimate of equivalence; important in situations when two forms (e.g., Form A and Form B) of the same measure are used; also referred to as *parallel forms* (Waldon)

alternative hypothesis, H_1: posits that an intervention will have an effect (Meadows)

AMSTAR (Assessment of Multiple Systematic Reviews): an 11-item questionnaire that can be used to assess the methodological quality of systematic reviews (Bradt)

applied behavior analysis (ABA): a type of therapy that uses principles of learning theory such as reinforcement, extinction, shaping, and punishment to change behavior (Jones & Brown)

applied research: research performed to solve a practical problem; purpose is to test a hypothesis or model in a real situation of interest to the researcher (Wheeler & Bruscia)

artifacts: physical objects that are the results of human behavior from the past

arts-based research: an umbrella term that comprises a research method, where the art forms are primary in the research process and an overall methodology, where a creative worldview forms the philosophical foundation for an inquiry; also called *art–based research, a/r/tography, arts-informed, artistic inquiry, artistically crafted inquiry, aesthetically based research,* and *critical arts-based research* (Viega & Forinash)

assumption of linearity: states that the relationship between each covariate and the dependent variable must be independently linear (i.e., data points fall in a straight line) and not curvilinear (i.e., data points fall in a curved line)

assumptions: conditions that must be met in the design of the study and in the data in order to apply certain statistical tests; parametric statistical tests require normally distributed data, equal variance in groups, and data on an interval or ratio scale; nonparametric tests do not require a specific distribution, they require that the data be collected from an independent, random sample; additional assumptions may be required for specific parametric or nonparametric tests; may also refer to things that are taken for granted in designing a study, generally clarified as part of the design

autocorrelation: when one measure influences the next measure, violating assumptions of parametric statistical testing (Ridder & Fachner)

autoethnography: a form of writing that has both ethnographic and autobiographical features

axiology: the branch of philosophy dealing with questions of value

baseline: the level or strength of a behavior before any intervention is introduced; a stable level of behavior serves as a basis for comparison when a new treatment or technique is begun

basic research: research performed primarily to increase the scientific body of knowledge without necessarily having in mind an application of the research findings; most often done in a laboratory or other setting in which all conceivable variables are controlled; also called *pure* or *fundamental research* (Wheeler & Bruscia)

biofeedback: auditory or visual feedback given to provide feedback on physiological functions to help a person gain some control over physiological processes

biography: the study of people and their contributions; a topic of historical research (Solomon & Davis)

bivariate correlation: determines the relationship between two variables; may represent the relationship between a single independent variable and a single dependent variable, or the relationship between any two independent or dependent variables (Ghetti)

bivariate linear regression: uses an equation to describe the relationship between a single independent variable and a dependent variable; analyzes the variability of a dependent variable by examining information available on an independent variable; also called *simple regression* (Ghetti)

Boolean operators: simple words (e.g., "or," "and," "not") used as conjunctions to combine or exclude keywords in a search (Abbott)

bracket: phenomenological research technique in which researcher attempts to hold in abeyance all preconceptions regarding an experience while undergoing it

case study: the study of a bounded system; can be objectivist or interpretivist (Murphy)

case-control study: retrospective study where study groups are defined by outcome (Ridder & Fachner)

categorical variable: a variable represented by numbers that identify separate, discrete categories

categories and *subcategories:* used to organize data in interpretivist research; built by looking at segmented data and determining the general topic of each segment

causal relationship: occurs when: (a) the cause precedes the effect; (b) the cause is related to the effect; and (c) no plausible alternative explanation exists for the effect other than the cause (Cohen)

changing criterion design: a type of single subject and small *n* research in which a long-term goal is established and incremental steps are taken along the way to bring the client closer to the goal (Napoles)

checklist: a list of behaviors that the observer can check off when they occur (Krout)

clinical importance: determined by calculations of the number needed to treat (NNT) and the number needed to harm (NNH); converts the results of studies of a treatment procedure into quantitative indicators of how many patients would have to be treated with the treatment method in order to bring about one good outcome or one harmful outcome (McKinney)

clinical research: research in which one is working directly with a client, observing the work as it is happening to further inform the clinical work, and studying these observations for research purposes; sometimes used to refer to applied research

closed-ended questions: a question followed by a set list of responses

coding: the interpretivist research procedure for assigning data segments to different categories by fixing a label on each unit of data to describe, represent, categorize, summarize, or symbolize the unit

coefficient of determination (r^2 or R^2): describes the amount of common or shared variance among variables, or how much of the variability in the criterion variable is accounted for by all predictors

cohort studies: gathers information from a specific cohort or population with changing members over time (Curtis)

collective case study: see *multiple case study*

Computer-Assisted Qualitative Data Analysis Software (CAQDAS): software to assist with qualitative data analysis (Baker)

concurrent validity: the degree to which a measure relates to a criterion (e.g., another measure or performance standard) established at the same time

confidence level: see *probability level*

confidence interval (C.I.): portrays the range of effects one might expect at a predetermined *p* level (e.g., *p* = .05 or 95% C.I.); when the confidence interval does not include zero, the estimated effect size is considered significant (Bradt)

confirmatory experiment: a type of experimental research that tests predictable outcomes and confirms previous findings

confirming case: can help researchers to elaborate on an initial analysis; a *disconfirming case* can reveal variations

conflict of interest: conflicting pressures and considerations that may influence the outcome of a research study

confounding variable: variable that inadvertently affects the independent variable in an experimental research study

consensual qualitative research (CQR): an interpretivist research method that requires consensual process in every step of data analysis in order to generate reliable results and, ultimately, applicable theories; incorporates elements from phenomenological research, grounded theory, and comprehensive process analysis (D. M. Kim)

consent form: a form that provides information on potential risks and benefits of participating in a research study; participant signs to indicate an understanding of the issues and willingness to participate in the study

CONSORT (Consolidated Standards for Reporting Trials) Statement: guidelines developed by an international group of medical editors and researchers to improve the quality of reports of clinical outcome studies (McKinney)

construct: a hypothetical concept or phenomenon (e.g., intelligence, depression, ability, or dysfunction) that cannot be observed directly, so one must infer the relative presence or absence of the construct through a measurable and observable event (Waldon)

construct validity: the degree to which a measure captures, or approximates, the phenomenon (i.e., the construct) under investigation; the validity of inferences that the observation methods or measurement tests and tools actually measure the construct that is being investigated

constructivism: a perspective that views meaningful human reality not as *out there* to be discovered or uncovered but rather as *constructed* by individuals through their interactions with and interpretations of the world and each other

content analysis: a method used to determine the presence of certain words or concepts within texts or sets of texts; can be either quantitative or qualitative; see also *qualitative content analysis*

content validity: a type of validity concerned with how well a measurement's procedures or a test's items accurately reflect the domain being measured (Waldon)

contingent design: a mixed methods synthesis design in which the results of synthesizing one group of studies (interpretivist, objectivist, or mixed methods primary research studies) are used to determine the next group of studies that will be retrieved and synthesized (which may, in turn, lead to another synthesis); this cyclic approach continues until the researcher has addressed the objectives of the synthesis (Meadows & Wimpenny)

continuous response digital interface (CRDI): an instrument that measures ongoing and fluctuating musical responses while people are listening to music; consists of a dial or a slide that can be manipulated by the listener as responses or perceptions vary; connected to a computer

continuous variable: a variable represented by numbers on a continuum

control: the extent in experimental research to which only the variable(s) intended to vary (the independent variables) differ(s) from condition to condition; also called *internal validity*

control group: a group in experimental research that does not receive the experimental treatment, thus providing a group against which the results of the treatment can be compared; may receive no treatment (a no-contact control group) or simply a different treatment

controlled observation: the precision of conditions under which data are collected (McKinney)

convenience sample: a sample selected because those comprising it are available or can attend certain scheduled sessions (as opposed to being randomly selected)

convergent parallel design: involves collecting quantitative and qualitative simultaneously, analyzing each strand separately, and merging the two data sets for final interpretation; strands are independent and equal in priority (Burns & Masko)

COREQ (Consolidated Criteria for Reporting Qualitative Research: a checklist that was designed to improve reporting in health- and mental health–care research (Gardstrom)

correlation: when one variable fluctuates in relation to another

correlation coefficient: states a relationship between two variables; a perfectly positive relationship is expressed by $r = +1.00$, a perfectly negative relationship by $r = -1.00$, and no relationship by $r = .00$

correlational research: research in which the researcher employs correlational analyses to determine the strength of the relationships among variables in the absence of any kind of experimental manipulation (Ghetti)

COSMIN (COnsensus-Based Standards for the Selection of Health Measurement INstruments): guidelines to evaluate the technical adequacy of research measures; include a checklist of methodological measurement qualities (including reliability, content validity, criterion-related validity, construct validity, measurement error, and responsiveness) and procedures for selecting and rating those qualities (Waldon)

cost–utility analysis; cost–benefit analysis; cost-effectiveness analysis; cost-minimization analysis: see Glossary of Terms at end of Chapter 29, Economic Analysis

counterbalanced design: a design in which the researcher determines the order in which subjects experience the experimental treatments so that each group experiences the conditions in a different order; used to ensure that order of presentation does not become a confounding variable

criterion case: looks at all cases that meet a certain criterion (Keith)

criterion variable: a behavioral measure of future performance to be predicted using a set of variables that are currently known; the predictor variable is used to predict the criterion variable in the context of nonexperimental research; see also *dependent variable*

criterion-referenced test: measures an individual's performance against a predetermined, fixed set of criteria; this criterion or benchmark might be a score required to be diagnosed with a certain disability or condition (Krout)

criterion-related validity: a type of validity concerned with whether a test that is intended to serve as a predictor or describer of an established behavior, the criterion, actually does so; the extent to which a measure relates to an independent (or external) measure or benchmark

critical ethnography: studies that describe and critique patterns of power and privilege as well as assumptions that are taken for granted in a culture

critical inquiries: a family of research strategies with a transformative agenda linked to various critical perspectives that challenge ideology and oppressive norms (Rolvsjord & Hadley)

critical interpretive synthesis (CIS): a type of qualitative synthesis that has the aim of synthesizing a diverse body of evidence that enables the generation of theory with strong explanatory power; focuses on interpreting a body of evidence to develop a theory grounded in the studies included for review (Meadows & Wimpenny)

critical theory: a school of thought that seeks to expose and therefore create an impetus for action against subjugation (Rolvsjord & Hadley)

critical value: the value needed to determine whether a finding is significant or not; the value that would be obtained if chance alone were operating; the researcher compares the statistic obtained through the statistical analysis with the critical value found in a table of critical values

criticism: the process by which historical researchers determine the credibility and accuracy of evidence; see also *external criticism, internal criticism*

cross-sectional design: samples are compared from different sets of participants who are at different stages or ages (Baker & Ledger)

crossover design: investigates two or more treatments over two or more periods of time; crossover trials provide each participant with two or more sequential treatments in a random order usually separated by a washout period (DeLoach, Wheeler, & Murphy)

culturally informed research: research that is concerned with cultural issues involved in music therapy research (Kim & Elefant)

data mining: the collection of previously existing data (Ridder & Fachner)

deception: the misrepresentation of facts related to the purpose, nature, or consequences of an investigation

deconstruction: one variant of poststructuralism; an approach to reading and writing texts; in deconstructionism, there is nothing outside the text (Hadley)

deduction or *deductive reasoning:* using theory, principles, or generalizations to develop hypotheses, gather data, and ultimately confirm or disconfirm the original theory; to test a theory through research; to move from the general to the specific

deductive analysis: an analytic approach where a framework of themes may be searched for in relevant data; used in thematic analysis (Hoskyns)

degrees of freedom (df): the number of observations in a linear distribution that are allowed to vary; determined by subtracting 1 from the actual number of items in the group (Meadows)

delimitations: internal limitations established by the researcher that limit the focus of a study; statements of what will and will not be included in a study (Cohen)

Delphi technique: the use of repeatedly refined questionnaires to gather data on a particular topic from experts in order to identify points of consensus and disagreement; may be used to produce consensus or to reveal differences of opinion among experts concerning a topic (Cassity)

demand characteristics: cues that influence participants to behave or respond differently because they know the purpose of the study (Waldon)

dependent variable: the variable that is observed for changes in order to assess the effects of manipulating the independent variable (Cohen)

descriptive research: research that aims at describing a phenomenon of interest

descriptive statistics: mathematical methods that are used to summarize and describe data (Meadows); includes mean, median, mode, standard deviation

design: the way that a research study is set up in order to investigate what is intended, including the independent and dependent variables and various aspects of the procedures; describes various ways of doing objectivist research (Cohen)

deviant case sampling: examining case(s) that are not the norm for the study being done; can provide data about special or unusual cases that may be troublesome or enlightening; also called *extreme sampling* (Keith)

directional prediction, one-tailed prediction, or *directional hypothesis:* assumes that the direction of an effect is known and can be expected based upon previous research

discipline research: research concerned with how music therapists interact with clients; one of three types of music therapy research (from Bruscia)

disconfirming case: see *confirming case*

discourse analysis: an approach that considers how meaning is socially, culturally, historically, and politically constructed and mediated through language (Talbot)

disordinal interaction: the order of the effects of one factor changes depending on the other factor (McKinney)

DOI (digital object identifier): a unique alphanumeric string assigned by a registration agency to identify content and provide a persistent link to its location on the Internet

dual relationship: more than one relationship between the researcher and research participants, as when one's students or clients are also participants in a research study conducted by the same person; a potentially conflictual situation

duration recording: observational method in which the length of time during which something occurs is measured (Krout)

effect size: a numerical way of expressing the strength or magnitude of a reported relationship between variables; quantifies the magnitude and association between the variables (Meadows)

effectiveness research: research conducted in settings that are close to those in which actual clinical work occurs; see also *pragmatic research* (DeLoach, Wheeler, & Murphy)

efficacy research: research conducted in an ideal laboratory situation; assesses the outcome that is associated with an intervention under ideal circumstances that allow for tight control; offers enhanced internal validity but may have limited generalizability to real-world settings; see also *explanatory research* (DeLoach, Wheeler, & Murphy)

emergent design, emergent process: a design typical of interpretative research in which the methods of engagement and data collection procedures emerge as the research progresses (Wheeler)

emic: analysis of cultural phenomena from the perspective of one who participates in the culture being studied; the inside view (Stige & Ledger)

empiricism: the theory that all knowledge is derived from one's own senses

empirical: based on, concerned with, or verifiable by observation or experience rather than theory or pure logic

empirical method: testing of theories through procedures for scientific objectivity, including careful observation of behavior, the isolation and manipulation of variables, and hypothesis testing

empirical phenomenology: focuses on understanding the meaning of a lived experience through multiple experiencers' descriptions of the phenomenon (Jackson)

empirical verification: verification through observation or experimentation

ENTREQ (*Enhancing Transparency in Reporting the Synthesis of Qualitative Research*): guidelines for reporting meta-syntheses of qualitative research

EPICURE: an evaluation agenda for interpretivist research; has two dimensions: (a) EPIC—refers to the challenge of producing rich and substantive accounts base on engagement, processing, interpretation, and (self-)critique; and (b) CURE—refers to the challenge of dealing with preconditions and consequences of research, with a focus on (social) critique, usefulness, relevance, and ethics

epistemology: the branch of philosophy dealing with what it is possible to know; a theory of knowledge concerning beliefs about how phenomena can come to be known, that is, how valid knowledge is produced (Hiller)

epoché: the theoretical moment where all judgments about the existence of the external world are suspended; used by phenomenological researchers

equal variance: similar amounts of variability in the data of two or more groups

essence: in phenomenology, essential parts of an experience that must be present so that the experience is recognizable

essential phenomenology: the discovery of structures that are implicit in a given phenomenon that allow it to be recognized as such (Jackson)

ethics: the branch of philosophy dealing with what is good and bad, moral and immoral

ethnography/ethnographic research: the firsthand study of how individuals and groups understand, accommodate, and resist a presumably shared order, achieved through a careful accumulation of data, aimed at examining the multifarious relationships that exist between the participants and their shared order, either within particular a context or culture or between them (Stige & Ledger)

etic: knowledge and values that researchers bring with them to the field; analysis of cultural phenomena from the perspective of one who does not participate in the culture being studied; the outside view (Stige & Ledger)

evaluation research: discipline research topic concerned with the outcomes or effects, as, for example, effects of music therapy on clients

event recording: see *tallying*

evidence-based practice (EBP): the use of current best evidence in making decisions about the care of individual patients

ex post facto research: quantitative research in which the researcher does not have direct control of the independent variables because they have either already occurred or are inherently not manipulable

existential phenomenology: a type of phenomenological inquiry that seeks to explicate the essence, structure, or form of both human experience and human behaviors as revealed through essentially descriptive techniques, including disciplined reflection (Jackson)

experimental design: a way to structure conditions in scientific inquiry so that researchers may test hypotheses by controlling certain variables and allowing others to change so that their effects can be observed; see also *design*

experimental engagement: the researcher sets up specific tasks or situations in order to engage participants in the phenomenon of interest; one of three levels of engagement in interpretivist research; see also *naturalistic engagement, retrospective engagement* (Keith)

experimental research: an objectivist research approach that involves comparing two or more groups that are similar in all important ways except for one factor (the independent variable) that has been deliberately set to differ between or among the groups; done to determine cause-and-effect relationships

explanatory research: assesses the outcome that is associated with an intervention under ideal circumstances that allow for tight control; see also *efficacy research* (DeLoach, Wheeler, & Murphy)

explanatory sequential design: a mixed methods design that consistently prioritizes quantitative data over qualitative data; in this design, quantitative data are collected first, followed by qualitative data; most common mixed methods design within music therapy (Burns & Masko)

exploratory sequential design: a mixed methods design that prioritizes the use of qualitative (interpretivist) methods in a mixed methods design; the first phase of the research collects qualitative data and uses qualitative methods of analysis; the findings from this initial qualitative phase are then used to plan a successive phase that uses objectivist methods; then, finally, the findings of the two discrete phases are integrated during a phase of interpretation of the entire analysis (Magee)

external criticism: techniques used by historians to determine the authenticity of a source of historical evidence; helps us determine whether the evidence is what we think it is, what it appears to be, or what someone claims it to be (Solomon & Davis)

external culture: relates to political and organizational aspects in a social and ecological context, including economic status and climate (Kim & Elefant)

external validity: establishes to what extent one can generalize the results of a research study to other populations, settings, times, measurements, and characteristics outside of those specifically used in the study (Cohen)

extraneous variable: see *confounding variable*

face validity: the degree to which a test seems to measure what it reports to measure

factorial design: a between-groups design based on analysis of variance that has more than one independent variable and one dependent variable; each level of each independent variable is *crossed* or evaluated in combination with each level of the other independent variable (McKinney)

feminism (or feminisms): broadly construed, a critical perspective concerned with gender equality and the intersections of identity, including but not limited to gender identity, gender expression, sexuality, race, class, and disability (Rolvsjord & Hadley)

feminist empiricism: focuses on how scientific methods can be improved by the identification and elimination of gender bias and the influence of social and political factors in research (Rolvsjord & Hadley)

feminist postmodernism: emphasizes the instability and multiplicity of social identities along with constructivist and poststructuralist perspectives, and delegitimizes dominating ideas and *grand narratives* (Rolvsjord & Hadley)

first-person research (FPR): uses data gathered from a first-person perspective—that is, data that come from the self; the aim is to acquire firsthand, personal accounts of subjective experience with the phenomenon of interest as directly experienced by the self (Hunt)

fixed effects model: a factorial design that identifies specific levels of the independent variables or categories of a factor that are of interest (McKinney)

focus group: a group of people assembled to collect data on particular experiences that people in the group may have had; participants are generally encouraged to share their feelings, insights, and opinions in a nonthreatening and permissive environment; may be called a *group interview* (Keith)

formal theory: a theory that can be used broadly (Amir, LaGasse, & Crowe)

foundational research: research that provides empirical support for concepts or notions related to music therapy, although not directly about music therapy; one of three types of music therapy research (from Bruscia)

frequency recording: see *tallying*

full factorial design: each level of each factor is crossed with all levels of the other factor(s) (McKinney)

generalize: to apply the results of research to people, settings, or conditions outside of those used in the experiment

gray literature: written material that is not published commercially or is not generally accessible (Abbott)

grounded theory: refers to both methods used to discover theory from data and the theory that the methods generate; grounded theory methods provide a framework, based on inductive logic, for collecting, managing, and rigorously analyzing qualitative data to construct descriptions with solid explanatory bases; data analysis involves the recognition of patterns and connections among elements of the data in a constant comparative procedure, a progressive and cyclic process of classifying, comparing, grouping, and refining labels representing data segments (O'Callaghan)

Hawthorne effect: when subjects' responses show changes due to the fact that the person is aware of being observed and acts accordingly (Ridder & Fachner)

health economics: the branch of economic theory dedicated to health-related topics; an applied field to systematically examine problems faced in promoting health (Else)

hermeneutic circle: in hermeneutic research, a constant analytic movement between phenomena of interest and the structures (theories) developed in order to better understand phenomena, so that theories are tentative and are constantly evaluated against the data, further refined, and then reapplied to the data

hermeneutic inquiry: a type of interpretivist research that has as its aim understanding meanings underlying human experiences, in contrast to, for instance, post-positivist explanations of causal relationships regarding phenomena or phenomenological pursuits of essences of objects, events, and experiences; can be divided into objectivist and alethic hermeneutics, with alethic including existential and poetic hermeneutics (see Loewy & Paulander for information on these divisions)

hermeneutic phenomenology: used to describe research in which the researcher seeks to understand human action through explicating an interpretation from textual data (Jackson)

heterogeneity of variance: high variability because numbers in a set are varied

heuristic inquiry: an approach to phenomenology in which the researcher utilizes personal experiences as data in order to understand and gain insight into a phenomenon through explication of meaning, essence, and quality; a type of first-person research (Jackson)

historical research: the systematic study of the past practices, materials, institutions, and people involved in therapeutic applications of music; involves gaining knowledge by studying evidence from the past; may refer to past events, things that have been written about the past, people's ideas, images, or memories of the past, a way of knowing about the past, or any combination of these (Solomon & Davis); see also *interpretivist historical research*

historiography: the process and product of presenting historical facts in a narrative based upon a critical examination of the sources (Solomon & Davis)

homogeneity of variance: low variability because numbers in a set are similar or homogeneous

human subject: defined by the Food and Drug Administration as an individual who participates in research either as a recipient of the experimental treatment or as a control

hypothesis: identifies a tentative relationship between the independent and dependent variables; a statement of what the researcher expects will occur in the study, or what will happen to the dependent variable as a result of the manipulation of the independent variable; often stated as: It is hypothesized that X (independent variable) will have an effect (or no effect) on Y (dependent variable)

hypothesis validity: the extent to which research results reflect theoretically derived predictions about the relations between or among constructs; the greater the hypothesis validity, the more a research study will contribute to the advancement of theory (McKinney)

hypothetico-deductive processes: seek to prove or disprove theoretically true statements through controlled experiments; also known as *hypothesis testing* or *falsification* (Hiller)

idealism: the belief that we humans construct experiences of reality in our minds through thoughts and ideas and that this reality is open to all varieties of interpretation; it is our consciousness that brings reality into being (Hiller)

implied consent: the assumption that a person who has received the information normally included in a consent form through a cover letter to a questionnaire, and returns the questionnaire, has consented to participate

incidence questions: objectivist research questions that are concerned with the prevalence of a certain variable or dimension along that variable within a particular stimulus array, environmental setting, subject population, response pattern, etc.

incident: see *segment*

independent group design: experimental research design in which two or more groups that bear no known relationship to one another are compared

independent variable: the variable that is manipulated, or varied, by the researcher; used primarily in experimental research or single subject and small *n* research designs; see also *predictor variable*

induction or *inductive reasoning:* finding patterns in data in order to formulate and test new hypotheses and/or theories; to generate a theory based on a logical and scientific analysis of data; to move from specific findings to generalizations

inductive inference: inferring general conclusions from particular phenomena; involves repeated empirical observations of similar phenomena, to make conclusions about their shared nature (Hiller)

inferential statistics: mathematical methods that employ probability theory to ascertain relationships between and among variables; statistics used to infer or estimate certain population characteristics based on a sample of the population (Meadows)

informed consent: the process by which a decision to participate in research is made by a competent individual after an investigator thoroughly explains the procedure, risks, and benefits of the study; allows individuals to make a decision to participate in a research study without coercion or fear of retribution (Murphy)

institutional review board (IRB): a group set up to review any research that receives funding from the Department of Health and Human Services, or other research as required by individual universities, clinical facilities, agencies, etc.

instrument: a general term used to describe the methods (e.g., observational techniques or interviews) or devices (e.g., tests or questionnaires) used in objectivist data collection (Waldon)

instrumental case design: a type of interpretivist case study; often used when a general understanding of a phenomenon or situation is needed; used to help researchers develop a better understanding of the theoretical underpinnings of a phenomenon (Murphy)

integrated design: a type of mixed methods synthesis design in which the methodological differences between interpretivist, objectivist, and mixed methods primary research studies are minimized, as findings from each are (to the greatest extent possible) transformed into one another (Meadows & Wimpenny)

integrative review: the broadest type of mixed methods synthesis, allowing for the inclusion of experimental and nonexperimental data that are compared and contrasted around a central concept, theory, or intervention (Meadows & Wimpenny)

interdisciplinary research: research in which team members develop new approaches to research by sharing differing epistemologies, starting with learning the language of the other disciplines (Magee & Heiderscheit)

internal consistency: method of determining reliability; important when multiple items within a single measure are used to measure a particular construct; these methods estimate the extent to which responses measuring one trait are consistent with other items purportedly measuring the same trait (Waldon)

internal criticism: techniques used by historians to determine the truthfulness of the information provided by written evidence (Solomon & Davis)

internal culture: relates to personal variables (e.g., one's values, knowledge, religion) (Kim & Elefant)

internal validity: reflects the degree to which the independent variable can be held responsible for a change in the dependent variable; also called *control*

interobserver reliability: see *interrater reliability*

interpretivism: holds that humans construct knowledge as they interpret their experiences of and in the world, rejecting the objectivist notion that knowledge is simply there to be identified and collected (Hiller)

interpretivist case study research: an in-depth empirical inquiry of a bounded system within a real-life setting (Murphy)

interpretivist historical research: a form of historical research that has been influenced by ideas from the *linguistic turn*, structuralism, poststructuralism, postmodernism, feminism, and deconstruction (Hadley)

interpretivist research: research intended to explore a particular phenomenon as it unfolds and reveals itself during the study, the aim being to explicate and understand the phenomenon; also called *qualitative research*

interpretivist synthesis: synthesis of interpretivist research, also called *qualitative synthesis, qualitative research synthesis, meta–ethnography,* and *qualitative meta–synthesis*; a way of combining and integrating interpretivist

research that addresses a similar topic, question, or population, developing a comprehensive picture of the findings, while ensuring the social, historical, and ideological context of the research is maintained; refers to a process and product of scientific inquiry aimed at systematically reviewing and formally integrating the findings and reports of completed qualitative studies (Meadows & Wimpenny)

interrater reliability: method of determining reliability, involves reliability based on agreement; the degree of agreement between raters or observers; essentially gives a score of how much consensus there is in the scores or ratings given by the observers; also referred to as *interrater agreement* or *concordance, interobserver reliability* (Waldon)

interval: scale or level of measurement that, because distances between adjacent values on the scale are equal, allows treatment of data by fundamental arithmetic functions such as addition, subtraction, multiplication, and division; suited for parametric statistical tests

interval recording: observational method in which the observation time is divided into small intervals within which the observer is instructed to observe and to record whether or not the behavior of interest occurred; sometimes called *time sampling* or *interval time sampling* (Krout)

interview guide: serves to structure the interview in order to obtain the best possible information from the interviewees; typically begins with general questions about the topic, and interviewers follow up with probes or clarifying questions (Keith)

interview-based surveys: a survey method in which a trained interviewer asks set questions and notates responses

intrinsic case design: a type of interpretivist case study; used when researchers are interested in learning more about a particular phenomenon; not looking to create theories or generalize their results (Murphy)

keywords: words relevant to a topic that are used in a literature search

latency recording: observational method in which the length of time before a behavior occurs is measured (Krout)

Latin square design: randomizes the first treatment assignment but gives each subject every treatment; each research subject must appear once and only once in each condition and level (DeLoach, Wheeler, & Murphy)

level: the divisions or values of an independent variable in experimental research

level of confidence: see *probability level*

level of significance: see *probability level*

Likert scale: items represent a dimensional construct (e.g., attitude, preference) requiring respondents to choose a value along that continuum representing the magnitude of their perception; has a written or pictorial descriptor at each degree along the scale (Waldon)

limitations: external conditions placed on the researcher that limit the focus of a study (Cohen)

linguistic turn: called into question the assumption that there is a reality outside of language to which we have direct access and argued for the position that language shapes and constitutes our understanding of reality; suggests that linguistic rules are arbitrary in the sense that they are arrived at by social agreement and understood differently by different linguistic communities (Hadley)

literature review: see *review of literature*

logistic regression: a form of regression employed when the dependent variable is categorical (Ghetti)

longitudinal design: studies how time, age, or interventions affect the variables of interest; done by collecting data from the same sample multiple times after different periods of time (Baker & Ledger)

main effect: the effect of an individual factor without regard to the effects of other factors in a factorial design (McKinney)

matched pairs design: experimental research design in which subjects are matched on relevant characteristics and assigned to different conditions

mean: descriptive statistic, average of scores, computed by first adding a set of numbers and then dividing that sum by the number of entries in the set (Meadows)

measurement: the assignment of numerals to objects or events according to rules (Waldon)

measurement error: the difference between the actual value of a quantity and the value obtained by a measurement; can be random or systematic

measures of central tendency, central value, or centrality: category of descriptive statistics that includes the mean, mode, and median

median: descriptive statistic identifying the midpoint of a distribution (Meadows)

mediational means: in discourse analysis, how objects or concepts are used and to what extent various participants internalize them as discourse (Talbot)

member checking: a procedure for establishing trustworthiness in interpretivist research in which the researcher provides the participants in a study with the data, categories in which the data are organized, and theories, conclusions, and other inferences that constitute the findings of the study in order to determine how well they match the experiences of the participants (Arnason)

meta-analysis: uses rigorous statistical techniques to combine and compare results (i.e., raw data) from independent, primary studies; a two-stage process: (a) an effect size or summary statistic is computed for each primary study, (b) a pooled estimate is calculated as a weighted average of the individual studies' effect sizes (Bradt)

meta-needs assessment: a type of meta-synthesis; a comprehensive analytic process focused on human service needs assessments using secondary data conducted by public, nonprofit, and private organizations in a particular community; based on meta-analysis and mixed methods research strategies (Meadows & Wimpenny)

method: the procedures or actions used to gather and analyze data (Hiller)

methodology: the supporting rationale for decisions made in designing methods for data collection and analysis; the justification for using a particular research method (Hiller)

microanalysis: research methods that investigate small units or microprocesses within one music therapy session or portions of a session (Wosch & Erkkilä)

mixed interpretivist research: incorporates data and analysis from more than one interpretivist research method (Zanders)

mixed methods research: collects and integrates both qualitative and quantitative data to answer one or more research question (Burns & Masko; Magee)

mixed methods synthesis: a process involving the integration of objectivist, interpretivist, and mixed methods research on a specific topic (Meadows & Wimpenny)

mode: descriptive statistic identifying the most frequently occurring score (Meadows)

model: a description or analogue used to help to visualize something that cannot be directly observed

morphological research: the study of the myriad relationships found among different aspects of a particular phenomenon based on the reflexive interpretations of independent observers; emphasis is given to understanding the *gestalt* of a phenomenon, which includes the whole, the parts in relation to the whole, and the parts in relationship to one another

mortality: the loss of participants from study groups (Cohen)

multicultural: refers to multiple cultures and indicates contrasting identities interacting or relating to one another in some way; among a wide range of individual identities, multicultural refers to a part of a person's race, ethnicity, age, gender, sexual orientation, language, religious or spiritual affiliation, marital status, ability, education, socioeconomic status, affiliation, and lifestyle.; can include the identities of an individual or the identities of many people (Kim & Elefant)

multicultural research: complex, contextual, and inclusive of multiple perspectives; includes cultural and musical plurality as well as its own conceptual limitations; also called *cross-cultural research* (Kim & Elefant)

multidisciplinary research: researchers from different disciplines approach a problem from their own discipline, working together at some point during a project, but they may have separate conclusions and disseminate the findings in different journals (Magee & Heiderscheit)

multi-element design: see *multiple treatment design*

multiple baseline design: a type of single subject/small *n* research in which individual baselines are established, consistent response patterns are observed, and then the independent variable is systematically introduced to one baseline at a time; sometimes referred to as a *staggered baseline design* (Napoles)

multiple or *collective case study:* a type of interpretivist case study; usually involves several instrumental case studies within a bounded system; the researcher starts with a theme or issue and studies multiple cases in the hope of enhancing the ability to theorize about a given phenomenon (Murphy)

multiple comparison procedure: see *post hoc test*

multiple regression: an equation that predicts values of the criterion variable using multiple independent variables (Ghetti)

multiple treatment design: single subject and small *n* design in which two or more interventions are compared in order to determine whether one is more effective than the other in changing a behavior; also called *multi-element design, multiple schedule design, simultaneous treatment design, alternating treatments, changing conditions, ABC design,* or *multiple treatment with reversal design* (Napoles)

narrative inquiry: the study of human lived experience portrayed through engaging, meaningful, and personal stories (Hadley & Edwards)

narrative literature review: a review that involves performing thorough literature searches, describing how these were done, grouping findings according to themes, critically discussing findings, and placing the proposed research in context; sometimes called *literature review* (Abbott)

narrative synthesis: an approach to the synthesis of relevant evidence that relies primarily on the use of words and text to summarize and explain the findings of multiple studies

naturalistic engagement: the researcher observes the phenomenon of interest in a natural, lived world; one of three levels of engagement in interpretivist research; see also *experimental engagement, retrospective engagement* (Keith)

naturalistic inquiry/research: an interactive process where a researcher enters the field and immerses her- or himself in the lived world of the phenomenon being studied; stems from the belief that human processes gain their meaning from their context and that to alter the context or to try to study phenomena by breaking them into constituents and bringing them into a laboratory is to fundamentally alter the social or psychological processes that one would like to study (Arnason)

negative case: data that contradict emerging findings

nexus analysis: includes tracing the histories of use of mediational means, considering such things as how current use is related to historical use of a particular musical instrument, vocables, and/or musical gesture; works to uncover how power relationships are complexly woven into the social practices at micro- and macro-levels (Talbot)

nominal: scale or level of measurement where numbers simply name or label; therefore, the numbers do not represent quantities (Waldon)

nondirectional hypothesis: a hypothesis that states that there will be a significant difference in effects but makes no prediction of the direction of the difference; appropriate if variables whose effects are unknown are being compared

nonexperimental research: any research design in which the researcher does not control and manipulate the independent variables (Ghetti)

nonparametric statistics: inferential statistical tests that require no assumptions about population characteristics, utilize nominal and ordinal scales of measurement, are amenable to nonnumeric data and small samples, and are relatively simple to compute; also called *distribution-free tests*

nonpositivist: one who does not subscribe to positivist beliefs but rather believes that truth and reality exist in the form of multiple, intangible mental constructions that are influenced by individuals and social experiences, all discoveries are bound to the time and context of the inquiry, and idiographic statements are more meaningful than generalizations

nonprobability sample: includes purposive (e.g., selection of specific individuals), convenience (e.g., selection of those most convenient to access), and snowballing sampling (e.g., selection of those recommended by others), all used in interpretivist research

norm-referenced test: standardized tests that are designed to compare and rank test-takers in relation to one another; allows the researcher to determine if an individual performed better or worse than a hypothetical average test-taker

normal distribution: sometimes called the *bell curve* or the *Gaussian curve;* the distribution of data as it occurs theoretically in a distribution with an infinitely large number of cases; normal distributions are symmetric around their mean, and the mean, median, and mode are equal; all members of a population are distributed under the bell curve, and 68% of the area of a normal distribution is within one standard deviation of the mean (95% of the area of a normal distribution is within two standard deviations of the mean) (Meadows)

null hypothesis, H_0: hypothesis predicting that there will be no difference between the sample mean and the mean of the population, or between two or more sample means;

if a difference is found, the null hypothesis is rejected and it is assumed that there is probably a real difference between the groups

objectivism: assumes that a reality exists *out there,* whether we are conscious of it or not, and that discovering the truth about that reality is best achieved through an accumulation of carefully planned observations; holds that we may come to know the truth about reality through repeated observations of it in highly controlled situations (Hiller)

objectivist case study: an intensive examination of an individual or group with the use of a quasi-experimental research design to determine the effect of an independent variable on one or more dependent variables; an in-depth study of a phenomenon within its real-life context and relevant in helping to understand complex social phenomena (Ridder & Fachner)

objectivist research: the purpose is to determine what is true or not true—to confirm or deny a focused and well-defined hypothesis established at the very beginning of a study; also called *quantitative research*

one-tail hypothesis, one-tailed prediction, one-tailed test: see *directional hypothesis*

online search: using an index by accessing a computer network directly

ontology: the study of being, of the nature of existence; it is the study of what exists, what is in reality, what is real (Hiller)

open-access literature: digital, free of charge, and compatible with features like peer review and copyright (Abbott)

open-ended questions: allow respondents to provide answers in their own words

open-format item: a type of measurement that allows the research participant to answer in an unrestricted manner because their responses are not constrained by predetermined choices or closed response modes (e.g., numeric responses) (Waldon)

operational definition: an outline of a construct in observable terms; an exact description of the behavior under consideration; describes specific and observable events so that others can independently observe and measure them

oral history: the verbal memories that a person has of his or her life; includes the individuals a person has known, the events in which a person has participated or observed, and the places a person has visited (Solomon & Davis)

ordinal: scale or level of measurement in which numbers imply the presence of order, that is, higher numeric values represent more of a particular construct than lower values; researchers to rank characteristics so that values can be compared to others as being equal to, less than, or greater than another (Waldon)

ordinal interaction: interaction in which the order of the effect does not change, although the magnitude does (McKinney)

outlier: deviant effect size (Bradt)

paradigm: a set of basic beliefs representing a worldview that defines, for its holder, the nature of the world, the individual's place in it, and the range of possible relationships to that world and its parts; provides unity to a scientific community; a set of shared assumptions, values, concepts, and practices

parallel group design: a two or more–group (or –arm) design wherein an experimental condition and an additional condition are compared in an attempt to determine potential between-group quantitative differences resulting from the experimental treatment (Silverman)

parametric statistics: inferential statistical tests that require normally distributed data to meet assumptions of normality: groups with equal variance and data on an interval or ratio scale; more powerful than nonparametric statistics (Meadows)

partial factorial design: uses a carefully selected subset of a full factorial design in order to focus on the central questions and conserve resources (McKinney)

participatory action research: see *action research*

pattern matching: an observed pattern, a pattern of measured values, is matched with an expected pattern or a proposition; patterns may be related to the dependent or the independent variables; if predicted values for each outcome have been found, strong causal inferences can be made (Ridder & Fachner)

peer debriefing: a procedure for establishing trustworthiness in interpretivist research in which the researcher meets with a peer who is free to pose questions regarding substantive, methodological, legal, ethical, or any other matters in order to increase the researcher's self-awareness of these matters (Arnason)

peer-review: a process by which a journal article is read by experts in the same field to make sure that it meets the necessary standards of scholarship before it is published or accepted

phenomenological inquiry: a comprehensive term for numerous variations of interpretivist research, the purpose of which is to explore and explicate the nature of a phenomenon through first-person experience; seeks to discover and describe the structure and meaning of a phenomenon that makes it intrinsically what it *is*—its essence; see also specific types of phenomenological inquiry defined in this glossary (Jackson)

phenomenology: a broad philosophical method that is based on the premise that reality consists of objects and events (*phenomena*) as they are perceived or understood in the human consciousness, not of anything independent of human consciousness; the study of experience and how we experience

philosophical inquiry: a broad approach to research that involves speculation, analysis, and criticism; characteristic procedures are clarifying terms, exposing and evaluating underlying assumptions, relating ideas as a systematic theory and showing their connections to other systems, and using argument as a primary mode of inquiry and a presentational device

philosophy: the practice of critically examining lay and learned assumptions about human life and the world; may involve clarification of concepts or critical reflections on knowledge, ethics, and aesthetics, in dialogue with sciences and various human practices; a system of beliefs or principles set forth to guide practical action (Stige & Strand)

philosophy of science: deals with what science is, how it works, and the logic through which we build scientific knowledge

pilot study: a study performed to test previously untested hypotheses, investigate areas that lack a strong foundation in theory or background research, or try out a measurement instrument; the results of a pilot study or test are generally used in a more developed research study

population: the total number of people possible in the group; the entire group of objects or people in whom the researcher is interested (Cohen)

Portraiture: an arts-based phenomenological method of research, developed by Lawrence-Lightfoot, in which the researcher (portraitist) paints a narrative portrait of phenomena; shares features of ethnography, case study, and narrative research (Merrill)

positivism: an objectivist research perspective that undergirded most human and social science research throughout the 19th and into the 20th century and still has impact in the 21st century; a philosophical system of knowledge that accepts only observable or measurable (i.e., empirical) experiences of the world as data for analysis, the findings from which are considered positive or absolute truths about reality (Hiller)

post hoc test: a test done after statistically significant results are found to determine between which groups the significant differences are found

postpositivism: the theoretical perspective that allows that, regardless of a researcher's faithful adherence to objectivist *scientific* methods, findings are not considered absolute truths but rather are conjectural and circumstantial and that, given new evidence, it is always possible for alternate explanations of data and findings to be articulated (Hiller)

poststructuralism: a strand of postmodernism that embraces multiple perspectives; is based on assumptions that there is no single truth, but multiple truths, and no privileged positions from which truth might be known (Hadley)

posttest: a test or assessment given following a treatment or intervention

power: the probability of correctly rejecting a null hypothesis; a statistical procedure that helps to determine how large a sample size is needed for an experiment

pragmatic research: conducted in settings that are close to those in which actual clinical work occurs and offers enhanced external validity; because it is less controlled, the assumptions that can be made about causality are limited; see also *effectiveness research* (DeLoach, Wheeler, & Murphy)

pragmatism: a philosophy that assesses the truth of meaning of theories or beliefs in terms of the success of their practical application; advocated by some as a useful model for conceptual agreement on how to conduct mixed methods research (Magee)

predictive validity: based on a measure's ability to predict a future outcome or performance

predictor variables: those variables chosen to statistically predict the criterion variable in multiple correlation and related techniques

pre-experimental one-sample design: only one group of participants receives a treatment, and measures are taken to determine the effects of treatment on the same group; two main types: (a) posttest-only design, and (b) one-group pretest–posttest design (Jones)

pre-experimental research: designs in which only one group of participants receives a treatment, and measures are taken to determine the effects of treatment on the same group

pretest: a test or assessment given prior to implementing experimental conditions

pretest sensitization: the effects of having been administered a pretest; a threat to ecological (external) validity in objectivist research; also called *pretesting effects*

pretesting effects: see *pretest sensitization*

primary source: information obtained from the source in which it was initially contained; in historical research, a firsthand witness of a historical event under study (Solomon & Davis)

principal investigator (PI): the researcher who takes primary responsibility for a study

PRISMA (Preferred Reporting Items for Systematic Reviews and Meta-Analyses) Statement: provides a minimum set of items for reporting systematic reviews and meta-analyses; consists of a 27-item checklist and a flow diagram detailing the number of studies identified, included, and excluded and reasons for exclusion (Bradt)

privacy: the right of an individual to choose if and what personal information will be shared or not shared with others

probability level: the likelihood that the data collected occurred by chance; used interchangeably with level of confidence, level of significance, confidence level, significance level, and alpha (a) level

problem statement: a statement of the problem or question for a study; also a step in developing the topic for such a study

profession research: research concerned with how music therapists interact with one another and with other professionals, along with the socioeconomic, political, and educational conditions affecting the discipline of music therapy; one of three types of music therapy research (from Bruscia)

prolonged engagement: a procedure for establishing trustworthiness in qualitative research in which the researcher spends sufficient time in the research site for learning the culture, testing for misinformation introduced by distortions either of the self or of the respondents, and building trust (Arnason)

protocol: a plan for research or treatment that is spelled out in detail so that it can be used repeatedly as a clinical procedure and/or tested with other samples and in other settings utilizing experimental research methods; see also *research protocol*

pure research: see *basic research*

purposive sampling: allows researchers to choose participants or other data sources that they believe will provide useful data; also called *purposeful sampling* (Keith)

quadrant model: quadrants graphically represent perspectives/phenomena as a matrix combining interior versus exterior and individual versus collective phenomena; developed by Wilber (Hunt)

qualitative content analysis: an approach of empirical, methodological, controlled analysis of texts within their context of communication, following content analytical rules and step-by-step models, without rash quantification (Ghetti & Keith)

qualitative research: a broad category of research whose followers believe that not all that is important can be reduced to measurements, it is essential to take into account the interaction between the researcher and the participant(s) being studied, findings cannot be generalized beyond the context in which they are discovered, and values are inherent in and central to any investigation; a process wherein one human being genuinely attempts to understand something about another human being or about the conditions of being human by using approaches that take full advantage of being human; also known as *interpretivist research* (definition from Bruscia)

qualitative synthesis: see *interpretivist synthesis*

quantitative research: research that attempts to answer questions about music therapy practices and patients' responses by quantifying or ascribing importance to the number or size of reactions or results, as, for example, in studying music therapy practices and patients' responses; also called *objectivist research*

quantitizing: the process of assigning numerical (nominal or ordinal) values to data conceived as not numerical (Magee)

quasi-experimental design: compares the effects of treatment on an existing group with another existing and closely matched group that has not received the treatment; two types: (a) static group design, and (b) pretest–posttest static group comparison design (de L'Etoile)

questionnaire-based survey: involves a set of questions (which can be both closed-ended and open-ended) to be answered by the survey respondent (Curtis)

random assignment: assigning subjects to groups or conditions so that there is an equal probability that an individual will be assigned to one condition as opposed to any other condition

random effects model: levels of an independent variable are randomly selected from a much larger or even infinite set (McKinney)

random sample: in objectivist research, those selected for the sample from the largest group the researcher has in mind, so that each member of the subset has an equal probability of being chosen

random selection: selecting subjects in such a manner that any subject in the population has an equal chance of being selected; ensures that the sample represents the population at large

randomization: selecting or assigning subjects randomly

randomized controlled trial (RCT): an experimental study that consists of at least two groups of participants, or conditions, with each participant having been randomly assigned to one of the groups; one of these groups, known as the treatment group, receives the independent or treatment variable, and the other group, the control group, receives a different treatment or no special treatment; the groups are treated identically (or with no systematic differences between them), with the exception of the addition of the independent variable for the treatment group(s)

range: descriptive statistic giving the difference (distance) between the highest score and the lowest score (Meadows)

rating scale: consists of statements or behavioral descriptors that are then evaluated and rated on some kind of dimension or scale; may be used when the degree or quality of the behavior, trait, or attitude is of interest to the researcher (Krout)

ratio: scale or level of measurement that includes all of the characteristics of the interval scale but also has an absolute or meaningful zero, so that values can be doubled or tripled and can also be zero; suited for parametric statistical tests

realism: the belief that a reality exists outside of our consciousness of it and that certain fixed laws of nature are permanent fixtures of that reality; once discovered, these laws are considered true and reliable toward explaining the natural world (Hiller)

reductive phenomenology: a type of phenomenological inquiry that places a strong emphasis on the assumption of the phenomenological attitude; this process can be described as taking a new, fresh look at a phenomenon by leaving behind what the researcher has already determined to be the reality of it (Jackson)

reflexivity: the process of examining oneself as researcher and the research relationship; takes into consideration that one's categories of observation are theoretically biased and also that they determine what one hears and how those sounds are perceived or interpreted, which in turn creates a basis for the choice of methods

regression: an extension of correlation with the aim of developing an equation that predicts values of the criterion variable

regression-discontinuity design: permits the research treatment to be provided to the subjects most in need of it while obtaining results of a fully randomized trial; used when random assignment is impractical or unethical and there are more eligible subjects for the research than can be accommodated (Sullivan & Sullivan)

regression to the mean: the statistical tendency of a numerical value that is extreme on the first measurement to move towards the mean when measured again

relationship: see *correlation coefficient*

reliability: the extent to which a measurement consistently measures a given construct on multiple occasions, assuming that there is no change in the underlying phenomenon being studied (Waldon); see *test–retest reliability, alternate forms reliability, internal consistency, interrater reliability*

reliability coefficient: used to describe the degree to which a set of scores is reliable and, therefore, free from error (Waldon)

repeated measures design: experimental research design that calls for subjects to act as their own controls; each subject is observed under every condition

RepGrid Technique (repertory grid technique): a computerized method for clarifying the constructs that an individual uses to understand a phenomenon, and for analyzing how these constructs fit together into a meaningful whole; each construct is examined according to a unique continuum of opposite characteristics or qualities assigned to the construct by the individual; based on personal construct psychology, the theory of personality developed by Kelly

replication/replicability: studies by different researchers working at different times yield the same results when using the identical techniques; results that can be replicated are less likely to have been due to chance

Reporting Guidelines for Music-Based Interventions: guidelines for how to report music interventions; developed by Robb, Carpenter, and Burns

research: a systematic, self-monitored inquiry that leads to a discovery or new insight, which, when documented and disseminated, contributes to or modifies existing knowledge or practice (from Bruscia)

research hypothesis: see *alternate hypothesis*

research protocol: a document that describes all aspects of a proposed research study (Murphy)

retrospective engagement: participants have already encountered the phenomenon of interest, and the researcher gathers data that are already available; one of three levels of engagement in interpretivist research; see also *experimental engagement, naturalistic engagement* (Keith)

reversal design: see *withdrawal design*

review of literature: a discussion that identifies important previous investigations and theoretical perspectives related to a research topic; orients readers to key issues on a topic and describes a rationale for a study; begins the article or other presentation of the research; also called *literature review*

risk–benefit ratio: the comparison of the potential risks with the potential benefits of the study

risk of bias: the possibility that systematic error, or deviation from the truth, in results or inferences occurs in a research study; risk of bias is assessed based on a number of criteria (Cohen)

sample: a part of the larger population that is used to gather information about and to represent the entire population; the group of people from whom data are collected (Cohen)

sampling: the procedures employed by the researcher to select participants for a study

scaled items: response options arranged along a dimension (Waldon)

scientific method: involves formulating specific questions based on one's empirical observations and then systematically finding answers to those questions (Cohen)

scientific phenomenology: also called *descriptive phenomenology;* the researcher resists assuming that the phenomenon itself actually exists in the real world, but instead regards the phenomenon merely as an appearance to human consciousness (Jackson)

secondary source: information that is not collected firsthand; any source that is not primary; used in historical research and in reviewing literature for other types of research (Solomon & Davis)

segment: a unit of processing in interpretivist research in which the items comprising the segment are classified together because they share a common trait or traits; also called *item, incident, meaning unit,* or *analysis unit*

segregated design: a mixed methods synthesis design in which the traditional distinction between quantitative and qualitative research is maintained (Meadows & Wimpenny)

self-hermeneutic: see *stance of the researcher;* applies to hermeneutic research

semiological tripartition: an analytic process developed by Nattiez, covering three dimensions of a symbolic phenomenon (music): (a) the poietic dimension, that is, the symbolic form as a result of a process of creation; (b) the aesthesic dimension, or the assignment of meaning to the form by the receivers; and (c) the trace, or the physical and material form in which the symbolic form is accessible to the five senses (Bonde)

shared order: a particular culture of interest

significance level: see *probability level*

simple effects: examine each level of one factor with each of the levels of the other factor or factors; sometimes called *simple main effects*

single subject research designs: a subset of objectivist case study research; systematically investigate anticipated effects of specified treatments on an individual or group treated as a single case through repeated measurement; also called *single case designs;* referred to as *applied behavior analysis designs* in the previous edition of this book (Jones & Brown)

snowball sampling: a process in which the researcher asks a research participant to put him or her in contact with similar people who might provide useful data for the research project; also called *chain sampling* (Keith)

Solomon four group design: a complex version of a parallel group design; uses a pre- and posttest design with two additional posttest-only groups: a second experimental group that receives only a posttest and a second control group that receives only the posttest (Silverman)

source method: the method upon which the research design is based; applies to mixed methods interpretivist studies (Zanders)

split-plot factorial: combines between-groups and within-groups analyses; also called *mixed design* (McKinney)

stance of the researcher: the acknowledgment and articulation of the researcher's perspective, allowing the reader to understand the preconceptions and influences that the researcher brings to the event and enabling the researcher to be conscious of potential biases and therefore less influenced by them; called *epoché* or *self-hermeneutic* in some types of research

standard deviation (s.d. or s): descriptive statistic that describes how varied the numbers in a set are; the average deviation of scores within a sample; sometimes described with the symbol (sigma)

standardized test: a collection of measurement items that are written, administered, scored, and interpreted in a consistent manner to yield a score representing a factor, ability, or trait in an examinee (or research participant) (Waldon)

standpoint epistemology: advocates a particular social perspective as epistemically privileged; developed within the context of Marxist politics and has traditionally been linked to a materialist feminist perspective; the particular vantage point of the marginal or subjugated is often privileged in standpoint epistemology (Rolvsjord & Hadley)

static group comparison design: one group that experiences a treatment is compared with one that has not; differences that occur between the two groups are assumed to be a result of the treatment; classified as quasi-experimental (de l'Etoile)

statistic: the value that is calculated by a statistical test

statistical inference: a set of procedures followed by a researcher in order to make decisions about an unknown population from studying a known sample; involves formulating a hypothesis, choosing a probability level, selecting a statistical test, predicting the direction of the difference, calculating a statistical value, comparing the statistical value to a critical value in the appropriate statistical table, and accepting or rejecting the null hypothesis

statistical power: see *power*

statistical significance: results achieved when a statistical test finds the variability between groups to be significantly greater than the variability within each group, suggesting that the results that were achieved did not occur by chance and resulting in the isolation of the independent variable as the most probable cause of changes in the dependent variable; sometimes called (only) *significance*

structuralism: a science of linguistics developed by linguist Ferdinand de Saussure; can be understood as a system of language where the meaning of an element in the system, or term, is determined in relationship to other elements of the same system; furthermore, an element of language acquires value or meaning in reciprocal relationship to its binary opposite (Hadley)

subordinate problems or *questions:* questions related and auxiliary to the primary research problem or question; a step in developing a quantitative research topic

substantive theory: limited in scope and relevant to specific situations (Amir, LaGasse, & Crowe)

survey: gathers information from a group of individuals in a systematic fashion, making use of a variety of methods, including questionnaires and interviews administered online, in person, or by telephone (Curtis)

systematic review: synthesizes the best available research evidence on a specific question; assembles evidence from clinical trials that meet predetermined eligibility criteria in terms of study design, population, intervention, and outcomes; characterized by systematic and transparent methods that are aimed at minimizing bias (Bradt)

tacit knowledge: knowledge that a person has but is not aware of; general information; knowledge that is difficult to write down, visualize, or transfer from one person to another

tallying: observational method in which the observer marks every time that a discrete behavior occurs; also called *frequency* or *event recording* (Krout)

TAU: acroynym for *treatment as usual,* a type of control condition wherein control participants receive exactly the same treatments as experimental participants, and the only between-group difference is the treatment (independent variable) under investigation (Silverman)

test: any device used to evaluate the behavior or performance of a person (Waldon); see specific types: *criterion-referenced, norm-referenced, standardized*

test–retest reliability: method of determining reliability that involves administering the same measure on two occasions in order to obtain an estimate of stability (Waldon)

thematic analysis: a common general approach to analyzing qualitative data that does not rely on the specialized procedures of other means of analysis; not constrained by specific methodology but serves the purpose of a wide range of interpretivist research practices; the analyst codes sections of a text according to whether they appear to contribute to emerging themes; sometimes called *qualitative thematic analysis, interpretive content analysis, applied thematic analysis* (Hoskyns)

theoretical grounding: theory generates research hypotheses that are tested quantitatively through objectivist research studies; conversely, inference from the results of objectivist research studies corroborates or falsifies theory (McKinney)

theoretical sampling: the researcher continues to sample on the basis of the evolving findings and possibly emerging theory (Keith)

theoretical saturation: a phase or theoretical point where a researcher, after continuous sampling and analysis, finds no new data and where no new concepts appear in the analysis (Keith)

theory: an organized, coherent, and systematic articulation of a set of issues that are communicated as a meaningful whole; can be *formal* and *substantive* (Amir, LaGasse, & Crowe)

time series analysis (TSA): used when observations are made repeatedly over several time periods in order to identify patterns in the sequence of numbers over time (Ridder & Fachner)

transcendental phenomenological inquiry: a type of research that is most closely aligned with the philosophy of Husserl. It focuses on understanding a phenomenon by means of analyzing its essential structure and thoroughly describing it (Jackson)

transformative research: a wide range of approaches such as critical theory, feminism, postcolonialism, critical theories of race, disability studies, and gender studies and queer theory; the aim is to reveal mechanisms of oppression with the endeavor to contribute to the liberation of those who are oppressed (Rolvsjord & Hadley)

treatment fidelity: confirmation that the music therapy protocol is being delivered as described

TREND (Transparent Reporting of Evaluations with Nonrandomized Designs) statement: provides guidelines for increasing the transparency and clarity of nonrandomized controlled trials (Silverman)

triangulation: a procedure for establishing trustworthiness that uses multiple data sources or methods in order to ascertain the accuracy of data; used in both objectivist research (Ridder & Fachner) and interpretivist research (Keith)

trustworthiness: the credibility, transferability, dependability, and confirmability of an interpretivist research study

two-tail hypothesis, two-tailed prediction, two-tailed test: see *nondirectional hypothesis*

Type I error: rejecting a null hypothesis when it should be accepted; signified by (Meadows)

Type II error: accepting a null hypothesis when it should be rejected; signified by (Meadows)

user perspectives: incorporating the views and experiences of clients when planning research as well as other services (Keith)

validity: accuracy (in any context); the extent to which what you are claiming is actually occurring; includes measurement validity and design validity

validity, design: see *internal validity, external validity*

validity, measurement: the extent to which a measure or test actually measures the variable in question or the extent to which a study studies what it intends to study; see *content, criterion-related, concurrent, construct, face,* and *predictive validity*

variability: how widely scores are dispersed or how closely they are grouped around the mean; also refers to the dispersion of a characteristic among a research population

variable: something that changes or that can be changed; see also *independent* and *dependent variable, confounding variable*

variance: a descriptive statistic giving the average of the sum of the squared deviations for a population; uses the symbol σ^2

visual analog scale (VAS): consists of a single line (typically horizontal, with or without numbers) that have anchoring descriptors at both ends (Waldon)

wait-list control group: a group that serves as a control group in an experimental research study and, immediately following the study, receives the experimental procedure if the procedure was found to be helpful

washout period: a space between the interventions that is long enough to ensure that the effects from one treatment will not carry over to the next treatment (DeLoach, Wheeler, & Murphy)

whole interval recording: a type of interval recording in which the behavior of interest must occur during the entire interval in order to be counted; see also *interval recording*

withdrawal design: a single subject and small *n* research design that tests the effects of an intervention by comparing a treatment phase or phases with baseline phases, one of which occurs after the treatment is withdrawn; sometimes labeled as an ABA or ABAB design; the term *withdrawal* is preferred over *reversal* because withdrawal refers to the mechanics of the design (Jones & Brown)

within subjects design: see *repeated measures design*

SUBJECT INDEX

A

ABA (applied behavior analysis), 121, 154, 161, 232, 248
abstracts, 15, 38
action research, 7, 58, 68, 98, 102, 164–65, 172, 177, 232
age, 50, 53–55, 74, 77, 79, 85, 128, 132, 135, 138, 155, 157, 159, 213–14, 240
Alzheimer's disease, 70–72, 82, 157, 159–61, 169, 176
AME (Active Music Engagement), 212–15, 219
analysis, hermeneutic, 80, 166, 169, 175–76
Analytical Music Therapy, 12, 140, 151, 169, 175, 230
analyzing improvised music, 150
ANOVA, 114, 121–22, 125, 127–28, 131, 134–37, 139
anxiety, 33, 62–63, 92, 94, 96, 113, 116, 120, 122–23, 161, 191, 226
applied research, 4–6, 232–33
approaches
  meaning-focused, 7–8, 98
  natural setting, 7, 163
artifacts, 51, 75, 79, 122, 140–41, 143–50, 163, 168, 182, 197, 222, 232
Arts-Based Research (ABR), 8, 19, 27, 68, 102, 169–70, 177, 203–4, 206, 208, 232
assessment, 3, 19, 21, 57, 87–88, 92–94, 111, 117, 147, 150, 240, 243
assumptions, 28, 31–33, 65–66, 68, 78, 80, 90, 125, 131, 182–83, 187–88, 195, 197, 232, 240–43
autism, v, 77, 82, 129–30, 147, 155, 160–61, 177

B

baseline, 7, 18, 123, 154–55, 215, 232–33, 241
bell curve, 129, 241
biases, 12–13, 57, 59–60, 85, 87, 94–95, 110, 115, 169–70, 185–87, 189–91, 197, 199, 222, 227–28
  cultural, 57, 59
  risk of, 84, 94–95, 189, 245
BMGIM (Bonny Method of Guided Imagery and Music), 145, 151, 173–74, 177, 188, 230
Boolean operators, 38–40, 46, 233
bracketing, 76–77, 165–67

C

cases, disconfirming, 142, 233, 235
case studies, v, 21, 26, 68, 100, 104, 151, 154, 160–61, 172, 181, 230–31
causal relationships, 9, 78, 88, 127, 186, 233, 238

CIOMS (Council for International Organizations of Medical Sciences), 47–50, 52
clinical research, 16, 57, 127, 181, 192–93, 233
community, 23–24, 26–27, 48, 54, 56, 58–62, 66, 98, 145, 147–48, 167–68, 175–76, 196–97, 220, 222
Community Music Therapy, 22, 60, 64, 98, 142, 147, 152, 177
Community Music Therapy in action, 62, 64, 152, 177
comprehensibility, 201–3
confidence intervals, 125, 129–30, 188–89, 191, 233
confidentiality, 48, 51–53, 150, 204–5
confounding variables, 71, 92, 185–86, 215, 233–34, 237, 247
consensual qualitative research (CQR), 8, 172, 175, 207, 233
consent, 47, 49–51, 53–54
consent form, 49–50, 214, 234, 238
CONSORT (Consolidated Standards for Reporting Trials), 187, 189, 193, 210–11, 218–19, 234
constructions, 3–5, 67, 73, 75, 143, 164, 172, 196, 198, 200–201, 203, 220, 223, 227–28
constructivism, 4, 68, 72–74, 82, 95, 98–99, 164, 234
constructs, 57, 108, 111, 113, 140, 164, 171–72, 176, 185–86, 195, 197, 211, 226, 238, 245
content validity, 110, 112–13, 117, 186, 234
contextualization, 195–98, 205
contextualizing, 195–98, 205, 210, 216
control, 69, 71, 87–88, 94, 121, 123, 141, 185–86, 189–90, 209, 214, 233–34, 236–39, 241, 245
  experimental, 154–55, 232
control conditions, 158–59, 181, 214–15, 247
control group design, 44, 119, 122–23
control groups, 7, 15, 44, 90–92, 94, 119, 121–23, 129–30, 136, 158, 234, 244, 247
control participants, 92, 247
co-researchers, 167–68, 226
correlation, 88, 109, 111, 125, 135, 137–38, 155–56, 160, 234, 245
criterion validity, 110–11, 117
culture, 12–13, 16, 19–20, 22–23, 55–63, 74, 98–99, 147, 163, 180, 194, 196, 198, 206–7, 235–36
culture-related issues, 55, 57, 98, 107

D

data
  clinical, 8, 168
  nominal, 124, 128, 133, 136–37, 187
  quantitative, 5, 179, 181, 237, 240
data analysis, 53, 66, 69, 81, 93–94, 139, 142, 185, 187, 198–202, 205, 212, 215–16, 227, 229